INTRODUCTION TO
QUANTITATIVE CYTOCHEMISTRY

The PREFACE.

By the
help of Microſcopes, *there is nothing ſo* ſmall, *as to eſcape our inqui-*
ry ; hence there is a new viſible World diſcovered to the underſtanding.

   From hence the World may be aſſiſted with variety *of Inventions,* new
matter for Sciences may be collected, *the* old improv'd, *and their* ruſt
rubb'd away ·
                                                   By the
addition of ſuch artificial Inſtruments *and* methods, *there may be, in*
ſome manner, a reparation made for the miſchiefs, and imperfection,
mankind has drawn upon it ſelf, by negligence, and intemperance, and a
wilful and ſuperſtitious deſerting the Preſcripts and Rules of Nature,
whereby every man, both from a deriv'd corruption, innate and born
with him, and from his breeding and converſe with men, is very ſubject
to ſlip into all ſorts of errors.

Book written by Robert Hooke, Fellow of the Royal Society.
Entituled , Micrographia, or ſome Phyſiological Deſcriptions of
Minute Bodies, made by Magnifying Glaſſes, with Obſervations and
Inquiries thereupon.   *Novem.* 23.
                                 1664.

INTRODUCTION
TO
QUANTITATIVE
CYTOCHEMISTRY

Edited by

George L. Wied

Cytopathology Service
University of Chicago
Chicago, Illinois

1966

ACADEMIC PRESS   **NEW YORK and LONDON**

ACADEMIC PRESS INC.
111 Fifth Avenue, New York, New York 10003

United Kingdom Edition published by
ACADEMIC PRESS INC. (LONDON) LTD.
Berkeley Square House, London W.1

LIBRARY OF CONGRESS CATALOG CARD NUMBER: 66-26257

PRINTED IN THE UNITED STATES OF AMERICA

CONTRIBUTORS

Numbers in parentheses indicate the pages on which the authors' contributions begin.

G. F. Bahr, *Armed Forces Institute of Pathology, Washington, D.C.* (137, 469)

Peter H. Bartels, *Laboratory for Applied and Theoretical Microscopy, E. Leitz, Inc., New York, New York* (137, 469)

Guenther Beneke, *Department of Pathology, Justus Liebig University, Giessen, Germany* (63, 107)

Abraham Bloom, *National Instruments Laboratory, Rockville, Maryland* (437)

Arline D. Deitch, *Department of Microbiology, Columbia University, New York, New York* (327, 451)

A. Mariano Garcia, *Department of Anatomy, State University of New York, Upstate Medical Center, Syracuse, New York* (215, 239)

Arthur J. Hale, *Pathology Department, St. Thomas's Hospital Medical School, London, England* (153, 183)

Robert Iorio, *Department of Anatomy, State University of New York, Upstate Medical Center, Syracuse, New York* (215, 239)

John W. Kelly, *Department of Anatomy, Tufts University School of Medicine, Boston, Massachusetts* (247, 489)

Günter Kiefer, *Department of Pathology, Justus Liebig University, Giessen, Germany* (295)

Mortimer L. Mendelsohn, *Department of Radiology, University of Pennsylvania, Philadelphia, Pennsylvania* (201)

H. P. Missmahl, *Department of Medicine, University of Tübingen, Tübingen, Germany* (507, 539)

Oscar W. Richards, *American Optical Company, Research Center, Southbridge, Massachusetts* (43)

Wirnt Rick, *Department of Pathology, Justus Liebig University, Giessen, Germany* (295)

Fritz Ruch, *Department of General Botany, Swiss Federal Institute of Technology, Zürich, Switzerland* (281, 549)

George T. Rudkin, *The Institute for Cancer Research, Philadelphia, Pennsylvania* (387)

Walter Sandritter, *Department of Pathology, Justus Liebig University, Giessen, Germany* (159, 295)

HEWSON SWIFT, *Whitman Laboratory, University of Chicago, Chicago, Illinois* (1, 355)

ANDREAS A. THAER, *Ernst Leitz GmbH, Wetzler, Germany* (409)

LOTHAR TRAPP, *Laboratory for Microscopy at Carl Zeiss, Oberkochen, Germany* (427)

GEORGE L. WIED, *Laboratory of Exfoliative Cytology, University of Chicago, Chicago, Illinois* (559)

PREFACE

When a scientist sets out to solve a problem, he begins by observing similar problems which have previously been solved by others or by himself, and attempts to apply the same set of rules. However, certain problems involve facets which defy the traditional set of rules.

Both the applied cytologist and the analytic cytologist (or quantitative microscopist) have traditional sets of rules which they follow in their respective disciplines, and, as a rule, neither wishes to abandon his methods. However, it is felt that if each would become better acquainted with the other's rules so that the frames of reference could be fused, discoveries would be made in basic cellular research and in applied cytology which would not have been otherwise possible.

The applied cytologist should be fully aware of the potentialities and limitations of analytic cytology. He should know the language of quantitative cytochemistry and should be able to assess the ways in which quantitative microscopy can assist him in his work in applied or clinical cytology. The analytic cytologist, on the other hand, requires exposure to clinical problems, lest he work only as an instrumentationalist, merely testing one instrument against another.

The chief aim of this work is to acquaint applied cytologists, analytic cytologists, and other individuals interested in cytology with traditional sets of rules used in disciplines other than their own. In addition, it is hoped that this book will familiarize the reader with the latest quantitative cytochemical and histochemical methods used in the evaluation of cytologic material and that it will aid him to select the method which can be best applied to a specific problem.

I would like to thank Dr. Gunter F. Bahr, A. F. I. P., Washington, D.C., for his outstanding cooperation and advice in the completion of this work, as well as for his editorial assistance. Dr. Daniel G. Oldfield, Mrs. Patricia Berg, and Miss Anita M. Messina of our Cytology Laboratory at the University of Chicago have assisted me greatly in the editorial work. The cooperation of the editorial staff of Academic Press is gratefully acknowledged. Financial support by the Illinois Division of the American Cancer Society is gratefully acknowledged.

GEORGE L. WIED

August, 1966

CONTENTS

Sensitivity and Evaluation of Microspectrophotometric and Microinterferometric Measurements

PETER H. BARTELS

Historadiography

GUENTHER BENEKE

Quantitative Electron Microscopy: An Introduction to General Quantitative Measurements with the Electron Microscope with Special Reference to Dry Mass Determinations

G. F. BAHR

Electron Probe Microanalysis as a Quantitative Cytochemical Method

ARTHUR J. HALE

Part II. Quantitative Methods for Determination of Nucleic Acids

Methods and Results in Quantitative Cytochemistry

WALTER SANDRITTER

Determination of DNA Content by Microfluorometry

FRITZ RUCH

Gallocyanin Chrome Alum

WALTER SANDRITTER, GÜNTER KIEFER, AND WIRNT RICK

Cytophotometry of Nucleic Acids

ARLINE D. DEITCH

The Quantitative Cytochemistry of RNA

HEWSON SWIFT

Microspectrophotometry of Chromosomes

GEORGE T. RUDKIN

Instrumentation for Microfluorometry

ANDREAS A. THAER

Instrumentation for Recording Microspectrophotometry

LOTHAR TRAPP

Instruments and Techniques in Microdensitometry

ABRAHAM BLOOM

Part III. Methods for the Quantitative Assay of Proteins, Polysaccharides, and Lipids

Cytophotometry of Proteins

ARLINE D. DEITCH

Introduction to the Cytochemistry of Sulfhydryl and Disulfide Groups

Quantitative Cytochemistry of Acid Mucopolysaccharides

Polarization Optical Analysis of Lipid-Containing Structures with Weak Birefringence

Part IV. Optical Methods for the Analysis of Orientation of Biological Structures

Principles of Polarized Light

Peter H. Bartels

Birefringence and Dichroism of Dyes and Their Significance in the Detection of Oriented Structures

H. P. Missmahl

Dichroism and Difluorescence

Fritz Ruch

Glossary of Terms for Quantitative Cytochemistry

ANALYTICAL MICROSCOPY
OF BIOLOGICAL MATERIALS

A Brief History

Hewson Swift

WHITMAN LABORATORY,
UNIVERSITY OF CHICAGO, CHICAGO, ILLINOIS

I. Introduction

During the past century a small but significant number of biologists have been interested in the microscope as an instrument for the chemical analysis of cells and tissues, rather than as a strictly morphological tool. A great variety of instruments have been designed for microscopic analysis, from the simplest microspectroscopes with a prism placed in the optical path, to highly complex automated scanning instruments, with as yet unrealized possibilities for the programmed analysis of vast quantities of data. At all stages in its development, the analytical microscopy of cells has required the admixture of both physical and biological knowledge. This collaboration was sometimes highly successful but equally often was filled with disappointment, when instruments which required much effort in design and construction failed to be accepted and were for one or another reason not applied to the problems for which they were designed. In a classical example of serendipity, the quartz ultramicroscope manufactured to provide maximal resolution, but virtually unused by biologists, 30 years later provided the essential component for the cytological demonstration of nucleic acids. In a more recent example, the color translation microscope also failed to find an application in surgical pathology, for which it was intended, but appears to have led its designer into important findings in the very different field of color vision.

Probably the earliest use of the microscope in biological analysis was in the investigation of plant and animal pigments. Sorby in 1865 reported a "spectrum microscope," which he further developed and applied to the study of plant colors and mammalian blood. "My aim has been to con-

1

trive a special system of qualitative analysis of coloured substances applicable to minute quantities, and as independent of general chemistry as the blowpipe method is in the case of minerals. I may here say that in some very important practical applications to the detection of blood stains not above 1/100 of a grain was at disposal, and yet perfectly satisfactory results were obtained" (Sorby, 1867). Sorby's spectrum microscope contained an objective with a 3 inch focal length, a slit at the point of focus, and a small Amici prism between the slit and lens. Most spectra were studied in aqueous or alcoholic solutions, in small cuvettes "cut from barometer-tubes" viewed either from the side or end-on for more dilute solutions. In later modifications, Sorby placed a rectangular prism before the slit and a cylindrical lens behind it, so that two spectra were displayed side by side for comparative purposes. In addition to the usual calibration methods, employing the principal Fraunhofer lines of the sun's spectrum, Sorby developed an ingeneous interference system, with two Nicol prisms and a quartz plate, which projected 12 interference bands across the spectrum. The interference bands were adjusted so that the yellow sodium D line was always located between the third and fourth fringe, and thus by crossing and uncrossing the polarizing prisms, Sorby had objective reference points for absorption maxima. He spent much time in adding various reagents such as caustic potash and sulfite of soda to pigment solutions, and noting the shifts in absorption bands, concluding that "the action of many reagents is so intimately related to different parts of the spectrum, as to show that there must be some connection between so-called chemical reactions and optical phenomena."

Another early application of microspectroscopes involved the changes in hemoglobin spectra associated with oxidation and reduction. Preyer (1866) was interested in comparing the absorption spectrum in extracted solutions of hemoglobin with those in intact cells. In his instrument he merely projected the spectrum of the sun or oil lamp from a Bunsen–Kirchoff spectroscope onto the substage mirror of the microscope, using a telescope ocular as collimator. By a comparison of solutions made from crystalline oxyhemoglobin and fresh intact erythrocytes, he concluded that the hemoglobin possessed identical characteristics both outside and inside the red cell, and that the blood contained no other detectable pigments. He also noticed the dichroism of oxyhemoglobin crystals, and its absence in intact erythrocytes.

Studies on blood pigments were continued by an increasing number of investigators. The effects of various reagents were tried on hemoglobin solutions (Preyer, 1868), but also on whole blood subjected to a wide variety of treatments. Ray-Lankester (1871) constructed a small gas chamber under a watch glass which held the drop of frog or human blood under study. Various gases were added or removed through three small side tubes, while the same blood cell could be watched and its absorption spectrum studied. From these observations he concluded, "Carbonic oxide and sulphuretted hydrogen produce their respective changes on the haemoglobin, as demonstrated spectroscopically, without altering the form of the corpuscle, merely effecting the radiation of its body." On the other hand, "Steam, chloroform, benzine, bisulphide of carbon, ammonia and cyanogen, act on the red blood-corpuscle so as to cause the escape of the haemoglobin." Ray-Lankester concluded the erythrocyte possessed "a pellicle or membrane of great tenuity," surrounding the viscid hemo-globin-containing central mass.

These studies were among the first in a long series on hemoglobin and other cell pigments. In the numerous papers which followed, the biological questions of interest to more recent workers were often quite similar to those asked by these earliest investigators, concerning the chemical iden-tity of pigments, the comparison of absorption between extracts and the *in situ* conditions, and the shifts upon oxidation and reduction which might lead to an understanding of physiological function. The spectro-photometric data obtained became steadily more detailed as the tech-niques grew more sophisticated. In the papers of Sorby and Preyer ab-sorption data are presented merely as engravings of the dark and light regions in the spectroscope image, with the position of the Fraunhofer lines drawn for spectral reference. From the work of Ångstrom (1868) and Rowland (1887) the actual wavelengths of these lines became known, so that an objective wavelength scale could be placed on the abcissa. The earliest estimates of optical density at each wavelength were at first made by subjective judgment. Sorby in typical recordings used the terms "very dark band," "much less dark band," and "gradually shaded to very dark at the extreme blue end" to denote absorption in various regions of his 12-band scale. Replacing these terms with the detailed absorption curves of today primarily required the technical development of photometry— the science of light measurement.

In at least one instance the ingeneous control of biological materials circumvented the need for photometric equipment. Engelmann (1882) actually obtained action spectra of photosynthesis with a unique com-bination of living algal cells and aerobic bacteria. In these studies, living filaments of algae were illuminated by spectra stretching across the field of the microscope. The algal cells were thus illuminated with different wavelengths of sunlight or gas light in different regions of the field. Bac-teria were added to these preparations, and they became distributed along the algal filament in a manner that reflected the amount of oxygen lib-erated by the plant cells. Engelmann counted the number of bacteria in various segments of the spectrum. The red end of the spectrum, between lines B and C, contained most of the bacteria. He concluded that this region was most active in photosynthesis, and that his bacterial counts reflected relative amounts of oxygen produced by the plant cells. He noted that the active region was the same whether the cell was green (*Cladocera*), blue green (*Oscillatoria*), or yellow (diatoms). Drawings from his paper, showing some of the very first absorption curves made on intact cells, are reproduced in Fig. 1. The results of Engelmann thus

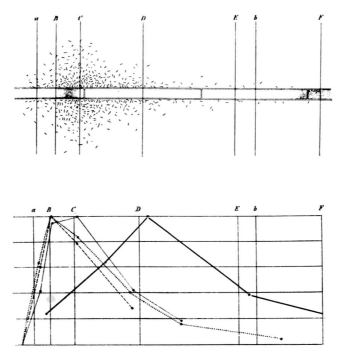

Fig. 1. Chlorophyll action spectra from Engelmann (1882). The upper drawing shows a filament of the alga *Cladophora* illuminated in a microspectrum from gas light surrounded with swarming bacteria concentrated in the red region of the spectrum where oxygen is liberated. The vertical lines are Fraunhofer lines for spectral calibration. The lower drawing shows a graph of bacterial cell counts for *Cladophora* (solid line), the diatom *Pinnularia* (dashed line), and the blue-green alga *Oscillaria* (dotted line) as compared with the curve for extracted *Elodea* pigments estimated by Pfeffer in 1881 (heavy line).

demonstrate both the red light absorption curve for chlorophyll and also the fact that red light is required for the liberation of oxygen in photosynthesis.

II. Photometric Methods

The science of light quantitation, as applied to absorption spectra, developed rapidly during the end of the 19th and the first part of the 20th century. The work of the early chemical spectroscopists laid the foundations required for the later quantitative analysis of biological material. The spectroscope took the form of an analytical instrument in the work of Bunsen, who with Kirchoff (1861) specified the optical requirements in a slit and prism system. Bunsen also defined the extinction coefficient (E), and its relation to the concentration (C) and thickness (d) of the absorbing material. Thus the Bunsen–Roscoe (1862) equation $E = kcd$, where k is a constant dependent on the absorbing substance and the wavelength, embodied the dependency of absorption both on thickness, as stated by Lambert in 1760, and on concentration, as shown by Beer in 1854.

Although the theoretical relationship between a substance and its light absorption was thus defined, and working spectroscopes developed, the practical study of absorption spectra still required methods for the measurement of light intensity. It was necessary to replace statements such as Sorby's "gradually shaded to very dark" with accurate points on a curve. The photometer was the last component of the spectrophotometric instrument to be developed. The earliest photometric determinations were made by eye, with the aid of adjustable comparators. Later, the photographic recording of spectra increased the ease and accuracy of the comparative process, and extended detection into the ultraviolet. Later still, with the development of photoelectric devices, human judgment of relative intensity was replaced by the greater objectivity of the galvanometer scale.

In the period between 1880 and 1900 most absorption studies utilized cuvettes of varying path width (Hartley, 1884). For each wavelength the minimal thickness of the solution at which the transmitted light was no longer detectable was recorded. For ultraviolet light these null transmission points were determined photographically. In later curves the logarithm of thickness was used to provide a better indication of the absorption characteristics. A number of cuvettes of variable optical path were developed to aid in these studies. These included the wedge-shaped cuvette, which was tapered from top to bottom (Mees, 1909) to provide a linear array of path lengths, the echelon-cell, where a number of steps were cut in the glass wall to give a series of discrete paths, and the Baly tube, where a glass plunger could be moved in and out of the chamber to provide a variable thickness of fluid, which could be read on a scale engraved along the side. Other curves were obtained by varying the concentration of measured substance, and keeping the path length constant (a method obviously inapplicable to substances showing shifts in absorption with concentration), or with the use of a neutral density wedge placed near the slit, so that the sample was viewed against a spectrum of high intensity at the bottom edge, fading to low intensities at the top (Mees, 1909).

Although this zero-transmission end point method was an attempt to provide objective evaluation of absorption, it was subject to large errors owing to the variation in spectral sensitivity of both the eye and photographic emulsion. The marked differences between the published absorption curves of the same compound obtained by different investigators provide a good indication of the inherent inaccuracies of the method. For example, the ultraviolet absorption maximum of phenylazophenol was indicated by different authors at wavelengths of either 260 or 280 mμ, with minimal values falling anywhere between 329 and 360 mμ (Tuck, 1907; Hantzsch and Robertson, 1910).

With the advent of double-beam instruments, one path containing the specimen, and the other for reference, results of far greater accuracy were obtainable. The reference beam was reduced in intensity for each wavelength reading by a variety of methods, to the point at which it matched the sample spectrum. Calibrated wire screens, screens etched on quartz plates, aluminized plates, adjustable diaphragms or slits, rotating sectors, neutral density wedges, and polarizing prisms were all used for quantitative matching of specimen and reference (see Brode, 1939, for review). Some of these techniques, particularly rotating sectors, have been adapted to later microphotometric studies on biological material. Although the eye can be a very poor judge of light intensity, and retinal sensitivity decreases abruptly at both red and blue ends of the spectrum, when confronted with the problem of matching a sample intensity with a continuously variable reference beam, accuracies down to 1 or 2% are obtainable. Instruments requiring intensity matching are still in use, for example, in interference microscopy with the Dyson photometer eyepiece, or the Baker half-shade ocular.

Intensity matching is simplified and made more objective on photographic recordings of spectroscopic data. In the important work of Hurter and Driffield (1890) the quantitative relation between light intensity and silver deposition in photographic plates was defined. Photographic densitometry is still an important technique in cytological studies, particularly where small, irregular objects such as single mammalian chromosomes are to be measured (see chapter by Rudkin in this volume). This method has as its basis the "H and D curve" of Hurter and Driffield, where plate density is plotted against the logarithm of light intensity.

These findings served to emphasize the fact that, although the relation between exposure and plate density is nonlinear, with standardized conditions it is sufficiently reproducible to make photographic recording of spectroscopic data both accurate and simple. In the period between 1910 and 1935 much of the basic work on molecular emission and absorption spectra was carried out on photographic spectrographs. A number of instruments, for instance, the Hilger-Spekker Photometer (Twyman, 1932), were designed to take a series of exposures on one photographic plate, the spectral images forming a set of evenly spaced bands from top to bottom. Each exposure contained the sample spectrum, and a reference spectrum reduced in intensity by linear units of extinction. To obtain an absorption curve from the photographic plate one merely had to place a spot at the edge of each image where reference and sample beams possessed equal intensity. The position of these spots outlined the absorption curve.

The development of photoelectric devices to replace the less dependable human eye markedly increased the precision and range of spectrophotometers, and opened the way for the development of modern instruments possessing a high degree of sensitivity and versatility. Light detectors of four types have been used, thermocouples, photoconductive cells, barrier cells (also called photovoltaic cells), and phototubes. Thermocouples depend upon the ability of absorbed light to raise the temperature of a bimetallic junction, often of constantan and copper. In the Boys (1889) radiomicrometer, one of the first photometric devices, the thermocouple junction was fastened against a blackened silver foil target, and leads were attached to a galvanometer for estimation of the amount of emitted current. This instrument was relatively insensitive, and obviously subject to fluctuations in room temperature. Sensitivity in later models was increased by the use of multiple thermocouple junctions, arranged in series to form the so-called thermopile. These detectors had the great advantage that their response was virtually independent of the illuminating wavelength. They thus afforded a good reference against which the highly wavelength-dependent photocells of other kinds could be compared. Thermocouple receptors have found application in plate densitometry, where high light sensitivity is not required. For example, chlorophyll absorption curves were obtained on single living *Euglena* cells with this detector by Baas-Becking and Ross (1925). Microspectra of *Euglena* cells were photographed on panchromatic film, using the Abbe microspectral ocular shown in Fig. 2. Film opacity was measured with a 6-volt tungsten lamp, the transmitted light falling on a thermocouple detector, with the current determined by galvanometer deflection. A similar detector, the bolometer, which still finds use as a detector in infrared spectroscopy,

also depends on the heating effect caused by incident radiation. The flux
to be measured falls upon a blackened coil of wire or thin metal strip,
and the increased resistance associated with the rise in temperature is
measured with a bridge circuit.

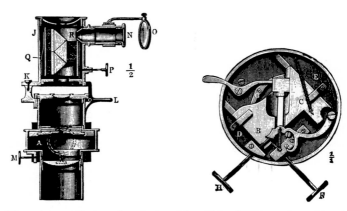

FIG. 2. The microspectral ocular, designed by Abbe (1870), and used in the studies
of MacMunn (1886), Keilin (1925), and many others is an example of the type of
instrument available in the late nineteenth century. A slit is present between the
two lenses of the Huygenian ocular (shown at the right). The side tube N projects a
wavelength scale on to the spectrum from light directed by the mirror O. In the
Amici prism, the central element of flint glass is inserted between two crown glass
prisms. (From the "Carl Zeiss Microscope Catalogue," 32nd edition, Jena, 1902.)

Although these temperature-estimating devices had an application in
plate densitometry and infrared photometry, photoelectric cells, employing photoconductive, photovoltaic, or photoemissive phenomena, were far
more selective and sensitive in their response, and thus applicable to
direct readings of absorption spectra. In 1873 Willoughby Smith discovered the photoconductive effect of sunlight on selenium rods, which he
was using as resistors in the experimental testing of circuits for sub-
marine cables. He noticed that resistance of the rods was almost twice as
great in the dark as in the sunlight. This finding stimulated the manufacture of many kinds of selenium cells, in which a thin film of the metal
filled the gap between two electrodes. Illumination of the selenium film
lowered the resistance of the cell a measurable amount. The early open
grids were subject to oxidation and deterioration by water vapor, and
thus required frequent calibration. In the later detectors selenium vapor
was deposited in vacuum on a gold or platinum grid on glass, and then
mounted in an evacuated tube. The similar photoconductive effect of
lead sulfide or galena crystals was discovered by Bose (1901), but was

virtually unused until the 1940's. These cells are highly sensitive to infrared radiation, and their use in applications involving "invisible" signaling was explored in World War II (Cashman, 1945). More recent photoconductive cells have utilized thallous sulfide (Case, 1920) to produce detectors of compact size and high sensitivity (Hewlett, 1947). Among the newest additions to the list are cells of silicon with intermediate sensitivity but high thermal stability, and also of cadmium sulfide (see Zworykin and Ramberg, 1949, for review).

In photoconductive cells, the effect of light on resistance of the element is measured. Detectors of this type thus demand a supply of stable electrical current for their operation. In photovoltaic cells, on the other hand, a current is generated by the photosensitive element itself, when subjected to illumination. These cells, called "barrier cells," since the current arises at the barrier between two surfaces, thus do not require an outside electrical source for their operation. The action of light in producing an electrical current (photovoltaic effect) was apparently first discovered by E. Becquerel in 1839 in his early experiments on wet cells. He reported that a current was generated when sunlight fell on an electrolyte solution in which two electrodes were immersed. The dry photovoltaic effect was first reported in 1878 by Adams and Day, who were stimulated to experiment with selenium by Willoughby Smith's discovery of the photoconductive effect. When crystalline selenium was deposited on an iron plate, and covered by a thin conducting film, a small current was detected upon illumination of the selenium layer through the covering electrode. A number of selenium barrier photocells, employing this principle, were made by Fruitts (1883), but received little attention and were never put to practical application. The principle was rediscovered more than 40 years later for coatings of cuprous oxide on copper, the covering electrode being first a spiral of lead wire (Grondahl, 1933), or later a sputtered film of gold or silver (B. Lange, 1930; Schottky, 1930). These and later investigators helped to develop the barrier cell into the familiar compact exposure meters that are in wide use today for exposure estimation in photography. The Photovolt barrier cell photometer, for example, is a rugged instrument designed for photomicrography. It has been used in the photometry of relatively large areas of tissue sections, for example, in the estimates of stained collagen in muscle (Wang, 1949).

Of all the light detectors so far available, phototubes have been the most sensitive and widely applicable to microphotometry of biological specimens. Light falling on certain photoemissive substances results in the release of electrons in direct proportion to the incident flux. This photoemissive effect was discovered by Hertz in 1887, in his classical experiments with spark gaps. Using a gap in which the electrode distance was carefully measured, he reported that the maximal jump distance was increased by the presence of a neighboring spark. He later showed with other light sources and a spectroscope that this lengthening of the jump distance was due to the effects of ultraviolet light upon the negative terminal of the gap. This phenomenon was explored further by several investigators. Hallwachs (1888) used a polished sphere of zinc, attached to a gold leaf spectroscope. If the sphere was negatively charged, it lost its charge quickly upon irradiation with ultraviolet light. If the sphere was positively charged, the light had no effect, but with two spheres one positive, one negative, placed side by side, ultraviolet irradiation of the negatively charged sphere resulted in the loss of charge from both. Hallwachs concluded that the ultraviolet light produced a flow of negative electricity along the electrostatic lines of force. In later experiments Stoletow (1890) attached a polished metal plate to the negative terminal of a voltaic pile battery. In front of the plate a coarse-mesh wire grid was placed, connected to a galvanometer which was in turn attached to the positive terminal of the battery. Illumination of the plate with ultraviolet light produced a flow of electrons from plate to grid, which was measured in the galvanometer.

In the transition from early experimental studies to working phototubes, the monumental work of Elster and Geitel (1890 et seq.) is undoubtedly the most significant. Since the photoemissive effect by 1890 was known to be a property of the electrochemically positive elements zinc, magnesium, and aluminum, it seemed probable to Elster and Geitel that the still more positive alkali metals sodium, potassium, cesium, and rubidium would exhibit the effect even more strongly. These substances oxidize so rapidly they could not be used alone, but were amalgamated with mercury, and the surfaces enclosed in a vacuum tube for protection. These first vacuum phototubes were found to be sensitive not only to ultraviolet radiation, but to visible light as well.

Much of the research on phototubes in the years that followed concentrated in the production of alkali-metal photoemissive surfaces. These compounds for the most part are highly reactive chemically, and the preparation of stable photocathodes required multiple applications of different interacting components applied *in vacuo,* demanding considerable engineering skill. Common multilayer surfaces now in commercial use include silver-cesium oxide-silver (S-1), silver-rubidium oxide-rubidium (S-3), antimony-cesium (S-4), or bismuth-cesium (S-8), each with characteristic sensitivities and wavelength response (see Zworykin and Ramberg, 1949).

The final, and highly important step in the development of modern phototubes, concerned the utilization of secondary emission within the detector. Secondary emission phototubes employ a series of emissive surfaces or dynodes, arranged in a linear or circular series, each with a stronger positive charge than the previous dynode. Light striking the photocathode, at zero potential, causes the emission of electrons, which are drawn to the first dynode, which carries a potential of approximately 100 volts. For every primary electron there is an emission of several secondary electrons, and these are drawn in turn to the second dynode, which carries a still larger potential. Each dynode stage thus involves an amplification of between 2 and 10 times the flux from the preceding surface. The nine dynodes of the commonly used 1P21 phototube involve a collective amplification factor of 2 million times at 100 volts per dynode, to provide a phototube with sensitivities of 40 amp per lumen. This may be compared with the approximate value 100 to 1000 microamperes per lumen obtainable with barrier cells, or one-stage phototubes.

These electron multiplier phototubes, aside from their extreme sensitivity, possess a rapid and linear response, and have surprisingly low dark currents, which may be reduced still further upon cooling the tube to liquid air temperatures. The standard 1P21 phototube, if cooled to $-180°C$, can detect light fluxes of 6×10^{-14} lumen, equivalent to about 260 quanta of green light per second. Although even greater sensitivities have recently been obtained, the simplicity, sensitivity, and linearity of photomultipliers make them convenient to many photometric applications. The end window tubes, where the photoemissive layer is deposited on a disk about 3 cm in diameter, have proven extremely useful for biological application in microphotometry.

Thus in the short period of a few decades photometry has emerged from the basic experiments on the effect of light on spark gaps and selenium rods, to provide the efficient and highly sensitive detectors in use today.

III. Applications

The biological advances in microphotometry must be interpreted against the rapidly changing techniques of spectroscopy and photometry outlined in the preceding section. The microphotometry of cells can be conveniently divided into three areas: (A) the study of naturally pigmented cell components by visible light, (B) the study of nucleic acids and proteins by ultraviolet light, and (C) the study of cytochemical reactions, mostly involving visible light microphotometry.

A. Cell Pigments

Most early workers on hemoglobin, such as Preyer, Hoppe-Seyler, and others, were primarily interested in the position of absorption bands, and the shifts in their position following various treatments of the sample. In many instances band positions were determined merely by eye in spectroscopic examination of hemoglobin solutions, with Fraunhofer lines and sodium arcs used for points of reference. For later studies on the kinetics of blood oxygenation and the formation of carboxyhemoglobin, it was necessary to perfect the methods of spectral analysis. The spectroscopic techniques of Hartridge on hemoglobin helped to prepare the necessary instrumentation for the monumental work to follow by Keilin on the cytochromes, and by Warburg on cytochrome oxidase.

Hartridge (1912) was interested in determining the ratio, in a small blood sample, of oxy- to carboxyhemoglobin. He demonstrated a shift in α and β absorption bands when oxygen was replaced by carbon monoxide, and devised a method for accurate determination of the position of the α band. From this he was able to calculate the oxy- to carboxyhemoglobin ratio. Band positions were determined by a "reversion spectroscope" in which two indentical spectra were presented side by side, one of which was reversed in polarity. The position of the spectra, with respect to one another, was changed by a prism until the points of peak absorption were matched by eye, and the degree of adjustment required was noted. This paper also presented some of the earliest absorption curves of hemoglobin solutions, apparently made by eye with the help of a wedge cuvette.

In a later paper on the same subject, Hartridge and Roughton (1928) stressed the greater accuracy obtainable with photographic methods in the estimation of oxy- to carboxyhemoglobin ratios, and also mentioned the advantage of having a permanent record of the data. In this study, spectra were photographed on Ilford chromatic plates, and the densities determined by a selenium photoconductive cell, the resistance being measured by a mirror galvanometer. To avoid the errors due to non-linearity and drift in the selenium cell response, plate density was compared in a double-beam system with a neutral density wedge. The wedge position was adjusted by hand, so that similar galvanometer readings were obtained for plate and wedge. The wedge position was then determined on a vernier scale, and from this the optical density was obtained.

The presence of a respiratory pigment in muscle and other tissues of both invertebrates and vertebrates was first described by MacMunn in 1886 using the Abbe microspectral ocular shown in Fig. 2. This pigment, which he called myohaematin or histohaematin, was characterized by four absorption bands in the reduced state, which disappeared on oxidation. "Myohaematin may be considered as the true intrinsic colouring matter of muscle, and the histohaematins the intrinsic colouring matters of the tissues and organs; both may be reinforced or replaced at times by haemoglobin when extra-activity of internal respiration is required;

probably the same radical may be made use of for building up all these pigments" (MacMunn, 1886). MacMunn's evidence was disputed by Hoppe-Seyler (1890), who claimed the four bands arose from the super-position of two reduced and two oxidized bands of hemoglobin, and who apparently totally ignored the findings MacMunn reported for inver-tebrates without hemoglobin. This opposition from a distinguished au-thority was enough to assure the lack of acceptance of MacMunn's new pigment, and it was largely forgotten until the work of Keilin 40 years later.

Keilin's (1925) observations on a wide variety of cell types, including bacteria, yeast, higher plants, and the muscles of various vertebrates and invertebrates, were made on fresh cells or tissues in small vessels or crushed between glass plates, and viewed with a microscope equipped with an Abbe ocular spectroscope. For accurate determination of band positions Keilin used the Hartridge reversion spectroscope, adapted for use with the microscope. In classical experiments, he described the pres-ence of the four absorption bands, in almost precisely the position es-timated by MacMunn. They were particularly evident in excised flight muscles of insects, vertebrate striated muscle, and baker's yeast. Keilin measured the light transmitted through the thorax of a living wax moth which had been cleaned of scales and fastened to a slide with gum arabic. When the animal was at rest the absorption bands were absent, but when the moth was struggling to free itself, the bands became faintly visible, only to vanish again when the animal stopped moving. In a gas chamber in the presence of nitrogen, coal gas, or potassium cyanide, the four bands became very pronounced, but faded when oxygen was again introduced and the animal began to recover. From these and other experiments Keilin defined the physiological properties of the cytochromes, and postulated that they were an essential component of aerobic metabolism.

In another classical use of spectroscopic techniques in the study of respiratory pigments, Warburg and Christian (1933) determined the absorption curve for cytochrome oxidase. The presence of an iron-con-taining respiratory enzyme in tissues was first suspected from the in-creased respiration produced in sea urchin cytoplasm by the addition of traces of iron. Carbon monoxide was also shown to affect the respiratory rate of yeast cells, but to a greater degree in the dark than in the light. Since Haldane had earlier shown that light similarly effects the release of carbon monoxide from hemoglobin, it was suspected that yeast pos-sessed a hemoporphyrin-containing respiratory enzyme, distinguishable from Keilin's cytochromes, which do not combine with carbon monoxide. This assumption was supported by studies on *in vitro* model systems in-volving the effects of light on complexes of carbon monoxide and hemoporphyrin. Warburg was able to determine the absorption spectrum of cytochrome oxidase, in spite of its exceedingly low concentration and instability to attempted isolation. This was done by treating suspensions of yeast cells with carbon monoxide in the dark, then illuminating them in monochromatic light of different wavelengths, and recording the efficiency of different regions of the spectrum in the photo-reversal of carbon monoxide inhibition. This ingenious method required adequate sources of intense monochromatic light, which were obtained by isolation of lines from a mercury lamp, and open arcs of magnesium, zinc, tungsten, and carbon. It also required the accurate estimation of line intensities, and for this purpose the amalgam photocell of Elster and Geitel was employed.

The brilliant studies of Keilin and Warburg, in which photometric methods have played an essential role, have laid the foundation for modern work on other cell components which possess specific absorption characteristics enabling them to be detected amid the complexities of cell metabolism. The kinetics of catalase–hydrogen peroxide interaction have been studied by Chance (1951). This enzyme, like cytochrome oxidase, also possesses a heme prosthetic group, and has an absorption maximum near 410 mμ. On association with hydrogen peroxide, or its methyl derivative, the absorption peak is depressed, so that the formation of the enzyme-substrate complex may be followed. The reaction is almost immediate, and its study required a rapidly acting mixing chamber, and an apparatus for rapid oscillograph recording of changes in optical density, utilizing photomultiplier tubes and a chopper amplifier. In other applications of recording spectrophotometers Chance (1951) has followed the changes in cytochrome absorption when an energy source, for instance, succinate, is added to the cell suspension. This results in the reduction of different cytochrome components at different times following succinate addition, each showing a characteristic shift in absorption. In this manner the sequential steps in the electron transport system can be followed. The simultaneous recording of two different signals was made possible by a vibrating mirror system, which alternately directed light from two different monochromators onto the same detector. The two paths could be employed to monitor changes with time at two different wavelengths in the same preparation. The difference between the two signals was relatively insensitive to total changes in absorbance or scatter in the system, provided both paths were affected equally. The recorder was highly sensitive, however, to any shifts affecting only one optical path. The instrument thus could be set to select and monitor specific alterations such as cytochrome oxidation involving shifts in single absorption bands.

There is a vast difference in instrumentation from the simple spectroscope and watch glass chamber of Ray-Lankester, to the elaborate oscillograph recordings of Chance. In the comparatively short span of less
than a century, the first simple studies on hemoglobin and chlorophyll
were later extended to a variety of other porphyrin-containing pigments,
and more recently to still other systems, such as visual pigments (Brown,
1961) and pyridine nucleotide fluorescence (Chance, 1962). Most visible
light studies have had the great advantage of being applicable to living
cells, where they may provide sensitive indications of shifts in cell
metabolism, in some cases even down to the level of single mitochondria
(Thorell, 1964), detecting metabolic changes in only 10^{-20} mole, or 6000
molecules, of cytochrome b.

B. Ultraviolet Absorption

The presence of infrared "heat" radiation beyond the visible limits of
the spectrum was first described by Herschel in 1801. Directly stimulated
by this discovery, Ritter in the same year looked for invisible rays at the
violet end of the sun's spectrum. He was able to detect "actinic" rays
from their action on silver chloride. This was the first of innumerable
studies on ultraviolet light. With the discovery in 1835 by Brewster of
fluorescence, a phenomenon he called "internal dispersion," the presence
of ultraviolet light became detectable by the use of fluorescent salts or
minerals. Provided the light source was intense enough, qualitative studies
could be thus made on the relative transparency or opacity of substances
placed in the ultraviolet light path. The fact that many biological substances fluoresce in ultraviolet light was determined by Stokes, who
published his monograph "On the change of refrangibility of light" in
1852. Stokes used two liquid filters for his studies, one filled with cupram-
monium as a dark blue filter, and as a yellow barrier filter a solution of
bichromate of potash. Sunlight was directed by mirrors through the blue
solution into a darkened room. Materials were illuminated with the blue
(and near ultraviolet) light, and viewed through the yellow filter. Stokes
described the "refrangible radiations" of bones, horn, ivory, leather, cork,
cotton, and many other biological substances.

The study of emission spectra advanced rapidly toward the end of the
19th century (see Brode, 1939, for review). With spectrographic instruments the positions of many emission lines were photographically
recorded and measured throughout the ultraviolet, visible, and infrared
spectrum. This active area of physical research provided spectroscopists
with a variety of monochromatic light sources which could be utilized for
absorption studies. Many of these early line sources were open spark gaps,
in which different metals could be used as electrodes. The specific spectral

lines were then isolated by prisms or gratings and passed through samples of biological material. For example, a crude absorption curve for muscle protein was determined by Soret in 1883. Ground calf muscle was extracted with 1% hydrochloric acid, the solution placed in a quartz cuvette, and studied under the ultraviolet emission lines from a cadmium spark. Soret reported that the solution was transparent to the Cd^{14} line ($\lambda = 325$), absorbed strongly with the Cd^{17} line ($\lambda = 275$) weakly at Cd^{18} ($\lambda = 257$), and heavily again at Cd^{20} ($\lambda = 232$). The characteristic ultraviolet absorption band of proteins in the vicinity of $\lambda = 280$ was thus described.

Quartz optics for ultraviolet microscopy were designed by Köhler and von Rohr in 1904. The impetus for this highly important work came not so much from an interest in the absorption characteristics of tissue components, as in a desire to increase the resolving power of the microscope. As such it was a logical continuation of the remarkable progress made in both the theory and practice of lens design during the end of the 19th century. The work of Lord Rayleigh and of Abbe served to emphasize the dependence of microscope resolution both on wavelength of light used and numerical aperture of the optical system. With the development of immersion objectives, perfected in the United States by R. B. Tolles in 1874 (see Cox, 1884), and the design of apochromatic objectives by Abbe (1886), the numerical aperture was pushed to the practical extreme of 1.40. But the wavelength could obviously be shortened by changing the illuminating light from visible to ultraviolet, with a theoretical gain in resolving power of about 2 times. The first ultraviolet lenses were designed for use with the magnesium spark line with a wavelength of 280 mμ. With this monochromatic light source, there was no need for color correction. The objectives were thus manufactured only of quartz, although fluorite components, a material also permeable to ultraviolet, were included in the oculars. Later a second series of quartz monochromats was designed for use with the cadmium spark line of 275 mμ.

Köhler (1904) described in detail the design and use of the ultraviolet system, which was manufactured by Carl Zeiss. The light source, both noisy and potentially lethal, was powered by a battery-operated transformer which provided 8000 volts at 2 to 5 amp. The spark gap could be fitted with either magnesium or cadmium electrodes, and a monochromator of two quartz prisms served to isolate either the magnesium 280 mμ or cadmium 275 mμ lines. Quartz collimator lenses, a quartz Abbe condenser, and quartz-fluorite oculars were provided, as well as a *Sucher* which fitted above the ocular, and focused the ultraviolet image upon a fluorescent screen of uranium glass. The apparatus also contained a camera for photographic recording of the ultraviolet images. A number of photomicrographs were published by Köhler, demonstrating that the expected increase in resolution was actually obtained, as shown by added detail in the structure of diatom shells. Also included were photomicrographs of an unstained section of frog eye, showing the heavy protein absorption at 275 mμ of the crystalline lens. In addition, as reproduced in Fig. 3, there were photomicrographs of unfixed salamander epidermis

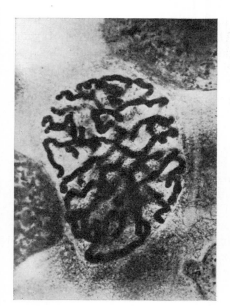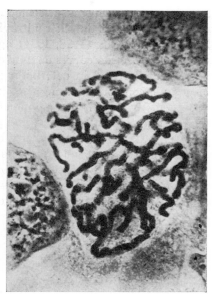

FIG. 3. Epidermal cells from *Salamander maculosa* larva, photographed by Köhler in 1904 at 275 mμ (left) and 280 mμ (right). Magnification 1300×; exposure 50 seconds at left, 10 seconds at right. Köhler remarked about the intense ultraviolet absorption shown by the prophase "spireme."

nuclei, mounted on glycerine, and photographed at 275 and 280 mμ. Köhler remarked about the intense ultraviolet absorption of the chromatin material.

The quartz monochromatic lenses of Köhler and von Rohr were expensive, and cumbersome for most biologists to use. In the decade that followed, the apparatus received scant attention and the few workers who used the equipment for the most part only emphasized the added resolving power obtained. Ernst and Wolbach (1906) published micrographs of a number of microorganisms, and concluded, "There is no question that much greater detail can be demonstrated with it than by any other method." Meigs (1908) showed micrographs of insect muscle fibers, but only in a footnote acknowledged the fact that ultraviolet light was employed. To Vlès (1911), however, the absorption characteristics shown by tissues in ultraviolet light were specifically of interest. He sited the early work of Soret (1883) on the ultraviolet absorption of muscle proteins, and with Köhler's ultraviolet microscope demonstrated the greater absorption at 275 mμ of the A band and the Z line in striated muscle of crayfish and house flies, indicative of their higher protein concentration. He also noted the strong ultraviolet absorption of muscle nuclei, but for some reason seemed more interested in the refractive index of the nuclei than in their ultraviolet absorption. A number of years later Vlès and Gex (1928, 1934) again utilized the Köhler quartz lenses to make absorption curves on unfixed sea urchin eggs. In the interim Vlès had been interested in determining the absorption spectra of a number of organic compounds, using the photographic recording spectrograph of Jobin and Yvon. This was a double-beam instrument utilizing mercury or hydrogen arcs as light source, and photographic recording. The reference spectrum was reduced in intensity by known amounts with an adjustable slit, and the intensity match points between sample and reference beams were marked on the plate as in the Spekker spectrograph mentioned above. Vlès (1934) presented a manual for the use of this apparatus, including directions for the timing of photographs by counting the "tops" on a metronome, and the use of a specially designed peg board for keeping track of the exposures. In applying the instrument to living unfertilized sea urchin eggs Vlès and Gex were hampered by the marked refractive index difference between egg and sea water, and also by the fact that the quartz monochromatic optics, if focused at one wavelength, were increasingly out of focus at other wavelengths and thus provided extinctions which were much too low. The quartz lenses were designed by Köhler and von Rohr to be used at a single wavelength, and possessed no color correction. They thus did not easily lend themselves to methods in which entire spectra are displayed in the photographic plate. Vlès and Gex were able partially to overcome this difficulty by making a composite absorption curve of eggs that had been focused at three different wavelengths (546, 340, and 260 mμ), providing a *spectre-enveloppe*. One such absorption curve is shown in Fig. 4, and demonstrates both the high nucleoprotein absorption at 260–280 mμ reported by these workers, and the absorption of the echinochrome pigment in the 350–400 mμ region. These pioneering studies of Vlès and Gex, in spite of their shortcomings, were among the first specifically to be directed toward the exploitation of ultraviolet absorption techniques in the analysis of cell components. As such they helped to attract the attention of other investigators to the potential importance of the method.

Studies on the ultraviolet absorption of tumor cells, grasshopper spermatocytes, and blue green algae were made at the Bell Telephone Laboratories by Lucas (1930, 1934). Besides noting the higher resolution obtainable in ultraviolet light, Lucas also emphasized the strong absorption of chromatin material. In addition, because of the narrow depth of focus of the quartz monochromats, he showed that it was possible to study in detail the distribution of chromatin within a nucleus by taking

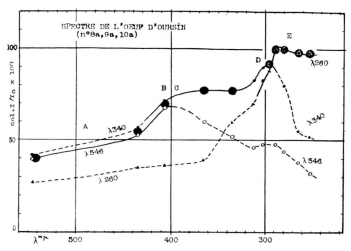

Fig. 4. Absorption spectrum of sea urchin eggs obtained by Vlès and Gex (1934). The large dark circles were considered to represent the "spectral envelope" of the cell. In other places the cell is out of focus. One curve was from a spectrum focused at 546 mμ, another at 340 mμ, and another at 260 mμ. The ultraviolet protein absorption is shown at E, and the near ultraviolet–visible absorption of echinochrome pigments at B and C.

a series of micrographs at different focal levels, a process which he called "optical sectioning." To analyze the chromatin distribution, positive transparencies of the micrographs were made and the density of absorbing material was determined for various transsects of the nuclear image with a recording densitometer, utilizing a thermopile as light detector. Although in these studies Lucas, as a metallurgist, was primarily interested in pointing out to biologists the possibilities of the instrument, they represent one of the first uses of densitometric recording equipment in the analysis of cytological material. Lucas also made the valuable discovery that the Köhler monochromats, although corrected for a wavelength of 275 mμ, nevertheless could provide good micrographs when used with line sources at other wavelengths. He published (1934) micrographs of the blue-green alga *Gleocapsa* taken at 275, 260, and 230 mμ, demonstrating the intense absorption of the cells at the lowest wavelength. He also reported the lethal effects of ultraviolet light, particularly at 230 mμ. He further suggested that studies on the comparative ultraviolet sensitivity of different cell types might prove of interest. The possible importance of ultraviolet photography in the analysis of chromosome structure was stressed by Lucas and Stark (1931), and a series of micrographs of stages in grasshopper spermatogenesis were presented. In the papers of Lucas, as in those of Vlès, the feeling is stated that ultraviolet techniques may be of potentially great cytological importance, provided certain technical details can be overcome. Lucas also stated, however, that "perhaps the greatest fault to be found with the ultraviolet microscope is its reaction on the operator. The concentration and the accuracy required for successful operation, the strain on the eyesight of the individual, and the nervous reaction prove tiring to the point of exhaustion at times" (Lucas and Stark, 1931). Anyone who has aligned and used a Köhler ultraviolet optical system will understand what he means.

Several other investigators during this period also used the Köhler quartz lenses. Wyckoff and Ter Louw (1931a,b), were interested in the lethal effects of ultraviolet light upon *Bacillus subtilus*, and showed that ultraviolet photomicrographs could be taken with exposures short enough to maintain cell viability. Later Wyckoff and Ebeling (1933) took ultraviolet micrographs of a variety of cell types, and concluded "that 2750 Å light is intensely absorbed by the chromosomes of many, if not all, dividing cells," and that photographs made with wavelengths above 3535 Å were indistinguishable from those made with visible light, showing only refraction and no absorption.

Micrographs of *Euglena* were made by Swann and del Rosario (1932), who noted the correspondence between the degree of ultraviolet absorption and the relative lethal effects, when light of 2435, 2894, 3132, and 3654 Å were compared. Similar results were found for *Euglena* by Allen *et al.* (1934), and were extended to a number of normal and neoplastic mammalian cells. These authors also emphasized, as did Lucas, that the quartz monochromats could provide good photomicrographs at a wide variety of wavelengths, provided the microscope was carefully refocused after each wavelength change. A graph of fine adjustment turns, plotted against wavelength, was provided to specify the focal point for each wavelength.

Up to this time a number of laboratories had used the Köhler objectives for studies of cell absorption. It was frequently stressed that cell components, particularly nuclei and chromosomes, showed strong ultraviolet absorption in the 260 mμ region. Although the fact that proteins absorbed ultraviolet light was well known at this time, most workers did not realize the important contribution made to cell absorbance by nucleic acids. It had even been suggested both by Policard (1928) and Scott (1932) that the strong ultraviolet absorption of nuclei and chromosomes might be due to their high content of calcium. This was in spite of the fact that the ultraviolet absorption of various purine and pyrimidine derivatives had been known for some time (Soret, 1883; Hartley, 1905; Dhéré, 1906). The possibility that nucleoproteins might be responsible for nuclear absorption was mentioned by von Schrötter in 1906, but he emphasized only the protein contribution.

It remained for Caspersson in his monumental thesis of 1936 to present the first definitive evidence of the importance of nucleic acids in the ultraviolet absorption of tissues. This was accomplished first by the theoretical analysis of absorbing and scattering properties of colloidal suspensions and refracting-absorbing spheres. It was concluded that the absorption curves obtainable could indeed provide an accurate representation of the absorbing materials of the cell (Caspersson, 1932b, 1933a,b). Second, photographic plate densitometry was developed to the greatest obtainable accuracy, to provide absorption curves of small cell regions, down to 1 mμ in diameter. Third, the absorption curves of biological material were compared with those from solutions of isolated nucleic acids and proteins.

The instrument used by Caspersson in his early photometric studies was essentially the Köhler ultraviolet microscope, with the improved rotating disk cadmium and magnesium electrodes described by Köhler in 1933. Individual ultraviolet photomicrographs were taken of each specimen at a variety of wavelengths. Each plate also included the image of a standard gray reference wedge, on which the optical densities were inscribed. Plate densities were determined, as in the studies of Lucas (1934), with a recording densitometer, utilizing a tungsten light source and a thermopile photometer. Each point on the absorption curve thus required a change in the monochromator to the proper line source, the refocusing of the microscope with the aid of the *Sucher*, taking and processing the photomicrograph, taking traces through object and background with the plate densitometer, and finally measuring the height of the tracing above background, and correcting the value by means of the gray wedge standard. This was a slow and painstaking process at best, and it is not surprising that the 1936 treatise was devoted largely to operational problems, both theoretical and practical, and comparatively little to actual biological data.

As an experimental proof of the method of photographic photometry, Caspersson devised a model system, in which small spheres of scharlach R dye dissolved in hexane were dispersed in a sugar solution of similar refractive index. Small spheres from 4 μ to 60 μ diameter were measured, and the maximal extinction of each sphere was plotted against its diameter. This provided a straight line relationship, except for the largest droplets, which showed a deformation due to gravity. Absorption curves of individual droplets were also made, and compared with absorption curves of the scharlach R dye obtained with a standard spectrophotometer. A photomicrograph of model spheres is shown in Fig. 5, together

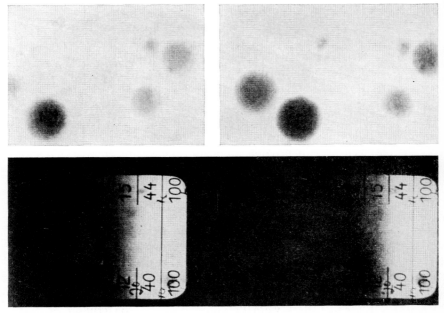

Fig. 5. A model system used to test the accuracy of microphotometric methods by Caspersson (1936). Spheres of scharlach R dye in hexane are suspended in a glucose solution, and photographed in visible light. Gray wedges for plate calibration are photographed on the same exposure (below). (cf. Fig. 6.)

with the image of the gray calibration wedge. In Fig. 6 are plotted the individual photometric measurements. This test afforded a simple and graphic demonstration of the linearity and accuracy of the microphotometric method, under conditions closely approaching those utilized with biological material.

Caspersson also demonstrated that the absorption curves actually obtained on cytological material in most cases could be resolved into only two components, attributable to overlapping absorption of nucleic acid and protein. In the upper part of Fig. 7 (from Caspersson, 1936) densitometer traces are shown superimposed for the same region of a grasshopper spermatocyte chromosome about 1.5 μ in diameter, made at different wavelengths on a 5 μ Carnoy-fixed section. In the bottom figure (Fig. 7) the same values are plotted in curve 1 for the center of the chromosome, and in curve 2 for the cytoplasm beside it. The chromosome was of course

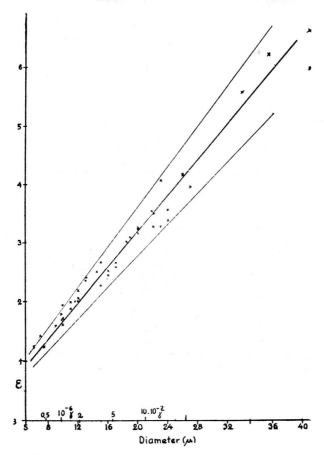

Fig. 6. A quantitative test of microphotometry (Caspersson, 1936). Measurements were made on the scharlach R spheres shown in Fig. 5, and the measured extinction of the sphere center was plotted against the sphere diameter, providing the expected linear relationship.

overlaid with cytoplasm through which the light passed. Thus to obtain the absorption of the chromosome alone, 0.7 times the cytoplasmic absorption was subtracted (curve 4), giving the difference curve (curve 3) for the chromosome alone. This was compared with the absorption of an 11% solution of nucleic acid with a 5 μ path length (curve 5). The curves for the chromosome and the nucleic acid solution are similar, but the chromosome shows added absorption particularly to the right of the peak. This is attributable largely to protein absorption, and also, in lesser degree, to light scatter.

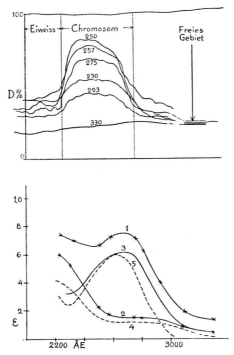

Fig. 7. Ultraviolet absorption measurements of a grasshopper (*Chorthippus*) metaphase chromosome (Caspersson, 1936). The upper figure shows densitometer traces made across a region of the same chromosome photographed at different wavelengths. The cytoplasmic (Eiweiss) absorption is at the left of the figure, and a background area (Freies Gebiet) at the right. In the lower figure, extinction values for chromosome (1) and cytoplasm (2) are plotted against wavelength. In curve (3) the absorption due to the chromosome alone has been estimated, by subtracting absorption from the cytoplasm lying above and below the chromosome (curve 1 minus curve 4 equals curve 3). Curve 5 is a nucleic acid curve for comparison (11% nucleic acid, 5 μ path length).

In the years that followed, Caspersson and his collaborators continually improved and extended photometric methods and equipment, in a series of brilliant developments in instrumentation. In 1940 an instrument designed for direct photometric recording of ultraviolet light absorption was described (Caspersson, 1940a), in which the microscope image was projected onto a screen by a movable quartz prism placed above the ocular. The screen contained an adjustable diaphragm, behind which was located a sensitive cadmium, sodium, or potassium phototube. Also in the light path, between prism and screen, was placed a rotating sector, which could be adjusted while in motion, to provide a continuously variable reduction in the light intensity. Direct photometric measurements were made by placing the cell region in the center of the microscope field, and projecting the image of the small area to be measured on the phototube. The phototube output for the object was then read on a sensitive galvanometer. The slide was then moved to an adjacent background area, and the background beam was dimmed by the rotating sector, until it matched the reading for the object. The extent to which the rotating sector was changed provided the measure of optical density.

Other modifications included provision for water-cooled high-pressure mercury arc and tungsten light sources in addition to the Köhler spark gap, and the design of a stage suspended by plates of quartz so that the cell could be moved aside to obtain background readings, but returned to its original position with great precision, so that precisely the same cell region could be measured at different wavelengths. These improved instruments were among the first in a long series, of which the Zeiss UMSP instrument described by Trapp in this volume represents one of the most recent contributions.

The early work of Caspersson and his collaborators undoubtedly did much to emphasize the importance of nucleic acids in gene structure and protein synthesis. Caspersson (1936) demonstrated that chromosomes of grasshopper testes and salivary glands of fly larvae (*Drosophila* and *Chironomus*) showed strong ultraviolet absorption at 260 mμ, associated with their content of DNA. He also showed that rapidly growing yeast cells absorbed much more strongly than old stationary cultures, a finding he associated with the fact that they were more rapidly dividing. The presence of high concentrations of nucleic acids, probably RNA, in the cytoplasm of *Drosophila* embryos and onion root meristems was described by Caspersson and Schultz (1939). Absorption curves from this paper, showing strong, predominantly nucleotide absorption in the growth zone and weak predominantly protein absorption in the root base, are graphed in Fig. 8. The authors concluded, "It seems likely that a high concentration of nucleic acids is the basis of the generally noted basophily of embryonic tissues. Those here discussed are strongly basophilic, in correlation with the high ultra-violet absorption. The presence of pentose nucleotides in high concentrations in rapidly dividing tissues is probably thus a general phenomenon." In later studies the role of cytoplasmic RNA in pancreatic protein synthesis was stressed (Caspersson *et al.*,

1941), and also in the functional relationships of the neuron (Hydén, 1943). Thus it was realized that RNA played an essential part in inter-phase synthesis, not in respect to mitosis alone. The studies of Hydén were of particular importance in their emphasis on the nucleolus. Since marked changes in nucleolar volume were observed during embryonic neuron development, and also in experimentally induced axon regenera-

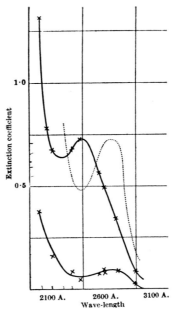

FIG. 8. A demonstration of the high nucleic acid concentration in growing cells of an onion root tip, and the low, predominantly protein, absorption in cells from the root base. In the dotted line, the lower curve has been multiplied by 8, to emphasize the difference in curve shape (Caspersson and Schultz, 1939).

tion, it became clear that the nucleolus also played some basic and essential role in the process of cytoplasmic synthesis. Changes in the heterochromatic material associated with the nucleolus were also noted, and it was concluded that these demonstrated the formation of nucleolar proteins by the heterochromatin.

These early studies in ultraviolet absorption were somewhat hampered by the difficulty of distinguishing DNA from RNA in chromosome ab-sorption, and also in the relative insensitivity of the method for the analysis of proteins. Caspersson (1939) described an increase in ab-sorbance per nucleus during the meiotic prophase in grasshopper testes. These determinations probably represent the first photometric estimates of the amount of nucleic acid per nucleus, but the presence of large amounts of chromosomal RNA was unsuspected, and so the increase was incorrectly attributed to the prophase synthesis of DNA. A great deal of effort was spent (Caspersson, 1940b, 1941) in the detailed analysis of protein absorption curves, and an interesting shift in the peak for protein-bound tryosine was demonstrated both in the heterochromatin and the nucleolus of a number of cell types. Both of these components also showed strong binding by acid dyes (Hydén, 1943) and were suspected of being rich in the "hexone bases" arginine, histidine, and lysine. Caspersson concluded that the shift in tyrosine absorption was due to the presence of histone proteins in nucleoli and heterochromatin, proteins known to contain high concentrations of these basic diamino acids, a conclusion not confirmed by later investigations (for instance, Mirsky and Pollister, 1946).

The general theory of the role of nuclear nucleic acids and proteins in cytoplasmic protein synthesis was summarized by Caspersson in 1950. "A certain part of the chromatin . . . , called the *nucleolus-associated chromatin,* produces substances of protein nature. There are indications that these substances contain considerable amounts of diamino acids. They accumulate and form the main bulk of a large nucleolus. From the nucleolus they diffuse towards the nuclear membrane, on the outside of which an intensive production of ribose nucleotides takes place. At the same time, the amount of cytoplasmic proteins increases." The theory was impressive in its universal application to all higher cells. It was widely if sometimes dogmatically reiterated, and had a very important influence upon the developing concepts of cellular synthetic mechanisms. Although later findings refuted the role of histones in nucleolar formation, Caspersson's theory correctly emphasized chromatin-nucleolus relationships and the important relation between the nucleolus and cytoplasmic RNA.

Ultraviolet photometry has been applied to a variety of other cytological problems, including the study of nucleic acids and proteins in tumor cells (Caspersson and Santesson, 1942), during erythrocyte formation (Thorell, 1947), and in the detailed study of salivary gland chromosomes, directed toward mechanisms of gene replication and gene action. Caspersson and Schultz (1938) reported a localized effect on the nucleic acids of single chromosome bands produced by a translocation involving heterochromatin. Cole and Sutton (1940), utilizing a photographic microphotometric method, in which each plate contained the image of a rotating sector step wedge (Cole and Bracket, 1940), were unable to confirm the effects of translocations on band contents. Ultraviolet absorption methods were later employed by Rudkin and Corlette (1957) to demonstrate an

increase during puffing in the DNA of certain chromosome regions of
Rhynchosciara. Nucleoproteins of growing fibroblasts in tissue culture
was studied by Walker and Yates (1952). Uber (1939) analyzed the
ultraviolet absorption characteristics of maize pollen, in which pollen
wall and cytoplasm were separately studied. Absorption curves for plant
cell wall components, particularly lignin, were also given by P. Lange
(1944).

Ultraviolet microphotometry has obviously been limited in its applicability only to those cell components with strong characteristic absorption. Also, results have frequently been difficult to interpret, since they
necessarily involve the superposition of absorption from nucleic acid,
protein, and nonspecific loss from scattered light. In addition, the needed
equipment has been expensive, and in many cases both awkward and
difficult to use. Probably for these reasons ultraviolet photometry has not
been widely used in cytological research, and has in many cases been
supplanted by the far simpler methods of staining and photometry with
visible light. Nevertheless, ultraviolet photometry has provided direct
estimations of cell components, without recourse to the complications of
cytochemical color reactions. Aside from their cytological importance,
however, the elegant studies of the Caspersson school represent the first
effective use of cytophotometric methods, providing a basis for the later
work of Pollister and collaborators, and also of Lison and Pasteels,
Walker, Rudkin, Sandritter, and many more.

C. Photometry of Cytochemical Reactions

It was evident early in the study of stained tissue sections that the
strong affinity shown by certain tissues for certain dyes was a function of
the chemical composition of the tissue itself. It was suggested by Mathews
(1898), for example, that the marked basophilia of rat pancreas cytoplasm was attributable to the high concentration of cytoplasmic "nu-
cleins." Similar conclusions are implied in the basiophilia of the "ergastoplasm" reported in guinea pig salivary glands by Garnier (1900), or in
the cytoplasmic "chromidia" of annelid eggs described by Lillie in 1906.
Cytoplasmic basophilia was further linked to the presence of RNA in the
ribonuclease studies of Van Herwerden (1913), which provided a background for the important cytochemical studies on developing sea urchin
and amphibian eggs by Brachet (1933, 1940a,b). Brachet clearly demonstrated, by the use of pyronin dye binding and ribonuclease extraction,
that RNA was a major component of oocyte nucleoli and cytoplasm, and
that these cell components underwent marked changes in RNA levels in
association with specific developmental stages.

A number of investigators (for instance, Stearn and Stearn, 1929) have pointed out that the binding of basic dyes by nucleic acids, and of acid dyes by proteins, is largely an electrostatic phenomenon. Important studies on nucleic acid–basic dye interaction were carried out by DeJong and Lens (1932) and Kelley (1939). The kinetics of acid dye–protein binding were similarly studied by Chapman *et al.* (1927), Fraenkel-Conrat and Cooper (1944), and Singer and Morrison (1948). All of these investigations served to show that, provided conditions of tissue fixation and staining were carefully controlled, reproducible relationships were obtainable between the number of charged residues available within the tissue, and the amount of dye bound.

With the discovery of the Feulgen reaction (Feulgen and Rossenbeck, 1924) the cytology of chromatin was immeasurably advanced. In most cells it became a simple matter to distinguish between the DNA-containing Feulgen positive chromatin, and RNA-containing Feulgen negative nucleoli. In cells with sufficient amounts of DNA, preparations were obtainable in which the mitotic chromosomes stood out clearly against an unstained background. The Feulgen reaction was soon applied to a wide variety of cytological problems, including the discovery of extranuclear DNA in trypanosomes (Bresslau and Scremin, 1924), and the distribution of DNA in bands and interbands of polytene chromosomes (Heitz and Bauer, 1933). (See Milovidov, 1936, for review.) It is of considerable interest that Caspersson (1932a) early investigated the quantitative relationships between DNA and Feulgen intensity, using solutions of DNA with various amounts of proteins added. Under these conditions Caspersson found, as later also did Sibatani (1950), that the Feulgen reaction was strongly influenced by the concentration and type of added proteins. It was concluded that the Feulgen reaction could not be utilized for quantitative photometric estimates of DNA.

One of the first investigators to estimate the amount of dye bound to individual nuclei was Mainland (1933). In his studies, the hematoxylin intensity of human uterine mucosa and carcinoma nuclei was estimated by comparison with a series of five water color squares painted on cards. The extinction equivalents for the cards were obtained by comparison with solutions of water color paints of known dilution. Nuclear outlines were traced from projections, and nuclear thickness was determined with the fine focusing knob of the microscope. Mainland divided the estimated stain intensity by the nuclear thickness, to obtain dye concentration. He then multiplied concentration by nuclear volume to obtain the total dye per nucleus. He reported a statistical correlation between dye concentration and nuclear volume of -0.49 ± 0.054. Thus the larger nuclei proved to be significantly paler, and the smaller nuclei darker. He concluded that "the most reasonable explanation of the relationship established is that the larger the nucleus, the greater the spreading apart of the stained particles and, consequently, the paler the total staining intensity. This explanation further suggests that the chromatic material in the various nuclei is the same in amount in any particular specimen." This probably represents the earliest expression of the DNA constancy hypothesis.

The first microphotometer designed specifically for use in quantitating cytochemical reactions was described by Pollister and Ris (1948). In its initial form the instrument used either a ribbon filament bulb and narrow band interference filters as light source, or green and blue lines from a low-pressure mercury arc isolated by appropriate filter combinations. The dimensions of the object under study were measured with an ocular micrometer, the area was delimited by a diaphragm placed in the image plane immediately below the photomultiplier phototube, and the amount of absorbing material was calculated from two consecutive readings made through the object, and a nearby background. The authors stressed the extreme simplicity of the apparatus ("in less than one hour a trained cytologist can master the entire technique"), and also the marked advantages in using visible light. They also showed how it was possible to subtract nonspecific absorption, if present, by the use of unstained "blank" slides. As an application of the apparatus, measurements on the total protein of maize nucleoli were presented, using the Millon reaction before and after an acid extraction suspected of removing histones. Since absorption characteristics of unextracted and extracted slides were similar, it was concluded that the nucleolus contains little if any histone protein.

The same instrument was applied to studies on the nucleic acids and proteins of onion root and grasshopper testis by Ris (1948). This study contained probably the first estimates of DNA per nucleus employing the Feulgen reaction, although possibly because large somewhat inhomogeneous regions were measured, a DNA increase during prophase was erroneously described. Measurements on the DNA in grasshopper spermatids were found to be roughly half the value for diploid premeiotic cells. This was probably the first published indication that gamete nuclei contain half the DNA of diploid cells.

A similar but more convenient photometer was subsequently described by Pollister and Moses (1949). Such instruments were used in the study of Feulgen intensities in rat liver nuclei by Ris and Mirsky (1949), in tissues of the plant *Tradescantia* by Schrader and Leuchtenberger (1949), in a variety of animal and plant tissues by Swift (1950a,b), and in mouse oogenesis and cleavage by Alfert (1950). An instrument for Feulgen photometry was also designed by Lison (1950), in which the image was projected upon a screen for the measuring of nuclear dimensions. The screen contained a diaphragm, behind which the phototube was placed, as in certain early Caspersson instruments. With this apparatus, Lison and Pasteels (1949) measured the amounts of Feulgen dye per nucleus in the testis of a mole, and Pasteels and Lison (1950) studied Feulgen values in liver and testis of the rat.

Although most of these investigators agreed that the amounts of Feulgen dye bound per nucleus, and presumably the DNA also, were distributed in a reproducible and meaningful pattern in different tissues, there was considerable disagreement as to the extent of variability actually occurring. Some workers maintained, on the basis of their photometric data, that the amounts of DNA per nucleus were under a precise quantitative biological control (the DNA constancy hypothesis) (Boivin et al., 1948; Mirsky and Ris, 1949; Swift, 1950a,b), while others maintained that DNA was subject to considerable metabolic variation (Schrader and Leuchtenberger, 1949; Leuchtenberger and Schrader 1952). Others strongly criticized the photometric method, as subject to major error through the uneven distribution of absorbing material (Fano, 1948; Glick et al., 1951), through the possible presence of dichroism (Commoner, 1949), or to serious lens flare in the optical system (Naora, 1951). The fact that distributional error in effect did not cause serious inaccuracies in Feulgen photometry was adequately shown through the independent development by Ornstein (1952) and Patau (1952) of the two wavelength method. This technique, as mentioned elsewhere in this volume, provides a powerful and flexible means of measuring absorbing material in heterogeneously distributed fields. With it, the manner of distribution of stained material within the measured area is of little consequence. It thus provided the direct demonstration that the criticisms of Glick et al. were unfounded, and also a means for the study of inhomogeneous objects such as mitotic figures (Patau and Swift, 1953). Dichroism as a possible source of error had previously been considered by Caspersson (1940c), and was also refuted by Pollister and Swift (1950). Appreciable lens flare was shown to be absent from properly constructed instruments by Caspersson (1936).

Many of these disagreements from the first days of Feulgen photometry were adequately settled in the years that followed (for reviews, see Swift, 1953; Swift and Rasch, 1956), and other chapters in this volume amply testify to the biological importance of the photometry of cytochemical reactions. It is of considerable interest, however, that in spite of significant improvements in photometric methods, and the better understanding and control of sources of error, some of the basic biological problems are still unsolved, for example, the major question as to how invariable the amounts of DNA per nucleus actually are, and how much they may be varied by localized changes in DNA amounts at specific regions of the chromosome.

Analytical microscopy has clearly left its mark on the history of biology. Among its greatest triumphs in the past have been the demonstration of respiratory pigments, the cytochromes and cytochrome oxidase, as universal constituents of aerobic cell metabolism. It has also been crucial in establishing the basic role of RNA in protein synthesis. More recently, Feulgen photometry has served to emphasize the quantitative control of DNA within the cell, a behavior clearly associated with the unique nature of genetic material. There is an increasing number of investigators utilizing the methods of quantitative cytology in basic research, and a growing series of new instruments is being developed, more powerful and with wider applicability than ever before, as evidenced both from recent symposia (for example, Montgomery, 1962) and by the later chapters in this volume. Many of these instruments, however, are relatively untested and as yet unapplied to current problems of biological research. It remains to be seen whether or not the newer and more complex additions to the arsenal of photometric tools, such as scanning with computer processing and storage, will provide the hoped for entrance into new domains. The challenge to photometry seems to lie in the creative application of good physical techniques properly oriented toward basic biological problems. As the history of photometry has shown, great precision and technical sophistication are often, but not always required. The very importance of some approaches has been in their simplicity.

There is also a major challenge to cytophotometry from the area of clinical cytology. Much research has demonstrated the importance of polyploidy and increased basophilia in the diagnosis of malignant tumors. The possibility of automated methods for cytological screening is apparent, and great importance should obviously be attached to the development of rapid and accurate photometric methods for exfoliative cell diagnosis. More subtle changes in the chromosome complement of man have also been implicated, both in certain tumors and in serious congenital anomalies. The quantitative detection and analysis of minute changes in the human karyotype presents another and more exacting problem for photometric instruments. A third application, recently suggested by Ornstein (1965), is the automated low-power scanning and processing of human serum samples separated on polyacrylamide gels. But whatever problems provide the focus for future photometric research, it is obvious that the instruments required must be adequately suited to the particular investigations at hand. They may possibly be as different from current instruments as the Zeiss UMSP is from the Abbe microspectral ocular first manufactured by the same company in Jena more than 80 years before.

REFERENCES

1. Abbe, E. (1870). Ueber einen Spectralapparat am Mikroskop. *Jena. Z. Med. Natur.* **5**, 459–470 (*in* "Gesammelte Abhandlungen," Vol. 1, pp. 1–13. Fischer, Jena, 1904).

2. Abbe, E. (1886). Ueber Verbesserungen des Mikroskops mit Hilfe neuer Arten optischen Glases. *Sitzungsber. Jena. Ges. Med. Naturwiss.* pp. 107–128 (*in* "Gesammelte Abhandlungen," Vol. 1, pp. 450–472. Fischer, Jena, 1904).

3. Alfert, M. (1950). A cytochemical study of oogenesis and cleavage in the mouse. *J. Cellular Comp. Physiol.* **36**, 381–406.

4. Allen, A. J., R. Franklin, and E. McDonald (1934). Photomicrography and radiation studies with various wavelengths of monochromatic ultraviolet radiation. *J. Franklin Inst.* **218**, 701–716.

5. Ångstrom, J. A. (1868). "Récherches sur le spectre solaire." Schultz, Uppsala.

6. Baas-Becking, L. G. M., and P. A. Ross (1925). Notes on microspectra. I. The absorption spectrum of *Euglena. J. Gen. Physiol.* **9**, 111–114.

7. Boivin, A., R. Vendrely, and C. Vendrely (1948). L'acide désoxyribonucléique du noyau cellulaire dépositaire des caracteres héréditaires; arguements d'ordre analytique. *Compt. Rend.* **226**, 1061–1063.

8. Bose, J. G. (1901). U.S. Patent 755,840.

9. Boys, C. V. (1889). A radiomicrometer for the measurement of light intensity. *Phil. Trans.* **A180**, 159–169.

10. Brachet, J. (1933). Récherches sur la syntheses de l'acide thymonucléique pendent le développement de l'oeuf d'oursin. *Arch. Biol. (Liege)* **44**, 519–576.

11. Brachet, J. (1940a). La detection histochimique des acides pentosenucléiques. *Compt. Rend. Soc. Biol.* **133**, 88–90.

12. Brachet, J. (1940b). La localisation des acides pentosenucléiques pendent le developpement des amphibiens. *Compt. Rend. Soc. Biol.* **133**, 90–91.

13. Bresslau, E., and L. Scremin (1924). Die Kerne der Trypanosomen und ihr Verhalten zur Nuclealreaktion. *Arch. Protistenk.* **48**, 509–516.

14. Brode, W. R. (1939). "Chemical Spectroscopy." Wiley, New York.

15. Brown, P. K. (1961). A system for microspectrophotometry employing a commercial recording spectrophotometer. *J. Opt. Soc. Am.* **51**, 1000–1008.

16. Bunsen, R. W., and G. Kirchoff (1861). *Poggendorfs Ann.* **113**, 337.

17. Bunsen, R. W., and H. E. Roscoe (1862). Photochemische Untersuchungen. *Poggendorfs Ann.* **117**, 529.

18. Case, T. W. (1920). Thalofide cell—a new photoelectric substance. *Phys. Rev.* **15**, 289–292.

19. Cashman, R. J. (1945). Development of sensitive lead sulfide photoconductive cells for detection of intermediate infra-red radiation. *Off. Sci. Res. Develop. Rept.* No. 5998. Washington, D.C.

20. Caspersson, T. (1932a). Die quantitative Bestimmung von Thymonucleinsäure mittels fuchsinschwefliger Säure. *Biochem. Z.* **253**, 97–110.

21. Caspersson, T. (1932b). Zur Kenntnis der Optik weisser Sole. I. Theoretische Ableitung des Absorptionkoeffizienten. *Kolloid-Z.* **60**, 151–159.

22. Caspersson, T. (1933a). Zur Kenntnis der Optik weisser Sole. II. Die diffuse Seitenstrahlung. *Kolloid-Z.* **65**, 162–170.
23. Caspersson, T. (1933b). Zur Kenntnis der Optik weisser Sole. III. Die optischen Verhältnisse bei der Koagulation. *Kolloid-Z.* **65**, 301–307.
24. Caspersson, T. (1936). Über den chemischen Aufbau der Strukturen des Zellkernes. *Skand. Arch. Physiol.* **73**, (Suppl. 8), 1–151.
25. Caspersson, T. (1939). Über die Rolle der Desoxyribosenukleinsäure bei der Zellteilung. *Chromosoma* **1**, 147–156.
26. Caspersson, T. (1940a). Methods for the determination of the absorption spectra of cell structures. *J. Roy. Microscop. Soc.* **60**, 8–25.
27. Caspersson, T. (1940b). Die Eiweissverteilung in den Strukturen des Zellkernes. *Chromosoma* **1**, 562–604.
28. Caspersson, T. (1940c). Nukleinsäureketten und Genevermehrung. *Chromosoma* **1**, 605–619.
29. Caspersson, T. (1941). Studien über den Eiweissumsatz der Zelle. *Naturwiss.* **29**, 33–43.
30. Caspersson, T. (1950). "Cell Growth and Cell Function." Norton, New York.
31. Caspersson, T., and L. Santesson (1942). Studies on protein metabolism in the cells of epithelial tumors. *Acta Radiol.* Suppl. 46 1–105.
32. Caspersson, T., and J. Schultz (1938). Nucleic acid metabolism of the chromosomes in relation to gene reproduction. *Nature* **142**, 294–295.
33. Caspersson, T., and J. Schultz (1939). Pentose nucleotides in the cytoplasm of growing tissues. *Nature* **143**, 602–603.
34. Caspersson, T., H. Landstrom-Hydén, and L. Aquilonius (1941). Cytoplasmanukleotide in eiweissproduzierenden Drüsenzellen. *Chromosoma* **2**, 111–131.
35. Chance, B. (1951). Rapid and sensitive spectrophotometry. *Rev. Sci. Instr.* **22**, 619–627, 627–634, and 634–638.
36. Chance, B. (1962). Kinetics of enzyme reactions within single cells. *Ann. N.Y. Acad. Sci.* **97**, 431–448.
37. Chapman, L. M., D. M. Greenberg, and G. L. A. Schmidt (1927). Studies on the nature of the combination between certain acid dyes and proteins. *J. Biol. Chem.* **72**, 707–729.
38. Cole, P. A., and F. S. Brackett (1940). Technical requirements in the determination of absorption spectra by the ultraviolet microscope. *Rev. Sci. Instr.* **11**, 419–427.
39. Cole, P. A., and E. Sutton (1940). The absorption of ultraviolet radiation by bands of the salivary gland chromosomes of *Drosophila melanogaster*. *Cold Spring Harbor Symp. Quant. Biol.* **9**, 66–71.
40. Commoner, B. (1949). On the interpretation of the absorption of ultraviolet light by cellular nucleic acids. *Science* **110**, 31–40.
41. Cox, J. D. (1884). Robert B. Tolles and the angular aperture question. *Trans. Am. Microscop. Soc.* pp. 5–39.
42. DeJong, H. G. B., and J. Lens (1932). Zur Kenntnis der Komplexkoazervation. XII. Einige orientierende Untersuchungen über die Koazervation hydrophiler Sole mit Farbstoffen, inbesondere von Gummi arabicum, mit Trypaflavin. *Biochem. Z.* **254**, 15–34.
43. Dhéré, C. (1906). Sur l'absorption des rayons ultra-violets par l'acide nucleique extrait de la levure de bière. *Compt. Rend. Soc. Biol.* **60**, 34 (Abstract).
44. Elster, J., and H. Geitel (1890). Ueber den hemmenden Einfluss des Magnetismus auf lichtelectrische Entladungen in verdünnten Gasen. *Ann. Physik* [3] **41**, 166–176.

45. Engelmann, T. W. (1882). Ueber Sauerstoffausscheidung von Pflanzenzellen im Mikrospektrum. *Arch. Ges. Physiol.* **27**, 485–490.
46. Ernst, H. C., and S. B. Wohlbach (1906). Ultra-violet photomicrography. *J. Med. Res.* **14**, 463–469.
47. Fano, U. (1948). Comments on paper of Pollister and Ris. *Cold Spring Harbor Symp. Quant. Biol.* **12**, 155–156.
48. Feulgen, R., and H. Rossenbeck (1924). Mikroskopisch-chemischer Nachweis einer Nucleinsäure vom Typus der Thymonucleinsäure und die darauf beruhende Elektiv Färbung von Zellkernen in mikroskopischen Präparaten. *Z. Physiol. Chem.* **135**, 203–248.
49. Fraenkel-Conrat, H., and M. Cooper (1944). The use of dyes for the determination of acid and basic groups in proteins. *J. Biol. Chem.* **154**, 239–246.
50. Fruitts, C. E. (1883). On a new form of the selenium cell and some electrical discoveries made with it. *Am. J. Sci.* **26**, 465–472.
51. Garnier, C. (1900). Contribution à l'étude de la structure et du fonctionnement des cellules glandulaires sereuses. Du rôle de l'ergastoplasme dans la sécrétion. *J. Anat. Physiol.* **36**, 22–98.
52. Glick, D., A. Engstrom, and B. G. Malmstrom (1951). A critical evaluation of quantitative histo- and cytochemical microscope techniques. *Science* **114**, 253–258.
53. Grondahl, O. (1933). The copper-cuprous-oxide rectifier and photoelectric cell. *Rev. Mod. Phys.* **5**, 141–168.
54. Hallwachs, W. (1888). Ueber den Einfluss des Lichtes auf electrostatisch geladene Körper. *Ann. Physik* [3] **33**, 301–312.
55. Hantzsch, A., and P. W. Robertson (1910). Gelbe und rote Formen von Salzen und Hydraten der Oxyazokörper. *Ber. Deut. Chem. Ges.* **43**, 106–122.
56. Hartley, W. N. (1884). Researches on spectrum photography in relation to new methods of quantitative chemical analysis. II. *Phil. Trans.* **175**, 325–342.
57. Hartley, W. N. (1905). The absorption spectra of uric acid, murexide, and the ureids in relation to colour and to their chemical structure. *J. Chem. Soc. (London)* **87**, 1796–1822.
58. Hartridge, H. (1912). A spectroscopic method of estimating carbon monoxide. *J. Physiol. (London)* **44**, 1-21.
59. Hartridge, H., and F. J. W. Roughton (1928). Photographic methods of estimating the percentage saturation of haemoglobin with various gases. I. The ratio of oxyhaemoglobin to carboxyhaemoglobin. *J. Physiol. (London)* **64**, 405–414.
60. Heitz, E., and H. Bauer (1933). Beweise für die Chromosomenstruktur der Kernschleifen in den Knauelkernen von *Bibio hortulans* L. (Cytologische Untersuchungen an Dipteran, I.). *Z. Zellforsch. Mikroskop. Anat.* **17**, 67–82.
61. Hertz, H. (1887). Ueber einen Einfluss des ultravioletten Lichtes auf die electrisches Entladung. *Ann. Physik* [3] **31**, 983–1000.
62. Hewlett, C. W. (1947). High-sensitivity photoconductive cell. *Gen. Elec. Rev.* **50**, No. 4, 22–25.
63. Hoppe-Seyler, F. (1890). Über Muskelfarbstoffe. *Z. Physiol. Chem.* **14**, 106–108.
64. Hurter, F., and V. C. Driffield (1890). Photo-chemical investigations and a new method of determination of the sensitiveness of photographic plates. *J. Soc. Chem. Ind.* **9**, 455–469.
65. Hydén, H. (1943). Protein metabolism in the nerve cell during growth and function. *Acta Physiol. Scand.* **6**, Suppl. 17, 1–136.

66. Keilin, D. (1925). On cytochrome, a respiratory pigment, common to animals, yeast, and higher plants. *Proc. Roy. Soc.* **B98**, 312–339.
67. Kelley, E. G. (1939). Reactions of dyes with cell substances. IV. Quantitative comparison of tissue nuclei and extracted nucleoproteins. V. Differential basic dye combination of tissue nuclei with special reference to resting and mitotic cells of tumor tissue. *J. Biol. Chem.* **127**, 55–72 and 73–86.
68. Köhler, A. (1904). Mikrophotographische Untersuchungen mit ultraviolettem Licht. *Z. Wiss. Mikroskopie* **21**, 129–165 and 272–304.
69. Köhler, A. (1933). Einige Neuerungen auf dem Gebiet der Mikrophotographie mit ultraviolettem Licht. *Naturwiss.* **21**, 165–173.
70. Köhler, A., and M. von Rohr (1904). Eine mikrophotographische Einrichtung für ultraviolettes Licht. *Z. Instrumentenk.* **24**, 341–348.
71. Lange, B. (1930). Über eine neue Art von Photozellen. *Physik. Z.* **31**, 139–140 and 964–969.
72. Lange, P. (1944). Om ligninets natur och fördelning i granued. *Svensk Papperstidn.* **11**, 262–280.
73. Leuchtenberger, C., and F. Schrader (1952). Variation in the amounts of desoxyribose nucleic acid (DNA) in cells of the same tissue and its correlation with secretory function. *Proc. Natl. Acad. Sci. U.S.* **38**, 99–105.
74. Lillie, F. R. (1906). Observations and experiments concerning the elementary phenomena of embryonic development in *Chaetopterus*. *J. Exp. Zool.* **3**, 153–268
75. Lison, L. (1950). Étude et réalisation d'un photomètre à l'usage histologique. *Acta Anat.* **10**, 333–347.
76. Lison, L., and J. Pasteels (1949). Sur l'évolution quantitative de l'acide thymonucleique pendent la spermatogenèse chez *Talpa*. *Compt. Rend. Soc. Biol.* **143**, 1607–1608.
77. Lucas, F. F. (1930). The architecture of living cells—recent advances in methods of biological research—optical sectioning with the ultraviolet microscope. *Proc. Natl. Acad. Sci. U.S.* **16**, 599–607.
78. Lucas, F. F. (1934). Late developments in microscopy. *J. Franklin Inst.* **217**, 661–707.
79. Lucas, F. F., and M. B. Stark (1931). A study of living sperm cells of certain grasshoppers by means of the ultraviolet microscope. *J. Morphol.* **52**, 91–113.
80. MacMunn, C. A. (1886). Further observations on enterochlorophyll, and allied pigments. *Phil. Trans.* **177**, 235–298.
81. Mainland, D. (1933). Colorimetric tests of nuclear staining. *Stain Technol.* **8**, 69–72.
82. Mathews, A. (1898). A contribution to the chemistry of cytological staining. *Am. J. Physiol.* **1**, 445–454.
83. Mees, C. E. K. (1909). "Atlas of Absorption Spectra." Longmans, Green, New York.
84. Meigs, E. B. (1908). The structure of the element of cross-striated muscle and the changes of form which it undergoes during contraction. *Z. Allgem. Physiol.* **8**, 81–120.
85. Milovidov, P. F. (1936). Zur Theorie und Technik der Nuklealfärbung. *Protoplasma* **25**, 570–597.
86. Mirsky, A. E., and A. W. Pollister (1946). The nucleoprotein of trout sperm chromosin, a desoxyribose nucleoprotein complex of the cell nucleus. *J. Gen. Physiol.* **30**, 101–148.

87. Mirsky, A. E., and H. Ris (1949). Variable and constant components of chromosomes. *Nature* **163**, 666–667.

88. Montgomery, P. O'B., ed. (1962). Scanning techniques in biology and medicine. *Ann. N.Y. Acad. Sci.* **97**, 329–526.

89. Naora, H. (1951). Microspectrophotometry and cytochemical analysis of nucleic acids. *Science* **114**, 279–280.

90. Ornstein, L. (1952). The distributional error in microspectrophotometry. *Lab. Invest.* **1**, 250–262.

91. Ornstein, L. (1965). Computer learning and the scientific method: A proposed solution to the information theoretical problem of meaning. *J. Mt. Sinai Hosp.* **32**, 437–494.

92. Pasteels, J., and L. Lison (1950). Teneur des noyaux au repos enacide désoxyribonucléique dans differents tissus chez le rat. *Compt. Rend.* **230**, 780–782.

93. Patau, K. (1952). Absorption microphotometry of irregular-shaped objects. *Chromosoma* **5**, 341–362.

94. Patau, K., and H. Swift (1953). The DNA-content (Feulgen) of nuclei during mitosis in a root tip of onion. *Chromosoma* **6**, 149–169.

95. Policard, A. (1928). Récherches histochimiques sur la teneur en cendres des diverses parties de la cellule. Teneur du noyeau en calcium. *Bull. Histol. Appl. Physiol. Pathol.* **5**, 260–265.

96. Pollister, A. W., and M. J. Moses (1949). A simplified apparatus for photometric analysis and photomicrography. *J. Gen. Physiol.* **32**, 567–577.

97. Pollister, A. W., and H. Ris (1948). Nucleoprotein determinations in cytological preparations. *Cold Spring Harbor Symp. Quant. Biol.* **12**, 147–157.

98. Pollister, A. W., and H. Swift (1950). Molecular orientation and intracellular photometric analysis. *Science* **111**, 68–71.

99. Preyer, W. (1866). Ueber das Verhalten der Blutkörper und einiger Farbstoffe im monochromatischen Lichte. *Arch. Mikroskop. Anat. Entwicklungsmech.* **2**, 93–101.

100. Preyer, W. (1868). Ueber einige Eigenschaften des Hämoglobins und des Methämoglobins. *Arch. Ges. Physiol.* **1**, 395–454.

101. Ray-Lankester, E. (1871). Observations and experiments on the red bloodcorpuscle, chiefly with regard to the action of gases and vapours. *Quart. J. Microscop. Sci.* **11**, 361–387.

102. Ris, H. (1948). The composition of chromosomes during mitosis and meiosis. *Cold Spring Harbor Symp. Quant. Biol.* **12**, 158–160.

103. Ris, H., and A. E. Mirsky (1949). Quantitative cytochemical determination of desoxyribonucleic acid with the Feulgen nucleal reaction. *J. Gen. Physiol.* **33**, 125–146.

104. Rowland, H. A. (1887). On the relative wavelengths of the lines of the solar spectrum. *Am. J. Sci.* **33**, 182–190.

105. Rudkin, G., and S. L. Corlette (1957). Disproportionate synthesis of DNA in a polytene chromosome region. *Proc. Natl. Acad. Sci. U.S.* **43**, 964–968.

106. Schottky, W. (1930). Über den Entstehungsort der Photoelektronen in Kupfer-Kupferoxydul-Photozellen. *Physik. Z.* **31**, 913–925.

107. Schrader, F., and C. Leuchtenberger (1949). Variation in the amount of desoxyribose nucleic acid in different tissues of *Tradescantia*. *Proc. Natl. Acad. Sci. U.S.* **35**, 464–468.

108. Scott, S. H. (1932). Topographic similarities between materials revealed by ultraviolet light photomicrography of living cells and by microincineration,

Science **76**, 148–150.

109. Sibatani, A. (1950). Effects of histone and other proteins on the Feulgen reaction. *Nature* **166**, 355–356.

110. Singer, M. and P. R. Morrison (1948). The influence of pH, dye, and salt concentration on the dye binding of modified and unmodified fibrin. *J. Biol. Chem.* **175**, 133–145.

111. Sorby, H. C. (1867). On a definite method of qualitative analysis of animal and vegetable colouring-matters by means of the spectrum microscope. *Proc. Roy. Soc. London* **15**, 433–455.

112. Soret, J. L. (1883). Récherches sur l'absorption des rayons ultraviolets par diverses substances. (Quartrième mémoire). *Arch. Sci. Phys. Nat.* **9**, 513–554.

113. Stearn, A. E., and E. W. Stearn (1929). The mechanism of staining explained on a chemical basis. I. The reaction between dyes, proteins and nucleic acid. *Stain Technol.* **4**, 111–119.

114. Stoletow, A. (1890). Sur les courants actino-életriques dans l'air raréfié. *J. Ann. Phys.* **9**, 468–473.

115. Swann, W. F. G., and C. del Rosario (1932). The effect of certain monochromatic ultraviolet radiation on *Euglena* cells. *J. Franklin Inst.* **213**, 549–560.

116. Swift, H. (1950a). The desoxyribose nucleic acid content of animal nuclei. *Physiol. Zool.* **23**, 169–198.

117. Swift, H. (1950b). The constancy of desoxyribose nucleic acid in plant nuclei, *Proc. Nat. Acad. Sci. U.S.* **36**, 643–654.

118. Swift, H. (1953). Quantitative aspects of nuclear nucleoproteins. *Intern. Rev. Cytol.* **2**, 1–76.

119. Swift, H. and E. Rasch (1956). Microphotometry with visible light. *In* "Physical Techniques in Biological Research" (G. Oster and A. W. Pollister, eds.), pp. 353–400. Academic Press, New York.

120. Thorell, B. (1947). Studies on the formation of cellular substances during blood cell production. *Acta Med. Scand.* Suppl. 200, 1–120.

121. Thorell, B. (1964). Design and performance of a microspectrophotometer for the determination of respiratory enzymes *in situ*. *Proc. 2nd Intern. Congr. Histo- Cytochem., Berlin, 1964* p. 85 (Abstract). Springer, Berlin.

122. Tuck, W. B. (1907). The constitution of hydroxyazo-compounds. *J. Chem. Soc. (London)* **91**, 449–457.

123. Twyman, F. (1932). "The Practice of Absorption Spectrophotometry." A. Hilger, London.

124. Uber, F. M. (1939). Ultra-violet spectrophotometry of *Zea mays* pollen with the quartz microscope. *Am. J. Botany* **26**, 799–807.

125. Van Herwerden, M. A. (1913). Über die Nucleasewirkulung auf tierische Zellen. Ein Beitrag zur Chromidienfrage. *Arch. Zellforsch.* **10**, 431–449.

126. Vlès, F. (1911). "Propriétés optiques des muscles." Hermann, Paris.

127. Vlès, F. (1934). Spectrographie et spectrophotométrie ultraviolettes d'absorption avec dispositif. II. *Arch. Phys. Biol.* **9**, 77–110.

128. Vlès, F. and M. Gex (1928). Recherches sur le spectre ultraviolot de l'oeuf d'oursin. *Arch. Phys. Biol.* **6**, 255–285; also in *Bull. Muse Oceanogr. Monaco* No. 518 (1928).

129. Vlès, F., and M. Gex (1934). Sur la structure des spectres ultraviolets de l'oeuf d'oursin. Introduction à une technique de microspectrophotométrie ultraviolette. *Arch. Phys. Biol.* **11**, 157–190; also in *Bull. Inst. Oceanogr. Monaco* No. 658, 1–23 (1934).

130. von Schrötter, H. (1906). Beitrag zur Mikrophotographie mit ultarviolettem

Licht nach Köhler. *Arch. Pathol. Anat. Physiol.* **183,** 343–376.

131. Walker, P. M. B., and H. B. Yates (1952). Ultraviolet absorption of living cell nuclei during growth and division. *Symp. Soc. Exptl. Biol.* **6,** 265–276.

132. Wang, H. (1949). A histo-photoelectric method of collagen determination in muscles. *Anat. Record* **105,** 537–538 (Abstract).

133. Warburg, O., and W. Christian (1933). Über das gelbe Ferment und seine Wirkungen. *Biochem. Z.* **266,** 375–411.

134. Wyckoff, R. W., and A. H. Ebeling (1933). Some ultraviolet photomicrographs made with different wave lengths. *J. Morphol.* **55,** 131–136.

135. Wyckoff, R. W. G., and A. L. Ter Louw (1931a). On the ultraviolet photomicrography of living cells. *Science* **74,** 664–665.

136. Wyckoff, R. W. G., and A. L. Ter Louw (1931b). Some ultraviolet photomicrographs of *B. subtilis. J. Exptl. Med.* **54,** 449–451.

137. Zworykin, V. K., and E. G. Ramberg (1949). "Photoelectricity and its Application." Wiley, New York.

Part *I*

QUANTITATIVE METHODS FOR DETERMINATION OF DRY MASS

AN INTRODUCTION TO THE THEORY
OF INTERFERENCE MICROSCOPY

Oscar W. Richards

AMERICAN OPTICAL COMPANY, RESEARCH CENTER, SOUTHBRIDGE, MASSACHUSETTS

During the first three and one-half centuries after the development of the microscope, most of its applications were examinations of natural objects. After 1825 achromatic lenses improved perception; during the third quarter of the nineteenth century the American makers Spencer and Tolles demonstrated the importance of large numerical apertures for resolution, and toward the end of that century Abbe and Schott developed apochromatic optics from new designs and materials. Improvement continues, fields of view are larger and flatter, aberrations fewer, and infinity-corrected objectives approach the limits set by light and diffraction.

Living cells and tissues are often too transparent for efficient examination with the brightfield microscope. Staining methods help, but few nontoxic dyes are available. Post-mortem study was complicated by questions about the changes induced by chemical agents used, and gave little information about the living process. When the details are anisotropic the polarized light microscope is available, but only in the past few years have rectified optics made its use possible at the high apertures needed for the finer structures (12). Darkfield methods are helpful, but of limited utility. Fluorescence microscopy has contributed information about cells and tissues. Friedman was using fluorescence microscopy for the examination of exfoliated cells some 15 years ago (8). Only within the past 20 years have interference and phase microscopes made possible observation of unstained, living cells and tissues.

I. Light and Optical Path Detail

The brightfield microscope suggests detail as we look at unstained, transparent materials. Closing the diaphragm of the condenser, one begins

43

to see structure, but then diffraction increases and resolution fails because the numerical aperture has been reduced too much. The ability to find detail depends on the nature of light, the materials within the specimen, and the sensitivity of the detector used (eye, camera, and so forth).

Light is radiant energy evaluated according to its capacity to produce visual sensation (1). For the average human eye, light is radiation from 380 to 760 nm,* although very intense radiation of 880 nm can be seen, and young people may see the 334 nm or even the 313 nm mercury, spectral lines. Vision is possible with the long-wavelength ultraviolet radiation after the lens of the eye is removed. A single ray of light vibrates at right angles to its direction of motion (Fig. 1). The distance from one crest to the next crest is called the wavelength, λ. The longer wavelengths of light appear red and the shorter ones violet. The amplitude, or excursion from peak to trough, is important because the energy present is equal to the second power of the amplitude.

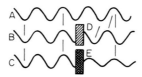

Fɪɢ. 1. Coherent light waves, absorption, and phase changes from retardation.

Figure 1 shows three coherent (that is, from the same source) light rays traveling parallel to each other in phase and of the same amplitudes. Placing a piece of transparent material, D, in the path of ray B slows the light, and the emerging ray is retarded, behind and out of phase with ray A, although the amplitude remains the same. Neither the eye nor the camera can detect changes in phase. However, an absorbing material, E, placed in the path of ray C can reduce the amplitude without changing the phase and the eye or camera can see and record the reduction of the light from the change in amplitude. The details of transparent tissues resemble the clear material D, which suggests that changing the phase alterations of the light passing through such specimens into amplitude changes should make the details visible. Phase and interference microscopes are constructed to do so.

The retardation of the material D depends on its thickness (t) and its increased optical density. (See also Fig. 12.) The optical density is expressed as refractive index, which is the ratio of the speed of light

* In microscopy, lengths are usually measured in microns (μ) and light waves in nanometers (nm), formerly called millimicrons (mμ), or angstroms (Å). 1 μ = 0.001 mm. 1 mμ = 0.001 μ = 1 nm = 10 Å

through the material to the speed of light in a vacuum. The optical path difference, $\Delta = (n_s - n_m)t$, is the difference between the refractive index of the specimen (n_s) and of the surrounding medium (n_m) times the distance the light must go through the specimen (t). The details of many living cells and tissues too transparent for brightfield microscopy consist of similar optical path differences.

Referring again to Fig. 1, when two rays of the same phase and amplitude, such as A, are combined, each reinforces the other and increased brightness results. Combining two rays of the same amplitude but of exactly opposite phase results in darkness from the destructive interference. Two or more rays not of the same phase and amplitude combine, giving grays. Figure 2 shows the wave formed by the combination of two dif-

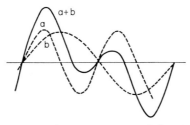

FIG. 2. Changed phase and amplitude in ray $a + b$ by the combination of ray a and ray b. After Edser (4).

ferent rays, a and b. When the light rays are of different wavelengths the combinations are more complex and are revealed by changes in color (38).

Optical path details can be made visible by changing the phase alterations made in the light by the specimen into amplitude differences. Phase and interference microscopes accomplish this by combining rays from the specimen and from the immediate surround of the specimen, either directly or after further modification of the path differences by diffraction plates or compensators. When the optical path of the surround is known, the path difference measurements can be used to determine the refractive index, thickness, and mass of the specimen.

II. Polarized Light

The light in a beam vibrates in all directions at right angles to its direction of travel. For analytical purposes it is desirable to limit the vibration to one plane; the light is then called plane polarized light. This can be done with a birefringent crystal, as shown in Fig. 5, or a sheet of plastic in which the molecules have all been oriented in one direction (as by stretching the film) so that light is transmitted through the film vibrating only in one direction. Polaroid film is an example of the latter. When crystals are used they are cut and reassembled so that one ray passes through the crystal and the other ray is passed to one side and absorbed. A second polarizer with its transmission axis at 90 degrees to that of the first polarizer will block the transmission of the beam. The ratio of the light passed in the latter crossed position to that when the polarizing axes are parallel is the extinction coefficient and a measure of the efficiency of the polarizing system. By adding retarding plates to the polarized beam, polarization can be changed from plane to circular or elliptical polarization. Polarized light is used in several kinds of interference microscopes (*4, 6, 11, 13, 16, 30, 33*).

III. Phase Microscopes

The phase microscope is a brightfield microscope with an added limiting, illuminated area (usually an annulus) placed at the front focal plane of the condenser and a diffraction plate at the back focal plane of the objective. An annulus for the condenser and a circular diffraction plate have the advantage of radial symmetry, although slits, crosses, and other shapes are used. The opening of the annulus is imaged at the back focal plane of the objective, and the diffraction plate is made to fit over this image. When no specimen is present, all of the light goes through this area. A specimen giving rise to optical path differences will deviate light, and the deviated light passes through all of the objective, mostly outside of the image area of the annulus. The two sets of light, from the specimen and its background, are recombined making the phase differences in the specimen visible.

The diffraction plate is made with retarding and absorbing areas that fit the image of the annulus and which selectively alter the light from the specimen and its surround so that a visible amplitude image is formed. Properly made diffraction plates can show the specimen details in bright or dark contrast and enhance or decrease the amount of contrast. Variable contrast (*22*) is possible, although not yet fully realized commercially. The Nikon Phase-Interference Microscope covers much of the possible range of contrast. Further details are available in many references (*2, 5, 16, 21, 26, 27, 30*).

Early phase microscopes of the late nineteenth and early twentieth centuries had diffraction plates made with soot and so were difficult to manufacture. Evaporation techniques were available in the early 1930's when Zernike applied phase methods to microscopy, and commercial production became possible. Köhler and Loos (*15*) reported on a Zeiss phase microscope in 1941. The first American phase microscope was exhibited in 1944, a Spencer with one bright and two kinds of dark contrast, each with several degrees of contrast (24; see also Bennett, 2a.) A year later the first Zeiss Phase Microscope with only one dark contrast was brought to the United States. Phase microscopes show changes in gradients (as at specimen edges) better than interference microscopes, are less effective for large areas of the same optical path difference, and are useful for the determination of refractive index (23), but do have the disadvantage of a halo surrounding the image. The halos are due to the way the light from the specimen and surround is combined and are less prominent with A+ and B− than with the A− dark contrast diffraction plate.

IV. Interference Microscopes

Over the past hundred years many ways have been found to separate a beam of coherent light into two or more beams (Figs. 3–6) and to re-

FIG. 3. A partially reflecting surface separates a light ray into two rays.

combine them after one beam has been altered by passing through a specimen, a compensator, or both. From the resulting diffraction patterns the optical path differences within the specimen can be made visible and measured. Coherent light from a single source must be used

FIG. 4. Ray separation obtained from diffraction and passing through slits.

(rays starting in phase), and for measurement monochromatic light is used. The green light from a mercury arc is readily isolated from the rays of other colors by filters (for instance, Corning CS-120), has a wavelength of 546 nm, and is often used for interference microscopy

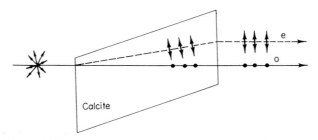

FIG. 5. A beam of unpolarized light is changed by a calcite crystal into two beams polarized at right angles to each other.

since this wavelength is close to 555 nm, where the human eye is most sensitive.

Interference methods have been applied to the microscope in many

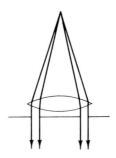

FIG. 6. Two beams separated from a beam by apertures masking the edge of a lens.

ways during the past 35 years and much literature is available (6, 11, 16, 21, 30, 32, 36, 39). Detailed descriptions and classifications are available (16). The following methods are found in biomedical areas:

   I. For the surface study of opaque specimens
      A. Multiple-beam methods
      B. Two-beam methods
  II. For the examination of transparent specimens
      A. Multiple-beam methods
      B. Shearing systems—interference oculars
      C. Two-beam systems
         a. Separation by reflection
         b. Separation by optical activity (birefringent materials).

Another method, using holograms, will not be discussed here (9).

When an optically flat glass surface is brought close to a reflecting surface and illuminated by coherent monochromatic light, the irregularities of the surface are seen in the alterations of the fringe patterns formed by the multiple interferences of the light. The surfaces of leaves have been examined in this manner (*10*). Most of the applications concern metal, crystal, and other highly reflecting surfaces (*36, 37*). The two-beam methods compare the surface with a known reference surface. There are a number of interference microscopes for the study of opaque specimens, but as there are few applications in the biomedical field further discussion of them will be omitted. The suggestion of putting the transparent biological specimen on a mirror for examination with these microscopes is usually found unsatisfactory owing to the high quality required of the mirror (so it does not contribute to optical path differences) and the problems of interpretation from the light passing through the specimen twice.

V. Multiple-Beam Methods for Transparent Objects

A brightfield microscope is easily converted into a multiple-beam microscope. Monochromatic light illumination is necessary, and the condenser iris is closed as much as possible. The specimen must be mounted on a slide that has been metallized with a coating which transmits 10% or less of the light and covered with a similarly metallized cover slip; the metallized sides both face the specimen (Fig. 7). Wet specimens

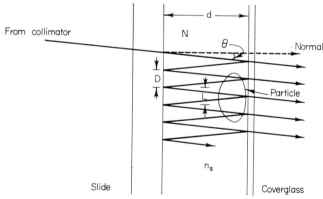

FIG. 7. Section through the specimen mount showing the light rays in a multiple-beam interference microscope. After Osterberg (*21*).

should be sealed with petrolatum jelly around the edges of the cover slip. On looking at such a specimen one usually sees alternating bands, or fringes of light and dark, which change direction as they pass through the specimen, giving the impression of contour lines (Fig. 8). When the

mount is a wedge, or can be converted into a wedge by pressing on one
edge of the cover glass with a dissecting needle, the fringes outside the
specimen usually are parallel and at right angles to the direction of the
wedge (Fig. 8a). The fringe passing through a disk-shaped specimen

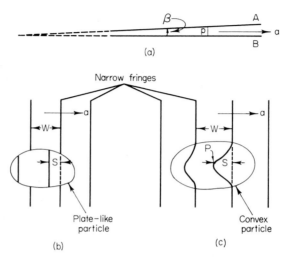

FIG. 8. Appearance of the field of view of a multiple-beam interference microscope
for platelike (b) and convex (c) particles with fringes from the wedge (a) in the
mount. After Osterberg (*21*).

will show a displacement S (Fig. 8b), while a convex specimen will displace the fringes into curved lines (Fig. 8c). The optical path difference
is given by

$$\Delta = (n_s - n_m)t = \lambda S/2W,$$

where S is the distance of the displacement, W is the distance between
the fringes, and λ is the wavelength of light used.

Sharper fringes can be obtained when the condenser of the microscope
is replaced with a 25-mm objective having a 1-mm pinhole mounted at
its focal plane. The monochromatic light from the illuminator is focused
on the pinhole (*21*). Light from the condenser at a slight angle from
the normal passes through the metallic coating of the slide and is
partly transmitted and partly reflected by the coating on the cover glass
(see Fig. 7). Continuing interreflections and transmission of light to the
objective cause interference, which is seen in the image as fringes. These
fringes are modified by any optical path detail within the specimen, and
the path differences can be computed from measurements of the displacements with the aid of an eyepiece micrometer. Measurement to a

tenth of a wavelength or about 0.05μ is possible, or the contour lines of the fringes can be used to make three-dimensional models of the specimen (25).

Some care is necessary for interpretation when there are abrupt changes in the specimen thickness, because the fringes may be too close for counting or may even be superimposed on each other. Sometimes the specimen can be flattened enough to aid the measurement of the fringes without undue damage.

The advantages of multiple-beam interference are the few changes necessary and the fact that the known wavelength of the light provides built-in calibration. The disadvantage is the cost of the metallized slides and cover glasses when the preparation is saved, or the loss of the specimen if the slide and cover glass are cleaned for reuse. Metallized slides and covers can be made using Merton's or other methods (19), or purchased commercially. Silver is toxic for most living specimens and cannot be used for the reflecting surfaces. Inconel or titanium is usually satisfactory. Osterberg has discussed the problems and precautions involved with multiple-beam interference microscopy (21). One of the earliest applications in biology was that of Frederikse (7) in 1933; more recent applications have been discussed by Merton (20), Mellors (18), and Richards (25).

VI. Interference Oculars

The interference oculars are so constructed that they may be put into the eyepiece tube of a monocular microscope in place of the usual ocular. Birefringent materials are used to shear the image so that light from the specimen and its surround can be reimaged together to reveal any optical path detail present in the specimen. A field lens may be added to reimage the back aperture of the objective into the shearing system.

Francon's Interference Oculars use polarized light, a Savart plate (made of two specially cut and oriented pieces of quartz), and a slit, or another Savart plate in front of the microscope condenser to separate and combine the two beams of light. The optical path details show in interference colors. The path difference can be estimated by transferring the sensitive purple tint from the surround to the specimen with the aid of a graduated control. The oculars are made in France by Barbier, Bénard & Turenne, Nachet, and by Optique et Précision de Levallois.

W. Schrader (Wenden bei Braunschweig) makes an interference eyepiece with one or two Wollaston prisms for shearing the image. The ocular with two Wollaston prisms can be adjusted to provide an image with fringes for measurement of path differences in a manner similar to that described in Section V. The Nife Microscope made by Aktiebolaget Jungner in Sweden has a more elaborate interference system in the eyepiece.

Personal experience has shown that neither the Francon nor the Schrader interference oculars provide as good images as the two-beam interference microscopes; the images are small and measurement is impractical with these oculars (*29*).

VII. Two-Beam Systems Using Reflection for Separation

The Cooke–Dyson Interference Microscope (3) (Fig. 9) separates the light into two beams with partially aluminized reflecting layers. The

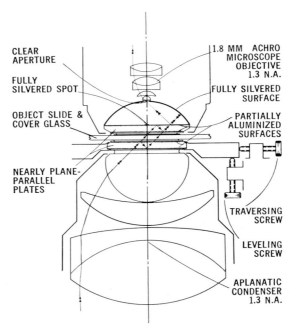

FIG. 9. Diagram of the Cooke–Dyson Interference Microscope. Courtesy of Mr. Robert Osgood, Vickers, Ltd., Belmont, Mass.

lower plate is mounted in an adjustable bar on the stage just above the microscope condenser. The upper plate is the front part of a catoptric (reflecting optics) unit magnification system which is part of the objective. This reflecting objective forms an image at the focus of the regular objective, thus extending the working distance for the interference system. Light from the condenser is partly reflected back from the top of the lower plate and partly transmitted through the specimen. The light reflected is turned back to the objective by the lower reflecting plate at some distance from the directly transmitted beam, giving rise to the two beams required for interference microscopy. The light that passed through the specimen is reflected back from the upper surface of the upper plate to the lower surface of the upper plate, where it is turned toward the objective and combined with the light that did not pass through the specimen. The combined light is reflected to the focal point of the objective by the catoptric system. The catoptric system has a fully silvered mirror except for the opening through which the light goes to the regular part of the objective. There is also a small, circular, fully silvered spot on the lower surface which blocks direct light from entering the objective.

The lower plate must be immersed to both the condenser top lens and the slide mount of the specimen. The upper plate must also be in immersion contact with the cover glass of the preparation. The nearly parallel plates can be adjusted so that a series of fringes passes through the specimen and measurements can be made using the calibrated tangent screw which displaces the lower plate. Note that while these fringes resemble those of a multiple-beam interference microscope, the distances apart are a full wavelength and not the half wavelength of the multiple beam system of Section V. With care, the optical path can be measured to about 1/200 wavelength of the monochromatic light used. The measurements can also be made with the aid of a microdensitometer from a photomicrograph.

By rotating the upper plate and adjusting the system so that a fringe is fully spread over the back aperture of the objective, no fringes are seen with the specimen, and the detail is revealed as differences in color with white light, or in intensity when monochromatic light is used to illuminate the instrument.

The specimen must be smaller than the separation of the two beams for accurate measurement. As with all reflecting systems the instrument is adversely affected by vibration. Air bubbles must be avoided in the three immersion contacts, or the specimen slide must be removed and the whole system cleaned and reimmersed.

The Leitz Interference Microscope (Fig. 10) also uses reflection to separate the coherent illuminating light into two beams which pass through separate objectives and are then recombined to show the path differences between the specimen and the reference path in the image. Using two objectives well separated, larger specimens can be examined and longer optical paths measured with the aid of compensators than with the single objective microscopes.

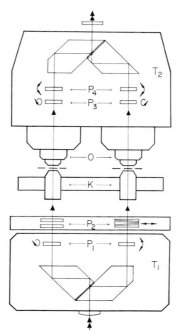

FIG. 10. Diagram of the Leitz Interference Microscope. Key: P_1, polarizers; P_2, wedge compensators; K, condensers; O, Objectives; P_3, P_4, plate compensators; T_1, beam separating prisms; T_2, beam combining prisms. Courtesy of Dr. Peter Bartels, E. Leitz, Inc., New York City.

VIII. Two-Beam Systems Using Optical Activity for Separation

Birefringent materials can be used to separate a beam of light into two beams (Fig. 6). In 1930 Lebedeff used this method for making an interference microscope (17). The Smith Interference Microscope (34, 35) is made by Baker (now part of Vickers, London) and their objectives and condensers were used in the AO-Baker Interference Microscope in the United States until 1964. Zeiss makes a similar instrument, and Nikon uses Savart plates to separate and recombine the two light beams in their Differential Interference Microscope.

Polarized light is used in these instruments, and birefringent specimens must be properly oriented to avoid error in measurement. The lateral resolution is no greater than that of other light microscopes and may be less because the condenser aperture is used below N.A. 0.6 to avoid obliquity error (see Fig. 13), but the vertical resolution is better than in multiple-beam methods.

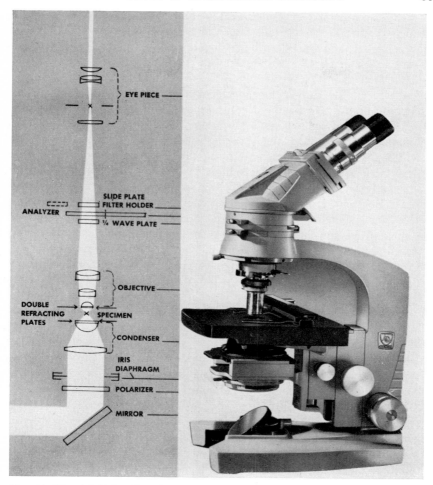

FIG. 11. The AO-Baker Interference Microscope and diagram of the light path.

The AO-Baker Interference Microscope in Fig. 11 will be used as an example. The entering coherent light is plane polarized at 45 degrees to the front-back axis of the microscope. A birefringent plate or lens (calcite or quartz) in the condenser divides the light into two beams. In the Shearing System the ordinary ray is the image-forming ray that passes through the specimen and the extraordinary ray passes to the right of the specimen, but is seen as an unfocusable, astigmatic image at the left of the specimen, because of the reversal of the compound microscope. In the Double Focus System the reference ray is passed around and focused above the specimen. Corresponding birefringent optics in the objective recombine the beams. The combined beam passes through a quarter-wave plate which plane polarizes the light, and an analyzer is used to find the plane of polarization. When no specimen is present this will be 45 degrees. Another position reveals change due to path differences in the specimen.

The size of the largest measurable specimen must be less than the separation of the two beams at the object plane or the measuring done along the edge of an extended specimen. The size limits vary with the different objectives. With the Shearing System optics the area to the apparent right of the specimen and the area where the reference beam passes must be clean, known medium to avoid errors of measurement.

The system is adjusted with leveling screws which tilt the condenser. Using a Bertrand lens, or phase telescope, the back aperture of the objective shows fringes; one is centered and then spread uniformly over the aperture. After the Bertrand lens is removed and the ocular is replaced, the microscope is ready for use. The aperture diaphragm is closed to increase contrast, but not enough to close off the reference beam of the Double Focus optics. (See also obliquity error below.) When white light is used, the specimen is seen in color; the colors can be varied for optimum contrast by turning the analyzer.

Measurement of the specimen requires monochromatic, mercury green light. Turn the analyzer until the region of the mounting medium close to the specimen is as dark as possible and read the scale on the analyzer (A_1); then turn the analyzer until the darkest region (extinction) is moved to the part of the specimen to be measured and again read the analyzer scale (A_2). The optical path difference is $\theta = 2(A_1 - A_2)$ in degrees, $2(A_1 - A_2)/360$ in wavelengths, or $2(A_1 - A_2)\lambda/360$ in microns when the wavelength λ is in microns $(\lambda = 0.564\ \mu)$. When the specimen is in a medium of known refractive index (n_m), or of known thickness (t), then either n or t can be determined.

$$\Delta = (n_s - n_m)t = \theta\lambda/360.$$

When the first medium (n_1) can be removed, and the specimen cleaned and mounted in a second medium (n_2), the two measurements can be used to determine both n_s and t;

$$(n_s - n_1) = \theta_1\lambda/360t \quad \text{and} \quad (n_s - n_2) = \theta_2\lambda/360t;$$

then

$$n_s = \frac{n_1\theta_2 - n_2\theta_1}{\theta_2 - \theta_1} \quad \text{and} \quad t = \frac{\theta_1 - \theta_2}{n_2 - n_1} \times \frac{\lambda}{360}.$$

The refractive indices may be known to 5 or more significant figures, but the difference rarely has more than 2 significant figures and the thickness cannot usually be known to greater than 2 significant figures (*31*). Also note that the refractive indices used must be for the 546 nm mercury green light and not the indices (n_D) for the sodium yellow line as in most tables of refractive indices.

The quarter-wave plate in the microscope is made to retard the light one fourth of 0.546 μ and therefore cannot be $\lambda/4$ for any other wavelength. Should it be used for light of another wavelength, the measurements will be in error, and the error will be greater as the light used departs from 0.546 μ. The maximum error, when the phase difference between the two polarizations (A_1 and A_2) is 45 degrees, is about 0.0006λ, or 0.2 degree for the $\lambda = 0.577$ μ mercury yellow light and about 0.012λ, or 4.3 degrees for the mercury blue light ($\lambda = 0.436$ μ). The corrections are difficult, must be made with each reading, and referred to the actual orientation of the $\lambda/4$ plate. It is recommended that the quarter-wave plate be replaced by one for the light to be used when measurements are to be made with other than 0.546 μ green light.

Instead of measuring a specimen in two known media of different refractive indices, it has been proposed that measurements be made with two wavelengths of light for thickness and index determination. This is not satisfactory for two reasons. First, another $\lambda/4$ plate must be used or the measurements corrected as discussed in the previous paragraph, and second, unless the dispersion of the specimen is sufficiently small, $n_{s\lambda_1} \neq n_{s\lambda_2}$, and a simultaneous solution of the two equations is ambiguous (*30, 31*).

A biological specimen such as the nucleus is usually measured within its cell, which is placed in an isosmotic medium, and the refractive indices of all three must be considered (Fig. 12). The matching method can be used and yields a value which can be checked with that from the ex-

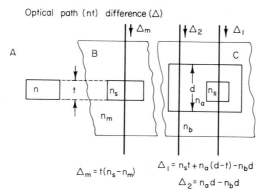

FIG. 12. Diagrams of optical path and optical path differences.

tinction transfer method. The analyzer reading is made for the extinction
of the medium (A_1) close to the specimen, and then the analyzer is turned
until the medium and cytoplasm are equally dark or match in intensity
and the analyzer is read again (A_3). The path difference from the matching method is $4(A_1 - A_3)$. The nucleus can be matched with the cytoplasm and its optical path determined (28, 30). When the mounting
medium is not an aqueous solution (for instance, an oil mount of bone),
problems of penetration enter into the measurements and calculations.
Details have been given by Hale (11) and others.

The refractive index of an aqueous solution increases as more solute
is dissolved in it. If the concentration (grams per 100 ml) is C, then
the specific refractive increment is $\alpha = (n - n_w)/C$. For a region containing a given material the dry mass is $M = AtC/100 = \Delta A/100\alpha =
A\Delta/\chi$ grams; since $\Delta = AtC$; A is the area of the specimen in square
centimeters, t is the thickness in centimeters, and it is convenient to use
$\chi = 100\alpha$. For proteins $\chi = 0.18$, for fats 0.14, and for starch 0.13; other
values are available (11). To determine the dry weight in this manner
assumes that the measured component is equally distributed in the volume (At) of the specimen measured. Rarely is this true for biomedical
specimens and the best value can be obtained by averaging or integration procedures.

The analyzer can be read to half a degree and the variation in readings for biological specimens averages ± 1 to 1.5 degrees. For better precision a halfshade eyepiece is available and the average readings are
± 0.2 degree. The measuring uncertainty, or sensitivity of the microscope,
is 1/240 to 1/1800 wavelength of mercury green light, depending on
whether the halfshade eyepiece is used. A known standard should be
measured occasionally to assure that the instrument and procedure are
in order, as in any quantitative procedure where the instrument is not
self-calibrating. For this kind of interference microscope, glass and thin
films make useful standards (30, 31).

Absorbing specimens up to a density of 0.5 (30% transmission) can
be measured using the halfshade eyepiece with the AO-Baker microscope.
Koester (14) has described a modification making possible amplitude as
well as phase measurement. The Baker Interference Microscope can be
provided with a fringe eyepiece for measurements from fringe shifts. Because the halfshade eyepiece is more accurate, no fringe eyepiece is
available for the AO-Baker microscope. The scale of the AO-Baker
microscope covers an optical path length of only one wavelength. When
the path in the specimen is greater, the specimen should be flattened
when this is appropriate, mounted in a medium of different refractive
index, or the multiple wavelengths determined with a quartz wedge eye-

piece (*30*). A nomogram is available for computing the index and thickness (*28, 30*).

A wedge in the specimen, or in the mount, in the direction of the shear in the microscope will not cause error. When in doubt it is well to rotate the stage and make several measurements. Measurement of a specimen with changing contour can be difficult (*16*). Looking down on a cylindrical object one sees the greatest optical path at the center, and the path diminishes rapidly at each side. Another difficulty is the obliquity error due to light passing through the specimen at any direction other than normal to it (Fig. 13). The formula in the figure is accurate to about

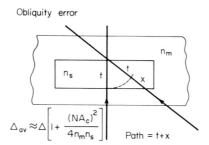

Obliquity error

n_m

n_s t

t x

$$\Delta_{av} \approx \Delta\left[1 + \frac{(NA_c)^2}{4n_m n_s}\right]$$ Path = $t+x$

Fig. 13. The obliquity error: $t + x$ is a greater path than t.

0.1% for numerical apertures to 0.6. Interference microscopes of this type are rarely used at a greater numerical aperture owing to the loss of contrast, as mentioned earlier. The obliquity error for the average biomedical specimen will be from 1 to 5% with the AO-Baker Interference Microscope at N.A. 0.5. To minimize the obliquity error without sacrificing numerical aperture and resolution, use the highest refractive index mounting medium that is practical for the measurement.

For further discussions of precision and errors and for specific microscopes the literature and the manufacturer's instruction books should be consulted.

REFERENCES

1. ASA Z7.1–1942, Illuminating engineering nomenclature and photometric standards. Am. Standards Assoc., New York.
2. Bennett, A. H., H. Jupnik, H. Osterberg, and O. W. Richards, "Phase Microscopy." Wiley, New York, 1951. (Out of print: copies available from University Microfilms, Ann Arbor, Michigan.)
2a. Bennett, A. H., Phase difference microscopy for transparent objects. *Anat. Record* **89**, 547 (1944).

3. Dyson, J., An interferometer microscope. *Proc. Roy. Soc.* **A204**, 170–187 (1950).

4. Edser, E., "Light for Students." Macmillan, New York.

5. Francon, M., "Progress in Microscopy." Harper, New York, 1961.

6. Francon, M., Polarization interference microscopes. *Appl. Opt.* **3**, 1033–1036 (1964).

7. Frederikse, A. M., Mikroskopische Beobachtung lebender Zellen. *Acta Brevia Neerl.* **3**, 121–122 (1933).

8. Friedman, H. P., Jr., The use of ultraviolet light and fluorescent dyes in the detection of uterine cancer by vaginal smear. *Am. J. Obstet. Gynecol.* **59**, 852–859 (1950).

9. Gabor, D., Improvements in and relating to optical apparatus for producing multiple interference patterns. U.S. Patent 2,770,166 (1956).

10. Greenham, C. G., Application of interferometry to biological surfaces. *Australian J. Sci.* **9**, 26 (1946).

11. Hale, A. J., "The Interference Microscope in Biological Research." Williams & Wilkins, Baltimore, Maryland, 1958.

12. Inoué, S., and W. L. Hyde, Studies on polarization of light at microscope lens surfaces. II. The simultaneous realization of high resolution and high sensitivity with the polarizing microscope. *J. Biophys. Biochem. Cytol.* **3**, 831–838 (1957).

13. Jenkins, F. E., and H. E. White, "Fundamentals of Optics," 3rd ed. McGraw-Hill, New York, 1957.

14. Koester, C. J., H. Osterberg, and H. E. Willman, Jr., Transmittance measurements with an interference microscope. *J. Opt. Soc. Am.* **50**, 477–482 (1960).

15. Köhler, A., and W. Loos, Das Phasenkontrastverfahren und seine Anwendungen in der Mikroskopie. *Naturwiss.* **29**, 49–61 (1941); Translation in *Textile Res. J.* **17**, 82–85.

16. Krug, W., J. Rienitz, and G. Schulz, "Contributions to Interference Microscopy." Hilger & Watts, London, 1964 (extensive bibliography).

17. Lebedeff, A. A., L'interférometrie a polarisation et ses applications. *Rev. Opt. (Paris)* **9**, 385–413 (1930).

18. Mellors, R. C., A. Kupfer, and A. Hollender, Quantitative cytology and cytopathology. *Cancer* **6**, 372–384 (1953).

19. Merton, T., On a method of increasing contrast in microscopy. *Proc. Roy Soc.* **A189**, 309–313 (1947).

20. Merton, T., On interference microscopy. *Proc. Roy. Soc.* **A191**, 1–6 (1947).

21. Osterberg, H., Phase and interference microscopy. *In* "Physical Techniques in Biological Research (G. Oster and A. W. Pollister, eds.), Vol. 1, pp. 378–437. Academic Press, New York, 1955.

22. Osterberg, H., The polanret microscope. *J. Opt. Soc. Am.* **37**, 726–730 (1947).

23. Osterberg, H., and A. J. Karlan, Determination of refractive indices by immersion methods and phase microscopy. *Trans. Am. Microscop. Soc.* **77**, 340–353 (1958).

24. Richards, O. W., Phase-difference microscopy for living unstained protoplasm. *Anat. Record* **89**, 548 (1944).

25. Richards, O. W., Tridimensional cytohistology. *J. Biol. Photogr. Assoc.* **19**, 7–15 1951).

26. Richards, O. W., Phase microscopy. *Science* **120**, 631–639 (1954).

27. Richards, O. W., Phase microscopy. II. Science, **124**, 810–814 (1956).

28. Richards, O. W., Measurement with phase and interference microscopes, *In* "Symposium on Microscopy," Spec. Tech. Publ. No. 257, pp. 6–18. Am. Soc. Testing Materials, Philadelphia, Pennsylvania, 1959.

29. Richards, O. W., Two interference oculars. *Proc. Intern. Microscopy Symp., Chicago, 1960,* p. 66, McCrone Associates, Chicago, Illinois, 1960.
30. Richards, O. W., "AO-Baker Interference Microscope Reference Manual," 2nd ed. Am. Opt. Co., Buffalo, New York, 1963 (extensive bibliography).
31. Richards, O. W., Measurement with the AO-Baker interference microscope. *Appl. Phys.* **3**, 1027–1030 (1964).
32. Richards, O. W., and C. J. Koester, Interference Microscopy, *In* "Medical Physics" (O. Glasser, ed.), Vol. 3, pp. 377–382. Year Book Publ., Chicago, Illinois, 1960.
33. Shurcliff, W. A., "Polarized Light Production and Use." Harvard Univ. Press, Cambridge, Massachusetts, 1962.
34. Smith, F. H., Interference microscope. U.S. Patent 2,601,175 (1952).
35. Smith, F. H., Microscopic interferometry. *Research* **8**, 385–395 (1955).
36. Tolansky, S., "Multiple Beam Interferometry of Surfaces and Films. Oxford Univ. Press, London and New York, 1948.
37. Tolansky, S., Applications of interferometry to biological microstructures. *Phys. Med. Biol.* **9**, 125–142 (1964).
38. Traub, A. C., A graphical demonstration of white light interference. *Am. J. Phys.* **21**, 75-82 (1953).
39. Williams, W. E., "Applications of Interferometry." Dutton, New York, 1930.

APPLICATION OF INTERFERENCE MICROSCOPY TO BIOLOGICAL MATERIAL

Guenther Beneke

DEPARTMENT OF PATHOLOGY, JUSTUS LIEBIG UNIVERSITY, GIESSEN, GERMANY

I. Introduction

During the past few years, the interference microscope has become increasingly important for the investigation of biological cell structures. In contrast to other quantitative histochemical methods, interference microscopy is especially suitable for the investigation of living cells, because this method as such does not damage the living cell during the short time of the measurement.

The designs of commercially available interference microscopes are based on two different systems. The first type of system consists of modified polarizing microscopes. It is used in the Baker interference microscope and in the Zeiss Jamin Lebedeff interference microscope.

The second system is called the Mach–Zehnder system. It is used in the Leitz interference microscope. Here, the light is divided by partially transmitting areas.

The lateral beam separation must be sufficiently wide to leave the reference beam completely unaffected by the specimen. Lateral beam separations between measuring and reference beam in these three designs are as given in Table I.

In the Zeiss Lebedeff system a double image of the specimen occurs at this distance, which might disturb the measurements. This is that it is safer to use the Baker and the Zeiss interference microscopes primarily for the measurement of isolated cells and small objects. The Leitz microscope is suitable for measurements in extended tissue sections.

The two light beams can be separately transmitted through the object or a medium around the object (Fig. 1). One beam is known as object beam, while the other is a reference beam. In this figure the light waves

fall on the object, as well as on the medium, in phase. As compared with
the light beam which passes through the medium, the one passing through
the object is retarded. The retardation is dependent on the refractive
index of the object and its thickness. When the refractive index is identical the retardation is dependent on the thickness. Light waves will result,
which exhibit a retardation of $\Delta\delta$. If these beams are reunited, interference of the beams occurs.

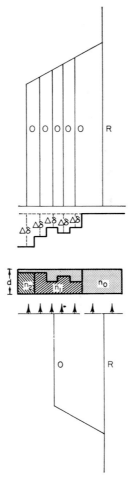

FIG. 1. Schematic representation of the optical path difference by objects having
different thickness and different refractive indexes. O, Object beam; R, reference
beam; $\Delta\delta$, optical path difference; n_0, n_1, n_2, refractive indexes; d, thickness;
$\Delta\delta = n_0 d_0 - n_1 d_1 = d(n_0 - n_1)$ (in nanometers).

TABLE I

Instrument	Objective	Lateral beam separation (μ)
Baker microscope		
Double focus system	10×	90
	40×	90
	100×	20
Shearing system	10×	330
	40×	160
	100×	27
Zeiss microscope	10×	546
	40×	175
	100×	54
Leitz microscope	—	62,000

This phase retardation cannot be visualized. It must, therefore, be translated into amplitude differences. The optical path difference (Table II), $\Delta\delta$, depends on the thickness (d), the refractive index of the object (n_0), and the refractive index of the medium (n_m) around the object.

TABLE II

EQUATIONS FOR CALCULATION OF REFRACTIVE INDEX, THICKNESS, WEIGHT OF DRY MASS, AND CONCENTRATION[a]

Measured or known values	Calculable values	Equation
$\Delta\delta$, Optical path difference [cm] d, Thickness [cm] n_m, Refractive index of the medium around the object	n_0, Refractive index of the object	$n_0 = \dfrac{\Delta\delta}{d} + n_m$
$\Delta\delta$, Optical path difference [cm] n_0, Refractive index of the object n_m, Refractive index of the medium around the object	d, Thickness of the object	$d = \dfrac{\Delta\delta}{n_0 - n_m}$ [cm]
$\Delta\delta$, Optical path difference [cm] F, Area of the cell [cm²] α, Specific refractive increment [cm³ g⁻¹ 100⁻¹]	M, Weight of the dry mass (dry weight)	$M = \dfrac{\Delta\delta \cdot F}{100\alpha}$ [g]
$\Delta\delta$, Optical path difference [cm] d, Thickness [cm] α, Specific refractive increment [cm³ g⁻¹ 100⁻¹]	c, Concentration	$c = \dfrac{\Delta\delta}{d \cdot 100\alpha}$ [g cm⁻³]

[a] See last paragraph of Section I for explanation.

The basic equation for interference microscopy is derived from the following formula:

$$\Delta\delta = (n_0 - n_m) \cdot d \quad [\text{cm}].$$

The refractive index of the object, the thickness of the object, the dry weight, and the dry mass concentration are thus assessed.

II. General Applications of Interference Microscopy

A. Determination of the Refractive Index of Biological Structures

The refractive index of the object is

$$n_0 = \frac{\Delta\delta}{d} + n_m.$$

When determining the refractive index, one must know the optical path difference ($\Delta\delta$), the thickness of the object (d), and the refractive index of the medium (n_m).

In certain cases it is difficult to determine the thickness of the object. These difficulties may be overcome by measuring the same object in two different media (2).

$$n_0 = \frac{\Delta\delta_2 \cdot n_{m1} - \Delta\delta_1 \cdot n_{m2}}{\Delta\delta_2 - \Delta\delta_1}.$$

Here $\Delta\delta_1$ is the measured path difference with embedding medium 1, which has a refractive index n_{m1}; $\Delta\delta_2$ is the measured path difference with embedding medium 2, which has a refractive index n_{m2}.

B. Determination of the Thickness of Biological Objects

The thickness of the object is assessed by the following equation:

$$d = \frac{\Delta\delta}{n_0 - n_m} \quad [\text{cm}].$$

The refractive index of the object (n_0) and of the embedding medium (n_m) must be known. The path difference of the object must also be determined in two different media (2) if the refractive index of the specimen is unknown.

$$d = \frac{\Delta\delta_1 - \Delta\delta_2}{n_{m2} - n_{m1}} \quad [\text{cm}].$$

Once again $\Delta\delta_1$ is the measured path difference with medium 1, with the refractive index n_{m1}, and $\Delta\delta_2$ is the measured path difference with medium 2 with refractive index n_{m2}.

Another method of determining the thickness of the section is to measure the path difference at two different wavelengths (*20*) or at different temperatures (*8*). Hallén (*14*) has described a different method for determination of the thickness: the object is embedded in soft plastic with known refractive index. Provided that the thickness of the tissue and the thickness of the simultaneously sectioned plastic medium are the same, the thickness of the sectioned plastic may be assessed.

C. DETERMINATION OF DRY WEIGHT

The determination of the dry weight of biological structures depends on certain conditions. These conditions are expressed in the mathematical equations for dry weight determination.

a. *The dry weight determination of a living cell embedded in a medium which is not a solution (e.g. water).* The dry weight is assessed according to the following equation:

$$M = \frac{\Delta \delta_w \cdot F}{100 \cdot \alpha} \quad [\text{g}].$$

The measured path difference when the cell is embedded in water is as follows:

$$\Delta \delta_w = (n_0 - n_w) \cdot d \quad [\text{cm}].$$

F is the area of the cell or the cell nucleus in the direction of observation. A determination of the thickness is not necessary under these conditions. α is a constant of the material. It is called the specific refractive increment and serves merely for the substance in solution. The specific refractive index may also be expressed as χ. The relation of α to χ is as follows:

$$\chi = \alpha \cdot 100.$$

Davies (*6*) and Hale (*11*) have collected a few χ values for important biological substances. For all substances not in a water solution, such as crystals and lipid droplets, χ is calculated as follows:

$$\chi = \frac{n_0 - n_w}{\rho} \quad \left[\frac{\text{g}}{\text{cm}^3}\right].$$

b. *The dry weight determination of a fixed cell embedded in a medium not a solution (e.g. water) which penetrates the cell.* In a fixed cell the distribution of substances is not homogeneous. The cell particles no longer occupy the total volume. Therefore, the measured path difference is as follows:

$$\Delta \delta = (n_p - n_w) \cdot d (1 - f) \quad [\text{cm}].$$

Instead of the refractive index of the dissolved cell substance, the refractive index of the fixed cell particles (n_p) is now found in the equation. As the fixed particles do not encompass the entire original cell volume, in the equation geometrical thickness is replaced by the effective thickness of the particles, $d \cdot (1 - f)$, where $(1 - f)$ is that part of the object thickness which is occupied by the fixed particles. This, however, is not important for the determination of the dry weight, when the cell is embedded in water. Dry weight is calculated according to the following equation:

$$M = \frac{\Delta\delta \cdot F}{100 \cdot \alpha} \quad [g].$$

c. *The dry weight determination of a living cell embedded in a medium which is a solution where only the solvent penetrates the cell.* It is often necessary to measure biological materials, such as living cells, in a solution like saline rather than in water, since water will damage the cell. When only the solvent of the solution penetrates the cell, the path difference that is measured is too small. This is caused by the volume of the displacement of the cell. The equation for path difference is as follows:

$$\Delta\delta_m = (n_0 - n_m) \cdot d - (n_m - n_w) \cdot d \quad [cm].$$

In this case the calculated dry weight would be too small. Therefore, a correction for the dry weight determination is necessary (*11*).

$$\text{Corr.} = (n_m - n_w) \cdot \frac{F \cdot d}{100 \cdot \alpha}.$$

This results in an equation for the dry weight determination:

$$M = \frac{\Delta\delta_m \cdot F}{100 \cdot \alpha} + (n_m - n_w) \cdot \frac{F \cdot d}{100 \cdot \alpha} \quad [g].$$

d. *The dry weight determination of a fixed cell embedded in a medium which is a solution and where only the solvent penetrates the cell.* The measured path difference is again composed of the refractive index of the fixed cell particles (n_p) and actual thickness of the fixed cell particles $d(1 - f)$. The measured path difference is again too small because of the volume of the displacement of the cell. The following equation is the result:

$$\Delta\delta_m = (n_P - n_m) \cdot d(1 - f) - (n_m - n_w) \cdot df \quad [cm].$$

Therefore, a correction is again necessary for the dry weight determination:

$$M = \frac{\Delta\delta_m \cdot F}{100 \cdot \alpha} + (n_m - n_w) \cdot \frac{F \cdot df}{100 \cdot \alpha} \quad [g].$$

III. Errors in Dry Weight Determination
by Interference Microscopy

A number of errors may occur. Most important are the errors caused by the object. Schiemer (*33*) has assessed the mean error according to Gauss's law of error for a number of errors occurring in the nuclear dry weight determination. The result is a mean error for dry weight determination of 15 to 20%. The error depends primarily on the measured phase difference and the area of the object.

A. ERRORS DUE TO SPHEROID CORRECTION OF NUCLEAR MEASUREMENTS

With interferometric nuclear measurements using the analyzer method, assessments on the nuclear center are usually the only possible determinations. However, as the nucleus is not a cylinder, but has the form of a rotated ellipsoid, a correction of $\frac{2}{3}$ should be made. This correction, however, does not always serve for the actual nuclear volume. The spheroid correction has an error of approximately 5% (*33*).

B. ERRORS OCCURRING IN DETERMINATION OF PHASE DIFFERENCE $\Delta\rho_G$ OR OF THE PATH DIFFERENCE $\Delta\delta$

When determining the phase difference, Davies (*6*) found a measuring accuracy of $\lambda/200$ (Dyson system). With the Baker interference microscope the measuring accuracy is found to be between $\lambda/200$ to $\lambda/300$. Schiemer (*33*) found a measuring accuracy of $\lambda/180$ for the Baker interference microscope. The Leitz interference microscope should have a measuring accuracy of $\lambda/1500$. In a study by Schiemer *et al.* (*34*), two investigators determined the values of $\Delta\rho_G$ using the analyzer method (Table III). The deviations in the values of small and relatively homo-

TABLE III
VALUES OF $\Delta\rho_G$ DETERMINED BY TWO INVESTIGATORS[a]

Cell no.	Nucleus		Cytoplasm		Background	
	A	B	A	B	A	B
1	160	166	124	122	111	103
2	168	162	123	125	110	105
3	163	167	122	116	105	108
4	169	163	116	110	108	107
5	164	165	126	115	110	106
M	164.8	164.6	122.2	117.6	108	105.8
% Diff.	0.13%		3.76%		2.23%	

[a] After Schiemer *et al.* (*34*).

geneous nuclei are minor (0.13%). Comparatively, the more inhomogeneous cytoplasm shows greater deviation of the values (3.76%). These figures show the subjective error that occurs when the analyzer values are read at optimal darkness.

This error may be decreased, according to Leuchtenberger *et al.* (*18*) and Caspersson *et al.* (*5*) by reading off the analyzer values at optimal lightness and optimal darkness in the object and the medium over a photomultiplier cell and with a galvanometer. Also, when measuring the deviation in the fringe method an error may occur in determining the path difference $\Delta\delta$. This is caused by relatively broad fringes. These difficulties are decreased with densitometry of the fringe field.

C. Errors Due to the χ Values

The χ values of the object depend on a number of factors:

a. *Dependence of the χ values on the chemical structure of the substance.* Table IV shows the dependence of the χ values on the structure of different chemical compounds. The value for unconjugated proteins is 0.17, for DNA approximately 0.175, for carbohydrates and for lipids approximately 0.14.

b. *Dependence of the χ values on the pH of the solution.* The pH value of the surrounding medium may cause changes of the χ values in the object (Fig. 2). Schiemer (*33*) demonstrated the dependence of

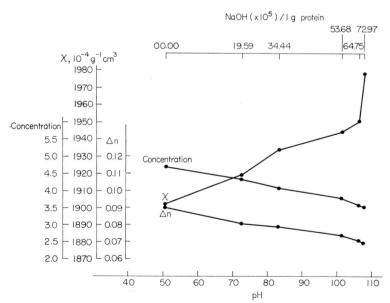

Fig. 2. Dependence of the value of the specific refractive increment (χ) on pH of the embedding solution (bovine serum albumin). From Schiemer (*33*).

TABLE IV

Value of χ for Biologically Important Materials*

Compound Class	Example	Physical state	Density	Refractive index	λ (mμ)	χ
Unconjugated proteins	Ovalbumin[a]	1.61% sol.	—	—	—	0.187
	Ovalbumin[a]	6.45% sol.	—	—	—	0.188
	Bovine plasma albumin[b]	0–50 g/100 ml solution	—	—	—	0.182
	Gelatin[c]	Dil. solution	—	—	—	0.18
	Gelatin[d]	Dry solid	1.27	1.525 av.	—	0.151
Amino acids	Glycine[e]	Dil. solution	—	—	—	0.179
	Alanine[e]	Dil. solution	—	—	—	0.171
	Valine[e]	Dil. solution	—	—	—	0.175
	Tryptophan[e]	Dil. solution	—	—	—	0.25
Nucleic acids	DNA[f]	Dil. solution	—	—	—	0.16
	DNA[g]	Dil. solution	—	—	—	0.20
	DNA[h]	Dil. solution	—	—	436	0.20
	DNA[i]	Dil. solution	—	—	546	0.175
	DNA[i]	Dil. solution	—	—	436	0.181
	DNA[j]	Dil. solution	—	—	436	0.188
	RNA[k]	Dil. solution	—	—	436	0.194
	RNA[l]	Dil. solution	—	—	—	0.168
Carbohydrates	Starch[d]	Solid	1.50	1 53	—	0.133
	Sucrose[d]	2% solution	—	—	—	0.141
	Sucrose[d]	Crystalline	1.588	1.558	—	0.141
Lipid	Fats[d]	Natural	0.93 av.	1.46 av.	—	0.14 av.
Salts	Sodium chloride[d]	5.25% solution	—	—	—	0.163
	Sodium chloride[d]	Crystalline	2.165	1.544	—	0.097
	Calcium chloride[a]	1.7% solution	—	—	—	0.21
	Calcium chloride[a]	Crystalline	2.512	1.52	—	0.075
	Potassium chloride[a]	10% solution	—	—	—	0.115
	Potassium chloride[a]	Crystalline	1.98	1.490	—	0.079
Conjugated proteins	β_1-lipoprotein[m]	Dil. solution	—	—	—	0.17
	Hemoglobin[n]	Dil. solution	—	—	—	0.193
	Turnip yellow mosaic virus[o]	Dil. solution	—	—	—	0.171
	Tobacco mosaic virus[p]	Dil. solution	—	—	—	0.17
	Tobacco mosaic virus	Dried gel	1.335 av.[q]	1.534av.[r]	—	0.151

* From Davies (6).
a Perlman, G. E., and Longsworth, L. G. (1948). J. Am. Chem. Soc. 70, 2719.
b Barer, R., and Tkaczyk, S. (1954). Nature 173, 84.
c Kenchengton, in Barer, R., and Joseph, S. (1954). Quart. J. Micrscop. Sci. 95, 399.
d "Handbook of Chemistry and Physics" (C. D. Hodgman, ed.), 30th ed. Chem. Rubber Publ. Co., Cleveland, Ohio, 1946.
e Adair, G. S., and Robinson, M. E. (1930). Biochem. J. 24, 993.
f Tennant, H. G., and Villbrandt, C. F. (1943). J. Am. Chem. Soc. 65, 424.
g Vincent, . ., in Barer, R. (1952). Nature 169, 366.
h Northrop, T. G., Nutter, R. L., and Sinsheimer, R. L. (1953). J. Am. Chem. Soc. 75, 5134.
i Brown, G. L., McEwen, M., and Pratt, M. (1955). Nature 176, 161.
j Reichmann, M. E., Rice, S. A., Thomas, C. A., and Doty, P. (1954). J. Am. Chem. Scc. 76, 3047.
k Northrup, T. G., and Sinsheimer, R. L. (1954). J. Chem. Phys. 22, 703.
l Davies, H. G., and Wilkins, M. H. F. (1900). Unpublished data.
m Armstrong, S. H., Jr., Budka, M. T. E., Morrison, K. C., and Hasson, M. (1947). J. Am. Chem. Soc 69, 1747.
n Adair, G. S., Ogston, A. L., and Johnston, J. P. (1946). Biochem. J. 40, 867.
o Markham, R. (1900). Private communication.
p Oster, G. (1900). Private communication.
q Bawden, F. C., and Pirie, N. W. (1937). Proc. Roy. Soc. B123, 274.
r Bernal, J., and Fankuchen, I. (1941). J. Gen. Physiol. 25, 111.

the χ values on pH using bovine serum albumin according to Perlmann and Longworth (21). The curves show that χ increased with increase in pH. The assessments of the concentration are either too small or too large when changes in pH occur.

c. *Dependence of the χ values on the wavelength of light.* Table V and Fig. 3 show the dependence of the χ values on the wavelength of light according to Hale (11) and Schiemer (33) respectively. It is seen that χ decreases with increasing wavelength.

TABLE V

DEPENDENCE OF χ ON WAVELENGTH OF LIGHT[a]

Wavelength λ (mμ)	Value of χ		
	Serum albumin	Serum globulin	Lactoglobulin
366	0.198	0.202	0.1963
436	0.190	0.195	0.1892
546	0.185	0.187	0.1818
579	0.183	0.186	0.1810
589	0.183	0.186	—
656	0.179	0.182	—

[a] After Hale (11).

For practical purposes the dry weight is determined according to a χ value of 0.18. One condition for this is that no increase in lipids and carbohydrates is found in the cell. Another condition is that measure-

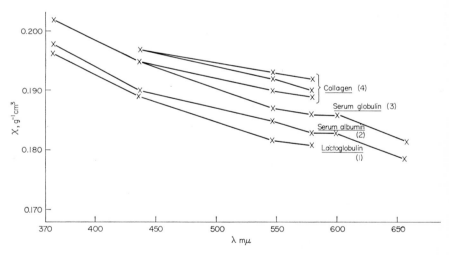

FIG. 3. Dependence of value of the specific refractive increment (χ) for different proteins on wavelength. From Schiemer (33).

ment of the phase difference is performed at the exact wavelength of 5462 Å. Under these conditions the deviation in χ is given by Davies (6), and Barer and Joseph (3), in the range from 0.177 to 0.186. The error is, therefore, 5%.

D. ERRORS IN DETERMINATION OF THE OBJECT AREA

An error may occur owing to indistinctness of the object border. With the Baker interference microscope at an object magnification of 100, an error of 0.5 μ will result (*33*). For the determination of object area the photographic image is most suitable. This photographic image may be projected, and the area then determined by means of planimetry. However, planimetric measurements are not free of errors. Figure 4

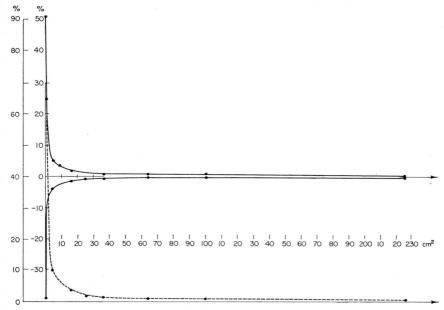

FIG. 4. Error caused by planimetry dependent on the size of the object area. The middle curves both show the deviation from the mean value in percentage. The lower curve shows the total deviation in percentage. From Schiemer (*33*).

shows a significant increase in planimetric error when the area is relatively small.

E. ERROR IN THE OBJECT THICKNESS

Determination of object thickness is always possible. Yet, difficulties may occur with any of the methods of thickness determination. For practical purposes, Sandritter *et al.* (*28*) provided an equation for interference microscopical measurements. With this equation it is possible to calculate the thickness of the nucleus when the area of the nucleus is known:

$$d = 2\sqrt{F_K/\pi} \quad [\text{cm}].$$

For practical purposes, the thickness of the cytoplasm is assumed to be the same as that of the cell nucleus.

F. Error Due to the Inhomogeneity of the Object

Biological objects such as cells and tissues are inhomogeneous, which also may cause errors. The more measuring points chosen, the smaller the error will become. However, according to Hale (10), as well as Hale and Kay (12, 13), it is better to measure with integrating methods. It is possible to measure the phase difference by integration over the total area of the object. Such apparatuses were designed by Lomakka (19) and Pörtner (22). Integration avoids the error due to inhomogeneity.

G. Error Due to Birefringence of the Object

When using the interference microscope based on polarized light, errors may occur owing to birefringence of the object. Birefringent objects have two or more refractive indexes. The path difference thus depends on the direction of the transmitted light. Therefore, when investigating birefringent objects it is essential to measure in a direction of the object which is parallel to the direction of the beam combiner; for instance, collagen fibers must be investigated lengthwise.

H. Errors in Preparation of the Specimen

Preparation of the specimen must be performed very carefully. In living cells, function of, for instance, the cell membrane, may be damaged. Cell substance may be lost or substances of the medium may penetrate into the cell. To prevent this error Bahr et al. (1), as well as Sandritter et al. (28), have used an embedding medium containing high molecular compounds or proteins. It is necessary to adjust for the pH values and the osmotic pressure. Also, special cell chambers may be used (32). When investigating air-dried smears of single cells, a loss of low molecular substances can occur during washing. This results in a decrease of the dry weight. On the other hand, washing is necessary because various substances can adhere to the surface of the cells. When these are not removed, the measured dry weight is erroneously increased. In addition, the adherent substances can be dissolved into the medium, which results in a change in the reference beam. The preparation of the object must also be exactly constant to avoid greater errors.

Chemically fixed cells and tissues are only to be used with great care. These fixatives cause various changes. Parts of the fixative may penetrate the specimen and be chemically bound there. This is the case, for example, with formalin fixation. Proteins and nucleic acids can be dissolved by hydrolysis when the fixative is acid containing. Alcoholic fixative dissolves lipids, and aqueous fixatives dissolve carbohydrates.

In addition, the refractive index and the specific refractive increment are changed by fixation. Finally, inhomogeneity of the object is increased by denaturation of proteins. From this it becomes apparent that the conditions for the investigation must be kept constant. Then the range of errors is between 10 and 15%. This seems to be an acceptable error for biological material.

IV. Example of the Calculation of Dry Weight

With the Zeiss interference microscope, one can measure squamous epithelial cells (extinction transfer method) embedded in water. First of all, the maximal darkness of the background (ρ_{GA}) is measured by turning the analyzer three times:

1st measurement: 49°.
2nd measurement: 50°.
3rd measurement: 51°.

The mean value of ρ_{GA} for the background is 50°.

Second, the maximal darkness (ρ_{GA}) of cytoplasm of the cell is measured three times:

1st measurement: 88°.
2nd measurement: 93°.
3rd measurement: 89°.

The mean value of ρ_{GA} for the cytoplasm is 90°.

Third, the analyzer of the microscope is again turned to the deepest darkness of the cell nucleus and the deepest darkness (ρ_{GA}) of the nucleus is also measured three times:

1st measurement: 125°.
2nd measurement: 126°.
3rd measurement: 139°.

The mean value of ρ_{GA} for the nucleus is, therefore, 130°.

A photograph of this cell is taken. Using this photograph the area (F) of the cytoplasm and the nucleus is determined by planimetry or by cutting out the cytoplasm and nucleus and weighing the nucleus and the cytoplasm separately.

In this example, the area of the cytoplasm has the following size:

1st measurement: 4980 /u^2.
2nd measurement: 4970 /u^2.
3rd measurement: 5050 /u^2.

The mean value for the area of the cytoplasm is 5000 /u^2.
In the same way the area of the nucleus is measured:

1st measurement: 99 /u^2.
2nd measurement: 100 /u^2.
3rd measurement: 101 /u^2.

The mean value for the area of the nucleus is 100 /u^2.
When an unfixed specimen is embedded in water the following equation is given for the calculation of the the dry weight (M):

$$M = \frac{\Delta\delta_w \cdot F}{\chi}.$$

Calculation of $\Delta\delta$ for the Cytoplasm. First the difference of the ρ value for the cytoplasm and the ρ value for the background is found:

ρ_{GA} cytoplasm	90°
ρ_{GA} background	50°
$\Delta\rho_{GA}$ cytoplasm	40°

In the Zeiss interference microscope the phase difference is measured in degrees. For calculation of the dry weight it is necessary to convert the phase difference ($\Delta\rho_{GA}$) in degrees into the path difference ($\Delta\delta$) in centimeters:

$$\Delta\delta = \frac{\Delta\rho_{GA} \times 2}{360} \times \lambda \quad [\text{cm}].$$

The multiplication of $\Delta\rho_{GA}$ by a factor of 2 is necessary because with the extinction transfer method the phase difference is only measured in $\lambda/2$ and not in 1λ ($1\lambda = 360°$). λ is the wavelength, which is used (5462×10^{-8} cm). Therefore,

$$\Delta\delta_{\text{cytoplasm}} = \frac{40 \times 2}{360} \times 5462 \times 10^{-8}$$

$$= \frac{80}{360} \times 5462 \times 10^{-8}$$

$$= 1216 \times 10^{-8} \text{ cm}.$$

Calculation of $\Delta\delta$ *for the Nucleus.* The difference between the ρ value for the nucleus and the ρ value for the background is

ρ_{GA} nucleus	130°
ρ_{GA} background	50°
$\Delta\rho_{GA}$ nucleus	80°

For the nucleus $\Delta\delta$ (cm) is

$$\Delta\delta_{\text{nucleus}} = \frac{80 \times 2}{360} \times 5462 \times 10^{-8}$$

$$= \frac{160}{360} \times 5462 \times 10^{-8}$$

$$= 2432 \times 10^{-8} \text{ cm.}$$

Calculation of the Dry Weight for Cytoplasm. The formula for the calculation of the dry weight is, under this condition,

$$M = \frac{\Delta\delta_w \cdot F}{\chi} \quad [\text{g}].$$

The χ value is used for a protein solution (0.18).

$$M_{\text{cytoplasm}} = \frac{1216 \times 10^{-8} \times 5 \times 10^3 \times 10^{-8}}{0.18}$$

$$= 33777 \times 10^{-13}$$

$$= 3377.7 \times 10^{-12} \text{ g.}$$

Calculation of the Dry Weight for the Nucleus. In the same way the dry weight of the nucleus is calculated:

$$M_{\text{nucleus}} = \frac{2432 \times 10^{-8} \times 10^2 \times 10^{-8}}{0.18}$$

$$= 13511 \times 10^{-14}$$

$$= 135.11 \times 10^{-12} \text{ g.}$$

V. Applications of Quantitative Interference Microscopy to Biological Material

A. EXAMINATIONS OF NORMAL CELLS

In Table VI the nuclear dry weight and the DNA content of haploid (sperms) and diploid cell (red blood cells, lymphocytes) nuclei are shown. It is seen that the values of the nuclear dry weight exhibit little change from species to species. It may be noticed that the dry weights of the nuclei exhibit the same relations as the DNA content of these

TABLE VI

Dry Weight Concentration, Dry Weight, and DNA Content
of Various Cells (Haploid and Diploid)[a]

Cells	n	μ^2	Concentration (10^{-8} g cm^{-2})	Dry weight (10^{-12} g)	Deviation	DNA (10^{-12} g)	Ratio of dry weight to DNA[b]
Human							
Spermatocytes	47	14.1	8061.6	6.08	0.54	3.12	1.91
Spermatocytes	10	14.3	8215.7	6.38	0.75	3.12	2.04
Thymus lymphocytes	115	26.6	5244.1	13.80	1.53	6.80	2.02
Bull							
Spermatocytes	175	41.1	2188.1	8.09	1.19	3.25	2.49
Thymus lymphocytes	96	26.1	5575.8	14.40	1.78	6.55	2.20
Rabbit							
Spermatocytes	34	30.3	2212.9	6.71	0.90	3.25	2.06
Spermatocytes	10	30.3	2236.6	6.79	1.16	3.25	2.09
Thymus lymphocytes	8	32.6	4130.3	13.53	2.56	5.75	2.35
Thymus lymphocytes	20	25.1	5207.1	13.02	1.29	5.75	2.26
Rat							
Spermatocytes	25	19.2	3039.0	5.82	0.51	3.11	1.87
Spermatocytes	16	17.5	3577.8	6.27	0.20	3.11	2.01
Thymus lymphocytes	30	21.8	4847.4	10.50	1.40	6.05	1.73
Thymus lymphocytes	31	24.9	4358.0	10.81	0.87	6.05	1.78
Thymus lymphocytes	14	25.5	4768.7	11.85	0.63	6.05	1.95
Cock							
Spermatocytes	44	11.5	2178.2	2.49	0.60	1.59	1.56
Erythrocytes	23	13.2	3489.0	4.59	0.52	3.30	1.39
Erythrocytes	32	14.3	5009.0	7.17	0.91	3.30	2.17
Erythrocytes	13	12.8	3836.0	4.93	0.21	3.30	1.49
Trout							
Spermatocytes	14	6.8	6350.0	4.29	0.22	2.52	1.70
Spermatocytes	33	7.7	5191.4	4.01	0.50	2.52	1.59
Spermatocytes	16	7.7	5760.0	4.43	0.32	2.52	1.75
Erythrocytes	29	25.9	3260.8	8.36	1.12	5.46	1.53
Rana temporaria							
Erythrocytes	26	70.7	3049.2	21.55	0.84	8.85	2.43
Bufo viridis							
Erythrocytes	35	50.2	3601.5	18.03	1.24	12.12	1.48

[a] From Sandritter et al. (25).

[b] DNA taken as 1.

cells. It is relatively constant in the ratio of 1 : 2. The relation of dry weight to DNA content is given by the quotient of 2. This means that with these cells, 50% of the nuclear dry weight is DNA. The other 50% of the nuclear dry weight is mainly protein, that is, histone and non-histone proteins.

This relation of DNA to dry weight is not the same in all cells. Table VII shows values from cells of the respiratory tract. Here cellular nuclei are found having ratio of DNA to dry weight such as 1 : 3.7 or 1 : 6.8. In these cells the greater nuclear mass is probably caused by an increase of non-histone proteins in the nuclei.

This is once again summarized in Fig. 5. The far left column shows the

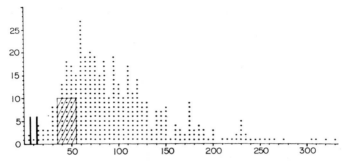

Fig. 5. Distribution of nuclear dry weight of various cells. Abscissa: dry weight in grams $\times$ 10^{-12}. Ordinate: number of cells.

dry weight of sperms. The next small column demonstrates the dry weight of lymphocytes, that is, the dry weights of haploid and diploid cells, respectively. Furthermore, these two cells have a ratio of DNA to dry weight of 1 : 2. Other diploid cells have a higher content of proteins in the nucleus. Therefore, the dry weight of the nucleus is also higher. These cells are summarized in the striped column. The other cellular nuclei in the figure having even higher dry weight are those of HeLa cells.

It is known that there exists a certain correlation between the nuclear volume and the cytoplasmic volume (nuclear-cytoplasmic ratio). In some cases the relationship is also applicable to dry weights. In cancer cells it has been found that nuclei with low dry weight have a low cytoplasmic dry weight and that with increasing nuclear dry weight the cytoplasmic dry weight becomes increasingly greater (Sandritter, unpublished findings, 1965). If we analyze this interrelationship for vaginal squamous epithelium, it is apparent (Fig. 6) that there is little evidence of such a relation. The grouping of measured cytoplasmic values indi-

TABLE VII

DRY WEIGHT, DRY WEIGHT CONCENTRATION, AND DNA CONTENT OF NUCLEI AND CYTOPLASM OF VARIOUS CELLS FROM THE RESPIRATORY TRACT[a]

Cells	Nucleus							Cytoplasm							Nucleoles						Relation of dry wt. of nucleus : cyto : nucleoles
	N[b]	Area (μ^2)	Vol. (μ^3)	Dry wt. (10^{-18} g)	a[c] (±)	Dry wt. (% in 100 ml)	Conc. (10^{-12} g/μ^3)	N[b]	Area (μ^2)	Vol. (μ^3)	Dry wt. (10^{-12} g)	a[c] (±)	Dry wt. (% in 100 ml)	Conc. (10^{-12} g/μ^3)	N[b]	Area (μ^2)	Vol. (μ^3)	Dry wt. (10^{-12} g)	Dry wt. (% in 100 ml)	Conc. (10^{-12} g/μ^3)	
Buccal epithelium cell	38	87	608	55.5	16	9.1	0.6550	37	4105	43.9 ×10	1941.2	381	4.45	0.4847	—	—	—	—	—	—	1 : 0.5
Ciliated columna cells	41	66	436	41.1	16	9.4	0.6299	41	159	1629	92.6	45	5.68	0.5960	6	2.0	2.25	0.6	26.7	0.3061	1 : 0.6 : 2.8
Basal cells	20	46	235	33.2	11	14.1	0.7332	7	27	324	11.1	4	3.43	0.4614	—	—	—	—	—	—	1 : 0.2
Pulmonary macrophages	25	79	528	47.5	20	8.9	0.6111	25	197	2238	101.9	251	4.56	0.5205	8	3.7	5.2	1.6	30.8	0.4444	1 : 0.5 : 3.5
Mean value of normal cells	124	72	477	45.5	20	10.8	0.6505	110	149	15939	86.9	251	4.87	0.5328	14	2.9	3.9	1.1	29.0	0.3851	

[a] From Sandritter et al. (28).
[b] The number of cells investigated.
[c] Standard deviation.

cates a slight increase in dry weight, although the values are generally widely scattered.

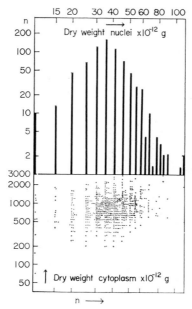

FIG. 6. Correlation between nuclear dry weight and cytoplasmic dry weight demonstrated on a double logarithmic scale. The cytoplasmic dry weight corresponding to the dry weight of each nucleus is plotted in the lower portion of the diagram. From Sandritter *et al.* (*31*).

Another possible use for the interference microscope is the determination of the chemical composition of biological structures, such as cellular nuclei. These measurements must be performed before and after specific extraction methods.

Davies *et al.* (*7*) have determined the dry weight of sperm heads before and after use of such extraction methods. With this method the sperm heads have a dry weight of 8×10^{-12} g. On the same sperms extractions are performed after these measurements, for example, the lipids are removed with ether; the RNA is eliminated with RNase; the DNA is extracted with trichloracetic acid. After each step of extraction the dry weight is measured and thus the chemical composition determined The sperms contain 10% lipids, 5% RNA, 40% DNA, and 40% proteins.

B. INVESTIGATIONS OF SPECIFIC CELLULAR FUNCTIONS

The interference microscope is also an important tool for the investigation of specific cellular functions. Barter *et al.* (*4*) investigated the ac-

tivity of alkaline phosphatase in the brush borders of kidney cells of
the rat and in the mucous cells of the duodenum of the rat. In Fig. 7,

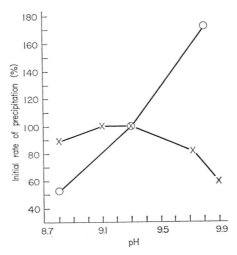

Fig. 7. Dependence of the alkaline phosphatase of rat kidney (○) and rat duodenum (×) cells on the pH of the incubation solution. From Barter *et al* (4).

the dependence of the activity of this enzyme on pH of the incubation
solution is shown. Alkaline phosphatase splits off the phosphate group
from the glycerophosphate. The phosphate group is bound with calcium
to form an insoluble salt. This salt is deposited in the tissue where the
enzyme is localized. The salt deposit can be measured by interference
microscopy because the dry weight is increased. The amount of the
calcium phosphate is directly proportional to enzyme activity. The figure
shows that the activity of the alkaline phosphatase in the rat duodenum
has an optimal pH of approximately 9.1. Contrary to this, the optimal
pH for alkaline phosphatase in the brush borders of the rat kidney is
more in the alkaline range.

Interesting investigations (Fig. 8) were performed by Lagerlöf *et al.*
(*16*) on matured and hemolytic red blood cells. The dry weight of these
cells was determined with the interference microscope. On the same cells
the hemoglobin content was measured with the cytophotometer. The
upper curves show an increase in proteins rather than an increase in
hemoglobin content in mature red blood cells. This indicates that the
protein is produced before the heme component is introduced into the
hemoglobin molecule. In normal erythrocytes (the lower curve in Fig. 8)
the relation between dry weight and hemoglobin content is linear.

Roels (*23*) has determined the dry weight of nuclei of cells of the
adrenal medulla. He found that stress, as well as splanchnicectomy,

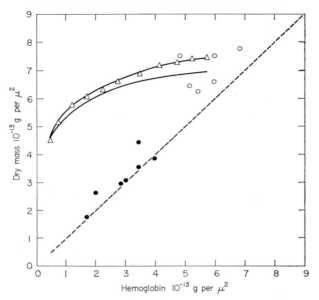

FIG. 8. Relation between the dry weight and the hemoglobin content of red blood cells. From Lagerlöf *et al.* (*16*). Red blood cells: △ matured, ○ normal, ● hemolytic.

causes an increase in the dry weight concentration of these cells. In comparative investigations he proved that the increase in dry weight is caused only by an increase of proteins in the nuclei. Up until then, no explanation for this phenomenon had been given.

Sandritter *et al.* (*24*), as well as Sandritter and Scomazzoni (*30*), have compared the dry weight of normal heart muscle fibers and heart muscle fibers in hypertrophy of the heart (Fig. 9). The curve shows that the dry

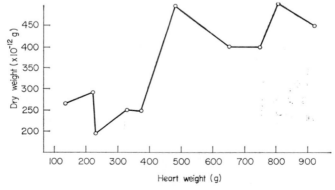

FIG. 9. Dependence of the dry weight of heart muscle fibers on the heart weight. From Sandritter and Scomazzoni (*30*).

weight of hypertrophic muscle fibers is twice as heavy as that of normal muscle fibers. The strain of the hypertrophic heart leads to a dry weight increase of the heart muscle fibers.

C. Cellular Growth

Sandritter *et al.* (*29*) have investigated the growth of single cells in tissue culture. The curves (Fig. 10) show measurements of the dry

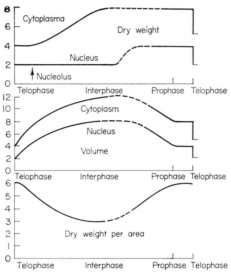

Fig. 10. Dry weight, volume, and concentration of nuclei and cytoplasm during the interphase of HeLa cells. From Sandritter *et al.* (*29*).

weight, the concentration, and the volume of cell nuclei and cytoplasm in interphase of the mitotic cycle. The volume (the middle curve) increases in early interphase. The increase in volume of the cytoplasm is greater than that of the nucleus. In the late interphase the volume is again decreased, but this decrease does not give the original value. The increase in volume compared with the curve of the dry weight (upper curve) shows that increase in volume is only partly caused by the increase in mass. The dry weight of cytoplasm and nucleus is doubled. The increase in dry weight begins earlier than that of the nucleus. The lower curve shows the dry weight in a specific area, that is, the concentration. This curve demonstrates that the decrease in the concentration begins approximately in the middle of interphase. At the end of interphase, the concentration again is the same as at the onset. These investigations lead to the following conclusions: In the beginning of interphase,

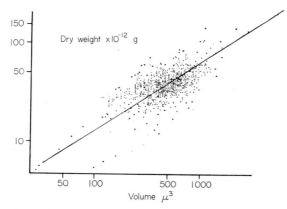

FIG. 11. Correlation between nuclear dry weight and volume demonstrated on a double logarithmic scale. From Sandritter *et al.* (*31*).

there is an uptake of water by the cytoplasm and the nucleus. This again leads to a doubling of the dry weight. At the end of interphase, water is released. In this phase cell enlargement is caused only by the doubling of the dry weight.

Cell growth may also be determined on squamous cells (*31*). There is a relation between the volume and the dry weight, which may be expressed in the following equation (also called allometric growth equation):

$$y = b \cdot x^{\alpha},$$

where y represents the dry weight and x is the volume; α represents the somatic exponent which indicates the ascent of the straight line, while

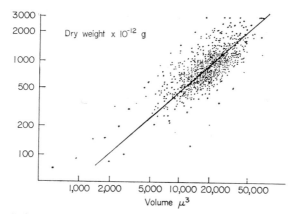

FIG. 12. Correlation between cytoplasmic dry weight and volume demonstrated on a double logarithmic scale. From Sandritter *et al.* (*31*).

b is to be interpreted as initial growth index. When α is 1, growth is isometric. If α is greater than 1, the dry weight will increase more than the volume. In Fig. 11 is demonstrated the correlation between the nuclear dry weight and volume on a double logarithmic scale; α is calculated as 0.68, and b is 0.56. In this case the volume increases more than the dry weight. In comparison with the nuclei the cytoplasm of the same cells shows another relation (Fig. 12). Here an α of 0.96 is found ($b = 0.68$). This shows that in the cytoplasm the dry weight increases proportionally to the volume (isometric growth).

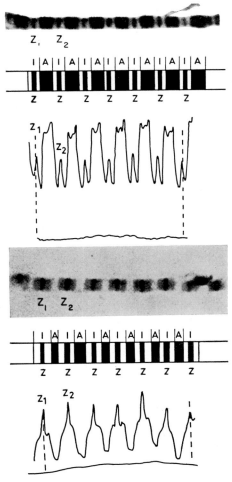

FIG. 13. Interferometric measurements on striated muscle fibers before (top) and after (bottom) extraction of actomyosine. From Huxley and Hanson (15).

D. COMPOSITION OF A FEW BIOLOGICAL STRUCTURES

Huxley and Hanson (15) investigated the composition of striated muscle fibers. Figure 13 (top) shows the interference pattern of such a striated muscle fiber. These fibers consist of 96% proteins (percentage of the total dry weight). It is seen that the concentration is considerably higher in the anisotropic stripes of the fiber (A) than in the isotropic stripes (I). This is also seen in the densitometer curve. The lower picture was taken under the same conditions. However, prior to measurement, the contractile protein, also called actomyosine, was extracted. The comparison of the two pictures shows that most of the actomyosine is localized in the anisotropic stripes of the muscle fibers.

Another application of the interference microscope for investigation

TABLE VIII

MASS AND RELATED DATA OF ELASTIC FIBERS OF THE AORTIC WALL[a,b]

	Adults	Children	t^c	p^d
Fiber characteristics				
Refractive index	1.55 ± 0.0028	1.55 ± 0.0026	0.0054	>0.9
Effective thickness, μ	3.62 ± 0.28	3.26 ± 0.18	1.076	$0.3 > p > 0.2$
Mass per unit area (1×10^{-12} g per μ^2)	4.36 ± 0.31	3.96 ± 0.19	1.097	$0.3 > p > 0.2$
Standard (50μ) fiber length				
Area μ^2	93.30 ± 2.22	102.15 ± 8.98	0.977	$0.4 > p > 0.3$
Dry mass ($\times 10^{-10}$ g per μ^2)	4.06 ± 0.31	4.09 ± 0.47	0.048	>0.9
Sample ($2,500\ \mu^2$) area				
Area occupied by fibers μ^2	270.37 ± 15.77	431.60 ± 43.24	3.501	$0.01 > p > 0.001$
Percentage area occupied by fibers	10.81 ± 0.62	17.26 ± 1.72	3.509	$0.01 > p > 0.001$
Dry mass of fibers in sample ($\times 10^{-10}$ g per μ^2)	11.75 ± 1.19	17.15 ± 2.12	2.301	$0.05 > p > 0.02$

[a] In 10 cases each of adults and children (mean values with standard errors).
[b] From Franca and Foraker (9).
[c] Standard deviation.
[d] Statistical significance.

TABLE IX

Dry Weight Distribution of Nuclei and Cytoplasm from Various Normal and Tumor Cells[a]

Cells	Nucleus						Cytoplasm					
	N[c]	Dry weight (10^-12 g)	a[d] (±)	Dry weight (% in 100 ml)	Mass per unit area (10^-12 g/μ²)	Area (μ²)	N[c]	Dry weight (10^-12 g)	a[d] (±)	Dry weight (% in 100 ml)	Mass per unit area (10^-12 g/μ²)	Area (μ²)
Spermatocytes	57	6.2	1.16	—	0.814	14.2	—	—	—	—	—	—
Thymus lymphocytes	116	13.7	1.5	13.2	0.524	27	—	—	—	—	—	—
Pleura mesothelial cells	254	37.4	16.2	5.7	0.450	88	254	50.4	27.4	2.6	0.340	152
Mean values of normal cells[b]	124	45.5	15.0	10.8	0.651	72	110	536.7	172	4.9	0.533	1122
Vaginal epithelial cells	211	37.9	1.7	7.3	0.417	82	211	949.3	12.1	4.2	0.326	2363
Mean value of all normal cells	(n = 705)	35.1	—	8.5	0.480	72	(n = 475)	512.1	—	3.6	0.399	1212
Oat cell bronchial carcinoma IV, V, XIV	281	34.5	19	8.2	0.493	71	—	—	—	—	—	—
Keratinizing squamous epithelial carcinomas												
VII	117	90.8	51	10.4	0.638	123	87	67.0	42	4.6	0.474	112
XIII	55	43.1	24	3.8	0.236	132	52	117.3	83	3.8	0.479	204
XV	40	124.8	58	10.4	0.806	141	40	172.0	115	5.2	0.646	223
XVI	143	64.1	56	10.2	0.603	92	—	—	—	—	—	—
Mean value	(n = 355)	80.7	—	8.7	0.571	122	(n = 179)	118.7	—	4.5	0.533	180
Nonkeratinizing squamous epithelial carcinomas												
II	20	58.6	16	7.2	0.510	105	19	24.3	17	2.0	0.517	47
III	24	247.3	103	4.8	0.667	357	21	113.3	109	2.0	0.493	230
VI	22	110.1	49	8.0	0.730	149	16	89.2	53	3.4	0.552	142
VIII	57	160.6	95	3.8	0.540	313	33	98.8	41	1.3	0.344	287
XII	105	198.5	101	15.9	1.234	147	105	254.1	216	6.5	0.936	231
Mean value	(n = 288)	155.0	—	7.9	0.736	214	(n = 194)	115.9	—	3.0	0.568	188
Mean value of all carcinoma cells	(n = 864)	90.0	—	8.3	0.600	—	(n = 373)	117.3	—	3.8	0.551	—
Tissue culture: HeLa cells	406	100.7	46	8.2	0.824	155	406	239.9	88	5.0	0.570	326
Amnion cells	102	117.7	44	4.3	0.473	244	102	257.1	95	2.7	0.272	461

a From Sandritter et al. (27).
b Squamous epithelial cells of the vagina, ciliated epithelium, basal cells, alveolar epithelium.
c The number of cells investigated.
d Standard deviation.

of biological structures has been given by Franca and Foraker (*9*). These authors investigated the elastic fibers of the aorta of children and adults (Table VIII). The investigations were performed under the assumption that elastic fibers of blood vessels change when aging. However, the values in Table VIII show that the dry weights of elastic fibers are the same in children and in adults. Children only show more elastic fibers per unit area.

E. Investigations on Tumor Cells

The interference microscope also plays an important role in tumor cell research. Table IX shows the dry weight values of the nucleus and the cytoplasm of sperms, thymocytes, squamous cells of the mouth and the vagina, and tumor cells. The mean values of the tumor cells vary from those of the normal cells. However, the tumor cells also show different dry weight values. These different values depend on the differentiation of the tumors. The dry weight of normal cells is approximately 35 $\times 10^{-12}$ g. The same nuclear dry weights (34.5×10^{-12} g) are found in oat cell carcinomas. An important higher nuclear dry weight is found in keratinizing squamous carcinomas. The middle absolute values are 80.7×10^{-12} g. Still higher is the nuclear dry weight of nonkeratinizing squamous carcinomas, 155×10^{-12} g, or of HeLa cells, 100.7×10^{-12} g.

Lee *et al.* (*17*) tried to investigate the influence of nitrogen mustard

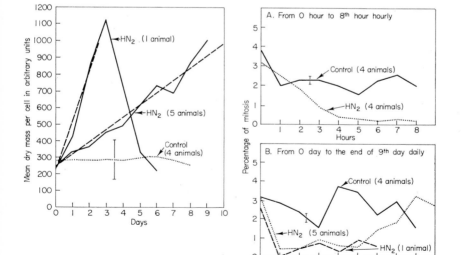

Fig. 14. Dry weight distribution of nuclei and mitotic index of Ehrlich ascites cells after treatment with nitrogen mustard. From Lee *et al.* (*17*).

on tumor cells with interference microscopy. They investigated Ehrlich ascites tumor cells that had been treated with nitrogen mustard (Fig. 14), and determined the dry weight of the nuclei and the rate of mitosis. The curves show that dry weight increases after only one treatment with nitrogen mustard. Contrary to this, in a range of 9 days the rate of mitosis is decreased as compared with untreated cells. These results show that the increase of substances is influenced by the treatment, but cell division is retarded.

These examples of applications of interference microscopy show that quantitative interference microscopy is an essential method for assessment of biological problems. Interference microscopy alone, as well as in comparison with other histochemical methods, provides new knowledge about the biological structure of the cell under normal and pathological conditions.

REFERENCES

1. Bahr, G. F., G. Bloom, and U. Fridberg, Volume changes of tissues in physiological fluid during fixation in osmium tetroxyde or formaldehyde and during subsequent treatment. *Exptl. Cell Res.* 12, 342–355 (1957).
2. Barer, R. Determination of dry mass, thickness, solid and water concentration in living cells. *Nature* 172, 1097–1098 (1953).
3. Barer, R., and S. Joseph, Refractometry of living cells. I. Basic principles. *Quart. J. Microscop. Sci.* 95, 399–423 (1954).
4. Barer, R., J. F. Danielli, and H. G. Davies, A quantitative cytochemical method for estimating alkaline phosphatase activity. *Proc. Roy. Soc.* 144, 412–426, 1955.
5. Caspersson, T., L. Carlsson, and G. Svensson, A scanning interference microscope arrangement. *Exptl. Cell Res.* 7, 601-602 (1954).
6. Davies, H. G., The determination of mass and concentration by microscope interferometry. *In* "General Cytochemical Methods" (J. F. Danielli, ed., Vol. 1, pp. 55–161. Academic Press, New York, 1958.
7. Davies, H. G., E. M. Deeley, and E. F. Denby, Attempts at measurement of lipid, nucleic acid and protein content of cell nuclei by microscope-interferometry. *Exptl. Cell Res.* Suppl. 4, 136–149 (1957).
8. Faust, R. G., The use of the Baker interference microscope for the study of optically heterogeneous specimens. *Quart. J. Microscop. Sci.* 97, 569–591 (1956).
9. Franca, L. C. M., and A. G. Foraker, Elastic fibre mass in human aorta: an interferometric approach. *Arch. Pathol.* 70, 216–219 (1960).
10. Hale, A. J., The application of interferic microscopy to a quantitative study of the colloid in the thyroid gland of the guinea-pig. *Exptl. Cell Res.* 10, 132–145 (1956).
11. Hale, A. J., "The Interference Microscope in Biological Research." Livingstone, Edinburgh and London, 1958.
12. Hale, A. J., and E. R. M. Kay, A comparison of the dry weights of isolated cell nuclei as determined by chemical and by interferometric methods. *Biochem. J.* 61, 22 (1955).

13. Hale, A. J., and E. R. M. Kay, A comparison of nuclear dry weights determined by chemical and by interferometric methods. *J. Biophys. Biochem. Cytol.* **2**, 147–158 (1956).

14. Hallén, O., Measurement of section thickness. *Acta Histochem.* Suppl. 6, 187–189 (1965).

15. Huxley, H. E., and J. Hanson, Quantitative studies on the structure of cross-striated myofibrils. I. Investigations by interference microscopy. *Biochim. Biophys. Acta* **23**, 229–260 (1957).

16. Lagerlöf, B., B. Thorell, and L. Akerman, Heme and dry mass formation during red cell development. *Exptl. Cell Res.* **10**, 752–754 (1956).

17. Lee, H., V. Richards, and A. Furst, Increase in dry mass of Ehrlich ascites tumor cells after treatment with nitrogen mustard. *Cancer Res.* **21**, 1108–1112 (1961).

18. Leuchtenberger, C., I. Murmanis, L. Murmanis, and D. R. Weir, Interferometric dry mass and microphotometric arginine determinations on bull sperm nuclei with normal and abnormal DNA content. *Chromosoma* **8**, 73–86 (1956).

19. Lomakka, G., A rapid scanning and integrating microinteferometer. *Acta Histochem.* Suppl. 6, 303–304 (1965).

20. Pehland, H., and H. Hager, Zur Theorie der interferenzmikroskopischen Trockengewichtsbestimmung an biologischen Objekten. *Z. Wiss. Mikroskopie* **64**, 271–285 (1959).

21. Perlmann, G. E., and L. G. Longworth, The specific refractive increment of some purified proteins. *J. Am. Chem. Soc.* **70**, 2719–2724 (1948).

22. Pörtner, J., Aufbau und Betrieb eines integrierenden Scanning Interferenzmikroskopes. Inaugural Dissertation, University of Giessen (1965).

23. Roels, H., Interferometric study of the cell nuclei of the adrenal medulla in different experimental conditions. *Exptl. Cell Res.* **30**, 437–440 (1963).

24. Sandritter, W., K. D. Grosser, and H. G. Schiemer, Trockengewichtsbestimmungen an normalen und pathologischen Herzmuskelfasern. *Verhandl. Deut. Ges. Pathol.* **44**, 192–194 (1960).

25. Sandritter, W., D. Müller, and H. G. Schiemer, Über den Nukleinsäuregehalt und das Trockengewicht von haploiden und diploiden Zellen. *Verhandl. Anat. Ges.* (*Jena*) **55**, 146–154 (1958).

26. Sandritter, W., and H. G. Schiemer, Histochemische Untersuchungen an HeLa-Zellen. *Verhandl. Deut. Ges. Pathol.* **42**, 449–458 (1958).

27. Sandritter, W., H. G. Schiemer, and W. Alt, Das Interferenzmikroskop im Dienste der Cytologie und Krebsforschung. *Klin. Wochschr.* **38**, 590–595 (1960).

28. Sandritter, W., H. G. Schiemer, W. Alt, R. D. Müller, and E. Behrouzi, Histochemie von Sputumzellen. III. Interferenzmikroskopische Trockengewichtsbestimmungen. *Frankf. Z. Pathol.* **69**, 167–193 (1958).

29. Sandritter, W., H. G. Schiemer, H. Kraus, and U. Dörrien, Interferenzmikroskopische Untersuchungen über das Wachstum von Einzelzellen (HeLa-Zellen) in der Gewebekultur. *Frankf. Z. Pathol.* **70**, 271–299 (1960).

30. Sandritter, W., and G. Scomazzoni, Deoxyribonucleic acid content (Feulgen photometry) and dry weight (interference microscopy) of normal and hypertrophic heart muscle fibres. *Nature* **202**, 100–101 (1964).

31. Sandritter, W., H. Zilles, and G. Kiefer, Interference microscopic dry weight determinations on cells from the vaginal epithelium. *Acta Cytol.* **7**, 45–53 (1963).

32. Schiemer, H. G., Beschreibung einer Zellkammer und Durchströmungseinrichtung zur Untersuchung von Gewebekulturen mit dem Interferenzmikroskop und UV-Mikrospektrographen. *Mikroskopie* **14**, 91–99 (1959).

33. Schiemer, H. G., Fehlerberechnungen für Trockengewichtsbestimmungen mit dem Bakerschen Interferenzmikroskop. *Ann. Histochim.* Suppl. 2, 25–36 (1962).
34. Schiemer, H. G., W. Alt, and W. Sandritter, Zur Methodik der Trockengewichtsbestimmungen mit dem Bakerschen Interferenzmikroskop. *Acta Histochem.* **4,** 325–360 (1957).

SENSITIVITY AND EVALUATION
OF MICROSPECTROPHOTOMETRIC
AND MICROINTERFEROMETRIC
MEASUREMENTS

Peter H. Bartels

LABORATORY FOR APPLIED AND THEORETICAL MICROSCOPY,
E. LEITZ, INC., NEW YORK, NEW YORK

Only a few years ago microspectrophotometry and quantitative interference microscopy were considered techniques of such advanced nature that they belonged in the hands of specialized experts only. This situation has changed. The recognized potential of both techniques in cytochemical research has led to an intense interest in their application. The main difficulty for anyone entering this field is not to see the capability of the method or to learn how to take measurements, but to learn to evaluate the results, to recognize sources of error, their effect and relative importance, to find ways of checking results, and to develop confidence based on experience.

To provide a background for the following discussion, a rough estimate of measuring range and limits of detection will be given for both methods.

I. Microspectrophotometry in Visible Light, Limit of Detection

In the equation

$$I = I_0 \times 10^{-\epsilon c d}, \tag{1}$$

I is the intensity transmitted by a homogeneously absorbing object; I_0 the intensity of the incident light. The thickness of the absorbing layer is denoted by d, and given in centimeters; c is the concentration of the absorbing substance in millimoles per cubic centimeter, and ϵ its molar decadic coefficient of extinction, having the dimension square centimeters per millimole. $E = \log (I_0/I)$ is called the decadic extinction.

The limit of detection is determined by the smallest difference between

I_0 and I that could be considered a signal. In the following, the conservative numerical value of 5% will be assumed, which is adequate for most routine measurements. For ϵ a value of 25,000 cm²/millimole constitutes an average value. Many organic dyes have molar decadic coefficients of extinction in the range from 25,000 to 40,000 cm²/millimole; for the products of many color reactions as they are used in colorimetry, ϵ values of around 10,000 are more frequently found.

The geometric thickness d of the absorbing layer in the microscopic object will be assumed as $10\,\mu = 1 \times 10^{-3}$ cm, which is well within the range of the usual section thickness from 3 to $15\,\mu$. Under these conditions the minimum detectable dye concentration is

$$\frac{1}{1 \times 10^{-3} \times 2.5 \times 10^4} \log \frac{100}{95} = c = 8.5 \times 10^{-4} \frac{\text{millimole}}{\text{cm}^3}. \tag{2}$$

It becomes immediately apparent that the high sensitivity of detection of the method does not lie in the photometric measurement, but in the microscopic dimensions of the measured volume. Provided homogeneous distribution exists in the specimen, a measuring area A of $20\,\mu^2 = 2 \times 10^{-7}$ cm² is not unusual; d has been taken as $10\,\mu = 1 \times 10^{-3}$ cm. Homogeneous distribution of the absorbing substance does not always exist over $20\,\mu^2$. In that case measuring areas of as small as $1\mu^2$ are frequently employed. In this volume of 2×10^{-10} cm³ the concentration of the absorbing substance had to reach a minimum of 8.5×10^{-4} millimole/cm³ to produce an absorption of 5%. The amount of substance m required for this follows from

$$c \times Ad = m, \tag{3}$$

$$8.5 \times 10^{-4} \times 2 \times 10^{-10} = 1.7 \times 10^{-13} \text{ millimole.} \tag{4}$$

For a substance with a molecular weight of 300 this sets the limit of detection under the assumed conditions at

$$300 \times 10^{-3} \times 1.7 \times 10^{-13} \text{ g} = 5 \times 10^{-14} \text{ g.} \tag{5}$$

II. Microinterferometry, Limit of Detection

The image of an interference microscope has an intensity distribution which quantitatively represents the distribution of dry mass in the microscopic specimen. Dry mass can therefore be measured by photometric means. Throughout the following discussion the specimen will be assumed to be a fixed tissue section, which is fully penetrated by the mounting medium, solvent, and solute.

Again, a 5% change in image intensity will be considered the minimum signal for the photometric device. On the nearly linear portion on the flank of an interference fringe this corresponds to an optic path difference of approximately 6 mμ. The optic path difference for any point is given by the equation

$$\Gamma = t(n_0 - n_m), \tag{6}$$

Where t is the geometric thickness of the section, n_0 the refractive index of the object, and n_m that of the mounting medium. The optical path difference between two points in the section is given by

$$\Gamma = t(n_2 - n_1) \tag{7}$$

with n_2 and n_1 denoting the refractive indices at the two points, and t assumed to be constant. From Eq. (7) one can compute the difference in refractive index that would produce an optical path difference of 6 m$\mu = 6 \times 10^{-3} \mu$. The geometric thickness t will be assumed as 5 μ for this numerical example:

$$\frac{6 \times 10^{-3}}{5} = 1.2 \times 10^{-3}. \tag{7a}$$

This is the minimum detectable refractive index difference in the 5-μ section, and it can be related to a corresponding difference of concentration c. In microinterferometry it is usual to express c in grams per 100 cm^3.

The specific refractive index increment α represents the change of refractive index for a change in concentration of 1%, that is,

$$\alpha c = \Delta n. \tag{8}$$

For protein, α has a value of 1.8×10^{-3} cm^3/g. To free the concentration c from the factor $1/100$, α is often replaced by $\chi = 100 \, \alpha$.

With a detectable $\Delta n = (n_2 - n_1)$ of 1.2×10^{-3}, the minimum detectable concentration difference follows from

$$\frac{1.2 \times 10^{-3}}{0.18 \text{ cm}^3/\text{g}} = 6.6 \times 10^{-3} \text{ g/cm}^3. \tag{9}$$

If we assume a relatively large measuring area of 5 μ^2 and consider the section thickness of 5 μ, the measured volume becomes 25 $\mu^3 = 25 \times 10^{-12}$ cm^3. In this volume a change of concentration by 6.6×10^{-3} g/cm^3 can be detected. In the present example this amounts to $25 \times 10^{-12} \times 6.6 \times 10^{-3} = 1.65 \times 10^{-13}$ g.

It is possible without too much difficulty to measure in considerably smaller areas. Even a measuring area of 1 μ^2 would lower the limit of detection by a factor of 5. In the numerical example above this would mean 5×10^{-14} g.

III. Evaluation of Measurements

The numerical values found in the previous paragraph immediately raise the question of how accurate such values are. The results of measurements of biological phenomena are affected by three different influences. The first is the variability of the biological material itself. Experimental results will, therefore, often have to be represented by a distribution curve rather than by a single value. The second influence is the combined effect of all statistical errors. Since these produce too high or too low a value with equal probability, and since the biological variability demands a minimum number of measurements, statistical errors in many cases are not too serious. They do not affect the position of the maximum of the distribution curve. Their influence is restricted to a slight broadening of the biological distribution curve, the extent of which will be discussed later. The third influence is systematic errors. These errors cause measurements persistently to come out too high or too low, thus displacing the maximum of the distribution curve. Systematic errors are often difficult to detect. When detected, they can be measured and eliminated by correction.

IV. Statistical Evaluation, Histogram and Distribution Curve

The variation of the measured values is caused by both the biological variability and statistical errors. The latter will for the first part of this discussion be considered as negligibly small. The variability of results under these conditions is determined solely by the "natural band width," the true biological variability which no further increase in measuring accuracy could narrow. There are biological populations that show almost no variability. In general the biological variability, however, is quite high, and it is not uncommon to find values in a single unimodal distribution that differ by as much as a factor of 2. In a typical case, the result of a series of measurements consists of a number of varying measured values.

It is quite evident that it is not sufficient to describe the measured results by their arithmetic means. Such a value cannot reveal whether the distribution is unimodal or bimodal. It also does not indicate how much the values vary. Whenever a pilot experiment or previous measurements have shown that these values form a unimodal distribution and that the distribution is regular, and when a sufficient number of measurements has been taken so that the arithmetic mean has stabilized itself, a simple evaluation technique can be employed which offers several advantages. First, it leads to a distribution curve rather than a histogram. A histogram is always based upon the actual number of occurrences in each interval. It is true that a histogram can be made more representative by using the same measured results and redistributing them again with class or interval boundaries displaced by one-half class width. Still, a histogram gives a discontinuous representation of a continuous distribution. A computed continuous distribution curve is based not on the actual number of counts in each class, but rather on the variance of the sample as such. The computed curve represents the distribution that an infinite number of measurements of a population with the same variance as the smaller sample would show. A higher number of measurements usually leads to a smaller variance, and by systematically finding the decrease of variance with an increasing number of measurements one can often obtain, after a relatively small number of measurements, a result which is indistinguishable from the result obtained after a very substantial number of measurements. A histogram does not give nearly as good a projection. The calculating schedule yields the standard deviation SD as a side product and is so short that it is worth using even when only SD is to be computed. Also, when a distribution curve has been computed, one can add or subtract known statistical influences; for example, when it is known that the statistical instrumental error is 5%, one can then compute for a given and measured distribution the new distribution curve with 5% less variability. This will be shown in a practical example: The total dry mass of a population of bacteria was measured. The 250 measurements were taken in 25 groups of 10 measurements each, and the arithmetic mean was computed. This turned out to be 7.6×10^{-13} g. Most values fell into the range from 3×10^{-13} g to 1.3×10^{-12} g, and the variance suggested dividing the population into seven classes of a class width of 2×10^{-13} g each. As a rule one should not choose more than $2 \times N^{1/3}$ classes, where N denotes the number of measurements taken. (See Table I.) The 250 meas-

TABLE I

TOTAL DRY MASS OF BACTERIA, FREQUENCY OF OCCURRENCE IN A POPULATION

| Class boundaries | | 0.6 | 2.6 | 4.6 | 6.6 | 8.6 | 10.6 | 12.6 | 14.6 |
($\times 10^{-13}$ g)	0.5	2.5	4.5	6.5	8.5	10.5	12.5	14.5	16.5
Frequency of occurrence	3	5	25	56	73	55	26	6	1

urements lead to a histogram with an almost perfect Gaussian distribution as represented by the continuous distribution curve in Figs. 1–3. The question naturally arises whether fewer measurements would not have produced the same result. Figures 1–3 show this attempt. Of the 250 available values, first 10, then 20, then 50 were distributed. By multiplying the obtained frequencies of occurrence with suitable factors the results were made directly comparable with those obtained from 250 measurements. The result is not too satisfactory. Even 50 measurements leave

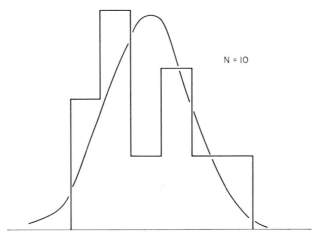

FIG. 1. The continuous curve shows the distribution of the total dry mass of a population of bacteria. Two hundred fifty cells were measured. The superposed histogram represents the distribution obtained after 10 measurements; ordinate values were multiplied by a factor of 25 to make results comparable.

much uncertainty about the distribution that one could expect to obtain after a very great number of measurements, and which is approximated by the sample of 250 measurements.

A better projection of the natural band width is obtained when not the histogram, but the variance of a smaller sample is used as a means of

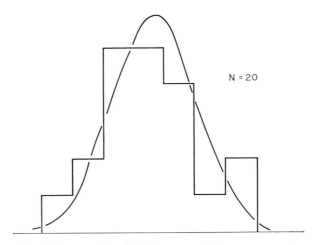

FIG. 2. Same as Fig. 1. Histogram of 20 measurements.

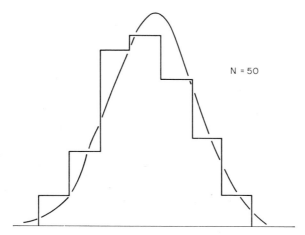

N = 50

FIG. 3. Same as Fig. 1. Histogram of 50 measurements.

approximating it. Using the same measured values as above, first the distribution curve for 250 values was computed, and then the curves obtained from 10, 20, 50, and 100 measurements. In the specific numerical example chosen here, the variance of the first group of 10 measurements was only 20% greater than that of the $N = 250$ sample, and the projection was fairly accurate. One must proceed with caution, however, and always take a sufficient number of measurements so that the arithmetic mean is known with sufficient reliability; it must also be known whether the distribution is unimodal or not. In the present example, the computation of the distribution function after 100 measurements gave a result that was indistinguishable from the one obtained after 250 measurements. The computation itself is very simple (1).

The frequency of occurrence dN is written under the mean deviation $\bar{x}$ of each class, as shown in Table II for the first 10 measurements. Then

TABLE II

COMPUTATION OF DISTRIBUTION FUNCTION, LIST OF FREQUENCY
OF OCCURRENCE PER CLASS

Class boundaries ($\times 10^{-13}$g)	0.6 2.5	2.6 4.5	4.6 6.5	6.6 8.5	8.6 10.5	10.6 12.5	12.6 14.5
Mean deviation $\bar{x}$	−6	−4	−2	0	+2	+4	+6
Frequency of occurrence dN	0	2	3	1	2	1	1

the products $\bar{x}\,dN$ are added, as shown on the left in Table III. As a control, as shown on the right in Table III, the products $\bar{x}^2\,dN$ are summed.

TABLE III

COMPUTATION OF DISTRIBUTION FUNCTION, FORMING
THE PRODUCTS "MEAN CLASS DEVIATION
TIMES FREQUENCY OF OCCURRENCE"

$\bar{x}\,dN$	$\bar{x}^2\,dN$
$6(0+1) = 6$	$36(0+1) = 36$
$4(2+1) = 12$	$16(2+1) = 48$
$2(3+2) = 10$	$4(3+2) = 20$
$W = 28$	$U = 104$

These two sums W and U are now used to compute the coefficients of precision, h_1 and h_2:

$$h_1 = \frac{N}{W\pi^{1/2}} = \frac{10}{28 \times 1.773} = 0.202, \quad h_2 = \left(\frac{N}{2U}\right)^{1/2} = \left(\frac{10}{2 \times 104}\right)^{1/2} = 0.219.$$

The arithmetic mean of these two is used:

$$h = \frac{h_1 + h_2}{2}, \qquad h_{10} = 0.210.$$

The arithmetic mean of the first 10 measurements was 7.4×10^{-13} g. The coefficient of precision h_{10} is now used to compute the distribution curve. For each class the corresponding ordinate follows from the relation

$$\eta = Nh\varphi(h\bar{x}).$$

The function $\varphi\,(h\bar{x})$ is tabulated in Table IV. Table V shows a numerical example for the first 50 measurements: h_{50} has been found to be 0.250. The η values are plotted directly over the centers of the corresponding classes. Zero must, of course, be placed at the arithmetic average for the sample of 50. Attention is called to the fact that φ has a value for $h\bar{x} = 0$. To make the η values directly comparable with those obtained from 250 measurements, they have to be multiplied by a factor of 5. The distribution function thus computed represents the results that could be expected from an infinite number of measurements which have the same variability as the selected sample of 10, 20, 50, or 100. It is, therefore, a much better approximation of the results expected from 250 measurements.

TABLE IV

COMPUTATION OF DISTRIBUTION FUNCTION, φ AS A FUNCTION OF $h\bar{x}$

$h\bar{x}$	φ	Φ	$h\bar{x}$	φ	Φ
0.00	0.564	0.000	1.05	0.187	0.862
0.05	0.563	0.056	1.10	0.168	0.880
0.10	0.559	0.113	1.15	0.150	0.896
0.15	0.552	0.168	1.20	0.134	0.910
0.20	0.542	0.223	1.25	0.118	0.923
0.25	0.530	0.276	1.30	0.104	0.934
0.30	0.516	0.329	1.35	0.091	0.944
0.35	0.499	0.379	1.40	0.079	0.952
0.40	0.481	0.428	1.45	0.069	0.960
0.45	0.461	0.476	1.50	0.059	0.966
0.50	0.439	0.521	1.55	0.051	0.972
0.55	0.417	0.563	1.60	0.044	0.976
0.60	0.394	0.604	1.65	0.037	0.980
0.65	0.370	0.642	1.70	0.031	0.984
0.70	0.346	0.678	1.75	0.026	0.987
0.75	0.321	0.711	1.80	0.022	0.989
0.80	0.297	0.742	1.85	0.018	0.991
0.85	0.274	0.771	1.90	0.015	0.993
0.90	0.251	0.797	1.95	0.013	0.994
0.95	0.229	0.821	2.00	0.010	0.995
1.00	0.208	0.843			

TABLE V

COMPUTATION OF DISTRIBUTION FUNCTION,
CALCULATION OF ORDINATES η

$\bar{x}$	$h\bar{x}$	φ
6	$6 \times 0.250 = 1.5$	0.059
4	$4 \times 0.250 = 1.0$	0.208
2	$2 \times 0.250 = 0.5$	0.439
0	$0 \times 0.250 = 0$	0.564

$\bar{x}$	$Nh\varphi(h\bar{x}) = \eta$	
6	$50 \times 0.250 \times 0.059 = 0.736$	
4	$50 \times 0.250 \times 0.208 = 2.6$	
2	$50 \times 0.250 \times 0.439 = 5.49$	
0	$50 \times 0.250 \times 0.564 = 7.05$	

TABLE VI

STABILIZATION OF h AND THE ARITHMETIC AVERAGE
WITH INCREASING SAMPLE SIZE

N	h	Arithmetic average ($\times 10^{-13}$ g)
10	0.210	7.4
20	0.196	7.2
50	0.250	7.12
100	0.255	7.6
200	0.244	7.6
250	0.246	7.6

Table VI lists the coefficients of precision obtained from the various samples. Figure 4 shows the distribution curves of the sample of 10 and

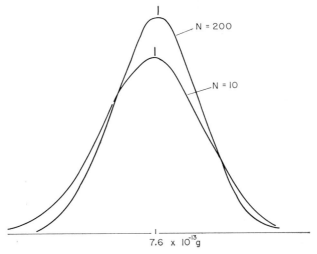

FIG. 4. Computed distribution curves for 10 and 200 measurements. The distribution computed from the variance of the first 10 measurements projects the distribution obtained after 200 or 250 measurements much more accurately than the histogram from 10 measurements shown in Fig. 1.

the sample of 200. If one now forms a weighted average over the coefficients of precision h obtained from the samples of 10, 20, 50, and 100 measurements, the coefficient h_{250} can be predicted fairly accurately.

These four samples represent a total of 180 measurements. $h_{10} = 0.210$ has to be given a weight of $10/180 = 0.055$, h_{20} a weight of $20/180 = 0.111$, and so on as follows:

$$0.055 \times 0.210 = 0.0115$$
$$0.111 \times 0.196 = 0.0217$$
$$0.277 \times 0.250 = 0.0692$$
$$\underline{0.555 \times 0.255 = 0.1416}$$
$$0.243$$

which yields an average precision coefficient of 0.243 for the first 100 measurements, which corresponds almost exactly to the value 0.246 found after a total of 250 measurements.

The coefficient of precision h is computed much faster than the standard deviation SD. The latter can immediately be read from Table IV. By definition, two thirds of a distribution fall within a distance of $\pm$SD from the arithmetic mean. This condition is fulfilled for an $h\bar{x}$ value of 0.7, where the function Φ assumes the value $0.67 = 2/3$. The value Φ in Table IV lists what percentage of the population lies between the boundaries given by the corresponding $\bar{x}$ in the $h\bar{x}$ -column. Numerical example:

$$h = 0.246, \qquad 0.246\bar{x} = 0.7,$$
$$\bar{x} = 2.86,$$
$$\mathrm{SD} = 2.86 \times 10^{-13} \text{ g.}$$

The numerical example chosen here had a particularly high variability, including values which even at the half-peak width differed by a factor of 2.5$\times$. Yet after 100 measurements and computation of the distribution function, no further change of the end result could be found. Direct plotting of the frequency of occurrences required 200 measurements to attain the same result.

It remains to be shown what influence statistical errors have upon the distribution curve. As mentioned before, they do not affect the position of the maximum on the abscissa. The same set of measured values may serve as a numerical example. The standard deviation, SD, had been found to be $\pm 2.86 \times 10^{-13}$ g. The initial assumption of negligible statistical errors is now abandoned. The natural band width, or biological variability, must, therefore, correspond to a distribution function with less variability. If statistical errors of the order of 5% are assumed, the relative variability of the natural band width must be 5% less. The relative variability is described by Pearson's coefficient of variation and is equal to

$$\nu = \frac{100 \times \mathrm{SD}}{\text{arithmetic mean}} \qquad \text{or} \qquad \frac{100 \times 2.86 \times 10^{-13}}{7.6 \times 10^{-13}} = 37.6\%.$$

From this, one can compute the SD of the pure natural band width, which should correspond to a distribution with 5% less variability. This is SD $= 2.47 \times 10^{-13}$ g. The coefficient of precision h of the new, less dispersed distribution follows from

$$\frac{0.7}{2.47} = 0.283 = h,$$

and Fig. 5 shows the two distributions, one broadened by 5% statistical error, the other the pure biological variability. The effect of statistical

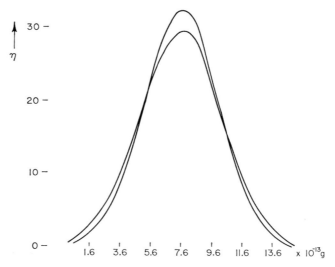

Fig. 5. The curve with the lower maximum is the measured mass distribution curve. The narrower, high curve represents a computed distribution with a 5% less variability, such as could have been caused by an instrumental error.

errors is, as one can see from Fig. 5, not too serious. Biological phenomena require a certain number of measurements in any case, and for most measuring techniques the statistical measuring errors are much smaller than the variability of the biological material. It is, therefore, good measuring advice not to attempt to eliminate the last percent of statistical error, but rather to take a greater number of measurements even though they may be burdened with slight statistical errors. The single measurement should be free from systematic errors, but it is also important that it does not require too much time, which would make the taking of the necessary number of readings impractical. The final result would be much more reliable with a faster technique and a greater number of measurements. Statistical errors should be kept in limits since they limit the differential sensitivity of the method.

It is rarely the purpose of a cytochemical investigation to measure just one value and its variability as, for example, the average total dry mass of bacteria. The true interest of the cytochemical problem lies in the systematic changes which a measured distribution undergoes when the experimental conditions are varied by a small amount. The ability to record such small changes could be called the differential sensitivity or the resolution of the method. It rests upon the method's capability to detect a small dip between two firmly established distribution functions, somewhat in analogy to light-microscopic resolution, which is also based upon the detector's capability to register a low-contrast intensity dip between the overlapping intensity distributions of two diffraction disks.

The usual agreement in statistical analysis is to consider two distributions as significantly different when the two maxima are separated by a distance equal to SD. This restriction applies only, of course, when the two dispersions are measured simultaneously and when in the overlapping range their frequencies of occurrence add up.

In the course of cytochemical experiments two distributions are usually measured consecutively. Whether or not a small shift of the maximum can be detected depends upon the difference in frequency of occurrence between the center class and the class immediately next to it. Statistical errors reduce this difference. This limits the method's usefulness to detecting small displacements of the distribution function during consecutive series of measurements.

REFERENCE

1. von Sanden, H., "Praktische Mathematik," Teubner, Leipzig, 1948.

HISTORADIOGRAPHY

Guenther Beneke

DEPARTMENT OF PATHOLOGY, JUSTUS LIEBIG UNIVERSITY, GIESSEN, GERMANY

The absorption of visible and ultraviolet light is dependent on the specific molecular configuration of the object. With higher-energy radiation (for instance, X-rays), on the other hand, there is interaction between the incident rays and the atoms of the object through which the rays penetrate.

First of all, some absorption (the photo effect) is noticeable. A photon with an energy of $h\nu$ strikes an orbital electron. If the energy of the impact is higher than the energy binding the electron in its orbit, the electron is expelled from its shell. The incident photon completely disappears.

Second, with higher-energy radiation the electrons are more or less free, and with low energy of the photon the electron is expelled from the orbit. Therefore, the energy of the photon is not completely dissipated. It scatters incoherently and inelastically. This is called the Compton effect.

Third, with very high-energy radiation, a so-called double-formation of electrons may occur. Here an electron unites with a positron, and the photon disappears. In addition, there is interaction between photons and the atomic nuclei. This process eliminates the involved photons.

These four effects all lead to a decrease in incident radiation. This decrease expresses itself as absorption on a photographic plate situated behind the object. In microradiography, the magnitude of the radiation energy is usually such that one is concerned mainly with the photo effect, that is, the absorption.

Two other effects occur that have nothing to do with absorption, emission and diffraction. (a) Emission occurs when an electron that is expelled from its orbit is replaced, either from without or from another orbit, the energy being set free as a photon. The energy of this emitted radiation is lower and its wavelength longer than that of the incident radiation (*12, 21, 49*). (b) Diffraction occurs if the material is crystalline (*12, 21, 49*).

X-Ray absorption, X-ray emission, and X-ray diffraction have all been used in micro-X-ray techniques (Fig. 1). *X-Ray absorption* is applied in three ways.

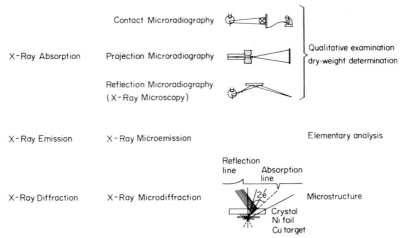

FIG. 1. Various applications of X-rays for investigations on biological objects.

a. *Contact Microradiography.* In contact microradiography, the specimen is directly on the photographic plate. Therefore, the size of the picture of the specimen is approximately the same as that of the specimen. With this method it is necessary to magnify the microradiogram secondarily with a normal microscope. The geometrical unsharpness of the picture in this method is not very great (approximately 0.3 μ). The secondary magnification of the microradiogram by the microscope is limited by the size of the grains of the film plate. For practical use a secondary magnification of 1 : 800 is possible. (*12, 19–23, 49*).

b. *Projection Microradiography.* Projection microradiography uses a primary magnification of the specimen by the microradiograph. With this method the geometrical unclearness is increased because the distance between the specimen and the photo plate is greater than in contact microradiography. Therefore, the focus of the X-ray tube must be very small. The advantage of projection microradiography is that the primary magnification of the specimen by the microradiograph and the secondary magnification of the microradiogram by the microscope is added. The total magnification, therefore, is higher in projection microradiography than in contact microradiography (*1, 10, 12–15, 21, 38, 44, 47–49*).

c. *Reflection Microradiography or X-Ray Microscopy.* Another method of receiving a higher resolution is reflection microradiography (X-ray microscope). This method uses the reflection of X-rays by metal mirrors. With a combination of several metal mirrors, a very high resolution is possible. However, this method is not yet ready for practical use (*12, 18, 21, 30–33, 46–49*).

In quantitative histochemistry, X-ray absorption may be used as contact microradiography for the determination of dry weight. Goby (*27*) made the first investigations with a similar simple method. The first investigations on tissue sections were done by Dauvillier (*16*), and Castel *et al.* (*7*). Engström (*19, 20*) and Engström and Lindström, (*22, 23*) have further developed this method for quantitative analytical purposes. Qualitative investigations, as well as dry weight determinations, can be performed on cells and tissue sections with microradiography.

In the following, microradiography is explained by using contact microradiography with the Philips microradiograph model CMR 5 according to the method of Müller *et al.* (*43*). This apparatus (Fig. 2) con-

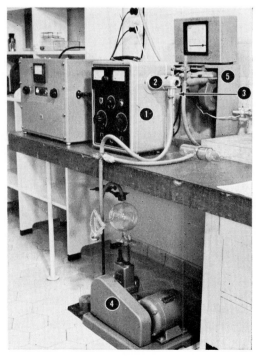

Fig. 2. Contact microradiograph equipment with the Philips microradiograph CMR 5. (1) High-voltage unit; (2) X-ray tube; (3) film holder; (4) vacuum pump; (5) ventilator. From Müller *et al.* (*43*).

sists of the high-voltage unit (1), the X-ray tube (2), the film holder (3), a vacuum pump (4) to evacuate the film holder, a ventilator (5) for cooling the X-ray tubes, and a voltage stabilizer. Inclusion of an ammeter and a voltmeter in the high-voltage unit permits control of the current and of the voltage.

Figure 3 shows a cross section of the X-ray tube. It includes the

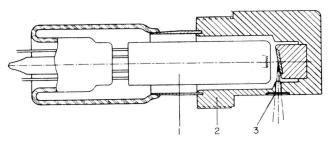

Fig. 3. Cross section of the X-ray tube for microradiography between 1.5 and 5.0 kV. (1) Cathode with tungsten filament; (2) anode with tungsten target; (3) beryllium window (thickness, 50 μ). Length of the tube: 8.0 cm. Size of the focal spot: 0.3 × 0.3 mm. From Combée and Recourt (11).

cathode (1) with the anode (2), the anticathode opposite it, and a beryllium window 50 μ thick (3). This beryllium window must absorb the visible light of the cathode. Furthermore, it makes evacuation of the X-ray tube prior to each exposure unnecessary. Beryllium is especially suitable for this purpose because its atomic number is low and its mass absorption coefficient is, therefore, also low. For mechanical stability, this window must be relatively thick. As a result it absorbs a considerable amount of soft X-rays.

Certain conditions must be met in contact microradiography: the intensity of absorption depends on the mass absorption coefficient of the object which is to be examined. In biology this is determined by the relative amounts of hydrogen, carbon, oxygen, and nitrogen. The mass absorption coefficient of these atoms increases with wavelength of the X-rays. To obtain measurable differences between object points, the absorption coefficient should be large and so long wavelengths must be used (soft X-rays).

The wavelength of the continuous X-ray spectrum depends on the voltage between cathode and anode. The shortest emitted wavelength, the distribution of intensity, and the wavelength with the highest intensity of a continuous X-ray spectrum are calculated according to the following equations:

(1) for the shortest wavelength of the spectrum

$$\lambda_0 = \frac{C}{V}, \qquad C = 12{,}365, \quad V = kV;$$

(2) for the intensity distribution in the continuous spectrum (Kramers, *34*, de Waard, *53.*)

$$I_{(\lambda)} = \frac{1}{\lambda^2}\left(\frac{1}{\lambda_0} - \frac{1}{\lambda}\right);$$

(3) for the wavelength with the highest intensity

$$\lambda_{I\ max} = \tfrac{3}{2}\lambda_0.$$

The curve of Fig. 4 shows the distribution of intensity of a continuous X-ray spectrum calculated for a voltage of 2 kV. The shortest wave-

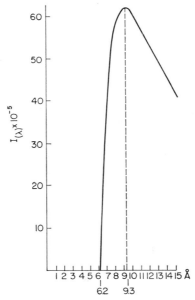

Fɪɢ. 4. Equations for the shortest wavelength, the intensity distribution, and the wavelength with the highest intensity of a continuous X-ray spectrum. Intensity distribution curve of the continuous X-ray spectrum at 2.0-kV voltage.

length is then 6.2 Å and greatest intensity is found at 9.3 Å. Therefore, the voltage and the wavelength of the emitted X-rays are related (Fig. 5). The shortest wavelength and the wavelength with the greatest intensity in these two curves are dependent on this relation.

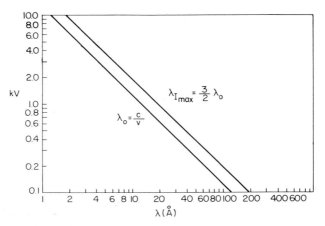

FIG. 5. Dependence of the shortest wavelength (λ_0) and the wavelength with the highest intensity ($\lambda_{I\,max}$) of a continuous X-ray spectrum on the anode voltage (kV) and wavelength (Å).

The design of the above-described apparatus, however, has certain drawbacks. Curve 1 in Fig. 6 shows that the transmission of a 50-μ beryllium window is dependent on the wavelength of the X-rays. As a

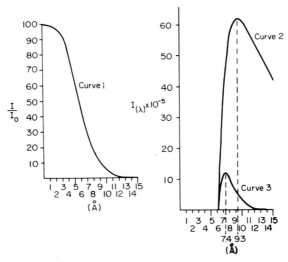

FIG. 6. Curve 1: Transmission of the 50-μ beryllium window depends on the wavelength of the incident X-rays. Curve 2: Intensity distribution curve of the continuous X-ray spectrum at 2.0 kV voltage. Curve 3: Intensity distribution curve of the continuous X-ray spectrum at 2.0-kV voltage after transmission through the 50-μ beryllium window.

result, from approximately 13 Å the beryllium window absorbs all of the radiation. Curve 2 again shows the distribution of intensity of a continuous X-ray spectrum. Curve 3 demonstrates the X-ray intensity beyond the beryllium window. In addition, the intensity maximum of the continuous X-ray spectrum is shifted toward the shorter wavelength and is found at approximately 7.4 Å.

From the relations shown in Fig. 7 it can be concluded that at 1.4 kV

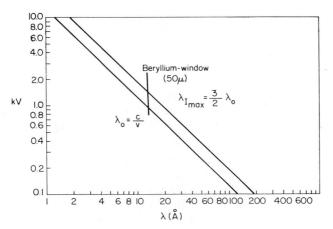

Fig. 7. Dependence of the shortest wavelength (λ_0) and the wavelength with the highest intensity ($\lambda_{I\,max}$) of a continuous X-ray spectrum on the anode voltage (kV) and wavelength (Å). Relation of the transmission of the beryllium window.

the wavelength in the intensity maximum is not transmitted. At 0.95 kV the shortest wavelength will not be transmitted either. Because of these limitations of the apparatus, the lower limit of radiation with maximal intensity is found at approximately 1.5 kV. This corresponds to a wavelength of approximately 12.5 Å.

The X-rays undergo further changes before reaching the film plate. Figure 8 shows a schematic cross section of the film holder. The focal point of the X-ray tube has a dimension of 0.3×0.3 mm. The distance from the focal point to the beryllium window is 11 mm and to the underside of the film emulsion it is 15 mm. Therefore, unsharpness (Og) of the picture (Fig. 9) is caused by the distance between focus and film emulsion. This is calculated from the size of the focal point of the tube (f), the distance between the tube focus and the film emulsion (a), and the distance between the object and the film emulsion (b):

$$Og = \frac{fb}{ab}.$$

In contact microradiography the histological section or the cells lie more or less directly on the film emulsion, so that b is relatively small. For example, with a section of 10 μ and a film emulsion of 5 μ, the maximal

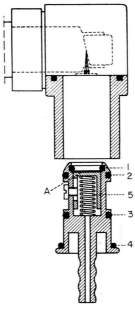

FIG. 8. Cross section of the target end of the X-ray tube and the film holder (microradiograph CMR 5). (A) Film plate with object, (1, 2, 3, 4) rubber rings; (5) a spring. From Combée and Recourt (*11*).

value for b is 15 μ or 0.015 mm. As already mentioned, a is 15 mm; f is 0.3 mm. This results in a very small geometrical unsharpness of 0.0003 mm or 0.3 μ.

Before the X-rays reach the histological section, a very significant

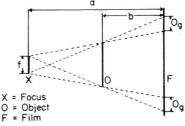

FIG. 9. The geometrical indistinctness of microradiography. See text for the equation for its determination.

absorption can occur in the air space of the film holder, approximately
4 mm high. Therefore, this space must be carefully evacuated. Figure
10 shows the effect of air on the absorption of X-rays. The curve has

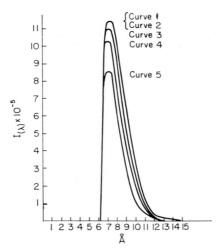

FIG. 10. The influence of the vacuum in the film holder on the intensity of the
X-ray spectrum (at 2 kV) after transmission through the beryllium window. Curve
1: Intensity of X-ray spectrum after transmission through a 50-μ beryllium window.
Curve 2: Intensity of X-ray spectrum after transmission through a 5-μ beryllium
window and a 4-mm air space at 0.76 mm Hg (10^{-3} atm). Curve 3: at 7.6 mm (10^{-2}
atm). Curve 4: at 76.0 mm (10^{-1} atm). Curve 5: at 760.0 mm (1 atm).

been calculated for a voltage of 2 kV. At a pressure of 1 atm (which is
760 mm Hg—see curve 5), 25% of the radiation emitted through the
beryllium window is absorbed by the air. The absorption of the air is
respectively lower at a pressure of 10^{-1} and 10^{-2} atm (curves 3 and 4).
The percentage decreases until, at a pressure of 10^{-3} atm (0.76 mm Hg)
(see curve 1), there is almost no absorption. It is therefore best to work
with a vacuum of at least 0.76 mm.

X-Irradiation passing through the cells or the tissue is further absorbed. This is the actual absorption, which is interesting to measure.
The absorption of the tissue is highly dependent on the thickness of
tissue, mass absorption coefficient, and preparation of the tissue.

Figure 11 (curve 2) shows the absorption of a 10-μ tissue section with
a certain mean absorption coefficient. The intensity of the incident X-irradiation (curve 1) is lessened to approximately 50% (2 kV, 50-μ beryllium window, 10^{-3} atm pressure) by the tissue section.

For sufficient absorption, the wavelength of the incident X-irradiation

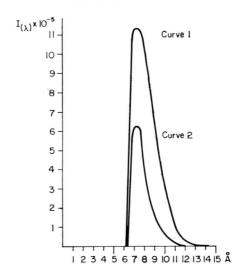

FIG. 11. Curve 1: Intensity of an X-ray spectrum (*a*/2 kV) transmitted through a 5-μ beryllium window and a 4-mm air space (0.76 mm Hg, 10⁻³ atm). Curve 2: Intensity of an X-ray spectrum (at 2 kV) transmitted through a 50-μ beryllium window, a 4-mm air space (0.76 mm Hg, 10⁻³ atm.), and 10-μ tissue section (middle dry weight).

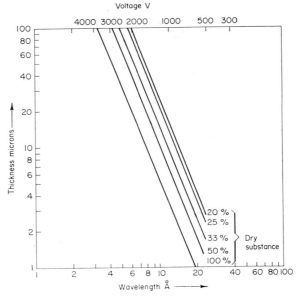

FIG. 12. The relation of tissue thickness, voltage, wavelength, and dry substance for microradiography of soft tissue. From Lindström (38).

must be changed, depending on the type of tissue. Figure 12 shows the relation between thickness of section, wavelength, and dry substance of the tissue. It shows that the thicker the tissue, the shorter must be the wavelength of the incident X-irradiation. In microradiography for dry weight determination, soft X-rays are suitable; it is, therefore, necessary to use very thin tissue sections.

The preparation of the tissue plays an important role in microradiography. Three points must be kept in mind: (1) As much water as possible should be extracted from the tissue. (2) No tissue components should be lost during fixation. (3) No excess fixative should remain after fixation.

As shown in Fig. 13, the absorption of X-rays depends on the water

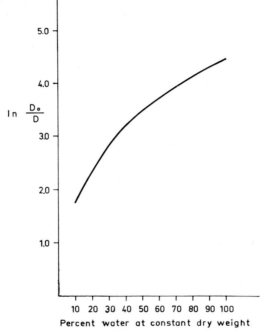

FIG. 13. Dependence of the film plate density ($\ln D_o/D$) on different water contents (percentage of the remaining water) of biological materials at constant dry weight.

content of the tissue because the atoms of water also absorb. The curve shows that the absorption at constant dry weight is considerably increased with increased water content. The logarithm of the absorption used in the calculation of the dry weight is twice as high at 100% water content as at 10% water content. This causes an error in the dry weight determination. Therefore, a method of fixation should be chosen that eliminates as much water as possible. Freeze drying is the optimal method, although with this method (2–4 hours at 0.01-mm pressure) 4 to 10% water still remains in the tissue. Fixation solutions containing acids dissolve nucleic acids and proteins of the tissue. On the other hand, there will be a remnant of a part of the fixation solution containing heavy metals. In the same way this is also true for formalin. Formalin is chemically bound by the proteins of the tissue. These errors have been pointed out by Nurnberger *et al.* (*45*) and Moberger and Engström (*39*), as well as Müller *et al.* (*43*).

As already shown in the schematic drawing (Fig. 8), the X-rays transmitted through the section will then reach the layer of the film plate. Figure 14 shows the continuous X-ray spectrum transmitted through a 10-μ tissue section at 2-kV voltage (50-μ beryllium window and 0.76-mm pressure). The lower curves represent the transmission of

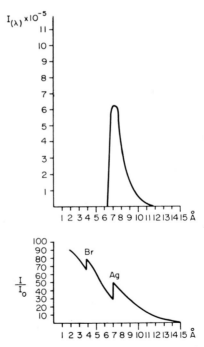

FIG. 14. (Top) Intensity of an X-ray spectrum (at 2 kV) transmitted through a 50-μ beryllium window, a 4-mm air space (0.76 mm, Hg, 10^{-3} atm), and a 10-μ tissue section (middle dry weight). (Bottom) Transmission of film emulsion (Kodak Maximum Resolution) with the absorption edges of Ag and Br.

TABLE I

DIFFERENT PROPERTIES OF FILM EMULSIONS SUITABLE FOR MICRORADIOGRAPHY

Emulsion	Resolution (lines/mm)	Size of grains	Thickness of layer	Light sensitivity	Preparation	Developer	Time of development (min)	Temperature of development (°C)
Gevaert Lippmann	2200	30 Å	—	—	—	Metinol U, Formel G 201	5	20
Agfa Mikrat	900	—	12 μ	—	Red light	Developer for Agfa Mikrat Plates	4	18
Eastman Kodak 649-0	—	—	—	—	—	—	—	—
Kodak Maximum Resolution	1000	450 Å 0.045 μ	5 μ	Green light, blue light, uv light	Orange light	Kodak D 158 Kodak D 178	4	20
						Gevaert G 209A	6	18

a 5-μ film emulsion of Kodak Maximum Resolution film. The discontinuity of the curve is caused by the K-absorption edges of silver and bromide. This means that the wavelength of the greatest intensity at 2 kV lies approximately in the area of the silver absorption edge.

By means of the photo-chemical effect, every photon which hits the emulsion leads to a reduction of the silver grains in the film emulsion. This causes blackening of the photographic plate where a large amount of rays strike, which means that there is slight absorption in the tissue. Light spaces on the photographic plate indicate that the impacted radiation on the film emulsion is small, that is, it shows where the absorption in the tissue is extensive.

For microradiography, special films should be used. The films generally used (Table I) are Gevaert Lippmann, Agfa Mikrat, Eastman Kodak No. 649-0, and Kodak Maximum Resolution film. These films have different degrees of resolution. The resolution of the Gevaert Lippmann film is 2200 lines per millimeter, that of the Agfa Mikrat film 900 lines per millimeter, and the Kodak Maximum Resolution film, 1000 lines per millimeter. Compared to normal photographic film, this resolution is relatively high. The size of the silver bromide granules of the Gevaert Lippmann film is 450 Å. However, the granules represent only a portion of the volume of the emulsion. In the Kodak Maximum Resolution film, approximately 200 granules are found evenly distributed in 1 μ^3. The

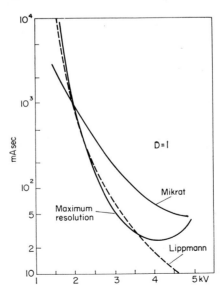

FIG. 15. Sensitivity (in milliampere seconds) of different film emulsions to soft X-rays (1–5 kV). From Combée and Recourt (10).

emulsion thickness is also of importance. In the Agfa Mikrat film it is 12 μ and in the Kodak Maximum Resolution film only 5 μ. Furthermore, optimal developing conditions have to be maintained for these films.

For microradiography, films with relatively high sensitivity are required. The curves in Fig. 15 show the time of exposure as milliampere seconds. This exposure time is dependent on the voltage to reach a density of one. The three films mentioned here are equally sensitive at a voltage of 2 kV. When the voltage is higher than 2 kV, Kodak Maximum Resolution film is the most sensitive of these three films. With voltages lower than 2 kV, the Agfa Mikrat film exhibits greater sensitivity.

Kodak has recently developed another new emulsion (Fig. 16). It

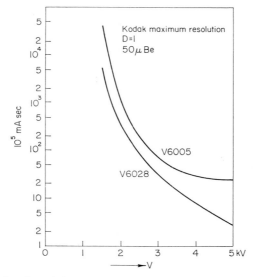

Fig. 16. Sensitivity (in milliampere seconds) of two different Kodak emulsions to soft X-rays. From Combée and Recourt (11).

contains 100 times more silver granules per the unit volume than the emulsion of the Kodak Maximum Resolution film and its thickness is only 1 μ. The sensitivity of the new emulsion is 2 to 10 times greater than the emulsion of the Kodak Maximum Resolution film. [For investigations of suitable film emulsions for microradiography, see Brattgård (5, 6), Combée (9, 10), and Engström (24).]

The commercial film plates are cut to 8 × 8 mm. The film plates are covered with a protective foil. The solution for the protective foil is prepared in the following way:

E 950 (Wolff & Co. Bomlitz/Walsrode, Germany)

or Parlodion	2.5 g
Amyl acetate	100.0 g

This results in a solution of 2.5 g %. The film plates are dipped into this solution. The foil solution may then run off in such a way that only a thin layer remains on the plates. This is then repeated. These plates covered with the protective foil are then left to dry for four hours.

The tissue sections are then placed on the emulsion side of the film plates, which have previously been covered with the protective foil. Cells may directly be spread out on the film plate. The paraffin of the tissue sections is removed in chloroform for 1 hour and afterwards in 90% ethanol for 10 minutes.

After exposure, the film plates are put into acetone for 15 minutes to remove the protective foil with the specimen. Then the film plates— without foil and object—are quickly washed in distilled water.

For the development of the film plates (Kodak Maximum Resolution), the developer Gevaert G 209 A (take daily from the stock solution) is suitable. This developer contains:

Methanol	4.0 g
Sodium carbonate cryst.	110.0 g
Sodium sulfite cryst.	130.0 g
Quinol	10.0 g
Potassium bromide	5.0 g
Distilled water	1000.0 ml

A suitable time for development is 6 minutes (during stirring) at a temperature of 18°C. The process of development is stopped by putting the film plates into 1% acetic acid or distilled water.

After development, the film plates are fixed in the following solution:

Potassium metabisulfite	25.0 g
Sodium thiosulfate	250.0 g
Distilled water	1000.0 ml

A suitable time for fixation is 30 minutes. Then the film plates are washed in clear water.

Afterwards, the film plates are dried with the specimen for approximately 1 hour in a vacuum. Then the glass side of the dried film plates is mounted on a slide with embedding medium. A cover slide is mounted on the emulsion side of the film plate.

Considering all of the above technical conditions, one obtains an optimal black and white negative using a continuous X-ray spectrum and using contact microradiography. The density of the negative is then directly related to the absorption of the biological tissue under investigation. To show this, the following examples are presented:

(a) Figure 17 shows a microradiogram of a tissue section of the calf

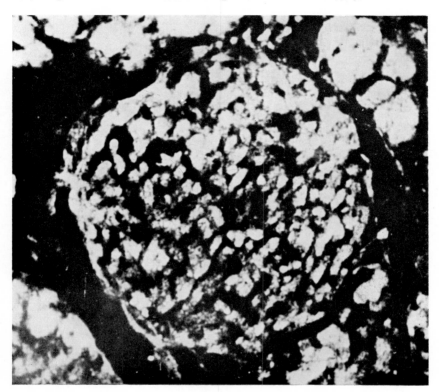

FIG. 17. Microradiogram of the pancreas. In the center of the picture a Langerhans isle is found. The light parts represent high absorption areas. From Müller and Sandritter (41).

pancreas. In the center a Langerhans islet can be seen. Around this, acini of the pancreas epithelium is found. The light areas are caused by high absorption in the tissue. With this method Müller and Sandritter (41) have found that the dry weight of the islet cells is 40% lower than that of the excretory pancreas cells.

(b) In Fig. 18 the absorption of kidney tissue is clearly seen. In the center is a glomerulus. The absorption of the Bowman capsule is the thin stripe. In the peripheral parts of the picture, tubules are shown. The absorption of the cell nucleus is very clearly seen.

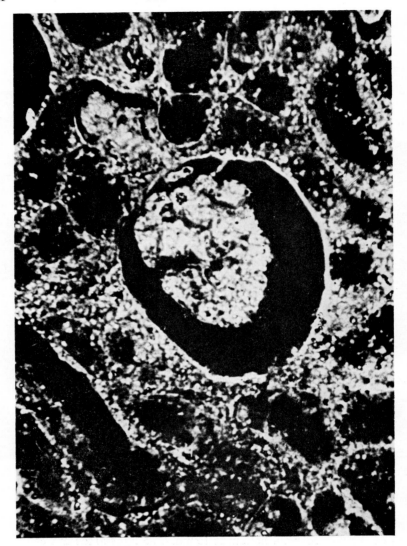

Fig. 18. Microradiogram of the kidney. In the center is a glomerulum. On the out-skirts tubules are found. The light parts show a high absorption. From Müller *et al.* (*43*).

(c) Figure 19 shows the microradiogram of a bone section. The bone trabecula are easily seen. They have a high absorption since they contain a high amount of calcium. Around the bone trabecula a small seam of uncalcified osteoid is visible. The microradiogram of this structure

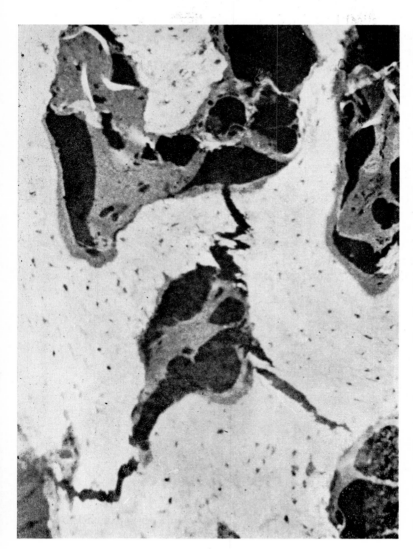

FIG. 19. Microradiogram of a bone section. The light parts represent the mineralized bone. At the outskirts of the bone trabecula a seam of nonmineralized osteoid is found.

shows a lower absorption; the same degree of absorption is seen in the connective tissue of the bone marrow.

These pictures can be examined quantitatively to demonstrate specific concentrations of chemical substances in the cell or in the tissue.

The theoretical base for the determination of the mass concentration and the dry weight in biological structures by use of microradiography is given by the X-ray absorption law and the Bunsen–Roscoe law. The X-ray absorption law is

$$I_{(\lambda)} = I_{0(\lambda)} \cdot \exp \left[-\left(\frac{\mu}{\rho}\right)_{\lambda} \cdot m \right]$$

or

$$m = \frac{\ln \left(I_{0(\lambda)}/I_{(\lambda)}\right)}{(\mu/\rho)_{\lambda}}.$$

I is the intensity of the incident X-rays and I_0 is the intensity of the transmitted X-rays, each at a specific wavelength; $(u/\rho)_2$ is the mass absorption coefficient of a specific substance at a specific wavelength. The mass m is weight per unit volume and has the dimension grams per cubic centimeter. I and I_0 cannot be measured with the given methodological conditions. However, the blackening of the film plate (density) can be measured outside (D_0) and inside (D_1) the object.

The density of a photographic emulsion (D) is

$$D = \log \frac{i_0}{i},$$

where i_0 is the intensity of visible light which passes through an unexposed area of the developed film emulsion and i is the intensity of visible light which passes through an exposed area of the developed film emulsion.

When one wishes to express I_0 with D_0 and I with D_1 in the X-ray absorption law, the following formula holds:

$$\frac{I_0}{I} = \frac{D_0}{D_1}.$$

According to the Bunsen–Roscoe law,

$$D = f(I \cdot t),$$

where t is the time of exposure, or, according to its modification by Schwarzschild,

$$D = f(I \cdot t^P).$$

The blackening of the film emulsion is dependent on a constant (f), the intensity of the X-ray radiation, and the time of X-irradiation. The

Schwarzschild exponent (P) should have a value of 0.98 (Glocker and Traub, *26*), 0.99 (Bouwers, *4*), or 1.0 (Mülbach, *40*).

To prove that the relation

$$I_0/I = D_0/D_1$$

holds under experimental conditions, a curve expressing time of exposure and intensity of X-irradiation per density of emulsion should be drawn. For this purpose, film plates without object (Kodak Maximum Resolution emulsion) are exposed at 1.55 kV for different time periods $(I \times t)$. The development of the film plates must be performed under constant conditions (Gevaert developer G 209 A for exactly 6 minutes at a temperature of 18°C). The blackening of the photographic plate (D) is measured. Under these conditions the measuring points lie on a straight line up to a density of 0.8 (see Müller *et al.*, *43*), so up to the density of 0.8 the above relation is fulfilled. Therefore, in the above equation, D_0 can be substituted for I_0 and D_1 for I.

From this results the equation for mass determinations (m) by means of microradiography:

$$m = \frac{\ln (D_0/D_1)}{(\mu/\rho)_\lambda}.$$

Thus, three values—D_0, D_1, and $(\mu/\rho)_\lambda$—must be measured. The density of an empty space in the preparation (D_0) and the density of the object (D_1) are determined by point measurement using the cytophotometer or densitometer. It is more complicated to determine the mass absorption coefficient. This can be done by calculation.

The mass absorption coefficient for wavelengths longer than 0.1 Å with a continuous increase is composed of the linear absorption coefficient (μ) divided by the density (ρ). The total mass absorption coefficient is the sum of the actual mass absorption coefficient (τ/ρ) and the mass scattering coefficient (σ/ρ):

$$\frac{\mu}{\rho} = \frac{\tau}{\rho} + \frac{\sigma}{\rho}.$$

The size of the mass absorption coefficient of regularly increasing absorption is as follows:

$$\frac{\tau}{\rho} = C \cdot Z^4 \cdot \lambda^3,$$

where C is a constant, Z is the periodic number of the specific element, and λ the wavelength.

The mass scattering coefficient (σ/ρ) is dependent on the atomic number (Z), the atomic weight (A), the scattering per electron (σ_e), and Avogadro's number (N_0), 6.0247×10^{23} molecules per mole.

$$\frac{\sigma}{\rho} = \sigma_e \cdot N_0 \cdot Z \cdot A_0$$

According to the classical wave theory of light, the mass scattering coefficient would be independent of the wavelength, but according to the quantum-mechanical theory, it is dependent on the wavelength (Lindström, 38).

The mass absorption coefficient of a chemical substance is the sum of the percentages of the weight of the individual elements (ai) on the total weight of the chemical substance and the mass absorption coefficients of the single elements:

$$\left(\frac{\mu}{\rho}\right)_{\text{total}} = \sum_{i=1}^{n} \frac{ai}{100} \cdot \left(\frac{\mu}{\rho}\right)_i.$$

Lindström (38) has calculated the mass absorption coefficient for a few important biological substances (Table II). The absorption coefficients may be directly used for the equation of mass determination.

For the determination of the mass concentration or the dry weight, it is necessary to have a reference system. A suitable material for the reference system is foil of cellulose nitrates. [The production of such foils is described by Hallén (28), Hallén and Ingelstam (29), Clemmons and Webster (8), and Lindström (38).] Pieces of the foil are stacked one above the other (Fig. 20). In this way a step wedge is formed. The weight of each piece of foil is determined, and the area of the foil is measured. By this means, the weight per unit area is determined. A microradiogram of such a step wedge shows the different densities of the film plate, which are measured with the densitometer. The measured densities are plotted against the weight per unit area which was assessed before. A curve of the mass absorption coefficient at a specific wavelength will result. The mass absorption coefficient may then be calculated by dividing the density by the known dry mass.

Lindström (38) (Table III) has determined the mass absorption coefficient of a few cellulose nitrates. He has also assessed the relation of the mass absorption coefficient of Parlodion to that of an animal protein. The values were between 1.1 and 1.3. There is, therefore, only a slight difference between the mass absorption coefficients of protein and cellulose nitrates. Cellulose nitrate foil is, then, suitable as a reference system for the determination of the mass absorption coefficient of a reference system which may be made (Lindström, 38) simultaneously with the examination of the tissue section. Therefore, a sufficiently large measuring field is necessary.

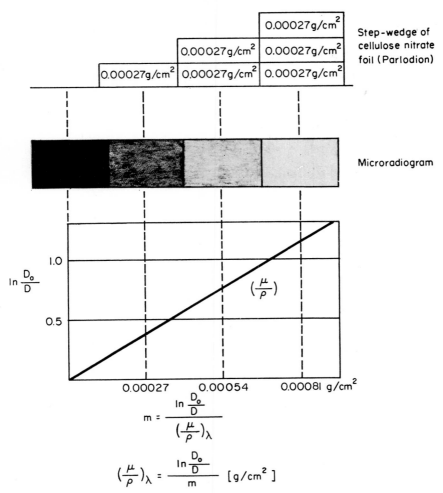

Fɪɢ. 20. Determination of the mass absorption coefficient of cellulose nitrate foils (reference system).

The simultaneous determination of the reference system and of the tissue is not possible in the commercially available microradiograph by Philips because of the relatively small measuring field. Müller *et al.* (*43*) have described a method for determination of dry weight with the Philips microradiograph without a simultaneous reference system and with which the absorption of a reference system need be determined only once. All other following investigations must then be done under the same conditions as for the reference system. The voltage of the tube,

TABLE II

CALCULATED MASS ABSORPTION COEFFICIENTS OF SOME COMMON ORGANIC COMPOUNDS[a,b]

Compound	2.5 kX.U.	3.0 kX.U.	3.5 kX.U.	4.0 kX.U.	5.0 kX.U.	6.0 kX.U.	7.0 kX.U.	8.0 kX.U.	9.0 kX.U.	10.0 kX.U.	11.0 kX.U.	12.0 kX.U.	13.0 kX.U.	14.0 kX.U.	15.0 kX.U.	16.0 kX.U.	18.0 kX.U.	20.0 kX.U.	22.0 kX.U.
Animal proteins	31.2	54.4	85.7	127.3	240	347	547	800	1111	1471	1932	2440	3020	3660	4420	5140	7030	9180	11640
Fibrin	29.9	52.4	82.6	122.9	233	348	548	802	1113	1475	1937	2450	3030	3670	4430	5150	7050	9210	11670
Elastin	26.9	47.7	75.6	112.9	215	349	550	804	1117	1479	1942	2460	3040	3680	4440	5170	7060	9210	11690
Collagen	28.9	50.8	80.4	120.0	228	357	562	821	1140	1510	1983	2510	3100	3750	4530	5270	7200	9400	11910
Amyloid	36.6	63.2	99.2	146.6	274	361	568	828	1149	1518	1993	2520	3120	3780	4550	5290	7230	9440	11950
Thymus histone	27.8	49.0	77.5	115.5	219	342	539	789	1096	1454	1908	2410	2990	3610	4370	5080	6950	9080	11520
Plant proteins	29.2	51.4	81.1	120.8	229	349	549	803	1115	1478	1941	2460	3040	3680	4440	5160	7060	9220	11690
Deoxyribonucleic acid	53.3	92.8	144.4	212	387	398	623	902	1254	1649	2170	2750	3380	4100	4940	5730	7820	10180	12870
Ribonucleic acid	55.4	96.5	150.1	220	401	401	627	908	1262	1659	2180	2760	3410	4130	4970	5770	7870	10240	12940
Glycogen	31.4	55.3	87.6	131.2	250	412	646	936	1297	1693	2230	2830	3460	4210	5050	5840	7950	10370	13030
Tripalmitin	20.2	35.9	56.9	84.6	161.5	265	421	623	862	1149	1502	1906	2350	2870	3460	4050	5550	7320	9350
Tristearin	19.8	35.2	55.9	83.1	158.7	260	413	612	847	1131	1479	1876	2320	2820	3410	3990	5470	7220	9230
Triolein	20.0	35.5	56.3	83.7	159.7	262	416	616	853	1139	1489	1888	2330	2840	3440	4020	5510	7270	9290
Trilinolein	20.1	35.7	56.7	84.3	160.8	264	419	621	859	1146	1499	1901	2350	2860	3460	4050	5550	7320	9350
Cerebrosides	27.5	48.3	76.0	112.3	211	297	470	690	957	1269	1662	2110	2600	3160	3820	4450	6090	8000	10170

[a] From Lindström (38).
[b] One kX.U. corresponds to 1.00206 Å.

TABLE III

MASS ABSORPTION COEFFICIENTS OF SOME CELLULOSE NITRATES AND RATIOS OF MASS ABSORPTION COEFFICIENTS OF PARLODION AND THE AVERAGE PROTEIN AT DIFFERENT WAVELENGTHS[a,b]

	2.5 kX.U.	3.0 kX.U.	3.5 kX.U.	4.0 kX.U.	5.0 kX.U.	6.0 kX.U.	7.0 kX.U.	8.0 kX.U.	9.0 kX.U.	10.0 kX.U.	11.0 kX.U.	12.0 kX.U.	13.0 kX.U.	14.0 kX.U.	15.0 kX.U.	16.0 kX.U.	18.0 kX.U.	20.0 kX.U.	22.0 kX.U.
Absorption coefficients																			
Parlodion	36.1	63.5	100.6	151.1	288	477	745	1074	1491	1944	2560	3250	3980	4830	5790	6690	9090	11820	14810
Zapon varnish	30.8	54.3	86.0	128.8	245	405	636	924	1280	1679	2210	2800	3440	4170	5020	5810	7910	10330	13010
Cellulose dinitrate	34.6	60.9	96.6	144.8	276	456	714	1031	1429	1865	2460	3120	3820	4630	5560	6420	8730	11360	14250
Cellulose trinitrate	35.5	62.5	99.0	148.5	283	468	732	1057	1466	1912	2520	3200	3910	4750	5700	6580	8940	11630	14580
Cellulose tetranitrate	36.2	63.7	101.0	151.6	289	478	747	1078	1495	1950	2570	3260	3990	4840	5810	6710	9120	11830	14830
Cellulose pentanitrate	36.8	64.8	102.6	154.1	293	486	760	1096	1520	1983	2610	3320	4060	4920	5910	6820	9270	12040	15080
Cellulose hexanitrate	37.3	65.7	104.1	156.3	298	493	771	1111	1541	2010	2650	3360	4120	4990	5990	6910	9390	12200	15280
Ratio of $(\mu/\rho)_{\text{ref}_j}$ to $(\mu/\rho)_{\text{prot}_j}$	1.157	1.167	1.174	1.187	1.200	1.375	1.362	1.343	1.342	1.322	1.325	1.332	1.318	1.320	1.310	1.302	1.293	1.288	1.272

[a] From Lindström (38).

[b] One kX.U. corresponds to 1.00206 Å.

the emission current, the time of exposure, the time of development, and temperature must especially be kept constant.

The determination of the mass concentration and the dry weight can be explained by a simple example. Assume that from a microradiogram, one obtains the following measurements: intensity of the visible light transmitted through the unexposed area of the developed film emulsion, $i_{00} = 100.0$; intensity of the visible light transmitted through the exposed area of the developed film emulsion outside of the object, $i_0 = 16.1$; intensity of the visible light transmitted through the exposed area of the developed film emulsion inside of the object, $i_1 = 17.3$. From these values the density of the photographic emulsion outside (D_0) and inside (D_1) the object is calculated:

$$D_0 = \log \frac{i_{00}}{i_0} = \log \frac{100}{16.1} = \log 6.20 = 0.7927,$$

$$D_1 = \log \frac{i_{00}}{i_1} = \log \frac{100}{17.3} = \log 5.77 = 0.7615.$$

The calculation of the mass concentration is as follows:

$$m = \frac{\ln (D_0/D_1)}{(\mu/\rho)_\lambda}.$$

The mass absorption coefficient is calculated for an animal protein at the wavelength of 9.0 Å with a mass absorption coefficient of 1111:

$$m = \frac{\ln (0.7927/0.7915)}{1111} = \frac{\ln 1.04}{1111}$$

$$= \frac{0.03922}{1111} = 0.0000035$$

$$= 3.52 \times 10^{-6} \left(\frac{9}{\text{cm}^2}\right).$$

For the determination of the dry weight, it is necessary to determine the area of the object. In this example the area is $A = 4105 \times 10^{-8}$ cm². The dry weight is calculated as follows:

$$\text{D.W.} = \frac{\ln (D_0/D_1) \cdot A}{(\mu/\rho)_\lambda},$$

$$= \frac{0.03922 \cdot 4105 \times 10^{-8}}{1111},$$

$$= 0.14482 \times 10^{-8},$$

$$= 1448.2 \times 10^{-12} \quad (\text{g}).$$

TABLE IV

DRY WEIGHT DETERMINATIONS BY VARIOUS METHODS

Cell population	Electron microscopy, $\times 10^{-12}$ (g)	Historadiography, $\times 10^{-12}$ (g)	Interference microscopy, $\times 10^{-12}$ (g)
Bull sperms			
Total	18.2 ± 0.085 (3)	—	—
Head	13.35 ± 0.7 (3)	7.87 ± 0.46 (50)	7.3–7.5 (17)
			7.1–7.3 (37)
			8.94 ± 1.17 (42)
Tail	4.85 ± 0.3 (3)	—	—
Midpiece	2.31 ± 0.15 (3)	—	—
Bull thymus			
lymphocytes			
(nucleus)	—	15.05 ± 0.53 (50)	14.40 ± 1.78 (51)
Frog erythrocytes			
(nucleus)	—	24.0 ± 0.69 (50)	21.55 ± 0.84 (51)
Squamous epithelium			
cells (human)			
Nucleus	—	70.36 ± 4.26 (50)	55.50 ± 2.6 (52)
Cytoplasm	—	1068.00 ± 84.00 (50)	1941.20 ± 61.5 (52)
Erythrocytes			
(human)	29.9 ± 0.050 (2)	33.7 ± 0.4 (25)	32.4 ± 0.2 (25)
			30.8 ± 0.1 (25)

Table IV demonstrates the agreement of the dry weight determinations with various histochemical methods (X-ray absorption, electron microscopy, interference microscopy).

A comparison of the dry weight values obtained with different methods shows that there is good agreement in the case of the human erythrocytes, the nucleus of lymphocytes, and frog erythrocytes. The agreement is not very good between the values from the bull sperms. Perhaps that is caused by the calculation of the mass absorption coefficient (microradiography) or the χ value (interference microscopy) for the nucleoprotein of the sperms, which is not exactly correct.

Under Müller et al., (43) the mean error of reproducibility was found to be 7.7%. This size error is small enough to make the studies acceptable for biological investigations.

In conclusion, it should once again be said that dry weight determination with the contact microradiograph is one of the possible applications of X-rays in experimental cell and tissue investigations. The application of X-rays has given much new information on biological structure.

REFERENCES

1. Ardenne, M. von, "Elektronen-Übermikroskopie." Springer, Berlin, 1940.
2. Bahr, G. F., and E. Zeitler, Determination of the total dry mass of human erythrocytes by quantitative electron microscopy. *Lab Invest.* **11**, 912–917 (1962).
3. Bahr, G. F., and E. Zeitler, Study of bull spermatozoa. Quantitative electron microscopy. *J. Cell Biol.* **21**, 175–189 (1964).
4. Bouwers, A., Über die Schwärzung der photographischen Platten durch Röntgenstrahlen und ihre Anwendung zur Intensitätsmessung. *Z. Physik* **14**, 374–382 (1923).
5. Brattgård, S. O., and O. Hallén, X-ray microradiography as a quantitative method. *Biochim. Biophys. Acta* **9**, 488–495 (1952).
6. Brattgård, S. O., and H. Hydén, Mass, lipids, pentose nucleoproteins and proteins determined in nerve cells by X-ray microradiography. *Acta Radiol.* Suppl. 94 (1952).
7. Castel, P., P. Lamarque, and J. Turchini, Historadiographie et localisation histologique de substances médicamentenses ou toxiques à poids atomique élevé. *Compt. Rend. Soc. Biol.* **123**, 1051–1052 (1936).
8. Clemmons, J. J., and T. S. Webster, An accurate reference system for historadiography. *Biochim. Biophys. Acta* **11**, 464–470 (1953).
9. Combée, B., J. Houtman, and A. Recourt, Microradiography. III. A sealed-off X-ray tube for contact-microradiography. *Brit. J. Radiol.* **28**, 537–542 (1955).
10. Combée, B., and A. Recourt, Historadiographie. *In* "Röntgenstrahlen, Geschichte und Gegenwart." C. F. H. Müller, Hamburg, 1955.
11. Combée, B., and A. Recourt, A simple apparatus for contact microradiography between 1.5 and 5 kV. Prepared by X-Ray Div. and Kodak Res. Lab., Eastman Kodak Co., Rochester, New York, 1957.
12. Cosslett, V. E., A. Engström, and H. H. Pattee, "X-ray Microscopy and Microradiography." Academic Press, New York, 1957.
13. Cosslett, V. E., and W. C. Nixon, X-ray shadow microscopy. *Nature* **168**, 24–25 (1951).
14. Cosslett, V. E., and W. C. Nixon, X-ray shadow microscopy. *Nature* **170**, 436–438 (1952).
15. Cosslett, V. E., and W. C. Nixon, The X-ray shadow microscope. *J. Appl. Phys.* **24**, 616-623 (1953).
16. Dauvillier, A., Réalisation de la microradiographie intégrale. *Comp. Rend. Soc. Biol.* **190**, 1287–1289 (1930).
17. Davies, H. G., E. M. Deeley, and E. F. Denby, Attempts and measurements of lipid, nucleic acid and protein content of cell nuclei by microscope-interferometry. *Exptl. Cell Res.* Suppl. 4, 136–149 (1957).
18. Dershem, E., and M. Schein, Über die Reflexion und Absorption langwelliger Röntgenstrahlen. *Z. Physik* **75**, 395–414 (1932).
19. Engström, A., Quantitative micro- and histochemical elementary analysis by roentgen absorption spectrography. *Acta Radiol.* Suppl. 63 (1946).
20. Engström, A., Microradiography. *Acta Radiol.* **31**, 503–521 (1949).
21. Engström, A., V. Cosslett, and H. Pattee, "X-ray Microscopy and X-ray Microanalysis." Elsevier, Amsterdam, 1960.
22. Engström, A., and B. Lindström, A new method for determining the weight of cellular structures. *Nature* **163**, 563–564 (1949).

23. Engström, A., and B. Lindström, A method for determination of the mass of extremely small biological objects. *Biochim. Biophys. Acta* **4**, 351–373 (1950).
24. Engström, A., and B. Lindström, The properties of finegrained photographic emulsions used for microradiography. *Acta Radiol.* **35**, 33–44, 1951.
25. Gamble, C. N., and D. J. Glick, Studies in histochemistry. LVII. Determination of the total dry mass of human erythrocytes by interference microscopy and X-ray microradiography. *J. Cell Biol.* **8**, 53–60 (1960).
26. Glocker, R., and W. Traub, Das photographische Schwärzungsgesetz der Röntgenstrahlen. *Physik. Z.* **22**, 345–352 (1921).
27. Goby, P., Une application nouvelle des rayons. X. la microradiographie. *Compt. Rend. Soc. Biol.* **156**, 686–688 (1913).
28. Hallén, O., A simplified method for the preparation of the reference system. *Exptl. Cell Res.* **4**, 494–495 (1953).
29. Hallén, O., and E. Engelstam, Determination by interferometric methods of the thickness of the reference system used in microradiography. *Exptl. Cell Res.* **3**, 248 (1952).
30. Johann, H. H., Die Erzeugung lichtstarker Röntgenspektren mit Hilfe von Konkavkristallen. *Z. Physik* **69**, 185–206 (1931).
31. Kirkpatrick, P., An approach to X-ray microscopy. *Nature* **166**, 251–253 (1950).
32. Kirkpatrick, P., and A. V. Baez, Formations of optical images by X-ray. *J. Opt. Soc. Am.* **38**, 766–774 (1948).
33. Kirkpatrick, P., and H. H. Pattee, Approaches to X-ray microscopy. *Advan. Biol. Med. Phys.* **3**, 123–127 (1953).
34. Kramers, H. A., On the theory of X-ray absorption and of the continuous X-ray spectrum. *Phil. Mag.* [6] **46**, 836–871 (1923).
35. Lamarque, P., Historadiography. New application of X-rays. *Radiology* **27**, 563–568 (1936).
36. Lamarque, P., Historadiography. *Brit. J. Radiol.* **11**, 425–435 (1938).
37. Leuchtenberger, C., I. Murmanis, L. Murmanis, S. Ito, and D. R. Weir, Interferometric dry mass and microphotometric arginine determinations on bull sperm nuclei with normal and abnormal DNA content. *Chromosoma* **8**, 73–86 (1956).
38. Lindström, B., Roentgen absorption spectrophotometry in quantitative histochemistry. *Acta Radiol.* Suppl. 125 (1955).
39. Moberger, G., and A. Engström, Historadiographic studies on normal, hyperplastic and cancerous epidermis. *J. Invest. Dermatol.* **22**, 477–491 (1954).
40. Mülbach, E., Untersuchungen über die Gültigkeit des Bunsen-Roscoeschen Gesetzes für die photographische Wirkung und den Verlauf der Schwärzungskurven langwelliger Röntgenstrahlen. *Z. Wiss. Phot.* **36**, 269–282 (1937).
41. Müller, D., and W. Sandritter, Röntgenhistoradiografische Untersuchungen an Inselzellen des Pankreas nach Stimulierung mit dem oralen Antidiabeticum D 860. *Exptl. Cell Res.* **13**, 441–443 (1959).
42. Müller, D., W. Sandritter, H. G. Schiemer, and K. Endres, Röntgenhistoradiographische und interferenzmikroskopische Trockengewichtsuntersuchungen an Zellausstrichen. *Histochemie* **1**, 438–444 (1959).
43. Müller, D., W. Sandritter, and G. Schwaiger, Eine Methode zur röntgenhistoradiographischen Trockengewichtsbestimmung ohne Verwendung eines Referenzsystems. *Histochemie* **1**, 420–437 (1959).
44. Nixon, W. C., and V. E. Cosslett, Microradiography. II. Projection microradiography. *Brit. J. Radiol.* **28**, 532–536 (1955).

136   GUENTHER BENEKE

45. Nurnberger, J., A. Engström, and B. Lindström, A study of the ventral horn cells of the adult cat by two independent cytochemical microabsorption techniques. *J. Cellular Comp. Physiol.* **39**, 215–254 (1952).
46. Ortner, G., Röntgenspektroskopie mit gebogenen Kristallen. *Oesterr. Chemiker-Ztg.* **44**, 110–114 (1941).
47. Pattee, H. H., The compound X-ray microscope. *Phys. Rev.* **85**, 764–768 (1952).
48. Pattee, H. H., The scanning X-ray microscope. *J. Opt. Soc. Am.* **43**; 61–62 (1953).
49. Pattee, H. H., V. E. Cosslett, and A. Engström, "X-ray Optics and X-ray Microanalysis." Academic Press, New York, 1963.
50. Sandritter, W., and D. Müller, Vergleichende röntgenhistoradiographische und interferenzmikroskopische Trockengewichtsbestimmungen. *Experientia* **15**, 158–161 (1959).
51. Sandritter, W., D. Müller, and H. G. Schiemer, Über den Nukleinsäuregehalt und das Trockengewicht von haploiden und diploiden Zellen. *Anat. Anz.* **105**, 146–156 (1958).
52. Sandritter, W., H. G. Schiemer, W. Alt, D. Müller, and E. Behrouzi, Histochemie von Sputumzellen. III. Interferenzmikroskopische Trockengewichtsbestimmungen. *Frankf. Z. Pathol.* **69**, 167–193 (1958).
53. Waard, R. H. de, A system of formulae and curves bearing on the distribution of energy on the continuous Roentgen spectrum. *Acta Radiol.* **28**, 37–48 (1947).

QUANTITATIVE ELECTRON MICROSCOPY

An Introduction to General Quantitative Measurements
with the Electron Microscope, with Special Reference to Dry
Mass Determinations

G. F. Bahr*

ARMED FORCES INSTITUTE OF PATHOLOGY,
WASHINGTON, D.C.

I. Introduction

On first sight it may appear premature to consider electron microscopy as a tool in quantitative cytochemistry alongside venerated techniques of light microscopy. If one realizes how profoundly the morphological analysis of cells and tissues, made possible by comparatively recent advances in electron microscopic techniques, has already influenced our cytological and cytochemical concepts and thinking, it seems not unrealistic to project an increasingly prominent role for the electron microscope in quantitative cytochemistry also.

This chapter intends to provide a review of electron microscopic techniques that the author considers of potential usefulness to the cytochemist, in particular when his investigations involve objects smaller than whole cells. As a prominent example, the essentials of the method for determination of dry mass with the electron microscope will be presented, extending the quantitative means of the cytochemist beyond the capabilities of interference microscopy into the study of subcellular particles.

The areas in which the electron microscope has already been used, though still to a rather limited extent, are conveniently divided into determinations of the following:

* This work was supported by the American Cancer Society, Grant No. P-259D.

137

An authoritative, comprehensive account of the state of the art of using the electron microscope for these purposes has recently been given (*27*).

II. Determination of Numbers

The desire to use the electron microscope as a counting device originated during work with objects clearly under the resolving power of the light microscope. It is, therefore, not surprising that virologists have pioneered in the development of the necessary methodology (*24*). The cytologist may wish to count the numbers of mitochondria or objects of comparable size in a suspension. He can then apply modifications of the virologist's approach (*3*): The technique involves combining known volumes of two or more different particle suspensions. One is a suspension of a known concentration of easily recognizable particles, identified as the dilution standard, while the others are of unknown concentration. The mixture of suspensions is sprayed, in the form of microdroplets, onto film-covered grids. A differential count of particles is then made in the electron microscope. On the basis of the relative concentrations so obtained and the known concentration in the dilution standard, the concentration of particles in the unknown, or unknowns, may be calculated. It should be mentioned here that another approach available to the cytologist is counting with a Coulter counter. The instrument was designed for counting cells and may, with proper precautions, be used for counting mitochondria (*16*).

III. Determination of Size

A. LENGTH, WIDTH, AND PROJECTED AREA

The high resolving power of the electron microscope makes it particularly suitable for determining the size of objects at or below the limits of resolution obtained with a light microscope. When measuring absolute size it is imperative to compare the object with an accurate magnification standard (*7*). Methods for the rapid statistical evaluation of size populations with the electron microscope have been described by Stoeber (*26*). At times the determination of length and width conveys limited information only. One may then resort to measurements of the projected area, for instance, of objects with such characteristic but unsymmetric shape as sperm heads (6). Planimetry on enlarged electron micrographs of whole mounted objects renders accurate values of the projected area of the one principal object plane that usually presents itself when the objects are drying down.

B. The Third Dimension of the Object

The thickness of an object, or its third dimension, cannot be determined in electron microscopy by focusing its upper and lower limits, since the depth of field at all times exceeds the thickness of the object. Therefore, several means of measuring the third dimension have been successfully used. Shadow casting is a popular technique in electron microscopy. A metal, such as aluminum or platinum, is heated in vacuum until it evaporates. The metal vapors leave as light would leave the filament of an incandescent lamp, that is, in a straight line of flight. The metal thus deposited around the object leaves the "shadow" of the object with respect to the "light" source free of metal. In the electron microscope, then, the shadow area will stand out brightly because it transmits more electrons than areas covered with the deposited metal. Knowledge of the evaporation geometry, namely the distance and angle of vapor source to object, permits the calculation of the dimensions of the object from the length of its shadow. Stereoscopy has been explored for the same purpose; it requires, however, rather complicated equipment (17). A third means is the measurement of contrast. This approach relies on the fact that contrast in electron microscopy is proportional to the mass per area of the object. For an exact determination of the third dimension, one must know the specific gravity of the object, which for dried biological objects, however, can only be given as an approximation. This technique has not been used to any great extent for determining dimensions, but the relationship of contrast to mass is the base for mass (or dry weight) determinations with the electron microscope (vide infra).

IV. Determination of the Relative Volume of Constituents of the Object

For the past 20 years electron microscopy has convinced us that the early cytologist's concept of the cell being a bag containing a sap or foam of cytoplasm with a number of granules suspended in it could be abandoned. The wealth of observations obtained with aid of the electron microscope leads us currently to believe that the interior of the cell is divided into distinct compartments, bound by lipid membranes and filled with a variety of substances and structures. We call these compartmentalizations mitochondria, lysosomes, endoplasmic reticulum, Golgi apparatus, and so forth.

In 1847 a French geologist, Delesse, showed that the fractional volume occupied by a distinguishable component in a body occupies an equal fraction of area on any random section through this body. The concept was brought about by the geologist's need to know the proportion of certain constituents in a piece of rock without resorting to cumbersome chemical analysis. Area determinations are tedious, and the procedure used today is the one proposed in 1898 in Vienna by Rosiwal, another geologist, who showed that the fractional length of lines superimposed on the section plane and traversing the component to be analyzed equals the fractional area of the component. Loud (22, 23) has summarized the consequences of Delesse's and Rosiwal's principles in a formula:

$$\frac{\text{length}_x}{\text{length}_{\text{total}}} = \frac{\text{area}_x}{\text{area}_{\text{total}}} = \frac{\text{volume}_x}{\text{volume}_{\text{total}}}.$$

It must be kept in mind that these relations hold true only for average values of statistically large and unbiased samples. The validity of these principles and their limitation have been given repeated mathematical analysis (14, 25, 29). In the biological literature we find these principles most often applied according to the procedure of Chalkley (12, 13). In 1945 Tomkeieff (28) elaborated an additional principle by which it is possible to deduce the surface area of membranous elements in a volume by counting the intersections of these membranes with the superimposed sampling lines.

The combined principles have been successfully applied by Loud (22, 23) in the analysis of electron micrographs of liver cells, and also in a study on the effects of various fixatives and embedding media on the fractional volume of cytoplasmic elements (23). The tediousness of the procedure has prompted Lazarow and Carpenter (11, 20) to propose and investigate a fast but fairly complicated electronic system for the registration of area intercepts, for both light and electron microscopic purposes. In want of such sophisticated instrumentation, the author has found the procedure of Loud (22, 23) very satisfactory. The reader is referred to these explicit descriptions of the method.

Unfortunately the measurement of size, and of volume in particular, has never enjoyed great popularity because it is usually cumbersome and, on the face of it, uninspiring. Such measurements may lead, however, to insight into fundamental relationships, of which the nuclear classes are a good example (10, 18, 19). In many instances a change in volume may be the only detectable indication of an altered function. A drug may affect the mitochondria of a cell in a morphologically unnoticeable way. So does, for example, X-irradiation, as a consequence of which rat liver mitochondria start to grow without giving any morphologic sign of being altered (2). In light and electron microscopy, measurements of object dimensions should be contemplated as an integral part of any approach to a cytochemical problem.

V. Determination of Total Dry Mass of the Object

If an electron beam transilluminates an object, its intensity, I_0, diminishes to I_1 by interactions between the beam and the object (Fig. 1). The

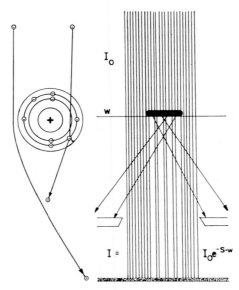

FIG. 1. Simplified schematic drawing of (left) elastic and inelastic electron scattering on an atomic nucleus of an electron microscopic object, and (right) the elimination of scattered electrons by a physical aperture. The decrease in electron intensity I_0 by I_1 by scattering events in the object w can be described by Beer's law.

most prominent of these interactions produces a deviation of the traveling electron from its original direction in the positive Coulomb field of an atomic nucleus in the object. This event is called elastic scattering. A small number of the electrons in the electron beam interacts with the shell electrons of the atoms in the object (Fig. 1). This event is called inelastic scattering. It produces ionization, X-rays, ultraviolet and visible light, thermal energy, and other phenomena. Inelastic scattering gives rise, as does elastic scattering, to a deviation of a beam electron from its original direction of flight.

If we insert a small physical aperture behind the object (right part of

Fig. 1) we shall prohibit most of the scattered electrons from continuing their travel down the microscope column. The electrons will fall upon the rim of this aperture, which is electrically at ground potential, and they will disappear. The smaller the aperture, the more scattered electrons will be eliminated. It is this very elimination of electrons from the beam that produces the image we observe in the electron microscope. Several important facts can be added to this rather simplified description of image formation in the electron microscope. Electron scattering is an atomic event, being independent of the chemical composition and the chemical bonds within the object. Also, it is not difficult to realize that the more atoms there are in the electron's path the greater the likelihood for it to interact and be scattered. It is, indeed, the total number of atoms per area that the electrons have to penetrate that determines the number of scattering events. A practical account of the losses suffered from the original electron beam through scattering in the object is given by Beer's law (Fig. 1),

$$I = I_0 e^{-\alpha S t}, \tag{1}$$

I_0 being the intensity entering the object and I the intensity remaining after scattering loss; αS is an equivalent of the absorption coefficient in spectrophotometry and t, the mass thickness of the object.

The unique relationship of the number of atoms per object area (mass per area) to the number of scattered electrons yields the basis for quantitative mass determinations. If we have a means of determining the magnitude of scattering losses from the beam (the analog to absorption of a beam of light), we will be able to deduce the amount of mass having caused this loss. We find a most suitable and practical recorder of electron intensities in the photographic emulsion. Considering the recording rather pragmatically, we find further that while the unscattered portion of the beam produces a certain photographic density, the image-forming portion of the beam produces less photographic density in proportion to the numbers of electrons lost through scattering in the object. The electron microscopist therefore commonly interprets areas of less exposure in his developed electron micrographic negative as being produced by "electron-dense" structures of the object. He is subjectively using the factual proportionality of object mass and transmission in the negative. For the purpose of this introduction to the quantitative use of the electron microscope, we will satisfy ourselves with the statement that the mass (dry mass) of a given object area (w_1) is proportional to the difference of transmission between the corresponding micrograph area and the transmission of another micrograph area exposed to the unscattered beam:

$$w_1 \sim T_1 - T_0. \tag{2}$$

This proportionality has been extensively tested in experiments as well as considered theoretically (8, 30, 31). Figure 2 summarizes the procedure

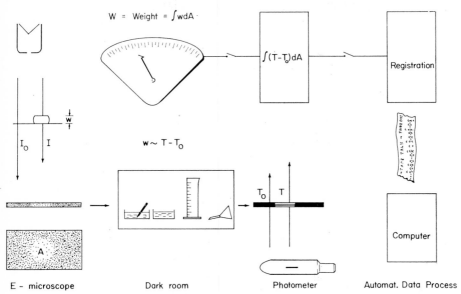

E - microscope   Dark room   Photometer   Automat. Data Process

FIG. 2. Scheme of the procedure of quantitative electron microscopy. From Bahr and Zeitler (8).

for mass determination. On the left side of the illustration an electron microscope is schematically indicated by its electron-emitting filament and grid cap (top). The electron intensity I_0 is passing down the microscope column. Interaction with the specimen of mass w scatters a portion of the beam electrons so that they will not pass through the physical aperture, but are eliminated. The electron intensity I_0 is reduced to I_1. The intensities are recorded in a photographic emulsion in which the image of the object A is now latently stored as a modulation of exposure corresponding to the intensity modulation experienced by the beam while passing through the object. The plate is developed under standard conditions, that is, at constant temperature and for a constant length of time. The electron micrograph (negative) thus obtained is now introduced into a special photometer for the measurement of transmissions. As we have seen before, the mass of each object point is represented in its image by the increased transmission T_1 over the background transmission T_0 (Eq. (2)). In order to arrive at the total mass of the object we must now sum up, or integrate, the transmissions of all image points in the micrograph, $T_1 + T_2 + T_3$, and so on, and indicate their numerical difference over an equal number of points with the background transmission T_0.

The photometer accomplishing this integration consists essentially of a telecentric lens system (31) that produces a parallel, homogeneous beam of light passing through the micrograph. By inserting physical apertures into this optical system and projecting their image into the plane of the micrograph, the transilluminated area of the micrograph can be variously restricted. The detector of the photometer (photomultiplier) sees the average transmission, $\overline{T}$, of this defined micrograph area. The proportionality of mass and transmission discussed above permits us, then, to say that the photometer sees the average mass per area encompassed by the area of the aperture:

$$w \sim \overline{T} - T_0. \tag{3}$$

If the entire image of our object is contained in the area of the measuring aperture, the total mass of the object will be represented in its transmission value. We now need to determine only the value of background transmission T_0, using the same area (aperture) of measurement. The difference of the two transmission values will be called "reading R." Readings can be obtained from either a galvanometer or another simple instrument, or the transmission values can be transferred to punched tape, which is then fed into an electronic computer suitably programmed for desired statistical analysis (Fig. 2).

We have, in fact, established a sensitive balance with this electron microscopic procedure. Like other balances, it has to be calibrated with objects of known weight. A number of different types of objects can be used for this purpose (8), of which polystyrene latex spheres are the easiest to use. The absolute weight of a sphere can simply be determined by measuring its diameter on an electron micrograph of known magnification, calculating its volume therefrom, and multiplying it by the specific gravity of polystyrene. Figure 3 is a calibration curve obtained with the aid of such spheres. In the upper half of the illustration electron micrographs of single spheres and accidental clusters are inserted as they appear enclosed in a measuring aperture of the photometer (Fig. 2) and as they would be "seen" by its photomultiplier. Calculated absolute mass values are represented on the abscissa. The ordinate gives the corresponding photometer reading R. The straight curve illustrates not only the proportionality of mass and reading, $w \sim R$, but contains the important evidence that the photometric response is independent of the shape and the inhomogeneities of the object, since readings of the total mass of a cluster, being the sum of its composing spheres, conform with the straight curve. Such a calibration curve enables us to convert any reading to absolute values of mass.

The slope of the curve, or our conversion factor α, is influenced by a

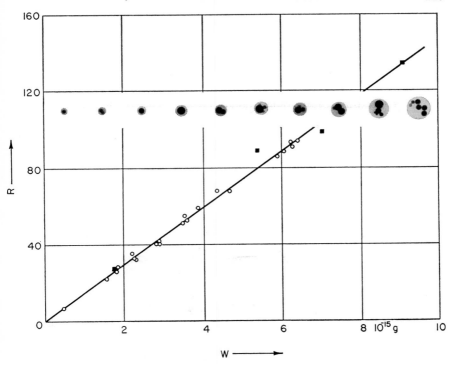

FIG. 3. Calibration curve for quantitative electron microscopy. The curve illustrates the straight-line relationship between absolute weights, w, and photometric readings, R. Polystyrene spheres (circles) and formvar (rectangles) were used for calibration. Electron micrographs of spheres accidentally clustered are inserted in the upper portion of the graph. The readings of these clusters, the weight of which can be determined by measuring the diameters of their constituent spheres, also fall onto the straight line, thereby proving that R is independent of the shape and the inhomogeneities of the object. From Zeitler and Bahr (*31*).

number of procedural parameters, such as the accelerating voltage of the electron microscope and the size of the objective aperture, the first of which influences the angular spread of electron scattering by the object while the second determines the number of electrons to be eliminated from the beam. Furthermore, conditions of exposure and photographic development of the micrograph influence α. One realizes that no exposure of the emulsion will lead to zero reading (both transmission values are at maximum $T_1 = T_0$), while overexposure will likewise produce zero reading, since both transmissions are zero. In between these two extremes, the curve for the slope α goes through a broad maximum. In practice one keeps conditions of exposure and development so that the background density of the plate falls between 0.5 and 0.7.

A. Limitations of Quantitative Mass Determinations

Quantitative measurements of dry mass are limited at the lower end of the method's working range $(10^{-17}–10^{-18}$ g) by the resolving power of the electron microscope and the adverse effects of high beam intensities required at high magnifications. Last but not least, the method is limited by the contrast (proportional to R) with which a small object can be recorded. At the upper end of its range, that is, in dealing with objects of a total dry mass of about 10^{-11} g, a limitation is set by the validity of Beer's law (30). It can safely be applied to objects having 34 μg/cm² using 50-kV accelerating voltage in the electron microscope, as well as up to 60 μg/cm² for 100 kV. The object has to be adequately penetrated by the electron beam in order to render a true photographic recording of the amount of matter it has passed. We see from the two values given that the higher the accelerating voltage used, the better will this condition be fulfilled. It is the thickness of the object or its mass in the third dimension that ultimately limits our approach. The extension of this object into the two dimensions of the object plane is of less concern, since it is in most instances possible to adjust the electron microscopic magnification so that the full image of the object is recorded on the photographic plate in proper size for photometric evaluation.

B. Instrumental Requirements

1. Electron Microscopy

The cytochemist will most probably deal with objects that are large compared with the resolving power of his electron microscope. With respect to what has been said in the preceding paragraph he will, therefore, prefer to use a microscope featuring a high accelerating voltage. Most conventional instruments are designed for up to 100 kV. One uses a contrast aperture (Fig. 1) of the maximum diameter compatible with the least amount of diffusely scattered electrons (stray light). This size usually produces little more contrast than one would obtain with no aperture at all.* It is our experience (4–6, 8) that a 100-μ aperture fulfills this requirement in the Siemens Elmiskop.

Photometry requires that the exposure of the photographic material be controlled. A sensor of the beam intensity and a shutter-timer device are needed to reproduce photographic densities in the image background within the stipulated range. Most modern instruments have built-in exposure meters. For others, attachments are available. Those devices that

---

* Elimination of scattered electrons is then brought about by the geometry of the design of the objective pole piece alone.

have a small area for direct measurement of the intensity of the electron beam allow measurement in an object-free background area and are superior to photometers that measure the response of a larger part of the fluorescent screen, since the latter will render average values irrespective of how great an area of the field of view is covered by the object.

2. Photometry

A special—though, in principle, simple—photometer is required for the determination of area transmission. Several generations of photometers for this purpose have been built in our laboratories since 1959 (*1, 8, 31*). Construction of a commercial unit* is at the time of this writing sufficiently advanced to anticipate availability soon. The use of a scanning photometer such as the Joyce–Loebel instrument has not yet been explored, since scanning measurements with this device will *a priori* be slow and unnecessarily cumbersome.

C. Working Range of Quantitative Dry Mass Determinations with the Election Microscope

In Fig. 4 the ranges of several conventional means for the determination of the mass of biological objects are indicated. There is a fortunate

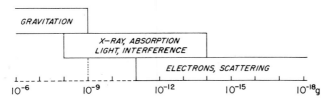

Fig. 4. Range of methods for the determination of mass.

overlap of the ranges of microradiography and interference microscopy with the range of quantitative electron microscopy, which enables us, at least in this weight range, to obtain several independent values on one object, providing a mutual check. Of these three methods, quantitative electron microscopy is the most sensitive one, making it possible to deal with objects that differ among each other by as little as 2%. Since the object has to be exposed to the vacuum of the electron microscope, it must be free of water, which limits the applicability to dehydrated objects. Interference microscopy has the prominent advantage over quantitative electron microscopy that it is applicable to living (hydrated) as well as dehydrated objects, but it is less sensitive, especially with objects

* Carl Zeiss, Oberkochen, Germany.

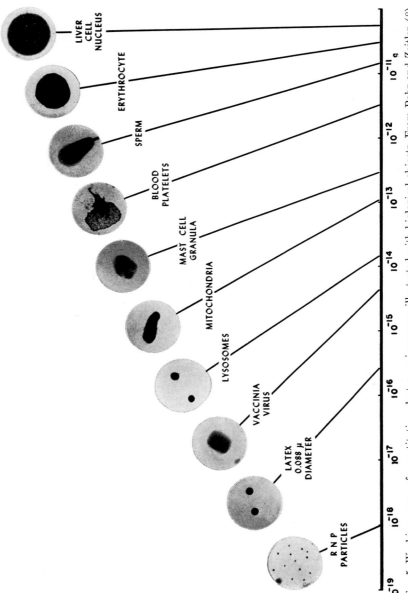

FIG. 5. Working range of quantitative electron microscopy, illustrated with biological objects. From Bahr and Zeitler (8).

weighing less than 10^{-12} g. On theoretical grounds microradiography has been considered a very accurate method (9, 15, 21). It requires dry objects, and its sensitivity is not better than that of interference microscopy.

The working range of quantitative dry mass determinations with the electron microscope is illustrated in Fig. 5 in terms of biological objects. It comprises cell nuclei at the heavier end (10^{-11} g) and macromolecules like ribonucleoprotein particles at the lighter end (10^{-18} g). In between, examples of recently studied objects are given. The value of direct quantitative study of individual particles as small as mitochondria is amplified by the fact that the method renders large amounts of data in a reasonable time, which makes it possible to analyze the material statistically for significant characteristics of the particle *population.*

Still largely unexplored, dry mass determinations with the electron microscope offer a means of following the enzymatic dissection of small objects in terms of lost mass. Furthermore, uptake of stains or antibody will produce mass increases that are amenable to quantitative analysis.

VI. Conclusion

Quantitative cytochemistry will find a rather versatile and precise tool in the electron microscope. Numbers, dimensions, volume, and dry mass of objects at or below the limit of resolution of other quantitative cytochemical techniques are quantities that may be obtained with this instrument.

Determinations of dry mass with the electron microscope extend the analytical means of the cytochemist into the realm of individual subcellular particles, covering a mass range from 10^{-11} g to 10^{-18} g, that is, in terms of biological objects from cell nuclei to macromolecules.

REFERENCES

1. Bahr, G. F., L. Carlsson, and E. Zeitler, Determination of the dry weight in populations of submicroscopic particles by means of quantitative electron microscopy. Presented at *Intern. Biophys. Congr., Stockholm, 1961.*
2. Bahr, G. F., and U. Glas, Effects of whole-body irradiation on rat liver mitochondria. *J. Cell Biol.* **23**, 8A (1964).
3. Bahr, G. F., G. H. Herbener, and U. Glas, A method for the counting of mitochondria. *Exptl. Cell Res.* **41**, 99–108 (1966).
4. Bahr, G. F., and E. Zeitler, Study of mitochondria in rat liver. Quantitative electron microscopy. *J. Cell Biol.* **15**, 489–501 (1962).
5. Bahr, G. F., and E. Zeitler, Determination of the total dry mass of human erythrocytes by quantitative electron microscopy. *Lab. Invest.* **11**, 912–917 (1964).
6. Bahr, G. F., and E. Zeitler, Study of bull spermatozoa: Quantitative electron microscopy. *J. Cell Biol.* **21**, 175-189 (1964).

7. Bahr, G. F., and E. Zeitler, The determination of magnification in the electron microscope. II. Means for the determination of magnification. *In* "Symposium on Quantitative Electron Microscopy" (G.F. Bahr and E. Zeitler, eds.), pp. 142–153. Williams & Wilkins, Baltimore, Maryland, 1965.

8. Bahr, G. F., and E. Zeitler, The determination of the dry mass in populations of isolated particles. *In* "Symposium on Quantitative Electron Microscopy," G. F. Bahr and E. Zeitler, eds.), pp. 217–239. Williams & Wilkins, Baltimore, Maryland, 1965.

9. Beneke, G., This volume, pp. 107–136.

10. Bucher, O., and R. Gattiker, Karyometrische Untersuchungen an Gewebekulturen. *Z. Mikroskop. Anat. Forsch.* **60**, 467–501 (1954).

11. Carpenter, A. M., and A. Lazarow, Component quantitation of tissue sections. II. A study of the factors which influence the accuracy of the method. *J. Histochem. Cytochem.* **10**, 329–340 (1962).

12. Chalkley, H. W., Method for the quantitative morphologic analysis of tissue. *J. Natl. Cancer Inst.* **4**, 47–53 (1943).

13. Chalkley, H. W., J. Cornfield, and H. Park, A method for estimating volume-surface ratios. *Science* **110**, 295–297 (1949).

14. Chayes, F., Determination of the relative volume by sectional analysis. *In* "Symposium on Quantitative Electron Microscopy" (G. F. Bahr and E. Zeitler, eds.), pp. 249–257. Williams & Wilkins, Baltimore, Maryland, 1965.

15. Engström, A., Quantitative micro- and histochemical elementary analysis by Roentgen absorption spectrography. *Acta Radiol.* Suppl. 63 (1946).

16. Glas, U., and G. F. Bahr, Study of mitochondria in rat liver; dry mass, wet mass, volume and concentration of solids. Submitted to *J. Cell Biol.* (1965).

17. Helmcke, J. G., Determination of the third dimension of objects by stereoscopy. *In* "Symposium on Quantitative Electron Microscopy" (G. F. Bahr and E. Zeitler, eds.), pp. 195–200. Williams & Wilkins, Baltimore, Maryland, 1965.

18. Helweg-Larsen, H. F., Nuclear class series. *Acta Pathol. Microbiol. Scand.* Suppl. 92 (1952).

19. Jacobj, W., Über das rhythmische Wachstum der Zellen durch Verdopplung ihres Volumens. *Arch. Entwicklungsmech. Organ.* **106**, 124–192 (1925).

20. Lazarow, A., and A. M. Carpenter, Component quantitation of tissue sections. I. Characterization of the instruments. *J. Histochem. Cytochem.* **10**, 324–328 (1962).

21. Lindström, B., Roentgen absorption spectrophotometry in quantitative cytochemistry. *Acta Radiol.* Suppl. 125 (1955).

22. Loud, A. V., A method for the quantitative estimation of cytoplasmic structures. *J. Cell Biol.* **15**, 481–487 (1962).

23. Loud, A. V., W. C. Barany, and B. A. Pack, Quantitative evaluation of cytoplasmic structures in electron micrographs. *In* "Symposium on Quantitative Electron Microscopy" (G. F. Bahr and E. Zeitler, eds.), pp. 258–270. Williams & Wilkins, Baltimore, Maryland, 1965.

24. Sharp, D. G., Quantitative use of the electron microscope in virus research: Methods and recent results of particle counting. *In* "Symposium on Quantitative Electron Microscopy" (G. F. Bahr and E. Zeitler, eds.), pp. 93–125. Williams & Wilkins, Baltimore, Maryland, 1965.

25. Smith, C. S., and L. Guttman, Measurement of internal boundaries in three-dimensional structures by random sectioning. *J. Metals* **5**, 81–87 (1953).

26. Stoeber, W., Statistical size distribution analysis. *In* "Symposium on Quantitative

Electron Microscopy" (G. F. Bahr and E. Zeitler, eds.), pp. 154–170. Williams & Wilkins, Baltimore, Maryland, 1965.

27. "Symposium on Quantitative Electron Microscopy" (G. F. Bahr and E. Zeitler, eds.). Williams & Wilkins, Baltimore, Maryland, 1965.

28. Tomkeieff, S. E., Linear intercepts, areas and volumes. *Nature* **155,** 24 (1945).

29. Weibel, E. R., Principles and methods for the morphometric study of the lung and other organs. *Lab. Invest.* **12,** 131–155 (1963).

30. Zeitler, E., and G. F. Bahr, Contrast and mass thickness. *In* "Symposium on Quantitative Electron Microscopy" (G. F. Bahr and E. Zeitler, eds.), pp. 208–216. Williams & Wilkins, Baltimore, Maryland, 1965.

31. Zeitler, E., and G. F. Bahr, A photometric procedure for weight determination of submicroscopic particles, quantitative electron microscopy. *J. Appl. Phys.* **33,** 847–853 (1962).

ELECTRON PROBE MICROANALYSIS AS A QUANTITATIVE CYTOCHEMICAL METHOD

Arthur J. Hale

PATHOLOGY DEPARTMENT,
ST. THOMAS'S HOSPITAL MEDICAL SCHOOL,
LONDON, ENGLAND

Electron probe microanalysis is a method that allows one to identify and localize elements within the microscopic structure of the tissue. The detection of the elements is independent of their molecular bonding; thus, although the method is highly specific for individual elements, it yields no information about the molecules in which they are present.

The method was introduced by Castaing and Guinier (4) and has been extensively used in metallurgical and mineralogical research. The principle of the method is that the specimen is probed using a finely focused beam of lectrons. X-ray and other wavelengths are emitted from the specimen as a result of the energy transitions induced by the electron probe, and the point of emission in the specimen can be identified and displayed on an oscilloscope. Using suitable spectrometers the different X-ray wavelengths can be separated, and thus the different elements responsible for the emission of these wavelengths can be identified (5). The apparatus is complex, consisting of an electron column, X-ray spectrometers, amplifiers, scaling, recording and display channels. In some instruments the electron probe can be scanned across the specimen, thus displaying the distribution of elements over the scanned area. There are at least six commercial electron probe microanalyzers available ranging in price from £16,000 to £30,000. Since many academic institutions are now using these instruments for anlaysis of metals and other hard samples, it may be possible for a biologist to gain access to them.

In analyzing biological samples, one of the main limitations is that the specimen may be destroyed by the electron beam because of its high thermal and electrical resistance (13, 14, 15). The burn marks thus pro-

duced can be prevented by covering the specimen with a conducting layer
(2, 8, 11, 16, 17). A suitable layer will produce stability of the specimen
and eliminate burn marks from it even after electron probes of high current are used for many hours (8). In this way it is possible to reanalyze
the same area for different elements. The sensitivity of the method permits detection of concentrations of 0.01% of an element or 10^{-15} g in an
area of 1 μ^2. Lack of suitable standards has, until now, prevented absolute quantitation on different specimens, but methods are at present being evolved to measure concentration variations within and between
specimens.

It is possible to detect all elements in the periodic table down to the
level of magnesium. The microscopic nature of the method permits one
to identify elements which have a suitably high local concentration in
the tissue, even though their bulk concentration in that same tissue may
be very low. In this way the distribution of calcium and iron in teeth
(1), tin inhaled into lungs (12), breakdown products of metal plates in
joints (11), iron absorbed from food of high iron content (9), calcium
in degenerating arteries (8), calcium and phosphorus in bone (3, 10),
copper in the lens in Wilson's disease (15), and iron in spermatocytes
(17) have been studied. This type of study of distribution of endogenous
elements will obviously be rapidly extended to analysis of iron in blood-
forming and -destroying tissues, copper and iron in liver disease, zinc
content of leukocytes and prostates, iodine content of thyroid glands, and
potassium and phosphorus content of a variety of tissues.

A further application is in the investigation of the distribution and
amount of stain bound to tissues where the stain contains an element
detectable by the electron probe. In this way enzyme reaction products
can be studied (7), and the distribution of stains selective for certain
molecular configurations can be correlated qualitatively and quantitatively with the presence of certain elements in these molecules. The scope
for this type of study is wide. Its advantages over conventional microspectrophotometry of stains are (1) high degree of specificity of detection, (2) high sensitivity, (3) correlation of stain with the elementary
composition of the stained molecules, and (4) design of new "stains"
with simpler molecular forms and different reaction characteristics.

The severest limitations of the method are its slowness and high cost,
but with development it may be that both of these factors will be reduced. The method is technically complex and as yet its application to
analysis of biological materials is in its infancy (6). With the development of more rapid and sensitive instruments and the solution of some
problems of specimen analysis it should, however, gain in popularity as
a quantitative cytochemical research method.

ACKNOWLEDGMENTS

This work was carried out in conjunction with Dr. T. Hall, Dr. V. R. Switsur, and Dr. R. C. Curran of the Pathology Department, St. Thomas's Hospital Medical School, London, and the Cavendish Laboratory, Cambridge, under the auspices of the Medical Research Council.

REFERENCES

1. Boyde, A., V. R. Switsur, and R. W. Fearnhead, Application of the scanning electron probe x-ray microanalyser to dental tissues. *J. Ultrastruct. Res.* **5**, 201–207 (1961).
2. Boyde, A., and V. R. Switsur, Problems associated with the preparation of biological specimens for microanalysis. *Proc. 3rd Intern. Symp. X-Ray Optics X-Ray Microanal., Stanford, 1962*, pp. 499–506. Academic Press, New York, 1963.
3. Brooks, E. J., A. J. Tousimis, and L. S. Birks, The distribution of calcium in the epiphyseal cartilage of the rat tibia measured with the electron probe microanalyzer. *J. Ultrastruct. Res.* **7**, 56–60 (1962).
4. Castaing, R., and A. Guinier, Application of electron probes to metallographic analysis. *Proc. Conf. Electron Microscopy, Delft, 1949*, p. 60. Nijhoff, The Hague, 1949.
5. Cosslett, V. E., Scanning electron and x-ray microscopy. *Ann. N.Y. Acad. Sci.* **97**, 464–481 (1962).
6. Cosslett, V. E., and V. R. Switsur, Some biological applications of the scanning microanalyzer. *Proc. 3rd Intern. Symp. X-Ray Optics X-Ray Microanal., Stanford, 1962*, pp. 507–512. Academic Press, New York, 1963.
7. Hale, A. J., Identification of cytochemical reaction products by scanning x-ray emission microanalysis. *J. Cell Biol.* **15**, 427–435 (1962).
8. Hall, T. A., A. J. Hale, and V. R. Switsur, Some applications of microprobe analysis in biology and medicine. The Electron Microprobe, 1966, pp. 805–833. John Wiley & Sons, New York, 1966.
9. Lever, J. D., and P. Duncumb, The detection of intracellular iron in rat duodenal epithelium. *In* "Electron Microscopy in Anatomy," p. 278. Arnold, London, 1960.
10. Mellors, R. C., Electron probe microanalysis. Calcium and phosphorus in normal human cortical bone. *Lab. Invest.* **13**, 183–195 (1964).
11. Mellors, R. C., and K. G. Carroll, A new method for local chemical analysis of human tissue. *Nature* **192**, 1090–1092 (1961).
12. Robertson, A. J., D. Rivers, G. Nagelschmidt, and P. Duncumb, Stannosis: benign pneumoconiosis due to tin dioxide. *Lancet* i, 1089 (1961).
13. Switsur, V. R., and A. Boyde, A consideration of some design features of a scanning microanalyser for biological applications. *Proc. 3rd Intern. Symp. X-Ray Optics X-Ray Microanal., Stanford, 1962*, pp. 495–497. Academic Press, New York, 1963.
14. Tousimis, A. J., Electron microprobe analysis of biological tissues. *ISA Proc.* **8**, 53–56 (1962).
15. Tousimis, A. J., and I. Adler, Electron probe x-ray microanalyzer study of copper within Descemet's membrane of Wilson's disease. *J. Histochem. Cytochem.* **11**, 40–47 (1963).

16. Yasuzumi, G., Electron microscopy and x-ray scanning microanalysis of needle biopsy material from human liver. *J. Cell Biol.* **14**, 421–431 (1962).
17. Yasuzumi, G., X-ray scanning microanalysis of elemental iron localized in testicular cells of *cipangopaludinia malleata reeve. J. Cell Biol.* **14**, 495–498 (1962).

Part II

QUANTITATIVE METHODS FOR DETERMINATION OF NUCLEIC ACIDS

METHODS AND RESULTS
IN QUANTITATIVE CYTOCHEMISTRY *

Walter Sandritter

DEPARTMENT OF PATHOLOGY, JUSTUS LIEBIG
UNIVERSITY, GIESSEN, GERMANY

The methods for quantitative histochemistry were developed by Caspersson (2). Two different fields of research are well combined in these methods. The milestones of this development were the discovery of nucleic acids by Miescher (10), the identification of ultraviolet light absorption of the purine and pyrimidine bases in UV light in the region of 260 mμ by Dhéré (4), the nucleal reaction for DNA of the biochemist Feulgen (6), and, on the other hand, the progress in microscopy starting with the UV microscope, by Köhler (9).

The methods used today derive from both lines of research. The techniques include a large spectrum of wavelengths, ranging from X-rays to infrared rays. The main principle of these methods is the measurement of the absorption of electromagnetic rays in biological objects. For this, one uses the properties of chromophores in biological objects, for example, the conjugated double bonds in nucleic acids or, on the other hand, the absorption of dyestuffs after specific and stoichiometric binding.

Table I shows a wavelength scale and the method to be applied in the different regions of the electromagnetic spectrum. One can see that there are two main types of methods:

(1) *Procedure for determining the dry weight.* Dry weight determinations provide useful information as a research tool in the field of quantitative histochemistry; we can use dry weight as a parameter to which other quantitative data can be related. X-Ray historadiography (5) and interference microscopy (1, 20) are two methods of determining dry weight, that is, mass, in two different ways. In one method the phase retardation of biological objects is used, while in the second method,

* With a grant from the Deutsche Forschungsgemeinschaft.

TABLE I

WAVELENGTH SCALE AND THE CORRELATED METHODS
OF QUANTITATIVE HISTOCHEMISTRY

Light range	λ (mμ)	Substance	Staining reaction	Method
Infrared	1000	RNS, DNS, carbohydrates	—	Infrared microphotometry
Infrared	800	Lipids, proteins	—	Infrared microphotometry
Visible	700	DNA	Feulgen, gallocyanin chrome alum–RNase, fluorescence	Cytophotometry
Visible		RNA	Gallocyanin chrome alum, Azure B, etc.	Cytophotometry
Visible		Histones	Fast Green pH 8.2, metaphosphate–gallocyanin chrome alum	Cytophotometry
Visible		Arginine	Deamination, Sakaguchi	Cytophotometry
Visible		(Dry weight determination)		Interference microscopy
Visible		Tyrosine, tryptophan	Millon	Cytophotometry
Visible		NH₂ (proteins)	Fast Green pH 1.2, Naphthol Yellow S	Cytophotometry
Visible		SS + SH	Bahr	Cytophotometry
Visible	500	Carbohydrates	PAS	Cytophotometry
Visible	400	Hemoglobin	Pigments, Fe(III), Lipofusin, DPN-DPNH, respiratory enzymes	Cytophotometry
UV	300	Tyrosine-tryptophan	—	UV microphotometry
UV	200	Nucleic acids	—	UV microphotometry
Vacuum UV	10	—	—	—
X-Ray	1	(Dry weight determination)		X-Ray microradiography
X-Ray	0.1	Na, Mg, P, S, Cl, K, Ca, Fe, Cu, Ag, I, etc.	—	X-Ray histospectroscopy
Electron microscopy	—	(Dry weight determination)		Bahr

X-ray historadiography, the absorption of elements like C, O, P, N, S in the region of 8–12 Å is employed to determine mass. Bahr and Zeitler (1) have made significant progress in the field of mass determination with their development of a technique that is applicable at the ultrastructure level with the electron microscope.

(2) *Cytophotometric methods for determining different chemical substances in the cell.* With cytophotometry in UV light, nucleic acids (DNA, RNA) can be determined; at wavelengths between 300 and 400 mμ pigments such as hemoglobin, hemosiderin, and respiratory enzymes can be studied.

Cytophotometry is used today mainly in visible light. Using different staining reactions one can determine nucleic acids and proteins, as well as carbohydrates.

The review of methods shows that there is more than one way of determining different chemical substances in the cell. Our opinion is that several independent methods should be used for the same biological program to check the quantitative data. Since errors do occur in all methods, it is absolutely necessary to test the results with more than one technique.

The chemical composition of the cellular nucleus can be used as an example of the combination of different methods (Table II). DNA can be measured by means of photometry in UV light, wavelength 260 mμ, after the Feulgen reaction or gallocyanin chrome alum staining and with the interference microscope after treatment with DNase. The RNA content is determined in UV light with measurements before and after RNase treatment in the same way as the interference microscope is used. For histones, Fast Green staining, pH 8.2, may be applied or the metaphosphate gallocyanin chrome alum staining (8). The extraction methods may also be used here. The non-histone proteins are not a well-defined group of proteins and can only be insufficiently determined by the Millon reaction or the staining reactions which identify the NH_2 groups. Perhaps the extraction methods in combination with interference microscopy are more useful for these problems. Quantitative cytochemistry of carbohydrates and enzymes is still an open field for research work.

Next we shall discuss in detail the methods of cytophotometry and give some of our results in the field of cancer research. (For the method of X-ray historadiography, see the chapter by Beneke (1a).) In a biological example I shall show how X-ray historadiography can be used with other methods.

Under pathological conditions one often sees inclusion bodies in cells; these bodies are very clearly seen in cytomegalia. The question is

TABLE II

CHEMICAL COMPOSITION OF A CELLULAR NUCLEUS AND THE DIFFERENT METHODS OF QUANTITATIVE CYTOCHEMISTRY

Substance	Method				
	UV photometry	Visible photometry	Interference microscopy[a]	X-Ray historadiography[a]	Autoradiography
DNA	260 mμ	Feulgen, gallocyanin chrome alum, methyl green	Extraction— DNase, TCA	—	Thymidine-H³
RNA	260 mμ (RNase)	Basic dyestuffs	Extraction—RNase	—	Uridine-H³
Histone	—	Fast Green pH 8.2, metaphosphate–gallocyanin chrome alum	Extraction— 0.2 N HCl, trypsin	—	Arginine-C¹⁴
Non-histone protein, globulin, lipoprotein	280 mμ	Millon, Naphthol-Yellow S, Fast Green pH 1.2	Extraction— 0.14 M NaCl + 0.2 N NaOH	—	Amino acid-C¹⁴
Carbohydrate	—	PAS	Extraction—diastase	—	—
Enzymes	DPN, TPN	—	Alkaline phosphatase	—	—

[a] Dry weight determinations.

whether these inclusion bodies are a product of virus infection. We have seen (15) that the dry weight of the inclusions is approximately 300×10^{-12} g. (Normal cell nuclei have a mass of 40×10^{-12} g.) The nucleic acid content is approximately 40×10^{-12} g, that is, 13% of the dry weight (Fig. 1). The Feulgen reaction of the inclusion body is strongly

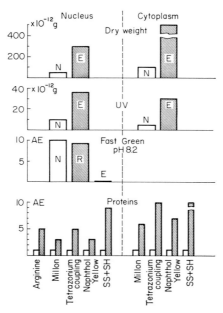

Fig. 1. Result of measurements on cytomegalia cells. Dry weight by X-ray historadiography. *N*, normal cells; *E*, inclusion bodies; *R*, chromatin ring around the inclusion body; *AE*, Arbitrary unit = relative dyestuff content.

positive, but the Fast Green staining, pH 8.2, is negative, and the chromatin ring around the inclusion body is positive. This means that the DNA of the inclusion body is associated with a nonhistone protein, so we can assume that the DNA is a virus DNA with a specific protein.

Interference microscopy has the advantage of allowing one to work with living cells. We use the Zeiss interference microscope that has been built into a scanning instrument to avoid the error of object inhomogeneity. One example demonstrates the manifold application of interference microscopy. The growth of single mammalian cells in the mitotic cycle can be measured (17). Figure 2 shows that the dry weight of the cytoplasm is doubled in the early interphase and is divided in mitosis. The mass of the nucleus is doubled only in late interphase. The changes in mass per square micron show that after cell division there is an up-

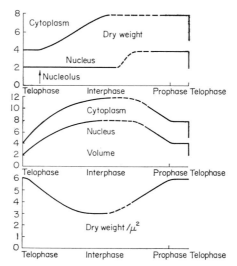

FIG. 2. Diagram of the dry weight, volume, and dry weight per square micron changes in single living HeLa cells. Measurements with the interference microscope.

take of water with a decrease of mass per square micron, while in late interphase there is an increase in mass due to loss of water. The changes in volume occur in the opposite manner.

Of all methods, microphotometry is the one most widely used today. Figure 3 shows the principle of this method, which is the same principle as in spectrophotometry; the same laws of photometry must be regarded.

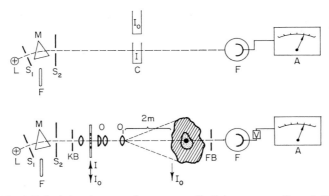

FIG. 3. (Top) Principle of macrophotometry. L, light source; S_1 and S_2, entrance and exit slit of monochromator (M); F, filter; C, cuvette; I_o, cuvette with blank solution; I, with solution to be measured; F, photomultiplier; A, galvanometer. (Below), Principle of microphotometry. KB, condenser, I, measuring point in the specimen; I_o, free space; O, objective; O_1, ocular; FB, measuring field; V, amplifier.

In microphotometry the microscope replaces the cuvette containing a solution and photometry is performed on the projected image of the cell. One is interested in obtaining the following data from microphotometry (Fig. 4): (1) the mass or the concentration of a substance; (2) the identification of a substance in a cell.

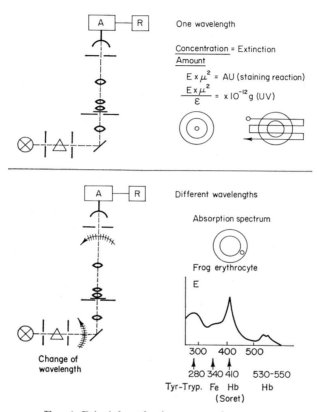

Fig. 4. Principles of microspectrophotometry.

The mass or the concentration is measured in the absorption maximum of the staining reaction or the substance at a defined wavelength. If only the concentration is wanted, then just the extinction is measured. In mass determination (for example, the amount of a dyestuff) the extinction times the area must be calculated.

For identification of cell substances one point in the cell must be measured at different wavelengths to obtain an absorption spectrum. For this, the Zeiss Universal Recording Microspectrophotometer can be used, where the measurements are performed at different wavelengths using the monochromator. Another possibility is realized in the spectro-graph by Leitz, where polychromatic light is used and a spectrograph behind the microscope gives the entire spectrum on a photographic plate.

The introduction of the microscope and the biological object in a photometer system leads to many disruptions of the light beam. Figure 5 shows those that may be introduced by the biological object. The bio-

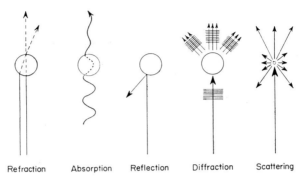

Refraction   Absorption   Reflection   Diffraction   Scattering

FIG. 5. Schematic representation of possible disturbances of a light beam intro-duced by biological objects.

logical object is in a mathematical sense a weakly defined object, so that the question arises whether correct measurements are possible under these conditions. Caspersson (2, 3) developed the theoretical background. After a 30-year period of development in this field, we have come to the conclusion that in order to avoid faulty measurements both the instru-ment and the object must fulfill certain conditions.

The first group of errors caused by the apparatus (Table III) plays almost no role today in the commercially available instrument. In the same way the lack of sufficiently monochromatic light or the Schwarz-schild–Villiger effect, that is, light glare on the glass-air surfaces of the lenses, can usually be well taken care of. An example of another error is the numerical aperture of the objective being too small; there is a nonabsorption light loss. The numerical aperture of the condenser is not as important as has been thought for a long time; it should be 0.3.

Errors introduced by the biological object are caused mainly by fixa-tion, light scattering, an abnormal dispersion, loss of absorbing sub-stances, and dichroism. Careful fixation (in most cases freeze-drying for UV-photometry) and matching of refractive indexes between object and medium can reduce these errors. Staining reactions include a possibility of many errors, and the adaption of a staining reaction for quantitative purposes is a very difficult and time consuming process. Finally, the bleaching of a dyestuff during measurement may be a source of error. For photometry in UV light special problems arise. Figure 6 shows

TABLE III

POSSIBLE ERRORS IN CYTOPHOTOMETRIC METHODS

Source of error	Effect on measurements[a]
Apparatus	
Nonlinearity	$\pm$
Noise	$\pm$
Cathode center	$\pm$
Light source variation	$\pm$
Monochromasia	$-$
Schwarzschild–Villiger effect	$-$
Focus	$-$
Numerical aperture,	
Of objective	$-$
Of condenser	$\pm$
Object	
Light scattering	$+$
Anomalous dispersion	$+$
Distributional error	$-$
Fixation artifacts	$\pm$
Loss of absorbing substances	$-$
Interference of absorbing substances	$\pm$
Variability of composition of chromophores	$\pm$
Unknown and changes of ϵ	$\pm$
Dichroism	$-$
Thickness of specimen	$\pm$
Staining reactions	
Lambert–Beer law	$-$
Dyestuff and staining (purity, pH, duration)	$\pm$
Reproducibility	$\pm$
Nonspecific staining	$+$
Shift in absorption maximum	$\pm$
Fading of dye	$-$

[a] $\pm$ indicates measurement will be either too high or too low; $-$ and $+$ indicate measurement is too low or too high, respectively.

that light scattering increases with shorter wavelengths. Furthermore, there is the problem of RNase treatment for determining DNA. Proteins also absorb at 260 mμ and must be taken in account. At the same time, one must not overlook the effect of hyperchromasia.

One of the most important sources of error is the absorption inhomogeneity of the object, that is, the *distributional error*. The laws of photometry hold only for pure solutions; biological systems are inhomogeneous objects with particles of different sizes and absorptions. All in-

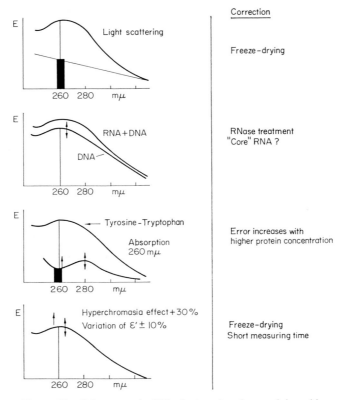

FIG. 6. Possible errors in UV photometry for nucleic acids.

struments must be constructed considering this aspect. The following ways have been chosen (Fig. 7):

(1) Keeping the measuring field so small that only homogeneous areas are measured. For this, the object has to be measured with a scanning system.

(2) Patau (12) has developed the two-wavelength method to avoid the distributional error (see also Garcia, 6a).

(3) In emission photometry, where the object serves as a light source, inhomogeneous distribution does not have to be taken into account (see Ruch (13b).

(4) In photographic colorimetry, which involves measurement of the silver content in solution, there is no error due to inhomogeneity.

(5) In the plug method (13) extensive error may be due to inhomogeneous distribution of chromophores. Only in cases of randomly distributed chromophores are the measurements correct.

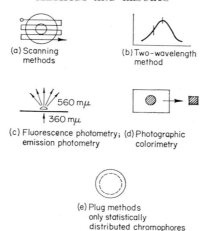

(a) Scanning
methods

(b) Two-wavelength
method

(c) Fluorescence photometry;
emission photometry

(d) Photographic
colorimetry

(e) Plug methods
only statistically
distributed chromophores

FIG. 7. Cytophotometric methods to avoid distributional error. See (a) Caspersson (*3*) (UMSP, photographic photometry); (b) Patau (*12*) and Ornstein (*11a*); (c) Rigler (*13a*), Ruch (*13c*), West (*22*) and Caspersson *et al.* (*3a*); (d) den Tonkelaar and van Duijn (*21*) and Kelly *et al.* (*8a*); (e) Pollister and Ris (*12a*).

Scanning instruments today have the broadest application. Different types of scanning systems have been used (Fig. 8). Scanning can be done by a mechanical scanner in the plane of the image (Deeley Instrument by Barr & Stroud), in which case the microscopic stage remains stationary. On the other hand, the biological object can be moved

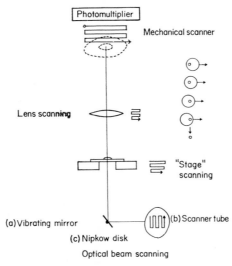

Photomultiplier

Mechanical scanner

Lens scanning

"Stage"
scanning

(a) Vibrating mirror

(b) Scanner tube

(c) Nipkow disk

Optical beam scanning

FIG. 8. Schematic representation of different scanning systems.

by shifting the microscopic stage (a system developed by Caspersson, *3*) or a scanning lens can be used for moving the biological object across the photomultiplier opening. During the past few years, more attention has been paid to optical beam scanning methods. Two systems have been developed: a scanner tube for the light source and a vibrating mirror in connection with a monochromator (see Montgomery, *11*).

All of these methods have various advantages and disadvantages, which are discussed using as examples the particular instruments with which we have had experience:

(1) The instrument from Barr & Stroud can only be used in visible light. Furthermore, only smears can be measured and the cells must not lie too closely together. Also, only staining reactions for cellular nuclei, the Feulgen reaction, for example, enable a measurement.

(2) The lens scanning system has been used only by Caspersson.

(3) The stage scanning method is realized in the Zeiss-UMSP. This method allows the broadest variation of application. It can be used in visible and in UV light.

(a) For photometry of sections in visible light a simple cytophotometer is used where measurements of the extinction are made from point to point in a cell, followed by calculation of the average after photometry and planimetry of cell nucleus.

FIG. 9. A self-constructed scanning cytophotometer (unpublished) with the scanning stage from the Zeiss UMSP.

(b) For automatic scanning purposes, a cytophotometer with a scanning stage of the type found on the Zeiss instrument was constructed (Fig. 9). This instrument has the advantage of allowing one to follow the measurement constantly during the entire scanning process.

(c) The Zeiss-UMSP for UV and visible light is used for measurements of the total content of absorbing material and for absorption spectra. The disadvantages found in using this instrument are that the scanning process is too slow and one cannot follow the scanning process during the measurement.

(4) Optical beam scanning system. We use an apparatus with a vibrating mirror which projects a small flying spot of monochromatic light over the cell. The advantage of this method is that the scanning process is very rapid and so living cells in tissue culture can be measured in UV light.

This review on instruments has shown that for different biological problems, various methods have to be applied. Special attention must be paid to the different possibilities of errors.

When instruments are tested, it is practical to use simple biological objects with relatively constant amounts of absorbing substances, such as sperms which have a haploid DNA content and cells having a diploid DNA content. Table IV shows the results of such measurements, which

TABLE IV

DNA CONTENT OF HAPLOID AND DIPLOID NUCLEI. COMPARISON
OF UV-CYTOPHOTOMETRIC AND CHEMICAL DETERMINATIONS

Species	Haploid (DNA $\times 10^{-12}$ g)		Diploid (DNA $\times 10^{-12}$ g)	
	UV	Chem.	UV	Chem.
Man	3.12	2.7	6.8	6.8
Bull	3.24	3.2	6.5	6.4
Rabbit	3.24	3.1	5.7	5.3–7.2
Rat	3.1	—	6.05	7.5
Rooster	1.5	1.3	3.3	2.4
Trout	2.5	2.5	5.4	5.3
Rana temporaria	—	—	8.8	8–9
Bufo viridis	5.3	—	12.1	—

agree very well with biochemical data (*14*). In Table V the dry weight determinations done with interference microscope (*18*) are seen. On the basis of the DNA determination with UV photometry, it is possible to

TABLE V

DRY WEIGHT (INTERFERENCE MICROSCOPY) AND PERCENTAGE OF DNA CONTENT
OF HAPLOID AND DIPLOID CELL NUCLEI

Species	Dry weight		Ratio dry weight to DNA	% DNA
	Sperm ($\times 10^{-12}$ g)	Thymus (erythrocytes) ($\times 10^{-12}$ g)		
Man	6.38	13.80	2.04	48
			2.02	49
Bull	8.09	14.40	2.49	40
			2.20	45
Rabbit	6.79	13.53	2.09	47
			2.35	42
Rat	6.27	11.85	2.01	49
			1.95	51
Rooster	2.49	4.93	1.56	63
			1.49	66
Trout	4.43	8.36	1.75	56
			1.53	65
Rana temporaria	—	21.55	2.43	41
Bufo viridis	—	18.03	1.48	67

calculate the percentage of DNA content of dry weight. These values also show good agreement with the biochemical data.

In simple biological objects the measuring data are comparatively easy to obtain and interpret. New problems arise if the measurements are done with mitotically active tissues. When comparing the mitotic cycle with the results of measurements, we can expect to obtain three different types of distributions of the measured values (Fig. 10).

(1) In mitotically inactive tissue, liver, for instance, diploid and tetraploid values were found, or only diploid cells, for example, the prickle cell layer of the epidermis.

(2) In mitotically active tissue, one must expect to find diploid and tetraploid cells and, in addition, cells with DNA values lying between diploid and tetraploid. These cells synthesize DNA in the S phase of the mitotic cycle. It is important to take into account that one cannot distinguish these cells from cells with an aneuploid chromosome number.

The problem of abnormal distribution of DNA values and chromosome aneuploidy is of great interest in cancer research. We have found that there is an abnormal distribution of DNA in human tumors with distribution patterns which can be compared with the chromosome stem line of tumor populations. Figure 11 shows an example of combined

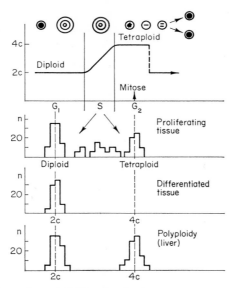

Fɪɢ. 10. Mitotic cycle and DNA distribution patterns of different tissues.

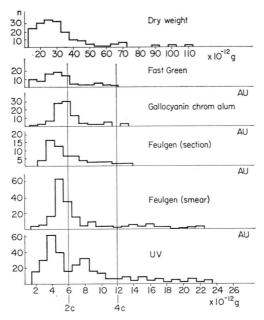

Fɪɢ. 11. Dry weight, histone protein content (Fast Green, pH 8.2), and DNA content of a bronchus carcinoma (oat cell carcinoma).

measurements on a human carcinoma (oat cell carcinoma) with measurements of the dry weight, the histone protein, and DNA content. DNA was estimated by three different methods. The nuclei have an average mass of approximately 25 to 30 $\times$ 10^{-12} g. Compared with these values, other cells of the bronchus have an average dry weight of approximately 40 $\times$ 10^{-12} g (16). The values of histone protein and DNA content are distributed in the hypodiploid region.

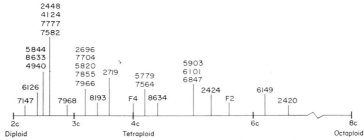

Fig. 12. Position of the DNA stem line of 30 human malignant tumors.

In Fig. 12 the positions of the stem line of 30 different human tumors are shown. Most of the tumors show a stem line different from the normal values. As opposed to malignant tumors (Fig. 13), benign tumors

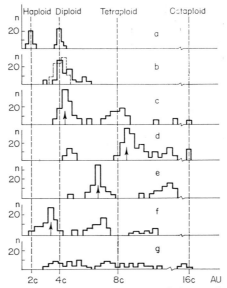

Fig. 13. DNA distribution pattern of (a) sperm and thymus lymphocytes; (b) adenoma (lung) and papilloma; (c,d) squamous cell carcinoma; (e) adenocarcinoma; (f) oat cell carcinoma; (g) undifferentiated carcinoma.

always have diploid values. In Fig. 13 it can also be seen that malignant tumors have a broader scattering of assessed values. This leads one to conclude that malignant tumors can be identified by an aneuploid DNA stem line. A regular DNA distribution, however, does not exclude a malignant tumor.

Regarding this conclusion, it will be most interesting to measure precancerous lesions. Carcinoma *in situ* of the uterine ectocervix has, contrary to the benign atypical epithelium, an aneuploid DNA stem line (Fig. 14). In 10 cases of carcinoma *in situ* (Fig. 15) this could be demon-

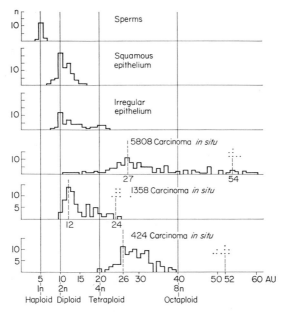

Fig. 14. DNA distribution pattern of normal ectocervix, epithelium dysplasia (irregular epithelium), and three cases of carcinoma *in situ*. Broken lines: DNA stem line.

strated. In cases of carcinoma *in situ* with attempt at differentiation and polymorphy of the cell nuclei, and in cases of basal cell hyperplasia no stem line was found. This DNA stem line could be found in all stages of progress in carcinoma *in situ* up to early invasive carcinoma (Fig. 16).

In a similar way we found that the intraalveolar cells of lung adenomatosis have the same atypical DNA distribution as the metastases in the lymph nodes (*19*).

These investigations seem to show that carcinoma *in situ* is a malignant epithelial alteration if the DNA content is taken into account. This

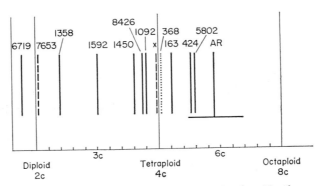

FIG. 15. DNA stem line of 13 cases of carcinoma *in situ*. Numbers and signs in the figure represent the registration number assigned to the different cases.

means that the problem of invasion of cancer cells depends on factors other than the atypical DNA distribution.

RNA distribution in carcinoma *in situ* also indicates the rapid growth rate of these epithelia. In normal epithelia only the basal cells have a high RNA concentration (Fig. 17a); in atypical epithelia of lower and

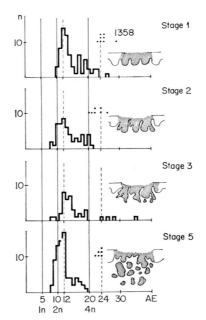

FIG. 16. DNA distribution pattern of carcinoma *in situ* and at different stages of invasion.

middle layers, the RNA concentration is increased (Fig. 17b), and in carcinoma *in situ* all layers are rich in RNA (Fig. 17c).

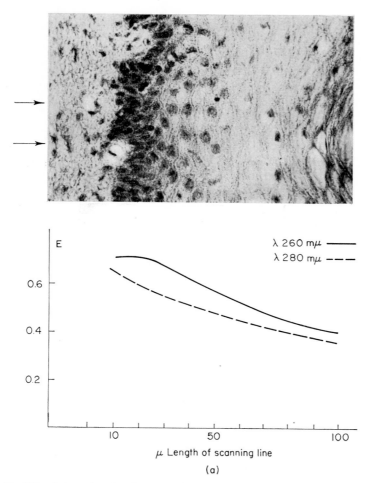

FIG. 17. UV photometry in the cytoplasm of (a) normal epithelium; See also following pages.

These measurements show that with the methods of quantitative histochemistry valuable results may be obtained. However, we agree that the amount of one substance is not a far-reaching result and qualitative deviations, for example, of the DNA and proteins of tumors, also have to be taken into consideration.

Indeed, there are indications that the hydrolysis curve of tumor cells

WALTER SANDRITTER

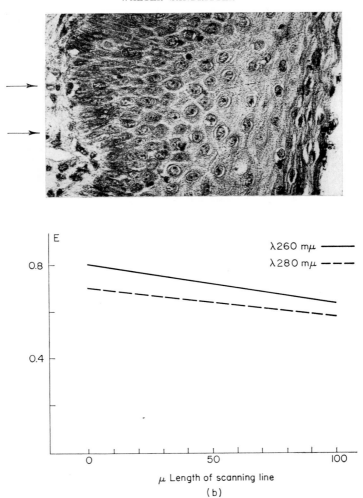

FIG. 17(b). UV photometry in the cytoplasm of dysplastic epithelium.

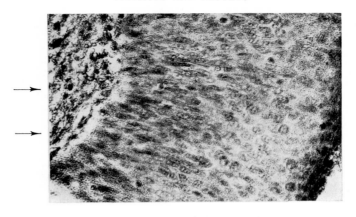

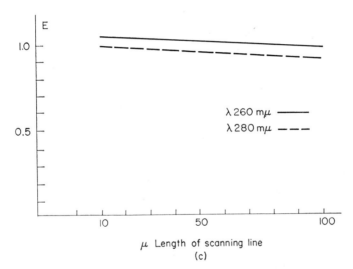

FIG. 17(c). UV photometry in the cytoplasm of carcinoma *in situ*.

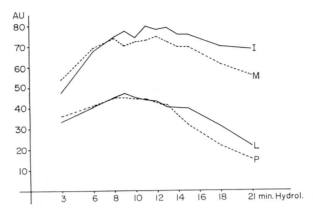

Fig. 18. Feulgen hydrolysis curve of (P) peritoneal mesothelial cells; (L) lymphocytes; (I) interphase cells of Ehrlich ascites tumor cells; (M) mitotic cells of
Ehrlich ascites tumor cells. AU = relative dyestuff content.

in the Feulgen reaction has a different course than in normal cells. Figure
18 demonstrates that in tumor cells the curve shows an inflection after
10 minutes. We presume that this atypical hydrolysis is related to a dis-
turbed euchromatin and heterochromatin ratio in tumor cells. This may
be more clearly shown if the hydrolysis curve is spread over a longer
time (Fig. 19). Then two phases of hydrolysis are seen. In the first
part, the euchromatin is hydrolyzed; in the second phase only the heterochromatin is stained. Both chromatins seem to react differently to hydrolysis.

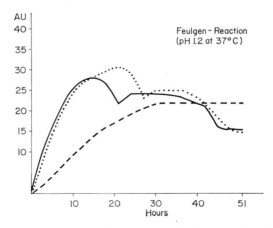

Fig. 19. Feulgen hydrolysis curve of liver cell nuclei (dotted line), thymus lymphocytes (solid line), and bull sperms (dashed line).

This review may have shown that the methods of quantitative histochemistry give some information on the chemical organization of the cell. On the other hand, one can see the difficulty and limitations on these methods.

The advantages and disadvantages of histochemistry become clear when one tries to compare them with biochemistry. Let us presume that we have any structured matter, for example, a cake with raisins. The biochemist can easily determine the chemical substances that are in the cake. He may also know that raisins are in the cake. The histochemist can, however, determine the topographical distribution of the raisins. It may be, however, that he does not know that they are raisins.

References

1. Bahr, G. F., and E. Zeitler, Study of mitochondria in rat liver. Quantitative electron microscopy. *J. Cell Biol.* **15**, 489–501 (1962).
1a. Beneke, G., this volume, pp. 107–136.
2. Caspersson, T., Über den chemischen Aufbau der Strukturen des Zellkerns. *Skand. Arch. Physiol.* **73**, Suppl. 8, 1–151 (1936).
3. Caspersson, T., "Cell Growth and Cell Function." Norton, New York, 1950.
3a. Caspersson, T., G. Lomakka, and R. Rigler, Jr., Registrierender Fluoreszenzmikrospektrograph zur Bestimmung der Primär- und Sekundärfluoreszenz verschiedener Zellsubstanzen. *Acta Histochem.* Suppl. VI, 123–126 (1965).
4. Dhéré, C., Sur l'absorption des rayons ultraviolets par l'acide nucléique extrait de la levure de bière. *Compt. Rend. Soc. Biol.* **1**, 34 (1906).
5. Engström, A., Microradiography. *Acta Radiol.* **31**, 503–521 (1949).
6. Feulgen, R., and H. Rossenbeck, Mikroskopisch-chemischer Nachweis einer Nukleinsäure vom Typus Thymusnukleinsäure und die darauf beruhende elektive Färbung von Zellkernen in mikroskopischen Präparaten. *Z. Physiol. Chem.* **135**, 203–248 (1924).
6a. Garcia, A. M., and R. Iorio, this volume, pp. 215–237.
7. Hale, A. J., "The Interference Microscope in Biological Research." Livingstone, Edinburgh and London, 1958.
8. Jobst, K., and W. Sandritter, Über den quantitativen histochemischen Nachweis von basischen Kernproteinen mit Gallocyaninchromalaun. *Histochemie* **4**, 277–285 (1964).
8a. Kelly, J. W., W. A. Clabaugh, and H. K. Hawkins, Photographic cytophotometry with a dual-microscope. II. Microscope assembly and film-dye extractions. *J. Histochem. Cytochem.* **12**, 600–607 (1964).
9. Köhler, A., and M. von Rohr, Eine mikrophotographische Einrichtung für ultraviolettes Licht. *Z. Instrumentenk.* **24**, 341–349 (1904).
10. Miescher, F., "Die histochemischen und physiologischen Arbeiten." Vogel, Leipzig, 1897.
11. Montgomery, P. O'B., Scanning techniques in biology and medicine. *Ann. N.Y. Acad. Sci.* **97**, Art. 2, 329–526 (1962).
11a. Ornstein, L., The distributional error in microspectrophotometry. *Lab. Invest.* **1**, 250–265 (1952).

12. Patau, K., Absorption microphotometry of irregular-shaped objects. *Chromosoma* **5**, 341–362 (1952).

12a. Pollister, A. W., and H. Ris, Nucleoprotein determination in cytological preparations. *Cold Spring Harbor Symp. Quant. Biol.* **XII**, 147–157 (1947).

13. Pollister, A. W., and L. Ornstein. *In* "Analytical Cytology" (R. C. Mellors, ed.), Chapter 1. McGraw-Hill, New York, 1955.

13a. Rigler, R., Jr., Mikroabsorptions- und Emissionsmessungen an Akridinorange-Nukleinsäure-Komplexen. *Acta Histochem.* Suppl. VI, 127–134 (1965).

13b. Ruch, F., this volume, p. 281–294.

13c. Ruch, F., Fluoreszenzphotometrie. *Acta Histochem.* Suppl. VI, 117–121 (1965).

14. Sandritter, W., D. Müller, and O. Gensecke, Ultraviolettmikrospektrophotometrische Messungen des Nukleinsäuregehaltes von haploiden und diploiden Zellen. *Acta Histochem.* **10**, 139–154 (1960).

15. Sandritter, W., D. Müller, and O. Mantz, Zur Histochemie der Cytomegalie. *Frankf. Z. Pathol.* **70**, 589–597 (1960).

16. Sandritter, W., H. G. Schiemer and W. Alt, Das Interferenzmikroskop im Dienste der Cytologie und Krebsforschung. *Klin. Wochschr.* **38**, 590–595 (1960).

17. Sandritter, W., H. G. Schiemer, H. Kraus, and U. Dörrien, Interferenzmikroskopische Untersuchungen über das Wachstum von Einzelzellen (HeLa-Zellen) in der Gewebekultur. *Frankf. Z. Pathol.* **70**, 271–299 (1960).

18. Sandritter, W., H. G. Schiemer, and H. Uhlig, Interferenzmikroskopische Trockengewichtsbestimmungen an haploiden und diploiden Zellen. *Acta Histochem.* **10**, 155–172 (1960).

19. Seidel, A., and W. Sandritter, Cytophotometrische Messungen des DNS-Gehaltes eines Lungenadenoms und einer malignen Lungenadenomatose. *Z. Krebsforsch.* **65**, 555–559 (1963).

20. Smith, F. H., Microscope interferometry. *Research* **8**, 385–395 (1955).

21. Tonkelaar, E. M. den, and P. van Duijn, Photographic colorimetry as a quantitative cytochemical method. I. Principles and practice of the method. *Histochemie* **4**, 1–9 (1964).

22. West, S. S., Fluorescence microspectroscopy of mouse leukocytes supravitally stained with acridine orange. *Acta Histochem.* Suppl. VI, 135–156 (1965).

FEULGEN MICROSPECTROPHOTOMETRY AND ITS CORRELATION WITH OTHER CYTOCHEMICAL METHODS

Arthur J. Hale

PATHOLOGY DEPARTMENT,
ST. THOMAS'S HOSPITAL MEDICAL SCHOOL,
LONDON, ENGLAND

A considerable amount of work has gone into the development of the theory and technique of microspectrophotometry in the visible wavelengths of light since the first publications appeared (*1, 91, 103, 131, 132*). Excellent reviews of the methods of measuring the amount of absorbing material in stained nuclei have been given by Davies and Walker (*28*), Pollister and Ornstein (*93*), and Walker and Richards (*140*). The original methods of measurement were effective in establishing the concept of constancy of relation between amount of DNA and the karyotype, but nevertheless they were inaccurate. In retrospect it may be that they showed constancy because they were too inaccurate to detect inconstancy. The main reasons for inaccuracy were the heterogeneous distribution of the absorbing material in nuclei prepared in a conventional manner, the high density of parts of these nuclei, the scattering effect of particulate nucleoprotein of high refractive index lying in a medium of lower refractive index, and out of focus effects, sampling errors, and light flare in the measuring system. These errors have been reduced from the original values of a coefficient of variation of ± 20–30% to around $\pm 5\%$ by detecting them as in the two-wavelength method (*77, 79*) and then applying corrections or by eliminating them as with scanning systems (*16, 31, 49*). These methods have been compared, and it has been found that they measured the same cells with a coefficient of variation of 3.9% (*74*). This means that differences of 10% between cells detected by these methods are significant.

The apparatus designed by Deeley has been available commercially for 6 years and has been used in many laboratories throughout the world. Its advantages are that it is accurate and extremely rapid. Approximately 25 nuclei can be measured and the final data on their individual total absorption calculated in 1 hour with a degree of reproducibility of about 5%. We have used it since its introduction.

Figure 1 shows a line diagram of the layout of the instrument and

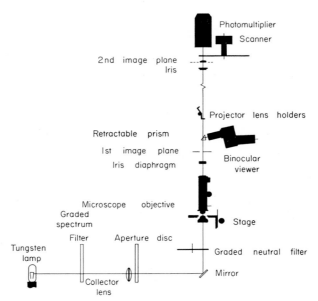

FIG. 1. Schematic arrangement of integrating microdensitometer.

Fig. 2 a photograph of the current model. The light source can be either a mercury arc with a feedback stabilizing circuit or a tungsten ribbon lamp operated from a high-stability, constant-voltage supply. The light from these sources may be fed into a monochromator which directs its output into the field lens. Beyond the field lens is a series of swing-out field stops of a size chosen to match the area of the field of view obtained with the objectives supplied. The light emerging from the stop that is selected then passes through a rotatable, continuous interference filter, which can be swung to an "cut" position, and which has a calibration scale to select the approximate wavelength required; the light is then deflected upward by a prism through a rotatable, continuous neutral filter. This filter is used to control the intensity of light passing through the microdensitometer. The filtered light enters the microscope condenser which can be of conventional type or can have a conical top lens essential for crushing suitably prepared specimens. The microscope objective and body tube are of conventional design. At the top of the body tube there is a series of swing-out circular apertures which can be selected to enclose the image of the object to be measured and to isolate it from adjacent objects. Above this aperture position there is a prism which

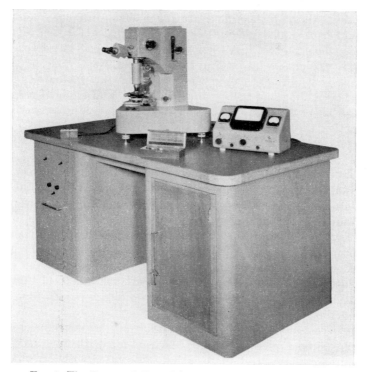

FIG. 2. The Barr and Stroud integrating microdensitometer.

deflects the image to the binocular eyepiece. This prism is automatically removed from the viewing position when the scanning system is running. When the prism is removed, the image passes upward, is deflected to the horizontal by another prism, passes through a projection lens which can be varied in magnification, is deflected downward by another prism, passes through an iris diaphragm, and falls on the scanning system. The iris diaphragm is used to reduce the scanned area to a size commensurate with the size of the image being measured and serves to reduce stray light in the system.

The scanner is mechanical and causes a small aperture to fly across the final image plane along 90 parallel lines in 3 seconds. The light passing through this scanning aperture falls on the end-window photomultiplier. The light signal is amplified, the contribution from each spot is added up, converted from transmission to density, and the total integrated density across the image of the object is recorded on the final reading meter immediately as the scanning mechanism comes to rest. To reduce statistical error three readings of the object and three readings of a closely adjacent clear field are taken. The difference between the object and background readings is the integrated absorption of the object. This whole process takes less than one minute. The reproducibility on a single Feulgen-stained sperm head is about $\pm 3\%$.

There is an additional meter which monitors the photomultiplier output during scanning and is used in setting up the instrument and detecting faults. There is also an extinction switch which permits one to determine whether the object has a density sufficiently low (< 1.0) to ensure accurate measurement. This switch can also be used to reduce the contribution of background light to the measurements.

To obtain optimal accuracy the specimen should be flattened in some way so that all parts of it come into focus and, in addition, areas of high density are made more transparent. One way of doing this is to fix wet smears made on a coverslip by freeze-substitution, stain them, flood the specimen with immersion oil, and lower a thin, pliable film of transparent cellulose or plastic onto the immersion oil. When inverted, this preparation can be clipped onto a holder on the microscope stage and the cells can be flattened by racking up the condenser with a conical top lens attached to it to crush the cell between the soft transparent film and the hard coverslip (29).

The low cost, high speed, and accuracy of the instrument make it popular for simple microphotometric measurement. In its standard form it is unsuitable for spectral analysis, but when fitted with a monochromator such analyses are possible.

The results are expressed in units of relative amount of stain, and if absolute amounts of the stained cellular component are desired then the usual form of calibration must be used. The absolute amount of DNA which can be measured in this way is about 0.5×10^{-13} g.

The majority of quantitative cytochemical studies have been on the amount of DNA in the cells. One of the important principles of cellular biology is that the amount of DNA in a cell is a constant with respect to the karyotype of the species. This amount will be constant in all tissues within the species, apart from polyploidy and polyteny. This principle was partly proven by biochemical and partly by cytochemical investigations. Various exceptions to it have been reported in mouse epidermis (78), in uterine and vaginal cells during the menstrual cycle (138), in the thyroid (105–107), in the effect of growth hormone on liver cells

(34), in compensatory hypertrophy of the kidney (35, 36), in the effect of low temperatures on plant nuclei (57), in liver (61), in the ovary of rats (136), and in the adrenal of rats exposed to cold (137). Many of these observations have been contradicted by others (2, 4, 22, 24, 37, 38, 90). The main difference between the data presented by these two groups is that the former only presents mean values for the samples of the cell population (the exceptions to this are La Cour et al. and Viola), whereas the latter group shows histograms. A skew distribution in a histogram will increase the mean value of the population forming the histogram. Ever since the work of Swift (132) it has been well established that proliferating cells synthesize and double their DNA prior to mitosis, and it is probable that the majority of exceptions to the rule of DNA constancy are explicable as a rise of the mean value due to synthesis prior to cell division in an appreciable number of cells in the population. If an exception to constancy of DNA is to be proven, then the following criteria must be satisfied (140): (1) The effect of synthesis of DNA must be eliminated; (2) the cells must have the normal karyotype for that species; (3) technical errors of measurement must be absent; (4) the cells being examined must have the same cytochemical reaction characteristics as those with which they are being compared. These criteria have rarely been satisfied in any quantitative investigation of DNA content.

With the development of the newer, more accurate methods of measuring the absorbance of single cells, it appears that more comparisons should be made of the amount of DNA in different cells. If a difference is found using these methods, then care must be taken in interpreting its meaning. This is illustrated by the work from my laboratory on the possible significance of the 10% difference in absorbance between human leukocytes and cervical epithelial cells reported by Atkin and Richards (5, 6). An investigation of the effect of time of hydrolysis, sulfite content and pH of the Schiff solution, and comparison with other cells showed that the mature polymorphonuclear leukocytes and small lymphocytes had a measured amount of Feulgen stain approximately 10% less than the nonsynthesizing ($2c : G_1$) cells of the bone marrow (41). That this reduction is not due to pyknosis and loss of DNA is shown by the ability of the small lymphocytes to enlarge their nucleus and cytoplasm, and transform themselves into cells capable of synthesizing DNA (25). It is possible that the measured reduction in the amount of Feulgen stain is a reflection of the compact manner in which the nucleoprotein is packed in the mature leukocytes. When the nucleus expands prior to DNA synthesis in culture, its measured Feulgen absorbance reverts to the higher normal diploid value.

The relation between karyotype and amount of DNA in the nucleus has been investigated in some detail. Richards *et al.* (*98*) showed a good correlation between chromosome number and amount of DNA in ascites tumors. In a later paper (*100*) they found in a variety of human cancers that most tumors contained more than the expected amount of DNA compared with their chromosome numbers. This could be explained, however, by the supernumerary chromosomes being larger than normal. The relation of chromosome size and number has been investigated (*104*) in the roots of two varieties of hyacinth which have specific chromosomal differences of a size amenable to investigation. It was found that the difference in DNA content between the two types of cells was proportional to the lengths of the chromosomes.

Comparison of the amount of DNA in the normal number 21 chromosome in man and the Ph_1 chromosome in the leukocytes in chronic myeloid leukemia, which may arise by deletion of part of the normal 21 chromosomes, has been made (*108*). The authors claimed that there is a diminished amount of DNA in the Ph_1 chromosome, but the technical difficulties of measuring accurately the amount of DNA in such a small, dense object are such that they tend toward giving an underestimate. In addition, the physical arrangement of the DNA in such a condensed structure may give an absorption coefficient which is different from that of extended DNA. Thus, although the amount measured may be less, the method of measurement may still be in error.

The correlation of the results of Feulgen microspectrophotometry with pathological conditions has been extensive. The large amount of work carried out by Leuchtenberger and her colleagues has been reviewed (*59, 60*). It extends in man to prostatic hypertrophy, precancerous lesions in skin, rectal polyps, malignant tumors of 14 organs, viral infections in skin, kidney, adrenal, seminal vesicle, and lung, and to the range of spermatogenic cells in infertility. Mellors (*73*) presented a comprehensive review of cancer cytochemistry which dealt with DNA distribution in a number of human cancers. The most comprehensive papers are those of Atkin and Richards (*5, 6, 99*), who investigated a variety of human tumors, but dealt mainly with those of the uterus and the relation of the DNA distribution to clinical progress and treatment. The earliest studies were those of Stowell (*131*) on 20 human tumors, and Carnes, Weissman, and Goldberg (*15*). Bader (*7, 8*) has also investigated several tumors. The distribution of DNA in human large intestinal polyps, adenocarcinomas, and a few other carcinomas has been reported (*128–130*). In addition, Stich (*127*) has also investigated rat hepatomas. Meek (*71*) has found that only in two cases out of ten was there an appreciable difference in the amount of DNA in the primary and secondary sites of human breast cancer. A comparison of DNA content in cystic adenoma and malignant pulmonary adenomatosis has been made (*120*). Lapham (*58*) has classified glioblastoma multiform according to the DNA distribution, and others have investigated human carcinoma in the cervix (*19, 55, 96*) and hypertrophied cardiac nuclei (*113*).

Investigations of the DNA content of human leukocytes have been numerous (*23, 41–44, 65–68, 80, 83, 85, 87–89, 131*). Mauri *et al.* (*69*) have investigated Hodgkin's disease, and Soldati and Torelli (*125*) reticulosarcoma. Reisner and Korson (*97*) and Marinone (*68*) have analyzed the erythroblast series. Several workers (*40, 81, 84*) have investigated animal leukocytes.

Changes in the DNA content of animal tissues have been reviewed (*60, 73*). Mouse cervical carcinomas (*114*) and ependymomas and rhabdomyosarcomas (*76*) have been investigated, and ascites tumors have received particular attention (*17, 60, 70, 72, 98, 135*). Cells in tissue culture have also been examined in detail (*13, 60, 116, 117*), particularly by Chèvremont's group, where spectrophotometry has been combined with other methods of analysis (*21*).

The majority of these investigations has been concerned with the DNA content of the cells and its relation to DNA synthesis or to changes in the karyotype. The value of such a limited approach is extended by examining other features of the Feulgen reaction or by comparing the amount of DNA with other parameters in the cell.

Now that the techniques are well established and the cytochemical staining methods which can be utilized with them have been extended, we should see a period of analytical quantitative cytochemistry developing (analytical in the technical sense that the reaction characteristics of the cytochemical methods can be analyzed). This has been done by Swift (*133*), Walker and Richards (*139, 140*), and Sandritter and Böhm (*110*) for the hydrolysis curve for the Feulgen reaction, and by Moses (*75*), Sibatani and Naora (*124*), Sibatani (*121–123*), Kasten (*50–53*), Barka and Ornstein (*10*), and Kasten, Kiefer, and Sandritter (*54*) for the effect of cytochemical variables on the absorption curve. In addition, other cytochemical methods have been studied. The alkaline fast green method for histone (*3*), the Millon reaction for tyrosine (*91, 92, 102, 115*), the Sakaguchi reaction for arginine (*64*), the naphthol yellow S method for protein (*32*), the Gallocyanin-chromalum method for DNA (*111*), the methyl green method for DNA (*56*), the dihydroxy-dinaphthyl coupling method for sulphydryl and disulphide groups (*14, 18, 134*), and the methylene blue method for nucleic acids (*33*) can all be used. Gahrton (*39*) has measured the carbohydrate content of neutrophile leukocytes stained by the periodic acid–Schiff method. In this way, correlations of the tyrosine and DNA content of canine liver cells (*24*) and the histone, non-histone protein, and DNA content of human leukocytes, normal and leukemic, have been studied (82, 86). The amount of protein and DNA in the abnormal cells in Hodgkin's disease (87) and in reticulosarcoma (125) have been reported. Meek (72) has investigated the protein and DNA content of ascites tumor cells. Comparisons of the amounts of Feulgen, Fast Green, and other stains in cells (94, 95) and of the ultraviolet absorption and the dry weight of cells measured by interference microscopy (17, 23, 30, 73, 101, 109, 112, 117–119) have been made.

These studies of the amounts of different nuclear components in similar samples of cell populations have yielded useful information, but the significance of the variations in different components is greatly increased if each can be measured in the same cell. Bloch and Godman (12) did this for histone and DNA of the same cells. In this way we have in our laboratory made detailed comparisons of the grain counts in autoradiographs over nuclei labeled with radioactive precursors of DNA and the amount of DNA in the same nuclei measured by Feulgen microspectrophotometry, as Looney (62, 63) has done for regenerating liver.

Our approach has been to label cells with radioactive precursors of DNA (usually thymidine, cytidine, and formate) under strictly specified conditions and then prepare smears. The smears are stained by the Feulgen method in which the acid hydrolysis also serves to remove all low molecular weight labeled precursors of DNA and the RNA. The smears are then covered with autoradiographic film which is exposed and developed under standard conditions. A photographic map of the smear is made, and using this map each cell is identified and numbered, the grain counts of each radioactive cell recorded, and the position of each nonradioactive cell indicated. The silver grains are then removed from the film; using the same map, the cells numbered on it are identified in the smear and the amount of DNA in them measured. Thus the DNA content of a cell can be correlated with its radioactivity measured as the number of grains overlying it. Several experiments to establish the validity of the method have been carried out.

The value of such a double analysis is best illustrated by discussing the type of problem that can be investigated. It is well known that the period of synthesis of DNA (the S phase) is related to the total generation time of a proliferating population of cells in the manner shown in Fig. 3. During the S phase the cell doubles its DNA content from the postmitotic (2c or G_1 value) to the premitotic amount (4c or G_2 value). At the end of G_2 the cell divides and the daughter cells enter the G_1 phase. The durations of S, G_2, and M in mammalian cells have been found to be approximately 6–12 hours, $\frac{1}{2}$–4 hours, and $\frac{1}{2}$–1$\frac{1}{2}$ hours, respectively. Knowing this, one can predict what the relation will be if a radioactive precursor is made available to all cells at different points in progression through the phases. The prediction will depend upon the time for which the precursor was available to the cells and the duration of each phase. If all cells faithfully follow the type of S curve shown in Fig. 3 and

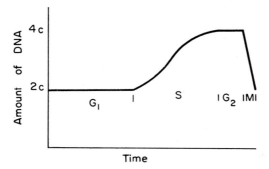

Fig. 3. The relation of the DNA synthetic (S), the postsynthetic (G₂), the mitotic (M), and postdivisional (G₁) phases of the cycle of cell proliferation.

if the precursor is available for a time which is short relative to the duration of S, then there will be a very simple relation of grain count to amount of DNA in single cells lying at different points on the S curve. Our experimental results did not fit the predicted pattern; thus we investigated variables such as use of different precursors, use of different isotopes, the effect of time of availability of precursor, the use of different cell systems, breakdown of precursor by cells, and so forth. We compared normal and leukemic leukocytes in this way and acquired useful information on the similarity and difference of results obtained. We have thus been able to demonstrate the variations in rate of uptake of tritiated thymidine, tritiated deoxycytidine monophosphate, and formate-C^{14} into normal human leukocytes induced to proliferate in culture, the lymphocytes from human thoracic duct, the atypical mononuclears in infectious mononucleosis, acute and chronic leukemic cells, regenerating liver cells in the rat, and mouse thymocytes, and to relate these variations to the increase in the amount of DNA prior to mitosis (25, 26, 45–48). Using Feulgen spectrophotometry, autoradiography, and fluorescence microscopy, the relation between DNA synthesis, protein synthesis, and antibody production can also be studied (9). Similarly, Rasch et al. (94) and Meek (78) have examined the relation between amounts of protein and DNA in plant tumors and ascites tumors, respectively, Ringertz (101) the relation between DNA and histone in irradiated cells, and Bassleer (11) the relation between the total mass of nuclei and the amount of DNA in cultured fibroblasts.

The questions which can be answered by such methods of double or triple analysis of the same cells are the following.

(1) What relations exist between the time and rate of synthesis of the components being studied?

(2) How do the absolute amounts of components being studied compare?

(3) How do experimental conditions vary these relations?

(4) How does the presence of one component influence the cytochemical reaction characteristics of the other?

(5) How do the cyclic changes in the amounts of any of these components vary with the phases of cell replication?

(6) What variations in these relations exist between different cell types?

Yet another way in which useful information can be obtained from quantitative cytochemical studies is that proposed by Walker (139). He pointed out that from a histogram of the distribution of DNA in a random sample of a proliferating population of cells one can deduce the time curve of synthesis of DNA provided that the cell population is homogeneous, that a large percentage of the cells sampled are participating in the proliferation, and that there is an equal increment of DNA with time at all stages of synthesis. There also should not be arrest of cells at any phase in the cell replication cycle. This approach has been used by Richards et al. (98) and Smith et al. (126) to obtain time curves of DNA synthesis. The biggest limitation of the method is that it is frequently not possible to estimate the number of cells in the G_1 phase that are taking part in the cell replication cycle but cannot be detected because they are in G_1.

Now that the apparatus required for such investigations is available commercially this type of approach will be more commonly followed. The information to be obtained using it is unique and forces one to look at classic cytological problems from the point of view of cell biology. It may seem astonishing to some that amounts of materials as small as 10^{-12} g can be measured with great accuracy within a single cell. This type of cytochemistry is, however, only in its infancy, and the introduction of new analytical techniques such as electron-probe X-ray emission analysis (27) and secondary ion emission microscopy (20) will considerably extend its scope in the next few years.

REFERENCES

1. Alfert, M., Cytochemical study of ovogenesis and cleavage in the mouse. J. Cellular Comp. Physiol. 36, 381–409 (1950).

2. Alfert, M., H. A. Bern, and R. H. Kahn, Hormonal influence on nuclear synthesis. *Acta Anat.* **23**, 185–205 (1955).
3. Alfert, M., and I. I. Geschwind, A selective staining method for the basic proteins of cell nuclei. *Proc. Natl. Acad. Sci. U.S.* **39**, 991–999 (1953).
4. Alfert, M., and H. Swift, Nuclear DNA constancy: A critical evaluation of some exceptions reported by Lison and Pasteels. *Exptl. Cell Res.* **5**, 455–460 (1953).
5. Atkin, N. B., and B. M. Richards, Deoxyribonucleic acid in human tumors as measured by microspectrophotometry of Feulgen stain. *Brit. J. Cancer* **10**, 769–786 (1956).
6. Atkin, N. B., B. M. Richards, and A. J. Ross, The deoxyribonucleic acid content of carcinoma of uterus. *Brit. J. Cancer* **13**, 773–787 (1959).
7. Bader, S., Distribution of deoxyribonucleic acid in tumor nuclei. *Proc. Soc. Exptl. Biol. Med.* **82**, 312–315 (1953).
8. Bader, S., A cytochemical study of the stem cell concept in specimens of a human ovarian tumor. *J. Biophys. Biochem. Cytol.* **5**, 217–229 (1959).
9. Balfour, B. M., E. H. Cooper, and E. S. Meek, Deoxyribonucleic acid content of antibody-containing cells in the rat lymph node. *Nature* **206**, 686–687 (1965).
10. Barka, T., and L. Ornstein, Some observations on the reaction of Schiff reagent with aldehydes. *J. Histochem. Cytochem.* **8**, 208–218 (1960).
11. Bassleer, R., Nouvelles recherches concernant les synthèsis de protéines nucléaires et d'acides désoxyribonucléiques au cours de la préparation à la mitose. *Compt. Rend.* **259**, 2683–2686 (1964).
12. Bloch, D. P., and G. C. Godman, A microphotometric study of the synthesis of deoxyribonucleic acid and nuclear histone. *J. Biophys. Biochem. Cytol.* **1**, 17–24 (1955).
13. Boyer, G. S., C. Leuchtenberger, and H. S. Ginsberg, Cytological and cytochemical studies of HeLa cells infected with adenociruses. *J. Exptl. Med.* **105**, 195–216 (1957).
14. Cafruny, E. J., H. S. Di Stefano, and A. Farah, Cytophotometric determination of protein-bound sulfhydryl groups. *J. Histochem. Cytochem.* **3**, 354–359 (1955).
15. Carnes, W. H., N. Weissman, and B. Goldberg, Desoxyribonucleic acid (DNA) content of tumor cells determined microphotometrically. *Federation Proc.* **11**, 410 (1952).
16. Caspersson, T. O., G. Lomakka, and G. Svensson, A coordinated set of instruments for optical quantitative high resolution cytochemistry. *Exptl. Cell Res.* Suppl. **4**, 9–24 (1957).
17. Caspersson, T. O., E. Klein, and N. R. Ringertz, Cytochemical studies on some effects of radiation on three ascites tumors. *Exptl. Cell Res* **18**, 857–862 (1958).
18. Caspersson, T. O., and L. Revesz, Cytochemical measurement of protein sulphydryls in cell lines of different radiosensitivity. *Nature* **199**, 153–155 (1963).
19. Caspersson, T. O., Quantitative cytochemical studies on normal, malignant, premalignant and atypical cell populations from the human uterine cervix. *Acta Cytol.* **8**, 45–60 (1964).
20. Castaing, R., B. Jouffrey, and G. Slodzian, Sur les possibilités d'analyse locale d'un echantillon par utilisation de son emission ionique secondaire. *Compt. Rend.* **251**, 1010–1012 (1960).
21. Chèvremont, M., Le mécanisme de l'action antimitotique *Pathol. Biol. Semaine Hop.* [N.S.] **9**, 973–1004 (1961).
22. Chèvremont, M., R. Bassleer, and E. Baeckeland, Nouvelles recherches sur les acides désoxyribonucleiques dans des cultures de fibroblastes refroidies puis réchauffées. *Arch. Biol. (Liege)* **72**, 501–524 (1961).

23. Christopherson, W. M., W. L. Broghamer, and F. J. Swartz, Deoxyribonucleic acid and anhydrous nuclear mass values in leukemia and normal lymphocytes. *Am. J. Pathol.* **42,** 337–344 (1963).
24. Cole, J. W., C. Leuchtenberger, P. Doolin, A. Kutsakis, and A. McKalen, Cellular changes during surgical stress. *Surgery* **40,** 113–120 (1956).
25. Cooper, E. H., P. Barkhan, and A. J. Hale, Observations on the proliferation of human leucocytes cultured with phytohaemagglutinin. *Brit. J. Haematol.* **9,** 101–111 (1963).
26. Cooper, E. M., A. J. Hale, and J. D. Milton, Studies on the kinetics of the proliferation of atypical mononuclears in infectious mononucleosis. *Acta Haematol.* In press.
27. Cosslett, V. E., Scanning electron and x-ray microscopy. *Ann. N.Y. Acad. Sci.* **97,** 464–481 (1962).
28. Davies, H. G., and P. M. B. Walker, Microspectrophotometry of living and fixed cells. *Progr. Biophys. Biophys. Chem.* **3,** 195–236 (1953).
29. Davies, H. G., M. H. F. Wilkins, and R. G. H. B. Boddy, Cell crushing: A technique for greatly reducing errors in microspectrometry. *Exptl. Cell Res.* **6,** 550–553 (1954).
30. Davies, H. G., M. H. F. Wilkins, J. Chayen, and L. F. La Cour, The use of the interference microscope to determine dry mass in living cells and as a quantitative cytochemical method. *Quart. J. Microscop. Sci.* **95,** 271–304 (1954).
31. Deeley, E. M., An integrating microdensitometer for biological cells. *J. Sci. Instr.* **32,** 263–267 (1955).
32. Deitch, A. D., Microspectrophotometric study of the binding of the anionic dye, Naphthol Yellow S, by tissue sections and by purified proteins. *Lab. Invest.* **4,** 324–351 (1955).
33. Deitch, A. D., A method for the cytophotometric estimation of nucleic acids using methylene blue. *J. Histochem. Cytochem.* **12,** 451–461 (1964).
34. Di Stefano, H. S., H. F. Diermeier, and J. Tepperman, Effects of growth hormone on nucleic acid and protein content of rat liver cells. *Endocrinology* **57,** 158–167 (1955).
35. Fautrez, J., G. Cavalli, and E. Pisi, Variation in the amounts of deoxyribonucleic acid in the cell nuclei and its correlation with mitotic activity. *Nature* **175,** 684–685 (1955).
36. Fautrez, J., E. Pisi, and G. Cavalli, Activité mitotique provoquée par la thiourée et teneur en acide désoxyribonucléique de la cellule hépatique. *Exptl. Cell Res.* **9,** 189–192 (1955).
37. Franck, G., Étude historadiographique des acides désoxyribonucléiques au cours de l'hypertrophie compensatrice du rein chez le rat blanc. *Compt. Rend.* **251,** 1300–1308 (1960).
38. Franck, G., Étude du métabolisime et de la synthèse des acides désoxyribonucléiques au cours de l'hypertrophie compensatirise du rein chez le rat jeune, par cytophotométric, caryometric et historadiographie. *Arch. Biol.* (*Liege*) **71,** 489–525 (1960).
39. Gahrton, G., Microspectrophotometric quantitation of the periodic acid–Schiff (PAS) reaction in human neutrophil leukocytes based on a model system of glycogen microdroplets. *Exptl. Cell Res.* **34,** 488–506 (1964).
40. Garcia, A. M., Studies on DNA in leucocytes and related cells of mammals. *Acta Histochem.* **17,** 230–245 and 246–258 (1964).
41. Hale, A. J., The leucocyte as a possible exception to the theory of DNA constancy. *J. Pathol. Bacteriol.* **85,** 311–326 (1963).

42. Hale, A. J., and S. J. Wilson, The deoxyribonucleic acid content of leukocytes in normal and leukemic human blood. *J. Pathol. Bacteriol.* **77**, 605–614 (1959).
43. Hale, A. J., and S. J. Wilson, The deoxyribonucleic acid content of the nuclei of leukaemic leukocytes. *Lancet* i, 577–578 (1960).
44. Hale, A. J., and S. J. Wilson, The deoxyribonucleic acid content of the leuko-cytes of human blood, bone marrow and lymph glands. *J. Pathol. Bacteriol.* **82**, 483–501 (1961).
45. Hale, A. J., and E. H. Cooper, DNA synthesis in infectious mononucleosis and acute leukemia. *Acta Haematol.* **29**, 257–266 (1963).
46. Hale, A. J., and E. H. Cooper, Studies on DNA replication in leukaemic and non-leukaemic leukocytes. *In* "*Current Research* in Leukaemia," pp. 95–107. Cambridge Univ. Press, London and New York, 1965.
47. Hale, A. J., E. H. Cooper, and J. D. Milton, Variability in grain count/DNA relation in mouse thymocytes labelled with thymidine. *Life Sciences* **4**, 509–513 (1965).
48. Hale, A. J., E. H. Cooper, and J. D. Milton, Studies of the incorporation of pyrimidines into DNA in single leukaemic and other proliferating leucocytes. *Brit. J. Haematol.* **11**, 144–161 (1965).
49. Jansen, M. T., A simple scanning cytophotometer. *Histochemie* **2**, 342–347 (1961).
50. Kasten, F. H., Stability of the Feulgen-deoxyribonucleic acid absorption curve *in situ* with variation in nuclear protein content and other factors. *J. Histochem. Cytochem.* **4**, 462–470 (1956).
51. Kasten, F. H., The Feulgen-deoxyribonucleic acid absorption curve in normal and tumorous tissues. *J. Histochem. Cytochem.* **5**, 398–402 (1957).
52. Kasten, F. H., The Feulgen-DNA absorption curve *in situ*. *Histochemie* **1**, 123–150 (1958).
53. Kasten, F. H., The chemistry of Schiff's reagent. *Intern. Rev. Cytol.* **10**, 1–100 (1960).
54 Kasten, F. H., G. Kiefer, and W. Sandritter, Bleaching of Feulgen stained nuclei and alteration of absorption curve after continuous exposure to visible light in a cytophotometer. *J. Histochem. Cytochem.* **10**, 547–555 (1962).
55. Kother, L., and W. Sandritter, Über den DNS-Gehalt des Carcinoma *in situ*. *Gynaecologia* **157**, 9–19 (1964).
56. Kurnick, N. B., The quantitative estimation of desoxyribosenucleic acid based on methyl green staining. *Exptl. Cell Res.* **1**, 151–158 (1950).
57. La Cour, L. F., E. M. Deeley, and J. Chayen, Variations in the amount of Feulgen stain in nuclei of plants grown at different temperatures. *Nature* **177**, 272–273 (1956).
58. Lapham, L. W., Subdivision of glioblastoma multiforme on a cytologic and cytochemical basis. *J. Neuropathol. Exptl. Neurol.* **18**, 244–262 (1959).
59. Leuchtenberger, C., G. S. Boyer, and J. J. Strain, Quantitative cytochemical investigations on the effect of virus on cells. *Ann. N.Y. Acad. Sci.* **81**, 73–83 (1959).
60. Leuchtenberger, C., and R. Leuchtenberger, Quantitative cytochemical studies on the relation of deoxyribonucleic acid of cells to various pathological condi-tions. *Biochem. Pharmacol.* **4**, 128–163 (1960).
61. Lison, L., and V. Valeri, L'erreur dans la détermination histophotométrique de l'acide désoxyribonucléique et la variation individuelle des noyaux en acide désoxyribonucléique. *Chromosoma* **7**, 497–507 (1956).
62. Looney, W. B., The replication of desoxyribonucleic acid in hepatocytes. *Proc. Natl. Acad. Sci. U.S.* **46**, 690–708 (1960).
63. Looney, W. B., R. C. Campbell, and B. E. Holmes, The effect of irradiation

on the replication of desoxyribonucleic acid in hepatocytes. *Proc. Natl. Acad. Sci. U.S.* **46**, 698–708 (1960).

64. McLeish, J., L. G. E. Bell, L. F. La Cour, and J. Chayen, The quantitative cytochemical estimation of arginine. *Exptl. Cell Res.* **12**, 120–125 (1957).

65. Marinone, G., Acido desossiribonucleinico ed empoiesi. *Haematologica* **35**, 85–100 (1951).

66. Marinone, G., Études cytophotométriques sur la teneur en acide désoxyribonucléique des cellules myéloïdes et lymphoïdes au cours de leur evolution et reproduction. *Rev. Belge. Pathol. Med. Exptl.* **21**, 333–354 (1951).

67. Marinone, G., Sur la teneur en acide désoxyribonucléique des noyaux au repos des cellules myéloïdes normales chez l'homme. *Sang* **bb**, 89–98 (1951).

68. Marinone, G., Problèmes de cytochimie quantitative des cellules des organes hemopoiétiques. *Rev. Hematol. (Paris)* **9**, 341–363 (1954).

69. Mauri, C., M. Soldati, and U. Torelli, La proteina istonica ei suoi rapporti con l'ADN nei nuclei degli istiociti normali e delle cellule di Sternberg. *Boll. Soc. Ital. Biol. Sper.* **34**, 29–32 (1958).

70. Meek, E. S., Deoxyribonucleic acid content of mouse ascites tumour cells in interphase and mitosis. *Brit. J. Cancer* **15**, 162–167 (1961).

71. Meek, E. S., The cellular distribution of deoxyribonucleic acid in primary and secondary growths of human breast cancer. *J. Pathol. Bacteriol.* **82**, 107–176 (1961).

72. Meek, E. S., Quantitative cytochemical analysis of protein and deoxyribonucleic acid in ascites tumour cells. *Brit. J. Cancer* **16**, 157–162 (1962).

73. Mellors, R. C., Microscopy III. Cancer cytology and cytochemistry. *Cancer Res.* **15**, 557–572 (1955).

74. Mendelsohn, M. L., and B. M. Richards, A comparison of scanning and two-wavelength microspectrophotometry. *J. Biophys. Biochem. Cytol.* **5**, 707–709 (1958).

75. Moses, M., Absorption spectrum of the Feulgen-nucleal complex *in vitro* and *in situ*. *J. Natl. Cancer Inst.* **12**, 257 (1951).

76. Ogawa, K., M. Himes, A. W. Pollister, and H. M. Zimmerman, Changes in deoxyribonucleic acid content of experimental tumors in C_3H mice. *Cancer Res.* **19**, 596–601 (1959).

77. Ornstein, L., The distributional error in microspectrophotometry. *Lab. Invest.* **1**, 250–265 (1952).

78. Pasteels, J., and W. S. Bullough, Augmentation expérimentale de la teneur en DNA des noyaux. *Arch. Biol. (Liege)* **64**, 271–294 (1953).

79. Patau, K., Absorption microphotometry of irregular-shaped objects. *Chromosoma* **5**, 341–362 (1952).

80. Perugini, S., M. Soldati, and V. Torelli, Il contenuto proteico del nucleo in rapporto al suo patrimonio di ac. desossiribonucleico: premesse dottrinali. *Riv. Istochim. Norm. Patol.* **2**, 441–448 (1956).

81. Perugini, S., M. Soldati, and V. Torelli, Il contenuto nucleare di proteine totali nei linfocite e negli epatociti del ratto normale. *Riv. Istochim. Norm. Patol.* **2**, 461–468 (1956).

82. Perugini, S., M. Soldati, and V. Torelli, Il contenuto nucleare di proteine totali nei linfocite e nei mielociti dell' uomo adulto normale. *Riv. Istochim. Norm. Patol.* **3**, 15–22 (1957).

83. Perugini, S., M. Soldati, and V. Torelli, Il contenuto nucleare di proteina isotonica e di acido desossiribonucleico nelle cellule della leucosi linfatica. *Riv. Istochim. Norm. Patol.* **3**, 95–104 (1957).

84. Perugini, S., V. Torelli, and M. Soldati, Il contenuto nucleare di proteina istonica e di ac. desossiribonucleico nei linfociti negli epatociti del ratto. *Riv. Istochim. Norm. Patol.* **2**, 449–460 (1956).

85. Perugini, S., V. Torelli, and M. Soldati, Il contenuto nucleare di proteina istonica e di ac. desossiribonucleico nei linfociti dell' uomo adulto normale. *Riv. Istochim. Norm. Patol.* **3**, 5–14 (1957).

86. Perugini, S., V. Torelli, and M. Soldati, Il contenuto nucleare di proteine totali nelle cellule della leucosi linfatica. *Riv. Istochim. Norm. Patol.* **3**, 105–112 (1957).

87. Perugini, S., V. Torelli, and M. Soldati, Differences in the desoxyribonucleoprotein complex of normal and leukemic human lymphocytes. *Experientia* **13**, 441–442 (1957).

88. Petrakis, N. L., Microspectrophotometric estimation of the desoxyribonucleic acid (DNA) content of individual normal and leukemic human lymphocytes. *Blood* **8**, 905–915 (1953).

89. Petrakis, N. L., and L. J. Folstad, Desoxyribonucleic acid content of individual lymphoma 1 and 2 tumor cells as determined by Feulgen microspectrophotometry. *J. Natl. Cancer Inst.* **15**, 63–66 (1954).

90. Pisi, E., and G. Cavalli, Teneur en acide désoxyribonucléique et activité mitotique dans le rien du rat blanc dans divers conditions expérimentales. *Arch. Biol. (Liege)* **66**, 439–482 (1955).

91. Pollister, A. W., and H. Ris, Nucleoprotein determinations in cytological preparations. *Cold Spring Harbor Symp. Quant. Biol.* **12**, 147–157 (1947).

92. Pollister, A. W., and C. Leuchtenberger, The nature of the specificity of methyl green for chromatin. *Proc. Natl. Acad. Sci. U.S.* **25**, 111–116 (1949).

93. Pollister, A. W., and L. Ornstein, The photometric analysis of cells. In "Analytical Cytology" (R. C. Mellors, ed.), 2nd ed., pp. 431–518. McGraw-Hill, New York, 1959.

94. Rasch, E., H. Swift, and R. M. Klein, Nucleoprotein changes in plant tumor growth. *J. Biophys. Biochem. Cytol.* **6**, 11–34 (1959).

95. Rasch, E., and J. W. Woodward, Basic proteins of plant nuclei during normal and pathological cell growth. *J. Biophys. Biochem. Cytol.* **6**, 203–276 (1959).

96. Reid, B. L., and S. Singh, Deoxyribonucleic acid values (Feulgen microspectrophotometry) in epithelium of human ectocervix, normal and cancerous. *J. Natl. Cancer Inst.* **25**, 1291–1302 (1960).

97. Reisner, E. H., and R. Korson, Microspectrophotometric determination of desoxyribonucleic acid in megaloblasts of pernicious anaemia. *Blood* **6**, 344–349 (1951).

98. Richards, B. M., P. M. B. Walker, and E. M. Deeley, Changes in nuclear DNA in normal and ascites tumor cells. *Ann. N.Y. Acad. Sci.* **63**, 831–846 (1956).

99. Richards, B. M., and N. B. Atkin, DNA content of human tumours; change in uterine tumours during radiotherapy and their response to treatment. *Brit. J. Cancer* **13**, 788–800 (1959).

100. Richards, B. M., and N. B. Atkin, The differences between normal and cancerous tissues with respect to the ratio of DNA content to chromosome number. *Acta Unio Intern. Contra Cancrum* **16**, 124–128 (1960).

101. Ringertz, N. R., The effect of x-radiation on nuclear histone content. *Exptl. Cell Res.* **32**, 401–404 (1963).

102. Ris, H., The composition of chromosomes during mitosis and meiosis. *Cold Spring Harbor Symp. Quant. Biol.* **12**, 158–160 (1947).

103. Ris, H., and A. E. Mirsky, Quantitative cytochemical determination of deoxyribonucleic acid with the Feulgen nucleal reaction. *J. Gen. Physiol.* **33**, 125–146, 1949.

104. Rodkiewicz, B., Measurement of desoxyribose nucleic acid by Feulgen-photometry in nuclei of roots of diploid and trisomic hyacinths. *Exptl. Cell Res.* **20**, 92–97 (1960).

105. Roels, H., Mitosis and deoxyribonucleic acid content of the nucleus. *Nature* **173**, 1039–1040 (1954).

106. Roels, H., Cell activity and deoxyribonucleic acid content of the nuclei of the thyroid gland of the white rat. *Nature* **174**, 514–515 (1954).

107. Roels, H., Le Teneur en acide désoxyribonucléique du noyau de la cellule thyroidiènne du rat blanc dans diverses conditions expérimentalles. *Arch. Biol.* (*Liege*) **67**, 211–268 (1956).

108. Rudkin, G. T., D. A. Hungerford, and P. C. Nowell, DNA contents of chromosome Ph[1] and chromosome 21 in human chronic granulocytic leukemia. *Science* **144**, 1229–1232 (1964).

109. Sandritter, W., Methoden und Ergebnisse der quantitativen Histochemie. *Deut. Med. Wochschr.* **45**, 2177–2183 (1961).

110. Sandritter, W., and N. L. Böhm, Atypische hydrolysekurve bei der Feulgenreaktion von Mäuseascites tumorzellen. *Naturwiss.* **51**, 273 (1964).

111. Sandritter, W., G. Kiefer, and W. Rick, Über die Stöchometric von Gallocyaninchromalous mit desoxyribonukleinsäure. *Histochemie* **3**, 315–340 (1963).

112. Sandritter, W., D. Muller, and H. G. Schiemer, Über der Nukleinsäuregehalt und das Trockengewicht von haploiden und diploiden Zellen. *Verhandl. Anat. Ges.* (*Jena*) **55**, 146–156 (1958).

113. Sandritter, W., and G. Scomazzoni, Deoxyribonucleic acid content (Feulgen photometry) and dry weight (interference microscopy) of normal and hypertrophic heart muscle fibres. *Nature* **202**, 100–101 (1964).

114. Scarpelli, D. G., and E. von Haam, The effect of croton oil and carcinogens on mitosis and the deoxyribonucleic acid content of cervical epithelial cells. *Cancer Res.* **18**, 657–663 (1958).

115. Schrader, F., and C. Leuchtenberger, A cytochemical analysis of the functional interrelations of various cell structures in *Arvelius albopunctatus* (de Geer). *Exptl. Cell Res.* **1**, 421–452 (1950).

116. Seed, J., Action of radiation on synthesis of deoxyribonucleic acid in normal and tumour strain cells. *Nature* **192**, 944–945 (1961).

117. Seed, J., The synthesis of deoxyribonucleic acid and nuclear protein in normal and tumour strain cells. *Proc. Roy. Soc.* **B156**, 41–56 (1962).

118. Seed, J., Studies of biochemistry and physiology of normal and tumour strain cells. *Nature* **198**, 147–153 (1963).

119. Seed, J., The relations between DNA, RNA, and protein in normal embryonic cell nuclei and spontaneous tumour cell nuclei. *J. Cell Biol.* **20**, 17–23 (1964).

120. Seidel, A., and W. Sandritter, Cytophotometrische messungen des DNS—gehaltes eines Luugenadenoms und einer malignen Luugenadenomatose. *Z. Krebsforsch.* **65**, 555–559 (1963).

121. Sibatani, A., Effects of histone and other proteins on the Feulgen reaction. *Nature* **166**, 355–356 (1950).

122. Sibatani, A., Feulgen reaction and quantitative cytochemistry of desoxypentose nucleic acid. II. Factors affecting the Feulgen reaction *in vitro*. *Cytologia* **18**, 1–12 (1953).

123. Sibatani, A., Feulgen reaction and quantitative cytochemistry of desoxypentose nucleic acid. III. Effects of histone on the Feulgen reaction *in vitro*. *J. Biochem.* (*Tokyo*) **40**, 119–134 (1953).

124. Sibatani, A., and H. Naora, Fixation artefact and intensity of histological staining: observations on mammalian liver cells. *Cytologia* **18**, 110–116 (1954).

125. Soldati, M., and V. Torelli, Ricerche citofotometriche sul contenuto nucleare di acido desossiribonucleico e di proteina istonica della cellula linfatica nel linfogranuloma maligno e nel reticulosarcoma. *Boll. Soc. Ital. Biol. Sper.* **34**, 32–35 (1958).

126. Smith, C. L., A. A. Newton, and P. Wildy, Deoxyribonucleic acid formation in multiplying HeLa cells. *Nature* **184**, 107–108 (1959).

127. Stich, H. F., The DNA content of tumour cells. *J. Natl. Cancer Inst.* **24**, 1283–1297 (1960).

128. Stich, H. F., and H. E. Emson, Aneuploid desoxyribonucleic acid content of human carcinomas. *Nature* **184**, 290–291 (1959).

129. Stich, H. F., S. F. Florian, and H. E. Emson, Deoxyribonucleic acid (DNA) content of human carcinoma cells. *Lancet* **ii**, 385–386 (1959).

130. Stich, H. F., S. F. Florian, and H. E. Emson, The DNA content of tumour cells. *J. Natl. Cancer Inst.* **24**, 471–482 (1960).

131. Stowell, R. E., Nucleic acids in human tumors. *Cancer Res.* **6**, 426–435 (1946).

132. Swift, H., The desoxyribose nucleic acid content of animal nuclei. *Physiol. Zool.* **23**, 169–198 (1950).

133. Swift, H., Cytochemical techniques for nucleic acids. *In* "The Nucleic Acids" E. Chargaff and J. N. Davidson, eds.), Vol. 2, pp. 51–92. Academic Press, New York, 1955.

134. Tieger, D. G., A. Farah, and H. S. Di Stefano, Cytophotometric determination of protein-bound disulphide groups. *J. Histochem. Cytochem.* **5**, 403–407, 1957.

135. Utsumi, K. R., Microspectrophotometric measurements of the deoxyribonucleic acid (DNA) content in two chromosomal lines of the Ehrlich ascites carcinoma. *Gann* **52**, 203–212 (1961).

136. Vandekerckhove, D., Nuclear deoxyribonucleic acid content in corona radiata of the ovary of the rat. *Nature* **197**, 190 (1963).

137. Viola, M., Marked decrease of DNA in the nuclei of the adrenal medulla of rats exposed to cold. *Nature* **204**, 1094–1095 (1964).

138. Vokae, R., C. Gompel, and A. Ghilain, Variations in the content of deoxyribonucleic acid in the human uterine and vaginal receptors during the menstrual cycle. *Nature* **172**, 31–32 (1953).

139. Walker, P. M. B., and B. M. Richards, A method for investigating the stoichiometry of the Feulgen stain. *Exptl. Cell Res.* Suppl. **4**, 97–102 (1957).

140. Walker, P. M. B., and B. M. Richards, Quantitative microscopical techniques for single cells. *In* "The Cell: Biochemistry, Physiology, Morphology" (J. Brachet and A. E. Mirsky, eds.), Vol. 1, pp. 91–138. Academic Press, New York, 1959.

ABSORPTION CYTOPHOTOMETRY: COMPARATIVE METHODOLOGY FOR HETEROGENEOUS OBJECTS, AND THE TWO-WAVELENGTH METHOD

*Mortimer L. Mendelsohn**

DEPARTMENT OF RADIOLOGY,
UNIVERSITY OF PENNSYLVANIA,
PHILADELPHIA, PENNSYLVANIA

By coupling the resolution and discriminatory power of the light microscope to the phenomena arising from the interaction of light with matter, cytophotometry brings the rich armamentarium of macroscopic chemical photometry into the cellular domain. Retardation, polarization, absorption, scattering, and emission can all be used to study the structure and chemical content of cells and cell parts, and natural subdivisions of cytophotometry have developed about each of these types of interaction. Absorption cytophotometry, the subject of this chapter, hinges on the ability of certain chemical groups to accept energy from light of particular wavelengths. These absorbing substances, or chromophores, may be endogenous to the cell or may be the product of chemical reactions used to stain a cell component selectively. Adapting the traditional methods of chemical spectrophotometry, absorption cytophotometry identifies and measures the chromophore by measuring the intensity of light before and after its passage through the region of interest.

As might be expected, serious problems are generated when a macroscopic method designed for dilute solutions under highly standardized conditions is extended to a microscopic domain in which there are no solutions, no standards, and nonrandom distributions of the material to be measured. An assortment of techniques has been developed to deal specifically with these problems, but these methods vary greatly in effectiveness, in suitability for particular material, and in demands on instrumentation.

* Supported by Grants 5-K5-CA-18,540 and 5 R01 CA03896 of the National Cancer Institute.

201

Although comprehensive information about individual techniques is available in the literature, few comparisons of one method with another will be found. The newcomer to the field may have great difficulty finding his bearings and choosing among the various alternatives. With this in mind, this chapter will review some of the unique problems of absorption photometry of microscopic objects, and insofar as possible will compare the various approaches available. In addition, a brief introduction to the two-wavelength method will be given.

I. Absorption Photometry

The Beer–Lambert law is the logical basis of absorption photometry. This law describes the exponential relationship between the absorption of monochromatic light and the amount of absorbing material the light traverses. In its simplest form, the law may be stated as

$$T = 10^{-kcl}, \tag{1}$$

where T, the transmittance, is defined as the probability that a photon of specified wavelength will not be absorbed in traversing a pathlength l containing material of concentration c and absorptivity k. The absorptivity is a characteristic of the absorbing material and is a measure of its capacity to interact with photons at the wavelength specified.

When light is measured with a photomultiplier or a similar photoelectric device, a current is produced in direct proportion to the intensity of light striking the detecting surface. Intensity, of course, is an expression of numbers of photons per unit time, and under stable conditions of illumination, transmittance can be redefined as

$$T = \frac{I}{I_0}, \tag{2}$$

where I_0 is the intensity of a beam of light incident on a photometric field, and I is the intensity of the beam after being transmitted through the photometric field. In practice I_0 is actually measured as the intensity transmitted through a reference field—a cuvette containing a zero concentration of the chromophore, or a clear area adjacent to the cell being measured. In this way, one detector measures both I and I_0, and spurious optical effects other than absorption can be automatically cancelled out.

The logarithmic form of Eq. (1) facilitates the calculation of concentration of chromophore from the measured transmittance. The form of the statement makes it clear that the negative logarithm of transmittance is proportional to the product of concentration and pathlength, and the term absorbance, synonymous with $-\log T$ and symbolized by A, has been introduced to represent the optical half of this simple proportion. Thus

$$-\log T = kcl = A. \tag{3}$$

When amounts of chromophore rather than concentrations are desired, Eq. (3) can be rearranged to give

$$m = \frac{(-\log T)B}{k} = \frac{AB}{k}, \tag{4}$$

where m is the mass of absorbing material in a photometric field, and B is the area of the photometric field. And finally, when the absorptivity is unknown and relative amount of chromophore is the desired parameter,

$$mk = (-\log T)B = AB. \tag{5}$$

II. Distributional Error

Most biological objects subjected to photometric measurement will have point-by-point variations in local transmittance. The effect of such heterogeneity on the absorption equations is easily shown by a two-component model. Consider, for example, a field made up of two regions of equal area. One region contains no absorbing material and therefore has a transmittance of 1.0 and an absorbance of zero. The other region contains absorbing material uniformly distributed within it such that the transmittance is 0.1 and the absorbance is 1.0. If the area of the combined regions is 1 μ^2 and the absorptivity of the chromophore is 1 unit/μ^2, the total amount of chromophore in the field can be calculated appropriately from Eq. (4) by summing the results for each region:

$$m = \frac{0 \times 0.5}{1} + \frac{1 \times 0.5}{1} = 0.5 \text{ units.}$$

Now suppose this same composite system is approached by taking an average transmittance across the entire field. This would be calculated to be

$$T = \frac{1 + 0.1}{2} = 0.55.$$

The negative logarithm of 0.55 is 0.26, and the calculated amount of chromophore using Eq. (4) would then be

$$m = \frac{0.26 \times 1}{1} = 0.26 \text{ units.}$$

Note that an error of 0.24 unit or 48% has been made by using the averaging approach. This is "distributional error" and it occurs whenever intensity measurements are made across a photometric field consisting of regions which are larger than the theoretical limit of optical resolution and have diverse transmittances.

The following summation for n equal areas each homogeneous within itself may give a clearer indication of why distributional error occurs:

$$m_1 = \frac{B}{k} A_1 \quad = -\frac{B}{k} \log T_1$$

$$m_2 = \frac{B}{k} A_2 \quad = -\frac{B}{k} \log T_2$$

$$\vdots \qquad \vdots \qquad \qquad \vdots$$

$$m_n = \frac{B}{k} A_n \quad = -\frac{B}{k} \log T_n$$

$$\sum_1^n m = \frac{B}{k} \sum_1^n A = -\frac{B}{k} \sum_1^n \log T \geq -n \frac{B}{k} \log \frac{\Sigma_1^n T}{n}.$$

When $T_1 = T_2 = \cdots = T_n$ the four terms below the line are equal and there is no distributional error. But when any inequality appears in the T series, the last term containing the average transmittance, $(\Sigma_1^n T)/n$, becomes smaller than the other terms. The magnitude of this negative error depends on the heterogeneity of the component transmittances. A graph of the relationship between heterogeneity and distributional error is shown in Fig. 1 for the two-component model. Similar graphs for more complex images have been given by Ornstein (*13*) and Patau (*14*). Patau has observed that as a general rule distributional error in a complex object

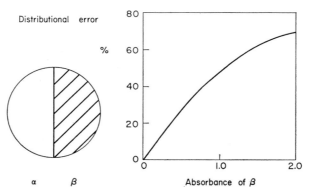

FIG. 1. Distributional error in a model photometric system. The photometric field is divided into two equal areas: α, containing no chromophore, and β, containing chromophore uniformly distributed, but varying in amount from one experiment to the next. Distributional error is calculated as $100(\overline{A} - A^*)/\overline{A}$, where $\overline{A}$ is the mean absorbance determined by measuring the transmittance of each area separately, and A^* is absorbance determined by measuring the transmittance of both areas simultaneously. The error increases as the absorbance of β increases, reflecting both the increase in $\overline{A}$ and the increase in the variance of local absorbance within the photometric field.

is proportional to the product of the mean absorbance and the statistical variance of local absorbances.

It is not generally appreciated that distributional error can also occur in the conventional absorption photometry of solutions. Variations in concentration of chromophore are not likely under these conditions, but there may be considerable variation in pathlength with some types of cuvettes and optical systems. This will produce a lack of proportionality between measured absorbance and concentration of absorbing material. Effects such as this are usually attributed to Beer's law failure—a phenomenon related to the increasing interaction of absorbing molecules as concentration increases—and the effect of distributional error is easily overlooked. As long as calibration curves using standard amounts of chromophore are the basis for calculating unknowns, and the measurements are done without changing the type of cuvette or the photometer, both types of errors completely cancel out. In cytophotometry, distributional error can be due to variation in both concentration and pathlength, and the unpredictability of differences from object to object eliminates any possibility of correcting for the error once it has occurred. The only hope of reliable measurements is to learn to avoid the error in the first place.

III. Methods of Absorption Cytophotometry

To demonstrate and compare the various methods of absorption cytophotometry, it is convenient to use what is probably the most frequently measured object in this field: the stained nucleus of a cell. If, in fact, we are attempting to estimate the DNA content of the nucleus, our goal might range from (1) a crude estimate of ploidy within a range of $\pm 40\%$ of the correct value through (2) a more demanding attempt to identify cells in DNA synthesis or to measure moderate amounts of aneuploidy within a range of perhaps $\pm 10\%$, to (3) an open-ended desire to test the hypothesis of constancy of DNA content or to measure minute amounts of aneuploidy where the smaller the error of measurement the better.

As described in detail elsewhere in this book (Bartels, 1) one can distinguish between two types of uncertainty in a measuring procedure. *Reproducibility* demonstrates the variables, random or otherwise, which cause fluctuations in the results when the same object is measured repeatedly; and *systematic error* is the consistent departure from a correct result due to inherent bias in the technique. Reproducibility is easy to determine, and is frequently stated in published reports of individual methods. Its impact on the over-all reliability of results can be reduced by increasing

the number of replicates one is willing to take for each object measured.
Systematic error is a more difficult problem, largely because there are no
absolute standards of reference available in the microscopic domain. In
discussing the various methods, the author has tried to assign overall
reliabilities by using a composite of the errors inherent in the logic of each
method, evaluation of published data, and his own experience. It should
be understood that these estimates are rough approximations and may not
be generally applicable.

The blunt, head-on approach to cytophotometry, as shown in Fig. 2,

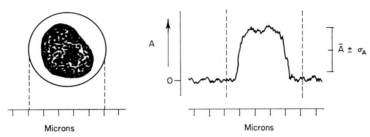

Microns   Microns

Fig. 2. Photometry with the entire object in the field. The relationship between
the nucleus and the photometric field is shown on the left, and a profile of local
absorbance along a line through the center of the nucleus is shown on the right.
σ_A is the standard deviation of local absorbance within the photometric field. In
comparing this figure with Figs. 3 and 4, the relative distributional error can be
visualized as the volume of a rectangular container having a base of $\sigma_A \times \sigma_A$ and a
height of $\bar{A}$. The error in this case is large, being similar in magnitude to the errors
in the model system.

is to include the entire nucleus and a surrounding rim of clear area within
the photometric field. The combined presence of clear field and the darkest
regions of the nucleus within the same photometric field produces errors
similar in magnitude to those generated by the two-component model just
described. Such errors can easily exceed the 40% limit of our least rigorous
criterion, particularly if the mean absorbance of the nucleus is relatively
high. Rendering the nucleus more transparent—by a change of wavelength
or of stain—decreases the distributional error, but it is impractical with
most instruments to make the nucleus transparent enough to eliminate
bias and still get a reliable measurement. Perhaps the only advantage
of this method is that it requires only one measurement of transmittance
and hence is relatively undemanding on time and equipment. Obviously
it is applicable only in cases in which a very wide uncertainty is tolerable.

An improvement on this approach is the use of the plug or core method.
As shown in Fig. 3, this method simplifies the photometry by restricting
the photometric field to a small area in the center of the nucleus. The

marked contrast between background and nucleus is thereby eliminated, and much of the variation in absorbance due to the three-dimensional shape and the internal structure of the nucleus is reduced as well. The effect on distributional error can be dramatic, and, in principle, when the effective diameter of the plug is smaller than the theoretical resolving power of the light microscope, the distributional error vanishes completely. One can then have great confidence in the local measurement of absorbance, but two difficulties remain. First there is a sampling problem in that the smaller the diameter of the plug, the less the measured absorb-

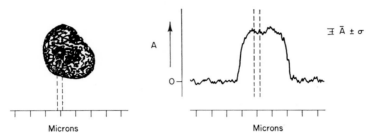

Fig. 3. Photometry by the plug method. σ_A, and therefore distributional error, has been greatly reduced by limiting the photometric field to a small plug containing little variation in local absorbance. However, $\overline{A}$ for the plug may not be representative of the local absorbances of the central region of the object, and the calculation of total chromophore content of the object also requires the estimation of relative volumes of plug and nucleus.

ance is likely to be representative of the population of absorbances across the nucleus. And second, the relative volumes of the plug and the nucleus must be calculated to convert the local amount of chromophore to the content for the entire nucleus. Because of these difficulties, the plug technique is limited to relatively homogeneous material with predictable and uncomplicated shapes. Under these circumstances, the technique involves relatively straightforward instrumentation and is capable of giving results within the 40% criterion, but probably not within 10%. The technique is particularly useful for sections with overlapping nuclei. Methods for extrapolating to nuclear volume and other details of the plug technique have been reviewed by Swift and Rasch (17). A novel approach to extrapolation is described by Garcia (4b) as the one-wavelength, two-area method.

By taking multiple plugs in the central region of the nucleus, one can extend the plug method to take full advantage of small plug sizes and yet avoid the uncertainties of sampling a minute area of a heterogeneous object. Absorbance for each plug is calculated and combined to give a mean absorbance for a typical plug. The results are then extrapolated to the entire nucleus as in the conventional plug procedure. This method eliminates or greatly reduces the sampling error, but at considerable cost in terms of time and effort. It is the procedure of choice for minimizing the errors in sectioned material with overlapping, heterogeneous nuclei. The reliability of the multiple plug method is limited by the reliability of the extrapolation from plug to nuclear volume, and it is doubtful that this error can be reduced below 10%.

The ultimate extension of the plug method is the systematic sampling of the entire object to be measured. This is the basis of scanning photometry where the small size of the scanning plug reduces or eliminates distributional error, the multitude of samples protects against sampling error, and the comprehensive inclusion of the entire object avoids the need to extrapolate on the basis of areas or volumes. In principle this is an extremely powerful approach; in practice it is probably the method of choice for measuring isolated, well-flattened nuclei, but it requires elaborate equipment and careful attention to detail. The plug or scanning spot may take several forms: the moving window of a mechanical scanner, such as in the Barr and Stroud device; a moving spot of light as in the flying-spot method; or a fixed aperture associated with a mechanism to move the cell or its image as in the scanners developed by the Caspersson group. The instantaneous intensity is measured and converted to its logarithm as the scan proceeds, and the logarithms are summed or integrated automatically over the entire scanned area. By using a reference beam or by repeating the scan over a clear area, the corresponding integral is developed for log I_0. The difference between the two sums is the integral of absorbance, and is directly related to the amount of chromophore in the scanned area. If distributional error is to be eliminated completely, the spot at any point in its travel must sample a portion of the cell no larger than the limit of optical resolution. When the spot is larger than this or equivalently when the cell is poorly resolved (out of focus owing to an overly thick specimen, or measured with inappropriate lenses or poor technique), boundaries and other sharp gradients within the object will be represented within the spot and will produce distributional error. Needless to say, the rapid measurement of very small intensities, the logarithmic transformation, the integration, the control of illumination, and the stability of the scan pattern can all be sources of both systematic and random error. But good equipment in good hands can give reproducibilities of 1% or better, and systematic error, at least in principle, should approach zero. Scanning is difficult to apply to overlapping objects, and it may be inappropriate for heterogeneous objects thicker than the depth of focus of an oil immersion objective.

The two-wavelength method is a somewhat different approach to cytophotometry. As in our first example (Fig. 2), the two-wavelength method measures average transmittance in a photometric field containing the entire nucleus; however, in this case two measurements are made using a pair of wavelengths predetermined to give absorptivities of 2 : 1 for the chromophore being studied. The method is based on a set of equations which solve for distributional error when the photometric field consists of one fraction free of chromophore and a second fraction containing chromophore homogeneously distributed. Although actual cellular images are seldom this simple, the same equations strikingly reduce distributional error for a wide variety of conceivable distributions of chromophore. In effect, the method operates as in Fig. 4, by establishing

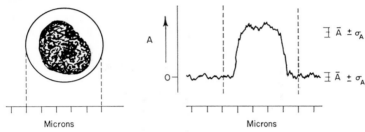

Fig. 4. Photometry by the two-wavelength method. Although the entire object is in the photometric field, measurements at two wavelengths and the appropriate mathematical manipulation of the transmittances effectively divide the field into an absorbing and a nonabsorbing component. The deviations of local absorbance comprising σ_A can now be taken to the nearest of the two diverse mean absorbances, thereby reducing distributional error considerably.

a mean for those absorbances near zero and a second mean for the high values over the nucleus. The reduction of distributional error is a reflection of the reduced variance of local absorbances about these two means. With the appropriate choice of stains and wavelengths it is practical to keep the distributional error to within 3% for the worst possible distributions of chromophore, and to within 1 or 2% for the cases likely to be encountered in biological work. Two-wavelength photometers are intermediate in complexity between plug machines and scanners. They require good monochromators, careful attention to optical alignment, and measurements of transmittance to better than 1%. Since sharp focus is not required, this is the only method capable of working effectively on heterogeneous objects thicker than the depth of focus of an oil immersion objective. But like the scanning method, the two-wavelength method is unsuited for overlapping objects. In practice it is a tedious method to use and yet it can give results reproducible to 3% with simple equipment and to even finer uncertainties with electronic methods for instrument stabilization. In spite of the small systematic errors which may remain uncorrected, one comparison of two-wavelength and scanning measurement on the same material has indicated that the discrepancies between the two methods are on the order of 3% for mammalian nuclei (12).

In addition to the methods of direct measurement which have just been described, cytophotometric procedures can be carried out on photographic images. Photographic techniques are discussed in detail elsewhere in this book, but for the sake of completeness a brief description is in order here. A good, conventional, photographic reproduction of a cell is essentially equivalent to a good optical image of the cell: it has the same attributes involving distributional error, sampling error, and extrapolation, and it can be measured by variants of the same techniques already described. In such measurements some simplicity is gained by having a macroscopic instead of a microscopic object, and some reliability is lost by introducing the uncertainties of the photographic process. There are also several photographic methods that have no counterpart in direct photometry. One such approach uses chemical methods to integrate the absorbance of the image, either measuring silver content (13), or using color photography and extracting and measuring the dyes (5, 10; see also Kelly 4c). Another unique variant of the photographic method involves the deliberate restriction of the range of image contrast to the narrow region at the foot of the photographic response curve. Under these conditions the photograph effectively performs a logarithmic transformation of the transmittance point by point in the object, thus avoiding the problems of distributional error (see Rudkin, 16a).

IV. The Two-Wavelength Procedure

The two-wavelength method was introduced simultaneously and independently by Ornstein (13) and Patau (14) in 1952. Although the two versions are basically the same, Patau's is the more convenient for manual operation and has been the method used in almost all published examples of the two-wavelength method. A third version of the method was introduced in 1961 (Mendelsohn, 11) for possible application to machine methods of computation. This last method differs in that the area of the photometric field is varied until the transmittances at the two wavelengths bear a definite relationship to each other; the corrected absorbance is then determined directly from one of the transmittances. The interested reader should refer to the original papers for the mathematical derivations, or to a recent summary by Garcia (3) showing the three derivations side by side.

The first step in the two-wavelength procedure is the selection of wavelengths appropriate for the chromophore under study. The stained material is searched carefully for examples of relatively transparent areas in which the chromophore is uniformly distributed. Defining a photometric field within each of several such areas, a pair of monochromator settings is selected to yield the following equivalent relationships:

$$A_1 = 2A_2, \qquad T_1 = T_2{}^2,$$

where the subscripts 1 and 2 refer to measurements at the first and second wavelength, respectively.

Once the wavelengths are established, the measurement of relative chromophore content is made by the following procedure modified from Patau:

(1) Select an object to be measured, checking only that it is completely surrounded by clear field.

(2) Move the object to the optical axis and define the photometric field with a calibrated measuring stop chosen and positioned to enclose the object completely. The avoidance of unnecessary clear area within the field is desirable, but not critical. Record the area, B, of the photometric field.

(3) Measure I and I_0 at both wavelengths. Since it is generally easier to change wavelengths than to move the object back and forth, the preferred method is to measure both I's and then both I_0's.

(4) Calculate

$$T_1 = \frac{I_1}{I_{10}}; \qquad T_2 = \frac{I_2}{I_{20}}.$$

(5) Calculate

$$L_1 = 1 - T_1; \qquad L_2 = 1 - T_2.$$

(6) Calculate

$$Q = \frac{L_1}{L_2} \qquad (L_1 > L_2).$$

(7) Calculate

$$C = \frac{1}{2 - Q} \ln \frac{1}{Q - 1},$$

or use Patau's table to find C as a function of Q.

(8) Calculate

$$m = \frac{L_2 C B}{k_2 \ln 10}.$$

Alternatively, steps (5) through (7) can be replaced by entering a set of two-wavelength tables (Mendelsohn, 8) with T_1 and T_2 and finding the value $L_2 C$.

The apparent simplicity of two-wavelength machines can be deceptive, and difficulties with the method are often due to inadequate or misunderstood instrumentation. Underlying many of the complications is the dramatic contrast between the two modes of operation that the method entails. For the selection of wavelengths, very small photometric fields are likely to be required, and the measurement of absorbance over a factor of 2 is highly vulnerable to the effects of glare in the optics. On the other hand, the large transparent fields of the measuring mode lead to transmittances approaching 1. In addition, an error is introduced into the measurements in this mode when the intensity of illumination or the efficiency of detection varies across the field. Thus, to be effective, the two-wavelength machine must have the optical and electronic capacity to deal with widely differing size of field, strength of signal, and range of transmittance. For replications of several percent, intensities should be measured to three significant places and drift should be minimal during each sequence of four measurements.

Another source of difficulty with the method stems from the involved series of entries and calculations required for each object measured. These represent a potential source of human error and make the method time consuming and fatiguing. For production work, it is impractical to do the calculations as the data are collected and hence one does not get meaningful results while the object is still under the microscope. The Canalco Ratio Recorder offers a distinct improvement in that this device temporarily stores the I and I_0 readings and automatically calculates the two transmittances. When combined with the two-wavelength tables, the recorder permits the calculation of final results as the data are taken. An even greater improvement is promised by a device in the final stages of development in this laboratory (Mayall et al., 7). By using a double beam to measure I and I_0 simultaneously, and double detectors to measure at the two wavelengths simultaneously, this new machine avoids the difficulty of having to measure four intensities sequentially. The electrical signals representing intensities are fed into a small, special-purpose analog computer, which performs the two-wavelength calculations and displays the relative chromophore content within seconds of when the measurement begins. Figure 5 gives an indication of the quality of the data currently obtained with this automatic two-wavelength machine. Several components of the device are not yet completed or are operating below specifications, and even better performance is anticipated in the near future.

Anyone seriously interested in the two-wavelength method would do well to begin by studying the original accounts by Patau (14), Ornstein (13), Pollister and Ornstein (16), and Patau and Swift (15). Important details of instrumentation and technique will also be found in articles

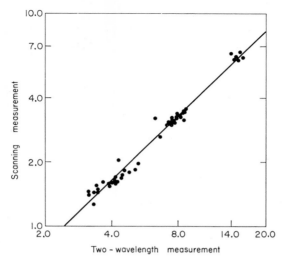

Fig. 5. A comparison of two-wavelength and scanning measurements taken from Mayall (*6*). Fifty liver nuclei stained with gallocyanin chrome alum were measured by two instruments: the automatic two-wavelength machine described in the text, and a mechanical scanner built by Airborne Instruments Laboratory (Bostrom and Holcomb, *1a*). The results are given in logarithmic scale and in arbitrary and independent units. The line through the graph represents the ratio of the two-wavelength to the scanning measurement for each nucleus averaged over the entire population, and the deviation of individual points from the line indicates the divergence of the two measurements. These deviations are well behaved over a fourfold range of values, and their magnitude suggests that the results with either instrument are meaningful well within the 10% criterion. Ordinarily one might be suspicious of a cytophotometer which gave the wide dispersal of values within the lowest ploidy class seen along either axis. The results of the cross check between instruments make it quite clear that in this case the spread of nuclear values is largely due to some source of variation other than the photometer. Nevertheless, there is a suggestion of systematic measuring error in the slight tendency for this cluster of points to be nonparallel with the line. In view of the preliminary status of the two-wavelength measurements, this should not be taken seriously, but rather it is pointed out as an indication of how cross checking can be used to evaluate machine performance in the absence of rigorous standards of measurement.

by Swift and Rasch (*17*), Mendelsohn (*8–11*), van Duijn *et al.* (*2*), and Garcia (*3, 4*). Garcia's most recent experiences with the method are reviewed in other chapters of this book (*4a, 4b*).

References

1. Bartels, P. H., This volume, p. 93.
1a. Bostrom, R. C., and W. G. Holcomb, CYDAC—a digital scanning cytophotometer. *IEEE Intern. Conv. Record* **9,** 110–119 (1963).

2. Duijn, P. van, E. M. den Tonkelaar, and M. J. Hardonk, An improved apparatus for quantitative cytochemical studies and its use in an experimental test for the two-wavelength method. *J. Histochem. Cytochem.* **10**, 473–481 (1962).

3. Garcia, A. M., Studies on DNA in leucocytes and related cells of mammals. II. On the Feulgen reaction and two-wavelength microspectrophotometry. *Histochemie* **3**, 178–194 (1962).

4. Garcia, A. M., Studies on DNA in leucocytes and related cells of mammals. III. The Feulgen-DNA content of human leucocytes. *Acta Histochem.* **17**, 230–245 (1964).

4a. Garcia, A. M., and R. Iorio, This volume, p. 215.

4b. Garcia, A. M., and R. Iorio, This volume, p. 239.

4c. Kelly, J. W., This volume, p. 247.

5. Kelly, J. W., W. A. Clabaugh, and H. K. Hawkins, Photographic cytophotometry with a dual-microscope. II. Microscope assembly and film-dye extractions. *J. Histochem. Cytochem.* **12**, 600–607 (1964).

6. Mayall, B. H., Unpublished observations (1965).

7. Mayall, B. H., R. C. Bateson, R. Q. Edwards, J. R. Connolly, and M. L. Mendelsohn, A dual-beam automatic two-wavelength microspectrophotometer. To be published.

8. Mendelsohn, M. L., The two-wavelength method of microspectrophotometry. I. A microspectrophotometer and tests on model systems. *J. Biophys. Biochem. Cytol.* **4**, 407–414 (1958).

9. Mendelsohn, M. L., The two-wavelength method of microspectrophotometry. II. A set of tables to facilitate the calculations. *J. Biophys. Biochem. Cytol.* **4**, 415–424 (1958).

10. Mendelsohn, M. L., The two-wavelength method of microspectrophotometry. III. An extension based on photographic color transparencies. *J. Biophys. Biochem. Cytol.* **4**, 425–431 (1958).

11. Mendelsohn, M. L., The two-wavelength method of microspectrophotometry. IV. A new solution. *J. Biophys. Biochem. Cytol.* **11**, 509–513 (1961).

12. Mendelsohn, M. L., and B. M. Richards, A comparison of scanning and two-wavelength microspectrophotometry. *J. Biophys. Biochem. Cytol.* **5**, 707–709 (1958).

13. Ornstein, L., The distributional error in microspectrophotometry. *Lab. Invest.* **1**, 250–262 (1952).

14. Patau, K., Absorption microphotometry of irregular-shaped objects. *Chromosoma* **5**, 341–362 (1952).

15. Patau, K., and H. Swift, The DNA-content (Feulgen) of nuclei during mitosis in a root tip of onion. *Chromosoma* **6**, 149–169 (1953).

16. Pollister, A. W., and L. Ornstein, The photometric chemical analysis of cells. *In* "Analytical Cytology" (R. C. Mellors, ed.), 2nd ed., pp. 413–518. McGraw-Hill, New York, 1959.

16a. Rudkin, G. T., This volume, p. 387.

17. Swift, H. H., and E. Rasch, Microphotometry with visible light. *In* "Physical Techniques in Biological Research" (G. Oster and A. W. Pollister, eds.), Vol. 3, pp. 353–400. Academic Press, New York, 1956.

POTENTIAL SOURCES OF ERROR
IN TWO-WAVELENGTH
CYTOPHOTOMETRY

A. Mariano Garcia

and

Robert Iorio*

DEPARTMENT OF ANATOMY, STATE UNIVERSITY OF NEW YORK,
UPSTATE MEDICAL CENTER,
SYRACUSE, NEW YORK

The most common sources of error in cytophotometry have been extensively reviewed in the past 15 years (*5, 6, 9, 16, 42, 44, 53, 54, 65, 67–71*). Similarly, a number of publications have dealt with the theory and practice of the two-wavelength method of Ornstein and Patau as a way to compensate for distributional errors (*15, 18, 35–38, 46, 48, 50, 56, 72*). Without dwelling on the problems pertaining to the stoichiometry of the staining reaction or those concerning optics, light source, and recording systems—all of which have received complete coverage in the abovementioned works—we shall attempt to limit ourselves to a consideration of the pitfalls of the two-wavelength method in an otherwise accurate cytophotometer. The following aspects of the procedure will be discussed: (1) preparation of the material, (2) selection of wavelengths, (3) the slope zero test, (4) the test of the five positions, (5) the error of the instrument, the "true" variation between cells after subtraction of the error due to the apparatus, and the third moment of the distributional curve as a measure of skewness, and (6) differential fading of Feulgen-stained nuclei.†

* Supported by NIH Training Program in Anatomical Sciences 5 T I GM 326.

† Most of the equipment used in the present study was purchased with the State University of New York funds.

I. Comments on Materials and Methods

The advantages of using smears of human and other mammalian leuko-cytes have been discussed elsewhere (17). Briefly, smears approach the "quasi two-dimensional structures" which are ideally suited for absorp-tion studies (9, 53). The thickness of the nuclei being minimal, all the absorbing molecules lie in the same focal plane. A narrow beam of light can be thought of as consisting of nearly parallel rays, and since the absorbing plate is normal to the beam, changes in the direction of the rays should be negligible (5, 9). Moreover, the three different populations (granulocytes, lymphocytes, monocytes) have the same diploid amount of DNA (1, 7, 8, 19, 23, 24, 34, 39).* Since the DNA synthesizing activity of leukocytes in blood, if existent, is minimal (4), the mean values ob-tained per cell type are nearly the same. The shape of the nuclei, ranging from the compact, discoid shape of the small lymphocyte to the irregular, lobulated nucleus of the granulocyte, presents a wide variety of distribu-tional problems. In short, mammalian leukocytes constitute an excellent test system for determining (a) DNA constancy, (b) uniformity of the response of the biological material to fixation and staining, (c) stoichiom-etry and specificity of the Feulgen-nucleal reaction, and (d) accuracy of the measuring procedure with respect to the method and to the instrument. Finally, blood smears have several advantages over histolog-ical sections: smears can be made quickly and easily, the risk of obtaining overlapping or incomplete nuclei is avoided, and the unstained red blood cells can be conveniently used for background reading, thereby canceling the effects of nonspecific light losses.

The use of clean slides is the best guarantee for keeping the smears or prints in place. "Factory clean" slides are hardly adequate since in most cases the material will fall off the slides during acid hydrolysis owing to a greasy film which coats the slides. An oil-free surface, on the other hand, will hold the smear or print firmly throughout the most drastic cytochemical treatment.

Smears for cytophotometry should be rather thick and quickly made so that the spread of the cell is kept to a minimum. It has been frequently pointed out that nuclei having high extinctions can cause departures from the Beer–Lambert law owing to distributional error, residual glare, or

---

* Hale, however, in 1963 challenged this view (22). He maintained that Feulgen-DNA values in mature leukocytes are lower than those in other diploid cells, the decrease being related to the maturation process. While this conclusion is logical in the case of granulocytes, it seems difficult to maintain the same view regarding monocytes and large lymphocytes, which are able to divide if put in a suitable en-vironment (45).

out-of-focus position of a large fraction of the absorbing particles. Consequently, caution is advised in working with extinctions above 1.5 (*9, 10, 65*). It is important to bear this in mind when dealing with sections greater than, or equal to, 10 μ in thickness. However, in our experience with smears, any inconsistencies found almost invariably originate from high transmittances owing to the fact that the noise of the photocathode in such cases tends to obscure differences between specimen and background signals (see discussion on curve shapes below). Because of the inconsistent results that can be obtained at high transmittances, the advantages of compact, flat absorbing structures is stressed.

After having been dried in air for at least 2 hours, the smears or prints are fixed in an 85 : 10 : 5 mixture of methanol–4% aqueous formaldehyde–glacial acetic acid. Fixation for 1 hour is sufficient, although it can be prolonged without any apparently adverse effects (*2*). After fixation, the smears are washed for 1 hour in running tap water to eliminate any excess formalin.

Hydrolysis can be performed in several ways, two of which we have used—the usual 1 N HCl at 60°C for 15–16 minutes for formalin-fixed tissues or 5 N HCl at 25°C (room temperature) for longer periods of time (*11, 26, 27*). The latter offers a wider and safer optimal plateau, thereby enhancing the reproducibility of the procedure (*11*).

After hydrolysis, the slides are washed repeatedly and then transferred to the Schiff reagent made according to Stowell (*61*), where they are kept in the dark at room temperature for 2 hours. Subsequently the slides are bleached and dehydrated [for complete technical directions see the review by Leuchtenberger (*33*)] and are then mounted in oil of 1.560 refractive index.

While it is easy to find unstained Feulgen-negative areas in blood smears, such is not the case with bone marrow or spleen prints. For reasons discussed elsewhere, it is convenient to stain only half of the slide, using the unstained portion for a blank. The tendency of the reagent to spread over the nonimmersed portion of the tissue is negligible, and with a minimum of care a good boundary is created between the stained and the unstained portions (*20*). However, the same is not true of hydrolysis. Theoretically, it should be better to hydrolyze half of the material and stain all of it so that the background reading would compensate for any nonspecific recoloration (*52*). Unfortunately this technique can lead to a fringe of partial hydrolysis causing a lower extinction value in the cells in this area, as will be illustrated in the results of set 3 (Section V).

Thus far, the most accurate procedure has been complete hydrolysis followed by partial staining. The fringe zone that occurs using this method is small and not significant.

The cells selected for measurement must be well stained, clear, and distinct. The belief that a random sampling should include all the specimens found, including broken or distorted ones, is misleading and results in a waste of time and effort. The three types of leukocytes, if properly preserved, will clearly show their nuclear characteristics, and with a minimum of training their identification poses no problem (3). All the measurements were performed using the monochromator and micro-spectrophotometer built by Canal Industrial Corporation, Bethesda, Maryland.

II. Selection of the Operating Wavelengths

The accuracy of the two-wavelength method depends upon the exact choice of wavelengths a and b such that, for a uniformly absorbing medium, $E_a = \frac{1}{2} E_b$. This prerequisite, which theoretically seems quite straightforward, poses a number of problems in practice. First of all, the Beer–Lambert law must be obeyed. If $E = kcd$, where E is the extinction, k the extinction coefficient, c the concentration of the absorbing substance, and d its thickness, then k must have a fixed value for each wavelength considered. Furthermore, k must be independent of the thickness of the absorbing structure and of the concentration of the chromophore in the solid state. This is not to imply that the value of k must be the same as the one found for liquid media, but merely that the curve shape and position in the spectrum must be reasonably constant within the working range. The simplest way to judge the constancy of curve shape is to determine complete extinction curves through nuclear plugs of different densities, since a nuclear plug can be used as a valid approximation of absorbing particles distributed at random within the field (53). In a subsequent step each curve is plotted in percentages of its own maximal extinction value, that is, the peak in each case becomes 100%. If the case for constant shape is upheld, all the profiles should overlap. The computations of the mean relative extinction and of the standard deviation for each wavelength considered become feasible.

Three major factors can alter the extinction patterns: (1) changes in the structure of the absorbing molecules (58); (2) distributional errors, which induce flattening of the curve (18); and (3) metachromasy, which in most cases will increase the values of k for lower wavelengths (2, 40, 51, 57, 66).

Each substance and each histochemical reaction whose quantitation is attempted poses its own set of problems regarding the proper choice of wavelength. For basic fuchsin-Feulgen in smears it is customary to choose the peak extinction, wavelength *b*, between 565 and 580 mμ, while the wavelength for 50% extinction, *a*, is in the green zone, usually between 505 and 510 mμ (*41, 63*). It appears less practical to select wavelength *a* from the red end of the spectrum, at a point beyond 600 mμ, since the sensitivity of the photocathode of the type used for the present study (1P28) decreases sharply after 580 mμ with a concomitant increase in noise. Moreover, the slope of the curve is highly negative in this region so that slight variations in the shape of the curve result in large changes in transmittance. In short, the right-hand slope of the curve is unsuitable for choosing wavelength *a* with any reliability. For a complete discussion of Feulgen-DNA curves *in situ* see Kasten (*30*).

The maximal extinction appears more as a plateau than as a peak, owing to the overlapping of two maxima at 550 mμ and 575 mμ (*41*). Small fluctuations in this zone are apt to go undetected. The point of 50% extinction in the green zone of the spectrum, on the other hand, is the most reliably sensitive spot on the curve for the detection of any departure from constancy due to distributional error or to metachromasy since either of these factors should, if present, displace the point of half-maximal extinction to a lower wavelength. However, if the point of 50% extinction remains "anchored" to the same position, with any random changes that might occur being attributable to fluctuations of the recorder, then any changes of the packed chromophores will affect all the cells to the same degree.

Forty-three curves were measured for the three types of leukocytes. Each curve was then expressed in terms of percentages of its own maximal value, and the entire set was analyzed for mean relative extinction, standard deviation, and coefficient of variation per wavelength.

The results of the above analyses are shown in Table I. As expected, the observable fluctuations at the peak of the curve are minimal; this is at least partly due to the fact that the higher the difference between the specimen and the background readings, the less significant the noise of the apparatus becomes. The two peaks mentioned by Moses (*41*) are noticeable, however. The coefficient of variation (that is, the standard deviation expressed as the percentage of the mean extinction for the corresponding wavelength) for the point of 50% extinction lies between 6 and 7% for 510 mμ and 505 mμ, respectively. If we assume that at least half of this variation is due to random fluctuation of the apparatus, we are left with an error of 3%; it is our belief that in any branch of quantitative biology, with the instruments presently in use, a variation of 5% or less, whether statistically significant or not, can be due to many factors other than biological. (See discussion of results in a later section.)

TABLE I

HUMAN LEUKOCYTES: BASIC FUCHSIN-FEULGEN-DNA. MEAN
RELATIVE EXTINCTION, STANDARD DEVIATION, AND
COEFFICIENT OF VARIATION WITH DIFFERENT
WAVELENGTHS (43 CURVES)

Wave-length $(m\mu)$	Mean relative extinction	SD	CV	Wave-length $(m\mu)$	Mean relative extinction	SD	CV
480	17.54	4.55	25.9%	560	96.89	2.72	2.8%
490	27.94	3.09	11.0%	565	96.89	2.28	2.3%
500	40.00	4.04	10.1%	570	97.92	2.80	2.9%
505	47.46	3.43	7.2%	575	98.00	1.90	1.9%
510	55.17	3.29	6.0%	580	98.49	2.20	2.2%
515	63.12	4.38	6.9%	585	96.40	2.96	3.1%
520	70.33	3.54	5.0%	590	89.86	3.62	4.0%
530	82.52	3.85	4.7%	600	78.47	6.96	8.9%
540	91.06	3.69	4.0%	610	57.06	9.51	16.7%
550	94.94	3.56	3.7%	620	36.35	10.65	29.3%

Figure 1 shows the mean extinction per cell type, while Fig. 2 shows
the relative values of these extinctions. It becomes evident that although
the lymphocyte profile seems slightly shifted to the right, its point of 50%

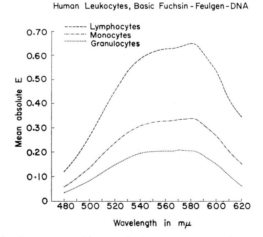

FIG. 1. Extinction curves of human leukocytes, mean values per cell type.

extinction is in line with the others. This result confirms our previous
findings (18), namely that the three types of cells studied have the same
absorption spectrum within 95% limits. The same conclusions have been

drawn by Kasten after extensive study of different tissues (*28, 29, 30*).

Another empirical finding is also worth stressing. Turning again to Figs. 1 and 2, it will be seen that the lymphocytes, with the highest extinction values, show almost the same absorbing pattern as the other cells so that any errors introduced by relatively lower transmittances are not significant in this case. On the other hand, the work reported here was done using a 3× ocular in order to minimize the image size. The use of this ocular made plug measurements difficult in distorted structures such as granulocyte and monocyte nuclei, so that errors due to inhomogeneous distribution of the nuclear material were likely to occur.

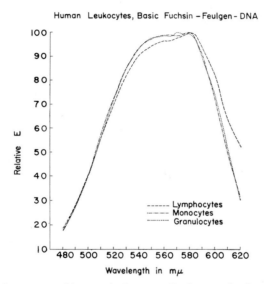

FIG. 2. Extinction curves of human leukocytes. Each curve is plotted in percentages of its own maximal value.

From what has been said regarding curve shape, it can be concluded that although our results favor the idea of constancy within 95% limits, this does not imply that we are denying the possibility of shifts in absorption spectra occurring between different tissues such as those recently reported by Hardonk and van Duijn (*25*). (See also Ornstein, *47.*) Moreover, the possibility of these variations must be kept in mind in discussing the spread of the histogram or "true" standard deviation between cells. Rather than attributing the variation to the DNA content, we must be aware of changes in extinction coefficients between cells as a contributing factor. Unfortunately, the amount of this variation (well below 10%) is quite small for any type of analysis since, owing to the limits of methodological accuracy, an overlapping of errors from different sources is likely to occur; any attempt to account for these errors must be confined to the realm of hypothesis.

The need for a careful selection of wavelengths based on at least 15 determinations cannot be too strongly emphasized. Random fluctuations in cell measurements can be overcome by increasing the size of the sample. However, the improper selection of wavelengths will introduce a systematic error, positive or negative, which will increase not only the spread, but also the asymmetry (skewness) of the distributional curve.

If one wishes to consider the differences in Feulgen-DNA values between sets, it is convenient to measure independently more than one slide per set so that an eventual wrong selection of wavelengths for a particular slide can be overcome, or at least minimized, by random sampling.

III. The Slope Zero Test and the Determination of the Cytophotometric Area

If it is assumed that the same two wavelengths chosen, a and b, will correct for distributional error whatever cell type may be present in the slide, we shall proceed to the next test. A cell nucleus, ideally that of a small lymphocyte, is chosen and measured at different diaphragm openings. If the two operating wavelengths bear the required ratio to each other, the results (Feulgen-DNA extinction times area) will be the same regardless of the area size used and the ratio of absorbing to nonabsorbing media. The fluctuations of the instrument should be random, that is, if the areas are plotted as abscissas and Feulgen-DNA estimates as ordinates, the slope of the lines should approach zero. If the ratio $E_a : E_b$ is less than 0.5 for a homogeneously absorbing medium, the estimates will become lower as the photometric field is increased in magnitude. Quite clearly, since the nuclear area is constant, any increase in the size of the photometric field results in an increase in free area, causing the slope of the line to be negative. Conversely, if the ratio of extinctions is greater than 0.5, this excess will overcompensate for the presence of nonabsorbing spaces and will result in an apparent increase in Feulgen-DNA values when larger diaphragm openings are used. The results of this test are shown in Table II, where the same cell has been measured with two different sets of wavelengths.

It has been found empirically that it is better to choose wavelength a slightly above the value of 50% maximal extinction (51 to 53%). Possibly, when the total area is much larger than the absorbing area (that is, A_2/A_1 is high) the glare introduced by the nonabsorbing space tends to increase the transmittances (*43, 49*) and this, in turn, causes the slope to be negative. This handicap, which depends upon the nature of light itself, exists in spite of the mathematical accuracy of the method. A cor-

TABLE II

Same Cell Measured with Different Areas[a]

Experiment 1[b] λ_b:578 (100%), λ_a:507 (51.5%)			Experiment 2[c] λ_b:578 (100%), λ_a:509 (54.5%)		
A_2	A_2/A_1	$E \cdot A_2$	A_2	A_2/A_1	$E \cdot A_2$
46.2	1.73	19.9	45.9	1.72	22.3
51.3	1.92	21.6	54.1	2.03	23.8
50.1	1.88	21.1	62.5	2.34	23.8
66.1	2.48	21.7	73.2	2.74	25.0
83.2	3.12	21.5	87.6	3.28	26.0
121.3	4.54	19.7	87.4	3.27	24.5
130.0	4.87	21.5	123.7	4.63	25.2
147.2	5.51	18.9	148.0	5.54	23.0
171.8	6.43	21.0	168.8	6.32	23.2
174.2	6.52	16.2	193.3	7.24	22.8
196.6	7.36	20.3	226.4	8.48	23.7
224.1	8.39	22.5			
302.4	11.33	17.6			

[a] Nuclear area $= A_1 = 26.7 \, \mu^2$. $A_2 =$ total area. $E \cdot A_2 =$ Feulgen-DNA value which should remain constant.
[b] Slope $= -0.0097$.
[c] Slope $= -0.0044$.

rectly built instrument will reduce the negativity to a minimum (see the Feulgen-DNA values obtained for large A_2/A_1 ratios), but the possibility of its exerting a systematically negative influence, although small, upon the final results, must be kept in mind. Since granulocytes and monocytes must necessarily include the presence of those nonabsorbing perinuclear spaces, the test discussed here offers a convenient way to check the accurate selection of both wavelengths.

The slope of the line representing the regression coefficient $\hat{b}$ can be found by the least square method $(14, 60)$ to be

$$\hat{b} = \frac{\Sigma^I x_i y_i}{\Sigma^I x_i^2} = \frac{\Sigma^I (X_i - \overline{X})(Y_i - \overline{Y})}{\Sigma^I (X_i - \overline{X})^2} = \frac{\Sigma^I X_i Y_i - (\Sigma^I X_i)(\Sigma^I Y_i)/I}{\Sigma^I X_i^2 - (\Sigma^I X_i)^2/I},$$

where X_i is any particular area used; Y_i represents the Feulgen-DNA value obtained for its corresponding area X_i;

$$\overline{X} = \Sigma^I X_i/I$$

is the mean area value;

$$\overline{Y} = \Sigma^I X_i/I$$

is the mean Feulgen-DNA value; I is the total number of measurements; and $x_i = X_i - \overline{X}$ and $y_i = Y_i - \overline{Y}$.

The estimate of the cytophotometric area can be another potential source of error. The iris diaphragm limits the diameter of the beam that reaches the photocathode. When the apparatus is set for linear response, the electron flow impinging upon the photocathode, observable as a galvanometer reading, is a linear function of the cytophotometric area.

The facts that the iris diaphragm is polygonal rather than perfectly circular, that there is an inherent error in a visual estimate of diameters which increases in the case of small openings and that such errors are squared when the readings are expressed as areas, point out the possible causes of the variation connected with this step. (See Garcia, *18*.) To circumvent these factors, areas are computed from galvanometer readings with the following conditions being maintained: (a) the linearity of the intensity reading against the area and (b) the constancy of this linearity for the working range of wavelengths and areas, regardless of any nonspecific light loss. A fixed stop is placed at the photocathode diaphragm; the area in square microns encompassed by the maximal aperture permitted to the diaphragm is determined several times with the aid of a stage micrometer. In the work reported here, the average value of this area, henceforth referred to as the "reference area," was found to be 608 μ^2. After background readings have been obtained for the cell, the diaphragm is opened to the maximum and the reading for the reference area is obtained. The actual value in square microns of the area used to measure the cell is obtained by the simple ratio

$$\frac{(\text{background reading for the cell}) \times 608 \ \mu^2}{\text{actual reading of the reference area}}.$$

IV. Test of the Five Positions

The purpose of this test is to check the homogeneity of the light and the uniformity of the photocathode response (*15, 18, 35*). As in the previous test, a small nucleus is chosen (if possible, the same nucleus used for the slope zero test) and the diaphragm is set to its maximal opening, the reference area. The cell is then measured in five different positions within the field (see Fig. 3).

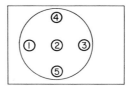

Fig. 3. The five positions used in the test checking homogeneity of light and uniformity of photocathode response.

Several estimates are obtained for each position. This test, quite clearly, introduces a maximal degree of inhomogeneity unlikely to be found in routine work, especially when a low-power ocular is used. A 10% variation between mean values per position is considered satisfactory. The results shown in Table III were obtained after the apparatus had been

TABLE III

Test of the Five Positions[a]

Position	Replicate readings (Basic Fuchsin-Feulgen-DNA)	Mean per position
1	17.6, 20.0, 17.4, 19.2, 20.0	18.8
2	19.2, 20.0, 18.2, 18.5, 19.6	19.1
3	21.8, 21.0, 18.0, 17.8, 19.8	19.7
4	18.4, 21.4, 21.1, 16.4, 19.2	19.3
5	20.7, 18.6, 18.8, 19.2, 18.4	19.1

[a] Nuclear area $(A_1) = 33 \ \mu^2$. Total area $(A_2) = 175 \ \mu^2$. $A_2/A_1 = 5.3$.

carefully aligned. The maximal difference found between positions 1 and 3 was 5%.

V. Feulgen-DNA Values in Cell Populations

Three different sets of slides were prepared and stained independently. Set 1, consisting of five slides, was hydrolyzed in $1 N$ HCl at 60°C for 15 minutes; set 2 (five slides), in $5 N$ HCl at 26°C for 35 minutes; and set 3 (four slides), in $5 N$ HCl at 26°C for 55 minutes. In sets 1 and 2 the entire slides were hydrolyzed and stained, whereas in the third set, only half of any one slide was hydrolyzed and stained, with the longer axis serving as the boundary between treated and untreated portions. In each case all the reagents were freshly prepared. The operating wavelengths were selected independently for each slide. Each cell was measured twice under independent conditions (nested replicas) and, in order to ascertain the maximal experimental variation under similar technical conditions, no corrections were made either for slides or for sets. To make an analysis of variance possible without such corrections, the statistical model proposed in a previous communication was used throughout (17). [For details, see Dixon (14) and Steel (60).]

Table IV is a general summary of the work where mean Feulgen-DNA values per set and per cell type are shown: the figure in parentheses indicates the number of cells measured in duplicate. The total number of data processed becomes 392 (the number of nuclei tested) times 2, or

TABLE IV

BASIC FUCHSIN-FEULGEN-DNA VALUES OF HUMAN LEUKOCYTES[a]

Set	Granulocytes	Lymphocytes	Monocytes	All types
1 (5 slides)	19.45 (45)	19.83 (44)	20.11 (29)	19.76 (118)
2 (5 slides)	22.05 (50)	21.03 (51)	23.68 (34)	22.07 (135)
3 (4 slides)	19.92 (47)	20.27 (48)	19.85 (44)	20.16 (139)
All (14 slides)	20.66 (142)	20.41 (143)	21.13 (107)	20.70 (392)

[a] Figure in parentheses indicates number of cells measured.

784. We shall comment upon differences between means in the general discussion of errors. It suffices to state here that the higher values for set 2 are due in part to an improper selection of wavelength a which overcompensates for the distributional error. As stated above, this excess becomes quite noticeable in the case of monocytes owing to the large areas occupied by these nuclei.

Table V shows the standard deviation of the cytophotometer and its

TABLE V

STANDARD DEVIATION AND COEFFICIENT OF VARIATION[a] OF THE APPARATUS

Set	Granulocytes	Lymphocytes	Monocytes	All types
1	1.38 (7.1%)	1.43 (7.2%)	2.41 (12.0%)	1.70 (8.6%)
2	1.72 (7.8%)	1.31 (6.2%)	2.03 (8.6%)	1.62 (7.3%)
3	1.37 (6.9%)	1.29 (6.4%)	1.92 (9.7%)	1.54 (7.6%)
All	1.51 (7.3%)	1.28 (6.3%)	2.09 (9.9%)	1.62 (7.8%)

[a] Numbers in parenthesis.

coefficient of variation, which is the former value expressed as percentage of the corresponding mean Feulgen-DNA content. As expected, the highest fluctuation is shown by monocytes since the error of the instrument increases as the extinction decreases. In general, this variation is random and does not affect the means. Since the duplicate estimates per cell constantly are a check of the instrumental error, they are considered quite advantageous. We do not believe that this error can be determined by measuring only one cell 10 times and then finding the mean and the standard deviation of the sample. To a certain extent, the error depends upon the intrinsic stability of the apparatus (light source and level of photomultiplier noise). However, the error also has an inverse relationship to the extinction value of the nucleus. Since we are dealing here with a wide range of extinctions which depend upon nuclear configuration and upon the degree of cellular stretching on the slide, it would seem inaccurate to extrapolate the standard deviations of 10 measurements of a single cell to different cell populations. In fact the evaluation of the photometric error and the estimate per cell must be simultaneous.

Figure 4 shows the histograms per set plotted in 10% increments. The

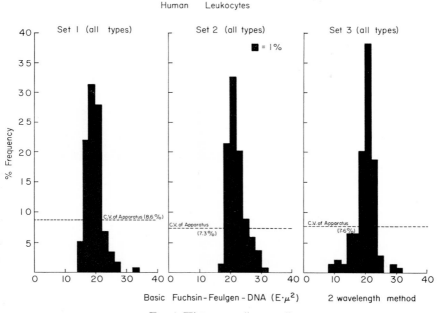

FIG. 4. Histograms "per set."

one corresponding to set 2 is skewed to the right, while the histogram of set 3 veers toward the left as a result of factors discussed below. The dotted line marks the level of instrumental error. Figure 5 shows the histograms per cell type also plotted in 10% increments; as expected, the narrowest distributional profile is that of the lymphocytes, while the histogram of the monocytes presents the broadest base. Nevertheless— and this can be observed in all six histograms—the frequencies which are above the line of error display a remarkably narrow spread of values, plus or minus 10% as a maximum. We consider this simultaneous plotting of frequencies and of instrumental variation a useful way to judge at first glance the significance of the experimental findings. Obviously, any frequency below the line of error can hardly be considered solid ground for further elaboration.

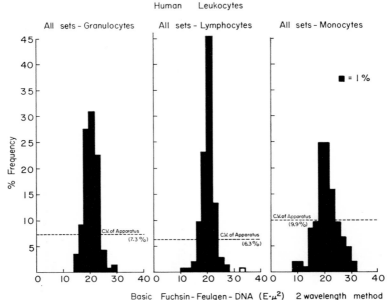

Fɪɢ. 5. Histograms per cell type.

Table VI shows the "true" standard deviation and the coefficient of variation between cells after the subtraction of the instrumental error. This is possible since each cell has been measured more than once (*14*,

TABLE VI

CORRECTED STANDARD DEVIATION AND COFFICIENT OF VARIATION[a] BETWEEN
BASIC FUCHSIN-FEULGEN-DNA CONTENT OF HUMAN LEUKOCYTES

Set	Granulocytes	Lymphocytes	Monocytes	All types
1	1.43 (7.4%)	2.13 (10.7%)	00	1.55 (7.8%)
2	1.48 (6.7%)	1.37 (6.5%)	2.60 (11.0%)	1.78 (8.1%)
3	1.80 (9.0%)	2.12 (10.4%)	4.83 (24.3%)	3.17 (15.7%)
All	1.52 (7.4%)	1.89 (9.3%)	3.47 (16.4%)	2.33 (11.2%)

[a] Numbers in parentheses.

60). The pertinent formulas have been discussed in a previous communication (*17*). Briefly, the true variance between cells is determined by means of the following formula:

$$\frac{\text{(mean square between cells)} - \text{(variance of the instrument)}}{\text{number of replicated measurements per cell}}.$$

There are several factors which may account for this "true" variance: (a) differences in hydrolysis and staining, (b) improper selection of wavelengths, and (c) differences in the DNA content.

Di Stefano (*13*) followed cytophotometrically the intensity of the reaction in cartilage nuclei after various times of hydrolysis (Table 1 of the reference quoted above). Ten nuclei were measured in each case, and the standard error exhibits only a moderate relative increase at both ends of the curve. This increase may be attributed to the instrument since the extinctions decrease in magnitude at these sites. Swift, in one of his comprehensive reviews of the problem (*64*), stated, "Although hydrolysis maxima may differ between species, there appears to be almost no evidence of a difference between tissues of the same species." Subsequently, he quotes some exceptions that have been reported in the literature; these differential responses to hydrolysis have been found between tissues, but not between cells of the same type as the lymphocytes of set 3 seem to indicate. Srinivasachar and Patau contend, "There is no reason for postulating that hydrolysis should affect different nuclei in strictly the same way" (*59*). This contention was not, however, shown to hold for the standard Feulgen procedures that they used, since differential destaining between nuclei was found to occur only after subsequent treatment with alcohol and with SO_2. Kasten (*31*) has studied the distribution of the Feulgen-DNA content in the three types of liver parenchymal cells after different hydrolysis times and has concluded that, at least within liver, depurination is a random process, that is, it affects most of the cells to the same degree. Caution against generalizations must be exercised, however. In a very recent publication Sandritter et al. (*55*) reported that euchromatin and heterochromatin respond differentially to hydrolysis. The latter type seems more resistant to depolymerization or solubilization of the apurinic acid, thus remaining a longer time than euchromatin in the optimal zone of the hydrolysis curve. This differential behavior could change the number of aldehyde groups available from cell to cell if the ratio of euchromatin to heterochromatin changes. The dissimilarities were pointed out among tissues. Whether they exist among cells of the same type or not is still an open question. In our results only two slides of set 3 yielded granulocytes and lymphocytes with hypodiploid values. Had the difference between the two kinds of chromatin been responsible for it, the occurrence of the phenomenon would have been more widespread. From these reports and from our own work, we believe that the small fraction of cells in set 3 with a Feulgen-DNA content of about 60% of the mode does not represent an individual preoptimal depurination or postoptimal solubilization of the DNA, which is inconsistent with the behavior shown by the other cells of the same population. More probably, the hydrolysis of only half of the slide is not an all-or-none event, and a middle zone of incomplete hydrolysis remains. Therefore, a warning must be given against hydrolyzing only a portion of a slide. The staining of half of a completely hydrolyzed slide, on the other hand, does not seem to offer such a setback as had been previously reported (20).

The errors arising from an improper selection of wavelengths have already been discussed. All we can say concerning the "real" differences in DNA content is that they are still open to discussion and that as techniques and instruments improve, the smaller the "true" standard deviation becomes. We believe that in our own results this deviation can be attributed to a large extent, if not entirely, to the factors already mentioned. DNA departures from constancy should be the last thing to blame for the spread of histograms within a class since Nature seems to be older, more stable, and more reliable than the experimental procedures of the biologists.

The way in which this variation between Feulgen-stained nuclei affects the distributional curve can be found with the aid of the third moment of this curve. Standard deviations, being square roots, have no sign. They are an average measure of spread but tell nothing about asymmetries, that is, whether such a spread is similar for both sides or whether it prevails for the higher values (positive skewness) or for the lower ones (negative skewness). This third moment is the sum of the cubes of the deviations between the data (X_i's) and the mean ($\overline{X}$) divided by the number of cases (N). If the curve is symmetrical, the value of the third moment should approach zero (21).

$$\sum^I \frac{(X_i - \overline{X})^3}{N} \sim 0.$$

If it does not approach zero, the expression

$$\left[\sum^I (X_i - \overline{X})^3/N\right]^{1/3} \times 100/\overline{X}$$

indicates the fraction of the curve which is asymmetric toward the right (positive sign) or toward the left (negative sign). Table VII summarizes

TABLE VII

CUBE ROOT AND PERCENTAGE OF THE MEAN CUBE

Set	Granulocytes	Lymphocytes	Monocytes
1	+1.543 (7.9%)	+1.825 (9.2%)	+1.145 (5.7%)
2	+1.705 (7.7%)	+1.304 (6.2%)	+1.112 (4.7%)
3	−1.478 (7.4%)	−2.079 (10.2%)	+1.846 (9.3%)
All	+1.226 (5.9%)	−0.709 (3.5%)	+1.940 (9.2%)

the values obtained with the latter formula; only three estimates out of the 12 that were made proved to be negative. It was reported previously (*19*) that the distributional curve of the Feulgen-DNA values in leukocytes shows a positive skewness of about 10%. The values for sets 1 and 2 are consistent with these findings. The negative skewness of set 3 is probably caused by a group of cells that are incompletely hydrolyzed. The statistical method used here is so sensitive that the lower values of a small fraction of the cells (5% of the total lymphocytic population) were enough to produce a negative value. In this sense, the cube root of the third moment may rightly be referred to as the "voice of the minority." The previous effect can be distinguished from the improper choice of wavelengths, if the inaccuracy is not gross, in that the influence of the wrong wavelength is less apparent and induces only gradual departures (compare the values for the monocytes between sets 2 and 3).

It has been previously reported that the relative values of the cube roots appear to exceed 15% only in systems that are undergoing DNA replication (*20*). Undoubtedly much more work is required in evaluating the significance of this parameter; nevertheless, we believe it could prove to be of assistance in the study of cell kinetics and of precancerous states.

Finally, we present the mean standard deviation and coefficient of variation (in parenthesis) (a) between slides of human blood (basic Fuchsin-Feulgen-DNA content)

Set 1	Set 2	Set 3	All Sets
2.24 (11.3%)	1.45 (6.6%)	1.01 (5%)	1.69 (8.2%)

and (b) between human leukocyte types (basic Fuchsin-Feulgen-DNA content).

Set 1	Set 2	Set 3	All Sets
0.33 (1.7%)	1.35 (6.1%)	0.29 (1.4%)	0.82 (4%)

The coefficient of variation between populations can be considered negligible if precautions are taken regarding the material, the cytophotometer, and the methods. Unfortunately, the rather unpredictable variation between slides of identically treated material is still large (8%), showing once more that a single slide as a control is not reliable enough. The only secure way to estimate and minimize this variation is by means of random sampling, using at least four different slides per tissue studied or two slides measured several times under independent conditions.

VI. Fading of the Feulgen Stain

It has been a customary practice among cytophotometrists to keep slides with known Feulgen-DNA values for various periods of time so that these measured slides could be used as controls in subsequent experiments. Recent publications, on the other hand, have pointed out that in doing this one runs the risk of using slides which are prone to fade after a certain time because of the pH of the reagent, the exposure of these "controls" to the light, and (or) the nature of the particular mounting medium used (*12, 32, 62*).

In a previous publication (*18*) we reported observations on two slides for periods of from 6 months to 1 year. The remarkable constancy of measurements shown led us to postulate the unlikelihood of any diminution of color intensity. After a period of $3\frac{1}{2}$ years, however, noticeable fading did occur in these slides.

A slide of human blood was stained in June 1960 using freshly prepared reagents. The means that were found in August 1960 were as follows (after having been corrected for the different systems of area values used):

Granulocytes	Lymphocytes	Monocytes	All
17.96	17.14	18.04	17.70

One year later (September 1961), the mean for the lymphocytes was 17.42. Three and one-half years later, it was our intention to use this same slide as a control for the overall performance of the cytophotometer presently in use. When not in use, this "control" slide was always kept in the dark; however, during this time the mounting oil had partially desiccated. The slide was remounted, and several sets of cells were analyzed with the two-wavelength method. The results obtained were quite unexpected. Believing that these results were due to misalignment of the apparatus or to improper use of the technique, we carefully realigned the instrument and changed the optics.

TABLE VIII
FEULGEN-DNA FADING AS A FUNCTION OF NUCLEAR AREA[a,b]

Set	Granulocytes Mean area	Granulocytes Mean Feulgen-DNA	Lymphocytes[c] Mean area	Lymphocytes[c] Mean Feulgen-DNA	Monocytes[c] Mean area	Monocytes[c] Mean Feulgen-DNA	Regression coefficient of Feulgen-DNA on nuclear sizes
1	90.73	13.51	54.56	15.09	124.6	14.20	−0.0128
2	103.45	14.52	79.05	15.39	—	—	−0.0231
3	91.83	12.97	61.39	15.26	—	—	−0.0597
4	96.00	14.00	56.40	16.28	—	—	−0.0411
All	96.27	13.77	72.08	15.32	—	—	−0.0257

[a] Point slope: 16.72-(Feulgen-DNA).

[b] Values obtained March 1964. Previous values (Feulgen-DNA, August 1960): Granulocytes, 17.96; Lymphocytes, 17.14; Monocytes, 1804; All, 17.70.

[c] From set 2 on, monocytes and lymphocytes were pooled together.

The results are summarized in Table VIII, where the lower values for the granulocytes are evident. Owing to the measuring procedure, nuclear areas were not computed as such. Instead, the total cytophotometric area, leaving only a rim of nonabsorbing perinuclear space, was used for statistical purposes as an approximation for nuclear areas. When these cytophotometric areas are plotted as abscissas and the product "extinction times area" as ordinates, the regression coefficient computed for such data is always negative. Therefore, the larger the area, or nuclear surface, the lower the Feulgen-DNA content (that is, the more intense the chromatic loss has been). Moreover, the "point slope" (Feulgen-DNA value) computed for an area of 0 μ^2 equals 16.72 units, only 5.5% different from the values obtained in August 1960, when totally different instruments with different calibrations were used. This 95% approximation reinforces our view that the decoloration of the DNA bound dye is directly proportional to the nuclear surface. A similar explanation has been suggested by Swartz and Nagy (62).

We believe that desiccation of the mounting oil is the major cause of the fading which occurred in these slides. Therefore, we advise the following precautions to be taken before and during the storage of slides: (1) Mount the material in immersion oil of suitable refractive index; (2) keep the material in light-tight boxes; (3) avoid any oil leaks which might leave parts of the tissues unprotected; and (4) do not trust slides that are over 1 year old.

VII. Conclusions

This has been a hurried glance at, rather than an inquisitive stroll through, a landscape of errors. Many variables remain as such, and more effort is demanded in order to control them. Others, however, can either be diminished by perfecting techniques and instruments or properly evaluated by statistical analysis so that correct inferences can be made. With up to 90% accuracy we can analyze DNA content in cells. Beyond that 90%, however, errors will make hypotheses risky.

It seems highly pertinent to quote, as a closing remark, the following statement of Srinivasachar and Patau (59): ". . . apparent deviations from constancy are usually small and often negligible, but are occasionally large enough to be misleading. Deviations from Feulgen-DNA constancy call for extended measurements on a variety of differently prepared Feulgen slides. Only if some deviations appear consistently, would there be any reason to consider them as deviation from DNA constancy."

References

1. Atkins, N. B., and B. M. Richards, Deoxyribonucleic acid in human tumors as measured by microspectrophotometry of Feulgen stain. A comparison of tumors arising at different sites. *Brit. J. Cancer* **10**, 769–786 (1956).
2. Baker, J. R., "Principles of Biological Microtechnique." Wiley, New York, 1958.
3. Bessis, M., "Traité de cytologie sanguine." Masson, Paris, 1954.
4. Bond, V. P., T. M. Fliedner, E. P. Cronkite, J. R. Rubini, G. Brecher, and P. K. Shork, Proliferative potentials of bone marrow and blood cells studied by "in vitro" uptake of H_3-thymidine. *Acta Haematol.* **21**, 1–15 (1959).
5. Caspersson, T., "Cell Growth and Cell Function." Norton, New York, 1950.
6. Caspersson, T., Quantitative cytochemical methods for the study of cell metabolism. *Experientia* **11**, 45-60 (1955).
7. Davidson, J. N., J. Leslie, and J. C. White, Quantitative studies on the content of nucleic acids in normal and leukemic cells from blood and bone marrow. *J. Pathol. Bacteriol.* **63**, 471–483 (1951).
8. Davidson, J. N., J. Leslie, and J. C. White, The nucleic acid content of the cell. *Lancet* **I**, 1287–1290 (1951).
9. Davies, H. G., and P. M. B. Walker, Microspectrophotometry of living and fixed cells. *Progr. Biophys. Biophys. Chem.* **3**, 195–236 (1953).
10. Davies, H. G., M. H. F. Wilkins, and R. G. Boddy, Cell crushing: A technique for greatly reducing errors in microspectrophotometry. *Exptl. Cell Res.* **6**, 550–553 (1954).
11. De Cosse, J., Submitted to the *J. Histochem. Cytochem.*
12. De la Torre, L., and G. W. Salisbury, Fading of Feulgen-stained bovine spermatozoa. *J. Histochem. Cytochem.* **10**, 39–41 (1962).
13. Di Stefano, H. S., A cytochemical study of the Feulgen nucleal reaction. *Chromosoma* **3**, 282–301 (1948).
14. Dixon, W. J., and F. J. Massey, "Introduction to Statistical Analysis," 2nd ed. McGraw Hill, New York, 1957.
15. Duijn, P. van, E. M. den Tonkelaar, and M. J. Hardonk, An improved apparatus for quantitative cytochemical model studies and its use in the experimental test of the two-wavelength method. *J. Histochem. Cytochem.* **10**, 473–481 (1962).
16. Eränkö, O., "Quantitative Methods in Histology and Microscopic Histochemistry." Karger, Basel, 1955.
17. Garcia, A. M., Studies on DNA on leucocytes and related cells of mammals. I: On microspectrophotometric errors and statistical models. *Histochemie* **3**, 170–177 (1962).
18. Garcia, A. M., Studies on DNA on leucocytes and related cells of mammals. II: On the Feulgen reaction and two-wavelength microspectrophotometry. *Histochemie* **3**, 178–194 (1962).
19. Garcia, A. M., Studies on DNA on leucocytes and related cells of mammals. III: The Feulgen-DNA content of human leucocytes. *Acta Histochem.* **17**, 230–245 (1964).
20. Garcia, A. M., Studies on DNA on leucocytes and related cells of mammals. IV: The Feulgen-DNA content of peripheral leucocytes, megakaryocytes and other bone marrow cell types of the rabbit. *Acta Histochem.* **17**, 246–258 (1964).
21. Goulden, C. H., "Methods of Statistical Analysis," 2nd ed. Wiley, New York, 1952.

22. Hale, A. J., The leucocyte as a possible exception to the theory of deoxyribonucleic acid constancy. *J. Pathol. Bacteriol.* **85**, 311–326 (1963).
23. Hale, A. J., and S. Wilson, The deoxyribonucleic acid content of leucocytes in normal and leukaemic human blood. *J. Pathol. Bacteriol.* **77**, 605–614 (1959).
24. Hale, A. J., and S. Wilson, The deoxyribonucleic acid content of the nuclei of leukaemic leucocytes. *Lancet* **I**, 577–578 (1960).
25. Hardonk, M. J., and P. van Duijn, Studies on the Feulgen reaction with histochemical model systems. *J. Histochem. Cytochem.* **12**, 758–767 (1964).
26. Itikawa, O., and Y. Ogura, The Feulgen reaction after hydrolysis at room temperature. *Stain Technol.* **29**, 13–15 (1954).
27. Jordanov, J., On the transition of desoxyribonucleic acid to apurinic acid and the loss of the latter from tissues during Feulgen reaction hydrolysis. *Acta Histochem.* **15**, 135–152 (1963).
28. Kasten, F. H., Stability of the Feulgen-deoxyribonucleic acid absorption curve *in situ* with variation in nuclear protein content and other factors. *J. Histochem. Cytochem.* **4**, 462–470 (1956).
29. Kasten, F. H., The Feulgen-deoxyribonucleic acid absorption curve in normal and tumorous tissues. *J. Histochem. Cytochem.* **5**, 398–402 (1957).
30. Kasten, F. H., The Feulgen-DNA absorption curve *in situ*. *Histochemie* **1**, 123–150 (1958).
31. Kasten, F. H., Evidence for a random loss of purines from DNA during acid hydrolysis. *J. Histochem. Cytochem.* **13**: 13–14, 1965.
32. Kasten, F. H., G. Kiefer, and W. Sandritter, Bleaching of Feulgen-stained nuclei and alteration of absorption curve after continuous exposure to visible light in a cytophotometer. *J. Histochem. Cytochem.* **10**, 547–555 (1962).
33. Leuchtenberger, C., Quantitative determination of DNA in cells by Feulgen microspectrophotometry. *In* "General Cytochemical Methods" (J. F. Danielli, ed.), Vol. 1, pp. 219–278. Academic Press, New York, 1958.
34. Mandel, P., P. Metais, and S. Cuny, Les quantités d'acide désoxyribonucléique des leucocytes chez les diverses espéces de mammifères. *Compt. Rend.* **231**, 1172–1174 (1950).
35. Mendelsohn, M. L., The two-wavelength method of microspectrophotometry. I: A microspectrophotometer and tests on model systems. *J. Biophys. Biochem. Cytol.* **4**, 407–414 (1958).
36. Mendelsohn, M. L., The two-wavelength method of microspectrophotometry. II: A set of tables to facilitate calculations. *J. Biophys. Biochem. Cytol.* **4**, 415–424 (1958).
37. Mendelsohn, M. L., The two-wavelength method of microspectrophotometry. IV: A new solution. *J. Biophys. Biochem. Cytol.* **11**, 509–513 (1961).
38. Mendelsohn, M. L., and B. M. Richards, A comparison of scanning and two-wavelength photometry. *J. Biophys. Biochem. Cytol.* **5**, 707–709 (1958).
39. Metais, P., and P. Mandel, La teneur en acide désoxypentosenucléique des leucocytes chez l'homme normal et a l'état pathologique. *Compt. Rend. Soc. Biol.* **144**, 277–279 (1950).
40. Michaelis, L., The nature of the interaction of nucleic acid and basic dyestuffs. *Cold Spring Harbor Symp. Quant. Biol.* **12**, 131–146 (1947).
41. Moses, M. J., Absorption spectrum of the Feulgen-nucleal complex *in vitro* and *in situ*. *J. Natl. Cancer Inst.* **12**, 257, 1951 (Abstract).
42. Moses, M. J., Quantitative optical techniques in the study of nuclear chemistry. *Exptl. Cell Res.* Suppl **2**, 75–102 (1952).

43. Naora, H., Schwarzschild-Villiger effect in microspectrophotometry. *Science* **115**, 248–249 (1952).
44. Naora, H., Microspectrophotometry in visible light range. *In* "Handbuch der Histochemie" (W. Graumann and K. Neumann, eds.), Vol. 1, Part 1, pp. 192–219. Fischer, Stuttgart, 1958.
45. Nowell, P. C., Differentiation of human leukemic lymphocytes in tissue culture. *Exptl. Cell Res.* **19**, 267–277 (1960).
46. Ornstein, L., The distributional error in microspectrophotometry. *Lab. Invest.* **1**, 250–265 (1952).
47. Ornstein, L., Discussion following J. F. Scott's Problems of scattering and spectral anomalies in microabsorption spectrophotometry. *Lab. Invest.* **1**, 73–84 (1952).
48. Ornstein, L., Doctoral Dissertation, Columbia University (1957). University Microfilms Inc., Ann Arbor, Michigan.
49. Ornstein, O., and A. W. Pollister, Schwarzschild-Villiger effect in microspectrophotometry. *Science* **116**, 203–204 (1952).
50. Patau, K., Absorption microphotometry of irregular shaped objects. *Chromosoma* **5**, 341–362 (1952).
51. Pearse, A. G. E., "Histochemistry, Theoretical and Applied," 2nd ed. Little, Brown, Boston, Massachusetts, 1960.
52. Persijn, J. P., and P. van Duijn, Studies of the Feulgen reaction with the aid of DNA incorporated cellulose films. *Histochemie* **2**, 283–297 (1961).
53. Pollister, A. W., and L. Ornstein, The photometric chemical analysis of cells. *In* "Analytical Cytology" (R. C. Mellors, ed.), 2nd ed., pp. 431–518. McGraw-Hill, New York, 1959.
54. Sandritter, W., Ultraviolettmikrospektrophotometrie. *In* "Handbuch der Histochemie" (W. Graumann and K. Neumann, eds.), Vol. 1, Part 1, pp. 220–338. Fischer, Stuttgart, 1958.
55. Sandritter, W., K. Jobst, L. Rakow, and K. Bosselmann, Zur Kinetik der Feulgenreaktion bei verlängerter Hydrolysezeit. Cytophotometrische Messungen im sichtbaren und ultravioletten Licht. *Histochemie* **4**, 420–437 (1965).
56. Schiemer, H. G., Inhomogenitätsfehler bei cytophotometrische Messungen. *Acta Histochem.* **9**, 174–179 (1960).
57. Schubert, M., and D. Hamerman, Metachromasia; chemical theory and histochemical use. *J. Histochem. Cytochem.* **4**, 159–189 (1956).
58. Scott, J. F., Ultraviolet absorption spectrophotometry. *In* "Physical Techniques in Biological Research" (G. Oster and A. W. Pollister, eds.), Vol. 1, pp. 131–203. Academic Press, New York, 1955.
59. Srinivasachar, D., and K. Patau, Proportionality between nuclear DNA-content and Feulgen-dye content. *Exptl. Cell Res.* **17**, 286–298 (1959).
60. Steel, R. G. D., and J. H. Torrie, Principles and procedures of statistics with special reference to the biological sciences. McGraw-Hill, New York, 1960.
61. Stowell, R. E., Feulgen reaction for thymonucleic acid. *Stain Technol.* **20**, 45–58 (1945).
62. Swartz, F. J., and E. R. Nagy, Feulgen stain stability in relation to three mounting media and exposure to light. *Stain Technol.* **38**, 179–185 (1962).
63. Swift, H., Quantitative aspects of nuclear nucleoproteins. *Intern. Rev. Cytol.* **2**, 1–77 (1953).
64. Swift, H., Cytochemical techniques for nucleic acids. *In* "The Nucleic Acids" (E. Chargaff and J. N. Davidson, eds.), Vol. 2, pp. 51–91. Academic Press, New York, 1955.

65. Swift, H., and E. Rasch, Microphotometry with visible light. *In* "Physical Techniques in Biological Research" (G. Oster and A. W. Pollister, eds.), Vol. 3, pp. 353–400. Academic Press, New York, 1956.
66. Sylvén, B., Metachromatic dye-substrate interaction. *Quart. J. Microscop. Sci.* **95**, 327–358 (1954).
67. Thorell, B., Cell studies with microspectrography. *Advan. Biol. Med. Phys.* **6**, 95–119 (1958).
68. Walker, P. M. B., Ultraviolet absorption techniques. *In* "Physical Techniques in Biological Research" (G. Oster and A. W. Pollister, eds.), Vol. 3, pp. 401–487. Academic Press, New York, 1956.
69. Walker, P. M. B., Ultraviolet microspectrophotometry. *In* "General Cytochemical Methods" (J. F. Danielli, ed.), Vol. 1, pp. 163–217. Academic Press, New York, 1958.
70. Walker, P. M. B., and B. M. Richards, Quantitative microscopical techniques for single cells. *In* "The Cell" (J. Brachet and A. E. Mirsky, eds.), Vol. 1, pp. 91–138. Academic Press, New York, 1959.
71. Zanker, V., Allgemeine Grundlagen der Photometrie und Spektrometrie. *Acta Histochem.* **9**, 101–112 (1960).
72. Zanotti, L., Rilevamento di curve spettrali per l'applicazione, in istofotometria, del metodo a "due lunghezze d'onde." *Mikroskopie* **17**, 285–290 (1962).

A ONE-WAVELENGTH, TWO-AREA METHOD IN CYTOPHOTOMETRY FOR CELLS IN SMEARS OR PRINTS

A. Mariano Garcia

and

Robert Iorio*

DEPARTMENT OF ANATOMY, STATE UNIVERSITY OF NEW YORK,
UPSTATE MEDICAL CENTER,
SYRACUSE, NEW YORK

The aim of the present chapter is to discuss a method which computes the extinction of flat absorbing structures, such as nuclei in smears, regardless of their shape. No changes in wavelength are required, so this technique can be used with simple instruments.† The equations involved and the preliminary results have been discussed elsewhere (*12*).

I. Derivation of the Formula

Let us consider a flat absorbing structure such as the nucleus of a monocyte, which has been stained by means of the Feulgen nuclear reaction. Assume for operating purposes that the solid "packed" chromophores are distributed at random within the nucleus (*15, 28*). If we call the nuclear area A_1, the total nuclear extinction E_1 becomes

$$E_1 A_1 = \left(\log \frac{1}{T_1} \right) A_1, \tag{1}$$

where T_1 is the transmittance obtained through a nuclear plug which should be approximately constant for that particular cell (*16*) provided, of course, that no perinuclear or nonabsorbing space is included in the plug.

*Supported by N.I.H. Training Program in Anatomical Sciences 5 T I GM 326.
† Most of the equipment used in the present study was purchased with State University of New York funds.

239

If the photometric area is enlarged to $A_i > A_1$ so that it encompasses not only the whole nucleus, A_1, but also some nonabsorbing space owing to the irregular shape of the latter, the total transmittance for A_i becomes

$$T_i = T_1 \frac{A_1}{A_i} + \frac{A_i - A_1}{A_i}, \tag{2}$$

where $T_1(A_1/A_i)$ is the transmittance of the nucleus times the fraction of the total area it occupies, and $(A_i - A_1)/A_i$ is the fraction of the area with transmittance equal to one. Therefore,

$$T_i A_i = T_1 A_1 + A_i - A_1 = (T_1 - 1)A_1 + A_i \tag{3}$$

and

$$T_i A_i - A_i = (T_i - 1)A_i = (T_1 - 1)A_1. \tag{4}$$

If the second and third expressions of Eq. (4) are multiplied by -1,

$$(1 - T_i)A_i = (1 - T_1)A_1. \tag{5}$$

From Eq. (5) it can be seen that "one minus transmittance" times its corresponding area is constant for a given nucleus (11, 12). The values of T_i and A_i can be readily obtained. [See the preceding chapter (13) for the computation of areas as a function of the phototube response.] From Eq. (5) the calculation of A_1 poses no problem, regardless of how irregular its shape might be, so that

$$A_1 = \frac{(1 - T_i)A_i}{(1 - T_1)}. \tag{6}$$

Finally, the Feulgen-DNA value per nucleus is found as

$$E_1 A_1 = \left(\log \frac{1}{T_1}\right) \frac{(1 - T_i)A_i}{(1 - T_1)}. \tag{7}$$

II. Steps for the Calculations

(1) Choose a nucleus and determine the transmittance (T_1) through a nuclear plug.

(2) Replace the cell in the center, open the photocathode diaphragm so that the whole nucleus and some free area are included, and find the transmittance T_i.

(3) Determine the value of A_i (the area used in step 2) by visual reading of diameters or as a function of photocathode response. Linearity should be checked if the second method is chosen.

(4) Compute $1 - T_i$ and multiply it by A_i.

(5) Compute $1 - T_1$.

(6) Divide (4) by (5). This will give the value of A_1.

(7) Obtain the extinction of the nuclear plug $(\log(1/T_1))$.

(8) Multiply the result of step 6 by that of step 7.

(9) If logarithms to the base 10 have been used, and a comparison is desired with results obtained by the two-wavelength method using Patau's or Mendelsohn's tables (*27, 19*), multiply the value of step 8 by 1.15. [See Garcia (*11*) or (*12*) for details.]

III. Material and Methods

"Set 3" of Feulgen-stained human leukocytes, discussed in the preceding chapter (*13*), and the cytophotometer built by the Canal Industrial Corp., Bethesda, Maryland, were used for the present study. Cells were measured simultaneously by the two-wavelength method of Ornstein and Patau (*25, 27*), and by the presently described procedure. As before, no correction was made between slides* to ascertain the maximal experimental variation. The statistical model discussed elsewhere (*10*) enables us to analyze and evaluate some of the factors contributing to the overall spread of results. The cytophotometer was equipped with a 3× ocular. This insures a minimal photometric area convenient for the two-wavelength technique, but sometimes makes obtaining nuclear plugs difficult, especially in the case of twisted nuclei such as granulocytes (see below).

IV. Results

The results are shown in Table I. With the exception of the monocytes,

TABLE I

BASIC FUCHSIN-FEULGEN-DNA VALUES OF HUMAN LEUKOCYTES.
ONE-WAVELENGTH, TWO-AREA METHOD

Statistics[a]	Granulocytes	Lymphocytes	Monocytes	All types
Means	19.47	20.07	17.80	19.14
Number of cells	12	46	35	93
SD apparatus	1.75	0.79	1.20	1.12
CV apparatus	9%	4%	7%	6%
SD between cells	0.12	2.07	2.92	2.34
CV between cells	0.6%	10%	16%	12%

[a] Mean SD (and CV) between slides: 1.37 (7%). Mean SD (and CV) between populations: 1.18 (6%).

the results are comparable with those obtained with the two-wavelength method. The lower mean of the monocytes stems from the difficulty in

* Expressions such as "between cells," "between slides," and so forth instead of "among cells" and "among slides" are used in statistics in discussing analysis of variance.

obtaining nuclear plugs without light leakage which reduces the extinctions. However, the coefficient of variation (CV), between populations is only 6%, in spite of the variety of distributional problems offered by leukocytes. The histograms are depicted in Fig. 1, and above the line of

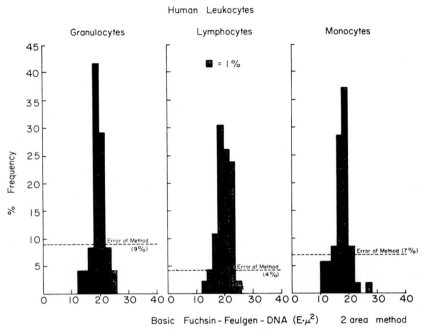

FIG. 1. Histograms per cell type.

experimental error they look strongly unimodal with a maximal spread of plus or minus 10%

V. Discussion

Scanning techniques and the two-wavelength method are unquestionably the best ways to solve for distributional errors. The first procedure requires a rather complex apparatus whose scanning device varies according to the model, plus a circuit with a logarithmic response and an integrator (1, 7, 9, 14, 15, 17, 21, 22). The second procedure must cope with stringent requirements of voltage stability, light purity, and accurately chosen wavelengths (8, 11, 13, 18–20, 25, 27–30). For minimal thickness, as in the case of smears, the transmittances increase so that the real differences between specimen and reference readings tend to be obscured by photomultiplier noise (*23, 28*). Even with the best instruments presently available, such as Deeley's microdensitometer (*6, 7*), Jansen's scanner (*15*), the Pollister-Ornstein double beam ratio reporter (*28*), or the Canalco cytophotometer, the total coefficient of variation ranges from 5 to 10%.

The method presented here must be judged empirically to evaluate its limitations and possible advantages, which are as follows:

(1) In comparison with the two-wavelength method there is some degree of distributional error. The mean for monocytes is lower than the corresponding figures for granulocytes and lymphocytes. This could be due to the small power of the ocular used. A 5× ocular might be preferable since obtaining pure nuclear plugs without concomitant glare would thus become feasible (*24, 26*).

(2) This variation in means is only 6% for three types of cells having quite different nuclear configurations. It seems difficult indeed to imagine or select a model system with a greater variety of distributional problems than peripheral leukocytes, and the method in question solves these problems within 6% limits. The grand mean is 5% lower than the one computed using the two-wavelength method, but the coefficients of variation fall within the same range (*13*). An inspection of the histograms corroborates the numerical findings; the mode lies at 19 units in the three cases, and above the line of error the frequencies spread out between 16 and 24 as maximal values. Assuming a similar spread for the tetraploid mode, at least 70% of the class intervals should remain free, so that any increase in spread due to DNA synthesis could be detected by the accurate tracing of the distributional profiles.

(3) It can be inferred from the preceding paragraphs that at least 94% of the errors of this method are nonsystematic ones. The similarity of means and the almost identical frequency curves for diversified absorbing textures are a good proof of its validity when used within the realm of its physical limitations. This is in agreement with Pollister and Ornstein's assertion that "the chromatin packages are for all practical purposes distributed at random within the nuclei" (*28*), and this seems to hold even for extreme cases such as the lobulated nucleus of the granulocyte where the plug must be small and confined to one particular lobe. A similar conclusion has been reached by Jansen (*15*).

(4) The method offers one practical advantage. Both measurements can be performed at the level of maximal absorbance, and the extinction is computed from the intranuclear transmittance so that the noise of the apparatus, which increases with the logarithmic conversion, is brought to a minimum. The computation of the area based in $(1 - T_i)$ shows, of course, a greater fluctuation owing to the inclusion of free areas, which

results in a rise in transmittance. However, since $(1 - T_i)$ is used as such, without further transformation, the errors do not increase significantly. This, in addition to the fact that only one wavelength is required and that monochromaticity of light and linearity of the photocathode are less important than with the two-wavelength method, where the very success of the operation depends upon them, makes this method advisable for those who work with simple machines and circuits not perfectly stabilized. It is by far more accurate than any procedure based on visual estimate of areas, provided that two limitations are kept in mind: (a) the method can be used only with smears, and (b) all specimens must be fixed and stained simultaneously in order to reduce differences in chromatin clumping brought about by more than one fixative.

REFERENCES

1. Box, H. C., and H. G. Freund, Flying-spot microscope adapted for quantitative measurements. *Rev. Sci. Instr.* **30,** 28–30 (1959).
2. Caspersson, T., Quantitative cytochemical methods for the study of cell metabolism. *Experientia* **11,** 45–60 (1955).
3. Caspersson, T., F. Jacobson, and G. Lomakka, An automatic scanning device for ultramicrospectrography. *Exptl. Cell Res.* **2,** 301–303 (1951).
4. Caspersson, T., G. Lomakka, and L. Carlsson, Eine Instrumentausrüstung für quantitative Cytochemie. *Acta Histochem.* **9,** 139–156 (1960).
5. Caspersson, T., A. Lomakka, and G. Svensson, A coordinated set of instruments for optical quantitative high resolution cytochemistry. *Exptl. Cell Res.* Suppl. **4,** 9–24 (1957).
6. Deeley, E. M., An integrating microdensitometer for biological cells. *J. Sci. Instr.* **32,** 263–267 (1955).
7. Deeley, E. M., Scanning apparatus for the quantitative estimation of deoxyribonucleic acid content. *Biochem. Pharmacol.* **4,** 104–112 (1960).
8. Duijn, P. van, E. M. den Tonkelaar, and M. J. Hardonk, An improved apparatus for quantitative cytochemical model studies and its use in an experimental test of the two-wavelength method. *J. Histochem. Cytochem.* **10,** 473–481 (1962).
9. Freed, J. J., and J. L. Engle, Development of the vibrating-mirror flying-spot microscope for ultraviolet spectrophotometry. *Ann. N.Y. Acad. Sci.* **97,** 412–430 (1962).
10. Garcia, A. M., Studies on DNA in leucocytes and related cells of mammals. I: On microspectrophotometric errors and statistical models. *Histochemie* **3,** 170–178 (1962).
11. Garcia, A. M., Studies on DNA in leucocytes and related cells of mammals. II: On the Feulgen reaction and two-wavelength microspectrophotometry. *Histochemie* **3,** 178–194 (1962).
12. Garcia, A. M., A one-wavelength, two-area method in microspectrophotometry for pure amplitude objects. *J. Histochem. Cytochem.* **13,** 161–167 (1965).
13. Garcia, A. M., and R. Iorio, Potential sources of error in two-wavelength cytophotometry. This volume, p. 215.

14. Hoffman, J. G., Flying spot methods for measuring DNA and the nucleocytoplasmic volume ratio in tissue cells. *Ann. N.Y. Acad. Sci.* **97**, 380–394 (1962).
15. Jansen, M. T., A simple scanning cytophotometer. *Histochemie* **2**, 342–347 (1961).
16. Korson, R., A microspectrophotometric study of red cell nuclei during pyknosis. *J. Exptl. Med.* **93**, 121–128 (1951).
17. Lomakka, G., A recording function transformer and integrator for microspectrophotometric use. *Exptl. Cell Res.* **9**, 434–445 (1955).
18. Mendelsohn, M. L., The two-wavelength method in microspectrophotometry. I: A microspectrophotometer and tests on model systems. *J. Biophys. Biochem. Cytol.* **4**, 407–414 (1958).
19. Mendelsohn, M. L., The two-wavelength method in microspectrophotometry. II: A set of tables to facilitate calculations. *J. Biophys. Biochem. Cytol.* **4**, 415–424 (1958).
20. Mendelsohn, M. L., The two-wavelength method in microspectrophotometry. IV: A new solution. *J. Biophys. Biochem. Cytol.* **11**, 509–513 (1961).
21. Mendelsohn, M. L., W. A. Kolman, and R. C. Bostorm, Initial approaches to the computer analysis of cytophotometric fields. *Ann. N.Y. Acad. Sci.* **115**, 998–1009 (1964).
22. Montgomery, P. O'B., W. A. Bonner, and J. E. Cook, Flying and stepping spot television microscopy. *J. Roy. Microscop. Soc.* **83**, 73–77 (1964).
23. Moses, M. J., Discussion following Richards, B. M., P. M. B. Walker, and E. M. Deeley, Changes in nuclear DNA in normal and ascites tumor cells. *Ann. N.Y. Acad. Sci.* **63**, 831–846 (1956).
24. Naora, H., Schwarzschild-Villiger effect in microspectrophotometry. *Science* **115**, 248–249 (1952).
25. Ornstein, L., The distributional error in microspectrophotometry. *Lab. Invest.* **1**, 250–265 (1952).
26. Ornstein, O., and A. W. Pollister, Schwarzschild-Villiger effect in microspectrophotometry. *Science* **116**, 203–204 (1952).
27. Patau, K., Absorption microphotometry of irregular shaped objects. *Chromosoma* **5**, 341–362 (1952).
28. Pollister, A. W., and L. Ornstein, The photometric chemical analysis of cells. *In* "Analytical Cytology" (R. C. Mellors, ed.), 2nd ed., pp. 431–518. McGraw-Hill, New York, 1959.
29. Schiemer, H. G., Inhomogenitätsfehler bei cytophotometrischen Messungen. *Acta Histochem.* **9**, 174–179 (1960).
30. Zanotti, L., Rilevamento di curve spettrali per l'applicazione, in istofotometria, del metodo a "due lunghezze d'onde." *Mikroskopie* **17**, 285–290 (1962).

COLOR FILM CYTOPHOTOMETRY

John W. Kelly*

DEPARTMENT OF ANATOMY,
TUFTS UNIVERSITY SCHOOL OF MEDICINE,
BOSTON, MASSACHUSETTS

"Cytophotometry" is a convenient term summarizing the application of photometric techniques to cells or to biological samples in the size range of cells (15). Some form of microscope must be introduced into the photometric train. Measurement of the light intensities encountered can be visual, although it is generally photoelectric or photographic. Analysis most commonly involves absorption of radiant energy by the object, with fluorescence emission or optical interference being increasingly exploited today.

It is the purpose of this chapter to describe the use of "white" light and ordinary color film, with or without a comparison microscope, as a combination for measuring the amount of absorbing chromophore (for example, stain or natural pigment) in a microscopic object. In most circumstances, it is believed that the method will prove as rapid as any photoelectric procedure for measuring absorption. Under the most favorable conditions, the color film method can be many times faster than any existing procedure. It is simple enough so that many types of problems can be immediately handled by the inexperienced investigator with the acquisition of essentially no highly specialized equipment.

I. General Background

Other authors in this volume have presented elements of the broad background necessary to understand the photographic method, especially Garcia and Iorio (6a), Hale (7a), Mendelsohn (14a), Rudkin (22a), Sandritter (23a,b), and Swift (25). The aims of photographic cytopho-

* Research underlying certain statements in this chapter was supported by grants from the National Institute for Arthritis and Metabolic Diseases (AM-06071, AM-08939) and National Heart Institute (H-1889).

tometry are identical with those of any photoelectric approach. However, two features of the pioneer work of Caspersson (*4*) are emphasized here. First, Caspersson used positive photographic images, not the objects themselves, for the final densitometry which gave essentially qualitative spectral analyses of cellular nucleoproteins. Second, the densitometry itself was laboriously carried out in many points over the object image, in order to approximate the average absorbance of the typically inhomogeneous cell. While measuring facility was a desirable goal, it was for far more fundamental reasons that Caspersson forecast in the early work the need for some rapid means of measuring the "total extinction" of a microphotometric field. In more or less chronological order, there followed the "spot-measuring" techniques of Pollister and his associates (*22*, *25*), scanning methods of Caspersson (*5*, *6*) and others, and the two-wavelength modification generally applied now in spot measuring to detect distributional error and measure in its presence (*19*, *21*).

There has curiously been no wide recognition of the novel photographic method of Ornstein (*19*), which seemed theoretically equivalent or superior to the most elegant scanning procedures. Given a perfect method of photographic reproduction, the following pertinent relations would exist:

(1) Optical properties of the object and its photographic image will correspond in every point, regardless of the image magnification.

(2) If absorbers in the object and its images conform to the same photometric laws, there will be proportionality between mass per unit area of the respective absorbers.

(3) "Optical advantage" of an enlarged image, with respect to mass per unit areas of the absorbers, will be proportional to the square of the magnification.

Thus, Ornstein considered the photomicrographic enlargement to be a scaled-up "chemical model" of an object too small to dissect and analyze by ordinary chemical means. A typical $2000\times$ print might contain 4 million times as much chromophore as the amount in the original object.

After making a positive black-and-white print of an object in monochromatic light, Ornstein extracted and measured the amount of reduced silver in the image, minus silver in a corresponding blank area, yielding an estimate of the total amount of chromophore in the microscopic object. The analogy to point-by-point densitometry of positive prints is obvious. It intuitively appears that the extraction method offers a better estimate of the "true" amount of silver in the image than the densitometric method. Only Niemi (*18*) applied the silver method in a study of erythrocytes in human anemias.

Photomicrographic control appeared about equally difficult, whether one applied chemical extraction or densitometry to silver analysis. Errors in the silver analysis by extraction were considered relatively high. Ornstein (20) later described the use of a type of color film that simplified the chemical manipulations and reduced over-all measuring error. The basis was the conversion of a black-and-white image to a monochrome image (blue azo dye, for instance), in which quantitative relationships are maintained. It then became much easier to extract and measure the monochrome dye than the original silver. While a marked net gain in precision was the important outcome of this modification, the monochrome method still required the same high degree of photomicrographic control as the silver analytical process, and the new requirement of making one's own monochromes seemed to equate with the technical difficulties of measuring the silver.

Monochromes were also prepared and tested by Mendelsohn (14), who measured the film dyes densitometrically in the intact transparencies, merely noting that the same results should be obtainable by extraction of the dyes for ordinary solution spectrophotometry. Mendelsohn found the photographic method in conjunction with the two-wavelength procedure generally equivalent to scanning methods. Unique advantages of photographic images over original objects were the possibilities of analysis (a) of low-contrast objects, including gray and black, (b) of objects stained with compound or metachromatic dyes, and (c) of objects stained with a single dye in the presence of nonspecific background staining. None of these is measurable by direct photoelectric approaches to the microscopic image of an object.

In summary, the following assumptions formed the immediate background for investigating the present photographic mode of cytophotometry:

(1) A photomicrograph appears capable of gathering more absorption information from a projected image than any scanning procedure, and only television scanning can match photography for speed.

(2) If a photographic image did not record the "photometric effect" (Section III, A) accurately in the first place, no form of photoelectric densitometry would exist. Therefore, the assumption is made here that chemical estimation of image silver is superior to photoelectric estimation (Section III, C).

(3) The chemical estimate made via monochromes is apparently much easier and more precise than classical silver analyses although equally tedious, since monochromes must be prepared in the investigator's own laboratory.

(4) In the absence of commercial supply and processing of mono-

chromes, it was finally assumed that ordinary commercial color films, which are convenient packages of *three* monochromes, might be adaptable to quantitative cytophotometry.

II. Outline of Photographic Cytophotometry

The details of photographic cytophotometry with color film and a dual microscope have been published elsewhere (*9, 11*). A single source feeds light through a beam-splitter to two microscopes. The microscopes are fitted with a comparison eyepiece to obtain a photomicrograph of both fields on the same film frame or plate. From appropriate areas cut out of the films, film dyes are extracted into known volumes of a solvent. The resulting solutions are measured, usually in a recording spectrophotometer, to obtain corresponding full spectra of the dyes. At present, the area under each spectrum (absorbance integral) is measured over the entire visible region to give relative amounts of film dye per unit area of film. The integrals are best estimates of "amount of chromophore" in the original microscopic object. This procedure will be described more fully below.

The original photographic method of Ornstein (*20*) called for the use of monochromatic light, monochrome positive prints, and a single microscope. It therefore seems necessary to explain briefly the rationale for substitution of polychromatic ("white") light, trichrome transparencies, and a dual microscope.

A. Color Films

Films of the type we are concerned with are called *trichrome* films because they depend upon only three dyes to reproduce the most complex of object colors. The translation of the complex color into a simpler language depends upon the removal (absorption) of varying proportions of major bands from the white light usually used for photography; such films are therefore called *subtractive* trichromes. In a transparency, the light is absorbed by only one passage through the film. Prints, including Polacolor, are simply transparencies fixed upon a dead-white matrix (for instance, baryta, barium oxide or sulfate) over a paper base. In the print, the light is absorbed once on the inbound passage and once more on the reflected, outbound passage. Thus, it was found that the relative absorptivities of Kodachrome II daylight and Polacolor films are approximately in the ratio 1.6 : 1. (This does not mean that amounts of dyes or magnitudes of visual effects are in the same ratio. The information was gained by integrating the absorbance of comparable areas of the two films between the limits of 380 and 720 mμ.)

The essential color process, a complex of many steps, may be considered in two major stages. The first stage is comparable with black-and-white photography, in which a latent image is formed by the action of light upon a photosensitive silver halide "emulsion" layer. The second stage is removal of the negative silver image that could have been formed, leaving in its place a positive colored reproduction in terms of one or more dyes. This is actually done by arranging the emulsion in three separate layers, each layer sensitized to a different region of the spectrum and filtered appropriately, so that silver activated by more or less of the selected spectral energy will "couple" with more or less of the three final dyes which form the transparency.

Some subtractive films (for instance, Kodachrome) are designed to allow the couplers to be added from solution during the film processing. Others (for example, Ektachrome) are "integral tripack" films in which the couplers are already components of the emulsion. The integral tripack might be better adapted to the present process than Kodachrome, which has been used for most of the investigations.

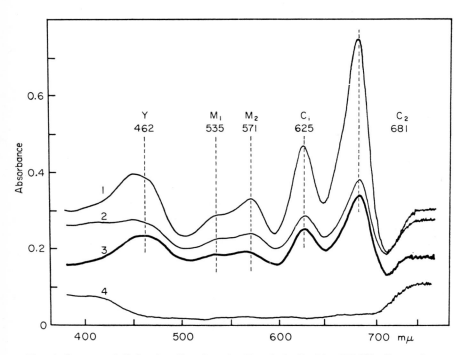

FIG. 1. Spectra of Polacolor film dyes in dimethylsulfoxide (DMS). Curve 1 was obtained from an *unexposed* 6.0-mm disk in 1.0-ml DMS. Curves 2 and 4 were obtained respectively from *unexposed* and fully *exposed* 7.15-mm disks in 3.0-ml DMS. These three solutions were read against DMS. Curve 3 is the "difference spectrum" of solution 2 when read against solution 4.

The spectral properties of Kodachrome II daylight dyes in solution have been shown elsewhere (11). The spectrum shows peaks of absorbance corresponding to the yellow (425 mμ), magenta (550 mμ), and cyan (695 mμ) dyes. In the subtractive language, it can be seen how these dyes may also be called "minus-blue," "minus-green," and "minus-red."

Figure 1 shows the spectral properties of Polacolor in solution. Polacolor is also a subtractive film, in which *all* processing steps take place by a proprietary transfer process, in terms of components incorporated into the film pack. There are only three final dyes, although the spectrum of Fig. 1 seems to show five. The yellow dye has an absorbance peak at 462 mμ. The magenta (525 mμ and 571 mμ) and cyan (625 mμ and 681 mμ) dyes are each associated with a double absorbance peak, in which the ratio between the peaks is a fixed value.

B. "White" versus Monochromatic Light

Under appropriate conditions, colorimetry by visual comparison or filter photometry may achieve a high degree of precision in problems involving the determination of concentration of a colored substance in solution. "While the eye can estimate only roughly the absolute magnitudes of photometric quantities, it can determine with considerable precision when the two properly juxtaposed parts of a photometric field are equally bright—provided, of course, that the two fields are of the same chromaticity, as is usually the case in visual spectrophotometry. In a visual spectrophotometer, therefore, the photometric part of the instrument includes (1) means for securing a uniformly bright two-part photometric field and (2) means for varying the luminance of one or both parts of the field in a continuous, easily adjustable, and known manner, so that when the eye indicates equality of match the desired spectrophotometric ratio can be determined" (7).

A "white light spectrophotometer" is easily conceived, but quite impractical. In such an instrument, an array of properly filtered photoreceivers would see the spectrum in more or less discrete, narrow bands, but would simultaneously record the total radiant flux. A system fundamentally analogous to this was actually used in early color photography when some films were made on the assumption that the best reproduction of a complex color would naturally require a large number of final dyes in the emulsion. An entirely satisfactory abridgment of the theoretical ideal has been effected in the current use of only three dyes.

C. The Comparison Microscope

Ornstein (20), Mendelsohn (14), and Niemi (18) have clearly shown that excellent quantitative absorption information may be obtained from a group of microscopic objects simultaneously photographed within a single field. Ornstein pointed out that a *second* field may be directly related to the first only if one microscopic object is made common to both fields. However, it is not always possible to relate fields geometrically— consider cytological preparations in which there is a sparse population of the cells of interest. It would never be possible to so relate two fields located in different preparations. Thus arose the idea of using a comparison microscope. The general management of temporary and permanent standards in a comparison microscope, to control variations among film frames, films, and emulsions and between the microscopes has been outlined elsewhere (*9*).

There are even more specific reasons for having a comparison microscope available than merely to cover adequately a single smear or encompass more than one smear. There is a need in microspectrophotometry to establish standards which compare to those universally employed in the ordinary spectrophotometric analysis of solutions. There can be no "ideal" standard for the microscopic work. Minute bits of natural fibers, paper, plastics, glasses, and various droplets have been used in the past, usually in a qualitative manner. The general applications of such microscopic standards have been discussed in relation to a quantitative study of dye binding by various protein microdroplets, using the Caspersson ultramicrospectrograph, microinterferometry, and X-ray microabsorption (*10*).

The special role of the comparison microscope is most evident when it is realized that a given standard object, for example, a "weighed" droplet of DNA or protein, cannot be placed into every preparation that might be of measuring interest. Therefore, it is highly desirable to have an option of photographically comparing the standard with any number of cytological objects, especially when the standard, or standards, and the cells have been treated identically in a cytochemical procedure.

D. SUMMARY: COLOR FILM, WHITE LIGHT, AND COMPARISON MICROSCOPY

There appear to be the following advantages in the combination which is now proposed for quantitative cytophotometry:

(1) Theoretically, photography is a better sampling and estimating procedure for heterogeneous absorption than any photoelectric procedure. It is faster than the latter, with the exception of television scanning, and requires no elaborate equipment.

(2) Primary absorption information may be obtained photographically from more than one object at a time in a single exposure. Only television can approach this performance. Spot-measuring or scanning procedures must be in effective contact with only one object at a time.

(3) Light source fluctuations, both in color balance and intensity, are eliminated by use of a single source and a beam splitter.

(4) Photographic variables, both in the films and in processing, are nullified by the act of taking two photomicrographs on the same frame or plate. This remains an area of undue critical control for any other photographic procedure, whenever it is impossible to perform all manipulations upon a single photomicrograph or two "interlocked" photomicrographs.

III. Photographic and Photometric Relationships

It is necessary here to emphasize only certain laws or relationships which are most closely related to the subject of this chapter. A background in photochemistry will be found in most textbooks of physical chemistry. Quantitative aspects of photography are treated in detail by Mees (13) and Baines (2). Unspecified references in this section may be found in one of the latter source books.

A. THE PHOTOCHEMICAL EFFECT: RECIPROCITY LAW

In an ideal photochemical reaction in solution, the product is a function of illumination intensity, I, and exposure time, t,

$$It = k. \tag{1}$$

Equation (1) is the Bunsen–Roscoe law, often called "reciprocity law" because of the reciprocal relation between intensity and exposure time. It may closely approximate the extent of a photochemical reaction in solution and even in a thin layer of photosensitive grains, but reciprocity law "failure" is the rule rather than the exception for practical film emulsions. In other words, an exposure of unit intensity and 100 seconds is almost never equivalent to that of 100 units intensity and one second. There is an optimal region of sensitivity for each photographic emulsion.

Within the optimal region and for a given intensity and exposure time, it is obvious that a variety of absorbers—chemical solutions, filters, smoke, stained objects—may be caused to modulate the extent of the photochemical reaction on a film emulsion. This is the basis for any application of the Bunsen–Roscoe relationship in photometry.

B. OPTICAL DENSITY AND EXPOSURE

In practical photography and in most applications of photometry, the actual amount of silver deposited in an emulsion by the action of light is not so important as reduction in the *transparency, T,* of a fully unexposed layer. In 1890, Hurter and Driffield published a definitive study of the relation between transparency, opacity $(1/T)$, and density $(\log 1/T)$.

They found that the density of a film should be proportional to the amount of silver per unit area and, by reciprocity law, to the logarithm of exposure time. For graphical convenience, but more particularly because ratios of intensities, that is, differences of log I, are more important for visual appreciation (cf. Weber–Fechner law) or photographic reproduction than the actual intensities themselves, Hurter and Driffield used the now well-known D-log E curves (Fig. 2). To call these "H-and-D curves" is en-

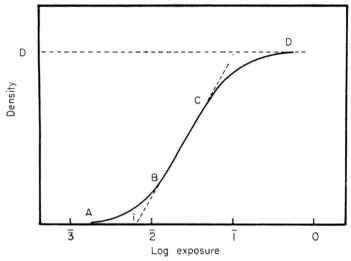

Fig. 2. A typical H-and-D curve. AB is the "toe" and CD is the "shoulder." The interval of correct exposure is the straight-line portion, BC, whose slope is γ. If density is measured above fog, i is the inertia point.

tirely unambiguous. While the slope, γ, of the curve is characteristic of the emulsion under specified conditions of processing—it is loosely used as a measure of contrast—there is a certain inaccuracy in calling it a "characteristic curve." The only objection to the widely used "D-log E" expression is that both E, meaning here exposure time, and D have been widely used in spectrophotometry to mean "extinction" and "optical density." However, partly for this reason, the latter terms have now been widely replaced by the term "absorbance," A (7).

In any application of photographic photometry, it will usually be specified that the correct exposure range must not extend beyond the limits of the straight-line portion of the appropriate H-and-D curve.

C. EVALUATION OF DENSITY

There are two ways of looking at the "amount" of a photographic image. One of these is chemical, being some suitable estimate of the actual amount of silver deposited per unit area. The other is physical, as in photoelectric densitometry. While the first method is more logical and usually more accurate (13), convenience has dictated that the latter is still more widely used in ordinary photometry and it was the method first applied by Caspersson (see Section I) in his early version of cytophotometry.

The classical method of silver analysis is gravimetry. In the present context, this method was abandoned by Ornstein (20), who found its contribution to over-all error in the photographic procedure intolerable. It is not known if other methods that have been applied by photographic chemists, always involving preliminary conversion of reduced silver to one of its salts, would be more suitable (13). These include microcolorimetry of colloidal silver sulfide, volumetry with potassium iodide in amperometric or potentiometric end points, and radioactivity measurement, using silver salts of Co^{60} or I^{131}.

However the measurement is made, the conclusion that density is directly proportional to the amount of silver per unit area of film is most usefully stated in terms of the photometric equivalent,

$$P = \frac{D \times 100 \text{ cm}^2}{\text{grams of Ag}}, \tag{2}$$

according to Hurter and Driffield. There is an important analogy between the photometric equivalent and the more general Bouguer–Beer law of ordinary optical theory. The Bouguer–Beer law says that the absorbance, A, of a solution is directly proportional to the concentration, c, of the absorbing solute,

$$A = kc. \tag{3}$$

If we give c the dimensions grams per square centimeter, and rearrange, Eq. (3) becomes

$$k = \frac{A \times \text{cm}^2}{\text{grams}}, \tag{4}$$

showing the identity of P and k. One expresses k in the term "absorptivity"; it may be specified as an "absorption coefficient" in various ways. But its fundamental dimensions are l^2/m or area per unit mass, A being dimensionless. As Hiskey (8) has pointed out, this means that absorptivity is a measure of the "light-blocking power" of a molecule, as if a given mass of substance could be assigned an area proportional to its absorbing ability.

D. Cytophotometry and the Photometric Equivalent

All that has so far been said in this section applies to areas of homogeneous density in the photographic emulsion, since these are the only conditions facing the photographic analyst. For heterogeneous absorption, as in most cellular objects, the prevailing choice has been to measure the object image directly and photoelectrically, eliminating photographic considerations. All photoelectric measurements of heterogeneous absorption, however, whether made on the projected image of the object in a microscope or on the photographic image, must be concerned with a further choice: shall the measurement be made in one large "spot" over the entire object, shall it be made in an arbitrary number of very much smaller spots, or shall it be scanned in a systematic way with a very small "moving" spot? It is unnecessary to enlarge upon this choice as one of the central problems of cytophotometry, since much of this volume is concerned with distributional error and the technical means of measuring in its presence.

Ornstein (19) and Patau (21) independently proposed the "two-wavelength method" for detecting distributional error and measuring absorption where it existed. (It is not widely recognized that the same mathematical treatment is applicable not only to the spot-measuring approach for which it was developed, but also to any system of cytophotometry.) Among the equations established for different cases of distributional error, Ornstein (20, 22) expressed the "amount of chromophore" in a whole photometric field as

$$Q = \sum_i^l \frac{(\log_{10} T_{i\lambda}{}^{-1})A_i}{k_\lambda},$$ (5)

where $T_{i\lambda} = 10^{-kc_i d_i}$, A_i is the area of small region with uniform $T_{i\lambda}$, l is the number of such regions, and k is the absorption coefficient. The photographic method is an application of Eq. (5) and entirely analogous to a scanning procedure. If F_i is the ratio of the area, A_i, to the area S of the entire photometric field, then

$$Q = \frac{S}{k_\lambda} \sum_i^l (\log_{10} T_{i\lambda}{}^{-1})F_i,$$ (6)

which is one form of the scanning equation originally used by Caspersson. Ornstein then developed an expression for the "perfect" negative-print combination based on the equivalent, showing how one term is comparable with superposition on the perfect photograph of a uniform density filter, and that this filter is analogous to a blank cutout area of the same size as the area cut out to include the object. In a simplified version of this expression, the amount of silver per unit area is

$$G_i = G_{ib} + G_{is}.$$ (7)

G_{ib} and G_{is} are the terms relating respectively to the cutout area of "clear" background, A_b, and the cutout area containing the whole image with a small rim, A_s. If the elemental area in the print is A_i, the total silver in the sample area and in the blank area respectively is

$$M_s = \sum_{A_s} G_i A_i \qquad (8)$$

and

$$M_b = \sum_{A_b} G_i A_i. \qquad (9)$$

Equations (7), (8), and (9) are now rewritten as

$$\sum_{A_s} G_i A_i = \sum_{A_s} G_{ib} A_i + \sum_{A_s} G_{is} A_i, \qquad (10)$$

$$M_s = G_{ib} A_s + \sum_{A_s} G_{is} A_i, \qquad (11)$$

and

$$M_b = G_{ib} A_b. \qquad (12)$$

The integrated silver content of the image is then

$$M = M_s - \frac{M_b A_s}{A_b} = \sum_{A_s} G_{is} A_i, \qquad (13)$$

which is directly proportional to the amount of primary chromophore in the object. Ornstein found that the approach based on Eq. (13) yielded data from within a single print with an error of ±3%, for a ±3% variation in illumination intensity and a ±10% variation in exposure and development. But at this point, the troublesome silver determinations were abandoned. Color monochromes were found to be at least as accurate as scanning, and faster and much simpler in terms of equipment. Implicitly, there should be no loss of absorption information in converting a silver image to its monochrome analog.

E. COLOR FILM DENSITOMETRY

The concepts and technology of black-and-white densitometry are applicable, in broad outline, to color film densitometry. Differences originate mainly in the need to analyze a trichrome emulsion in terms of individual dye components making up the image, to sum the total effect of these three absorbers, and to manage particularly the summation in terms of any mixture of radiations. An excellent classification of the modes of color densitometry (or sensitometry) is given by F. Williams (see Mees, 13).

Analytical spectral density is a measure of the proportions of the individual differentiable components making up the image. Although there is no exact analogy for this parameter in black-and-white photography, the H-and-D curve of a silver positive would resemble a single analytical density curve (Fig. 11). Two important features are shown in Fig. 11.

The most obvious is that no real straight-line portion exists in these curves. [There should, indeed, be no linear region of the H-and-D curve (13).] The lack of symmetry of the three curves reflects the differential sensitivity of the three emulsion layers over the entire exposure range, especially at short exposures. These characteristics explain the relatively narrow exposure limits of color films, within which relative densities of the three final dyes will remain in any practical degree of proportionality.

There are simple, if tedious, methods for critically determining the individual absorbers in a set of three from the composite spectrum (8, 13, 26). Based on the solution of three simultaneous equations, the calculations are best made with a desk calculator or special analog computers. Methods of matrix algebra are applicable in many of these analyses as well.

Integral spectral density is a measure of the integrated effect of the composite absorber on radiations of a particular energy distribution, including "white" light. Narrow-band or monochromatic radiations are included under this heading as a special case, spectral density.

While there are theoretical reasons for assuming that the wavelength of radiation should *not* be involved, it is a matter of experience that

$$D = f(I, t, \lambda). \tag{14}$$

The effect of wavelength should merely be to shift the D-log E curve along the log E axis without a change in γ. But γ depends markedly on wavelength, partly because the photoresponsive grains differ markedly in spectral sensitivity. Fortunately, the equation for monochromatic light has been generalized in several forms for mixed radiations, even for practical emulsions. The first of these was the van Kreveld addition law,

$$S(D, \lambda) = \chi(D, t), \tag{15}$$

where $S(D, \lambda)$ is the spectral sensitivity of the emulsion in reciprocal energy units required to produce a given D, that is, inversely proportional to the magnitude of exposure at a given wavelength required to reproduce D in any exposure time. It was then the remarkable conclusion that γ was independent of both t and λ, except that the D-log E curve was stretched along the log E axis by one factor, $f(\lambda) - \phi(t)$, and located on the same axis by a second factor, $f_i(\lambda) - \phi_i(t)$. In 1936, van Kreveld and Ornstein formulated the most general addition law:

$$D = F \frac{\log E - [f_i(\lambda) + \phi_i(t)]}{f(\lambda) + \phi(t)}. \tag{16}$$

Even successive exposures at two different wavelengths were additive.

A more useful analytical form of the addition law, where S is again the reciprocal energy required to produce a given density, is the sensitivity to any mixture of wavelengths,

$$S_m = \frac{aS_1}{a+b+c+\cdots} + \frac{bS_2}{a+b+c+\cdots} + \frac{cS_3}{a+b+c+\cdots} + \cdots, \quad (17)$$

and a, b, c, . . . are amounts of energy at λ_1, λ_2, λ_3, ... For a continuous band of wavelengths of energy distribution $M(\lambda)$, Eq. (17) becomes the integral

$$S_m = \frac{\int S(\lambda)M(\lambda)\,d\lambda}{\int M(\lambda)\,d\lambda}. \quad (18)$$

Thus, the addition law becomes the main basis for using white light in a quantitative application. If a given density is produced in an emulsion at λ_1, λ_2, λ_3, . . . , λ_n by energies e_{λ_1}, e_{λ_2}, e_{λ_3}, . . . , e_{λ_n}, the same density is produced by any combination of these wavelengths with total energy $ae_{\lambda_1} + be_{\lambda_2} + ce_{\lambda_3} + \cdots + ze_{\lambda_n}$, where $a+b+c+\cdots+z = 1$. If a series of color photographs were made of the same field under identical conditions, all photographs would bear the same absorption information unless absorbing objects were interposed in the fields. Then the deviation from unity of the energy factors would be a measure of the respective object chromophore contents.

IV. General Methods and Materials

The best descriptive approach to the methods of photographic cytophotometry appears to be in terms of equipment and materials that are now used. Earlier equipment will be mentioned if pertinent. Sources of supply will be given, unless they are considered to be common knowledge.

Most of the general ground rules that apply to any method of measuring absorbance in cells are applicable to photographic cytophotometry (*16*, *22*, *23*, *27*). This is particularly true in relation to alignment and testing of the photomicrographic assembly, which should always be maintained in optimal operating condition (*1*, *12*, *17*, *22*, *24*).

Photographic cytophotometry may be considered as three major operations: photomicrography, film handling, and spectrophotometry (or chemical photometry).

A. Photomicrography

1. *Light Source*

The first requirements of any light source are that it deliver sufficient power in correct color balance to the film plane. This obviously depends chiefly upon distances and numbers of surfaces in the optical system and upon the particular film used. Stability is highly desirable although stringency of this requirement is considerably reduced whenever the dual microscope is being used. It should be noted that control may be exerted over the color temperature of some lamps by varying the voltage. The lamp should be capable of critical illumination, either Nelson or Köhler type.

For 35-mm films, both tungsten (2900°–3200°K) and zirconium-arc (3100°–3200°K) lamps have proved satisfactory. The tungsten lamp is a typical research type, 6-volt, 15-amp ribbon filament unit. The zirconium-arc is a 15.4-volt, 6.25-amp lamp (Sylvania C-100) in a Mikrark illuminator with dc power supply (Boone Instrument Co., New York City). When the AO-Shea comparison microscope became available, the tungsten lamp was not able to supply the power needed.

Polacolor color balance and intensity requirements were met only by a xenon discharge lamp (Leitz #250 housing, Osram XBO/CSX-150W burner, Siemens VX 150-f-2b-1 power supply). The 6000°–7000°K color temperature of this lamp matches the Polacolor requirement without filtration, and its intensity permits exposures within the recommended reciprocity range of the film. If inhomogeneity of the arc image presents any problems, a Leitz diffusing disk is available.

TABLE I

FILTERS USED FOR VARIOUS FILM AND LIGHT-SOURCE COMBINATIONS

Type	Examples	Applications
Daylight blue	Corning 742, Bausch & Lomb 31-34-88	Color balance: Kodachrome II daylight or Kodachrome daylight with tungsten or zirconium arc lamps.
Heat-absorbing	Leitz KG-1	Remove for Polacolor (inside xenon housing).
	Leitz BG-32	Protection between exposures (in xenon rack).
	Water, approximately 8 cm	For Polacolor exposure. Use no other filters.
Neutral density	Bausch & Lomb 31-34-38-01	Intensity regulation: No significant change in color balance. Set of 0.3, 0.6, 0.9, 1.2 relative density.
Yellow-orange	Wratten G, Wratten E-2	Contrast: Focusing aid. For bluish stains.
Green	Wratten X-1 #11	For reddish stains.
Red	Wratten F, Klett #99	For greenish stains.

2. *Filters*

Filters are used here for several purposes. They may be required to regulate over-all light intensity and/or color balance, to absorb heat, or to adjust intensity between the two microscopes. They are useful for temporarily increasing visual contrast during focusing. The main filter is located between lamp and beam splitter, controlling both microscopes. Balance filters are located between the beam splitter and the microscopes. Table I summarizes the characteristics of some filters that have been used.

3. *Beam Splitter*

The function of the beam splitter is to provide light of equal intensity to each microscope and render the system independent of line-voltage fluctuations. Several schemes are shown in Fig. 3. Although it seems de-

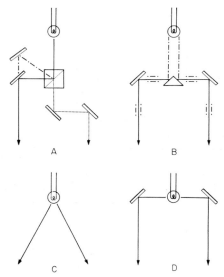

Fig. 3. Four "beam-splitting" schemes. Only *A* is a true beam splitter, in which both beams theoretically possess the same intensity, color, and source geometry. Some degree of intensity regulation is gained by movement of one or both lateral mirrors. *B* is a beam bisector (reversed comparison eyepiece); different cross-sectional halves of the source image go to each microscope. *C* and *D* seem relatively simple but do not meet the geometric requirement and are not adaptable to housed lamps. Collimating lenses are not shown in any of these plans.

sirable that the beam splitter present to each microscope the same source geometry, such a requirement may be too critical for many purposes. Therefore, while a beam splitter of type *A*, Fig. 3, is now used exclusively, others may be permissible.

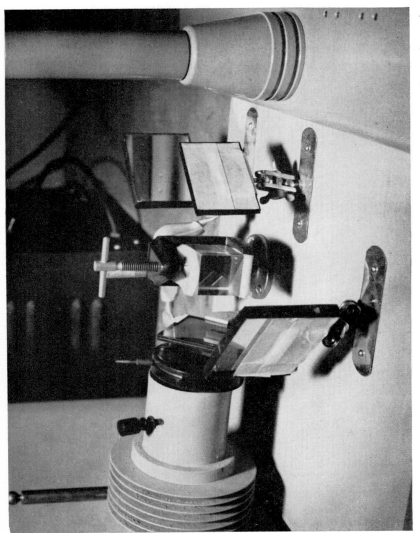

FIG. 4. Home-made beam-splitter assembly, showing the double-prism cube and three first-surface mirrors. Mirrors are mounted on ball-and-socket joints. Here the light source is a zirconium arc.

Commercial beam splitters to match the usual distances that would exist between comparison eyepieces are not available. With reference to *A*, Fig. 3, it would be desirable to be able to move all elements within rather wide limits and to lock them in final position. Stiff ball-and-socket joints for all mirrors in the present beam splitter (Fig. 4) have been useful, but should be replaced in a definitive model.

Beam-splitter units are usually in the form of simple plates or more expensive double-prism cubes. Originally the plate type was used (Bausch & Lomb #45-10, 3 × 50 × 50 mm) and then replaced by a double prism (Fish-Schurman Corp., 70 Portman Road, New Rochelle, New York, Type 74, A50/50N beam splitter). Both of these were satisfactory, although there were significant color differences in the transmitted and reflected beams. A double prism with Inconel coating is now used; it has practically no color difference between the beams (American Optical Co., 1¼-inch

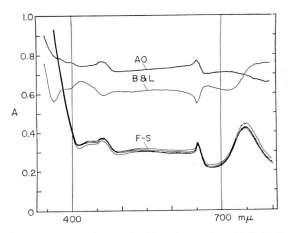

Fɪɢ. 5. Absorbance spectra of two double-prism cubes (AO, F-S) and a beam-splitting plate (B&L). Transmission: reflection ratios were close to 50 : 50 for all three units, though only the AO splitter yielded almost indistinguishable and neutral beams.

cube, crown spectacle glass, $n = 1.523$, mμ value (58.6). Absorbance spectra of these beam splitters are shown in Fig. 5.

4. *Comparison Microscope*

Any pair of "matched" monocular microscopes can be fitted with one of several available comparison eyepieces or bridges to make a comparison microscope. It is preferable that the microscopes focus by stage movement rather than body-tube movement, since the comparison eyepiece will otherwise bind upon the tubes. Apochromatic objectives are recommended, although achromats have been used.

A new comparison microscope assembly, employing the Shea Comparison Bridge, is available from the American Optical Company, completely

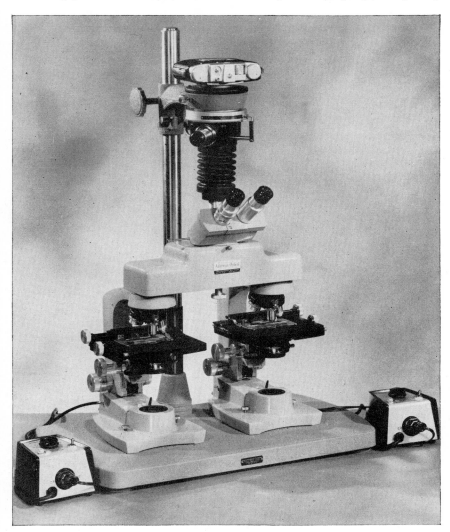

FIG. 6. Shea comparison microscope (American Optical Company). This is the assembly supplied with standard optics, two separate light sources, the Shea comparison bridge, and a 35-mm camera. A specially modified version is described in the text.

furnished for photomicrography (Fig. 6).* This is the best available unit, since the bridge is optically corrected for performance equivalent to that of a single microscope. Furthermore, the bridge permits selection of either left or right fields or any intermediate setting of the divider. Some technical comments detailed below will suggest to the user improvements in any assembly for critical microscopy and photomicrography.

a. *Mirrors.* First-surface mirrors should be used, preferably in a mounting which can be locked. This is a suitable place to point out that even good first-surface mirrors supplied with most microscopes are invariably mounted incorrectly. Unless the axis through the yoke pinions lies in the plane of the mirror surface, it will be impossible to truly align the center of the mirror with both the lamp axis and microscope body-tube axis. In most simple mirror mountings, the pinion axis lies behind the mirror surface. A more elaborate mirror-mounting, as suggested for the beam splitter, would be desirable for the microscopes. It is the ultimate intention to dispense with mirrors altogether by moving the lamp and beam splitter below the microscope table so that their mutual axis coincides with the microscope axis.

b. *Condensers.* For the apochromatic objectives, Abbe achromatic centerable condensers of numerical aperture 1.40 are used.

c. *Objectives.* Zeiss planapochromats are used. Each of these is fitted with its own centering mount, matching a single body part on the microscopes, although satisfactory work can be done with the usual rotating nosepiece. The Zeiss objectives are $10\times$ (numerical aperture 0.32), $25\times$ (numerical aperture 0.65), for coverslips of 0.17-mm thickness, best obtained from a batch of $\#1\frac{1}{2}$ coverslips, and $100\times$ oil-immersion (numerical aperture 1.40). American Optical, Bausch & Lomb, and Reichert objectives have also been used.

d. *Eyepieces.* Compensating eyepieces of $5\times$, $7.5\times$, $10\times$, and $12.5\times$ are available. Only one eyepiece of any particular magnification is required for the camera tube; visual eyepieces are not critical.

e. *Bridge (Comparison Eyepiece).* A Bausch & Lomb comparison eyepiece ($\#31$-15-99) was used for much of the original work. Its ocular is not compensating for apochromatic objectives and since it is an integral part of the unit, cannot be replaced with the correct ocular.

The AO-Shea comparison bridge (K-1418) is a well-designed eyepiece, which must be factory adjusted to the microscopes and body tube and set for the interpupillary distance of the major user. Correcting rings of

* The author is deeply indebted to the American Optical Company, particularly to Mr. D. R. Chamberlain, who was responsible for the loan of a special Shea comparison microscope with AO-Baker interference optics and standard optics, the gift of an Inconel beam splitter, and the benefit of valuable advice over the past 2 years.

8-mm height are used to match each objective to the altered basic tube length of the microscopes (160 mm).

5. *Cameras*

There is no restriction whatsoever on the cameras to be used, although it has been most convenient to use the base, stand, and universal shutter-viewer supplied with the 35-mm and Polaroid cameras for the AO-Shea comparison microscope. The basic size of the film has a direct bearing on the scale of the chemical work to follow (see Section B, 3 below). If a variety of films, including any Polaroid products, will be employed, the Polaroid MP-3 industrial camera is recommended.

6. *Photometers*

There are three basic uses of a photometer in this procedure. A simple exposure meter is needed for the photomicrography (for example, Leitz Microsix L). A more precise wide-range photomultiplier photometer is available to monitor light in any part of the optical train and to carry out photometry in the "spot-measuring" manner (Pacific Photometric Instruments, Box 996, Berkeley, California, Model 50 with RCA 931A, 1P28, and 1P29 photomultiplier tubes in a search unit; a Photovolt 520A instrument was formerly used).

B. FILMS AND FILM HANDLING

1. *Films*

The most experience so far has been with Kodachrome daylight and Kodachrome II daylight 35-mm films. These films now offer no technical difficulties and commercial processing is entirely satisfactory. Some experience with Agfacolor and Ektachrome shows that these and probably many other 35-mm reversal films can be used.

Polacolor work was somewhat spurred by the need at the Tutorial to work with a material that did not need 24–36 hours processing delay. Therefore, there can be no certainty yet that this remarkable film will prove as reliable for quantitation as the 35-mm films, however promising the preliminary work has been.

Polacolor Type 48 roll film is developed after exposure by hand-pulling, which is a feature of some concern in producing even density, as in the image of a clear field. This disadvantage might be eliminated by the use of single-sheet Polacolor. The film should not be mounted before cutting the desired disks for extraction. A print which is not fresh tends to crack and especially to radiate small fissures when the cutting punch is applied, which can cause unnoticed loss of chromophore. The original suppleness and cutting qualities are immediately and safely restored to the film by wiping its surface with a barely moist sponge.

The Kelvin rating of Polacolor is 6250°. Its optimal exposure range is 1/1000–1/10 second, which virtually demands a xenon lamp for the dual microscope.

2. *Film Disks*

Objects are punched or cut out of the films with a background rim as narrow as possible. Nearby blank areas are preferably cut out with the same size punch. However, it is possible to make the blank correction when there must be disparity between object and blank disk areas.

Circular paper punches in a range of sizes are generally used. The cutting edges should be polished by punching many times through the finest ruby cloth. The actual *measured* area of the cutouts must be known for certain critical work (Table II). Weighing of disks is probably not

TABLE II

AREAS OF DISKS CUT BY SARGENT PUNCHES

Die number	Nominal diameter		Area (mm^2)	
	Inches	mm	Calculated	Measured[a]
2	5/32	3.97	12.38	13.61
5	7/32	5.56	24.28	27.10
6	9/32	7.15	40.15	41.90

[a] Based on weights of large card areas and cutouts taken from these.

necessary for most work (Table III), but it is mandatory when irregular

TABLE III

POLACOLOR DISK WEIGHTS[a]

	Fresh	48 hours
Mean weight (mg)	10.283	10.118
Standard deviation	0.059 (0.57%)	0.0074 (0.07%)
Standard error	0.015	0.0018

[a] Sixteen disks were cut from the same unexposed frame, and weighed on the microbalance about 1 hour after development and again after 48 hours in the balance compartment.

cutouts are made, when punches of different sizes must be used, or when there is deliberate removal of extraneous areas from a regular cutout.

Cutouts are impaled on lengths of thin steel wire, in which a steplike kink has been pressed near one end to support the disks freely in the extraction tubes.

Almost any good paper punch will readily cut the films. Heavy-duty punches in a range of useful sizes are used (W. Schellhorn Co., New Haven, Connecticut, "Sargent looseleaf" punches).

The weight range of typical cutouts demands that a microbalance be used for all weighing (Mettler M-5, for example).

3. *Film Extractions*

The purpose of disk extraction is quantitative removal of all film dye from a given film area into solution for photometric measurement of the amount of dye. The solvent now used, dimethylsulfoxide or DMS, CH_3SOCH_3, is an extremely efficient general solvent of low volatility and no absorption in the visible region. It is dispensed from automatic pipettes of high precision in order to reduce this most significant point of error (20). The extractions are carried out in any tubes whose total

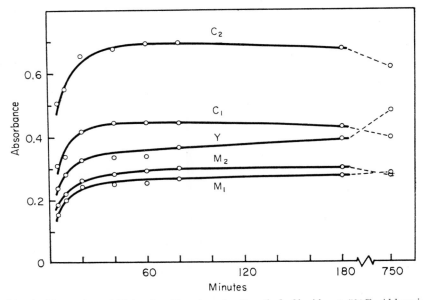

Fig. 7. Extraction of Polacolor film dyes in dimethylsulfoxide at 50°C. Abbreviations are Y, M, and C for the yellow, magenta, and cyan dyes, respectively. Only Y is seriously influenced by rising UV absorption (gelatin?) with prolonged extraction. However, the same experiment showed that there is also a delayed increase in absorption at the deep red end, about 760 mμ. Most points represent absorbance of dyes extracted from one 7.15-mm disk into 1.0-ml DMS. Values for 60 minutes are means of five replicates, with coefficients of variation not greater than 3%.

volumes are about twice the volumes of solvent used and which are tightly sealed with inert rubber (for example, Vacutainers), not glass, since DMS is a "creeper" which will pass through a standard taper joint.

Extractions are carried out in a waterbath or oven at 50°C for 60 minutes. The course of these extractions has been previously shown for Kodachrome in the form of a table (*11*); the same information is presented here for Polacolor graphically (Fig. 7). Film disks may remain in DMS at room temperature indefinitely before extraction and up to at least 24 hours between extraction and measuring. The solutions alone are stable for weeks in the dark. Extraction of disks is complete at room temperature in 12 hours. Kodachrome films leave an amber-stained (yellow filter layer) gelatinous residue after DMS extraction; the residue is not troublesome and the stain has no bearing on the measurement. Polacolor leaves an absolutely clear gelatinous residue which is so soft that it may fall back into the solution and interfere with measurement.

The usual Kodachrome and Kodachrome II disks of 5- to 9-mm diameter are extracted in 3.0 ml of DMS; Polacolor disks of the same size are extracted in 1.0 ml. These relationships insure that even fully unexposed disks will not yield absorbances greater than 0.8 and most cellular objects will yield absorbances of 0.05–0.4.

Automatic pipettes delivering 1.0 ml and 10 ml are used for dispensing of DMS (Labindustries Inc., 1740 University Ave., Berkeley 3, California, "Repipets" #3001, 1.0 ml, and #3010, 10 ml). In one series of 16 aliquots set for 1.0 ml, the smaller pipette delivered with a mean solvent weight of 1.107 g and coefficient of variation of 0.21%.

4. *Spectrophotometry*

A recording spectrophotometer (Bausch & Lomb 505) is used for all work, partly because much investigative interest still remains in the method itself. Routine studies might well be conducted with a manual spectrophotometer or filter photometer, after preliminary work has shown the spectral characteristics resulting from the particular biological material of interest. Cuvettes to contain approximately 0.5–3.0 ml minimum volumes lend versatility to the measuring procedure. All spectra in this laboratory are recorded routinely at 22°C by means of a circulating waterbath and constant-temperature cell holder.

Cuvettes of 1.0-cm path length and various widths are obtainable from several sources (for example, Scientific Cell Corp., 118–21 Queens Blvd., Forest Hills, New York).

No significant wavelength error was found in automatic recording with the present spectrophotometer, based on repeated calibration with a mercury lamp, didymium filter, and numerous familiar solutions. Absorbance error was from about 0.2% at $A = 0.7$ to about 5% at $A = 0.05$. Absorbance readings were arranged to fall within the limits 0.2–0.8 when possible. In a set of 42 duplicate readings made at the peak wavelengths of eight similar Kodachrome II film-dye solutions, the standard deviation of differences was greatest for the yellow dye, 0.8%, and least for the cyan dye. It was concluded that spectrophotometric error does not dominate the overall error of the dual-microscope procedure.

Absorbance, A, is read directly from recorded spectral curves at the peaks associated with the trichrome film dyes in DMS solution: yellow, Y, magenta, M, and cyan, C. The sum of absorbances at these three (Kodachrome II) or five (Polacolor) peaks is designated ΣA. The absorbance integral over the entire visible region is called $\int A$ and is obtained by direct planimetry or by weighing of carefully dissected spectral recordings or tracings. It will always be necessary to prove that the simplest possible reading, A_m for example, is permissible for a given problem.

In measuring cellular chromophore content, one necessarily obtains the *difference* between cell and blank areas, regardless of whether absorbance sums or integrals are used. If integrals are used, the quantities may be obtained in two ways. The first is a direct, one-step recording of the object solution against the blank solution (not against DMS). This procedure is similar to relative transmittancy measurement described by Hiskey (8) for increasing spectrophotometric accuracy. This is probably the method of choice for routine measurements. The second method is to record cell and blank solutions separately against DMS. The only advantage of this

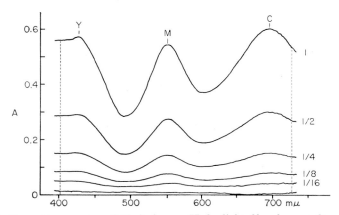

Fig. 8. Absorption spectra of Kodachrome II daylight film dyes at five concentrations in dimethylsulfoxide. The prime solution (1) was an extract of two 5-mm disks in 3.0 ml of solvent. Peak wavelengths are 426 mμ (Y), 552 mμ (M), and 696 mμ (C). Broken lines are limits of areas measured for Fig. 2.

method is that spectral shape relations are maintained. Both methods yield essentially the same data.

It is necessary to show that the particular film dyes used obey the Bouguer–Beer law (Section III, C) in the solvent of choice. Spectral results of a dilution experiment with Kodachrome II are shown in Fig. 8. The spectral data are used to show explicitly the adherence of the film dyes to the Bouguer–Beer law and also to compare different ways of measuring "amount of chromophore" in a given film area (Fig. 9). It

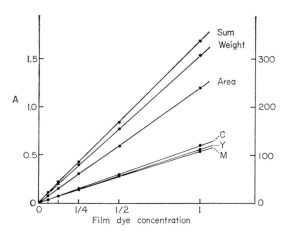

Fig. 9. Comparison among different modes of measuring "amount of dye" in a Kodachrome II daylight film disk, based on the spectra of Fig. 1. Individual peak absorbances, A_y, A_m, and A_c, sums of the peak absorbances ΣA, and weights (grams) of dissected spectral areas are plotted on the left ordinate against relative concentration. Areas (square centimeters) under the curves are similarly plotted on the right ordinate. Weights and areas are estimates of the absorbance integral, $\int A$.

can be seen that A_y, A_m, A_c, ΣA, and $\int A$ are all linearly related to relative concentration of film dyes. This relationship may or may not be true when certain photomicrographic and biological factors are imposed upon the basic spectrophotometric measurement. Numerous measurements of $\int A$ by weighing and planimetry have led to a personal preference for planimetry, although both methods are equally accurate and tedious.

V. Specific Methods

Although major technical aspects of photographic cytophotometry have been thoroughly investigated, especially with Kodacolor films, there has been no opportunity to apply it widely to critical biological materials. This section describes a few crucial tests that have been made with cells as objects.

A. EXPOSURE RANGE

Numerous exposure series have been made with Kodachrome II daylight film. A spectral family obtained from such a series, in which the same film frame was exposed in steps by masking, is shown in Fig. 10.

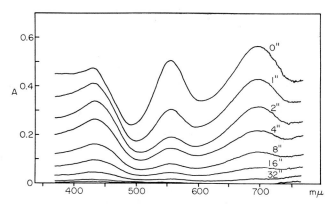

FIG. 10. Absorption spectra of Kodachrome II daylight film, in dimethylsulfoxide solutions (2–5 mm disks in 3.0 ml), exposed for 0–32 seconds to a clear microscopic field at 100× magnification.

Differential sensitivity of the three emulsion layers is reflected by the disproportional changes in curve shape. This is more clearly shown by corresponding analytical spectral density curves (Fig. 11), which are

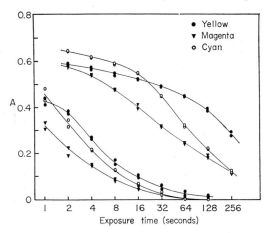

FIG. 11. Analytical spectral density curves. The lower set was constructed from the spectra of Fig. 10, showing a useful exposure range of approximately 3–10 seconds. The upper set was obtained from similar spectra where the film had been exposed to relatively low illumination, yielding no useful exposure range. Each of the sets was based on data from two experiments.

TABLE IV

Total Absorbance of the Image of a Stained Mast Cell at Three Magnification Levels

Square of magnification	Object	Disks		Absorbance, A			ΣA	$\int A$ (cm²)	$\int A_{cell} - \int A_{blank}$	
		Diameter (mm)	Weight (mg)	Yellow 424 mμ	Magenta 552 mμ	Cyan 697 mμ			Raw	Corrected[a]
67,080	Cell	3.6	2.33	0.044	0.037	0.030	0.111	18.1	7.6	5.2
	Blank	3.6	1.90	0.028	0.018	0.015	0.061	10.5		
136,160	Cell	5.5	9.50	0.095	0.084	0.078	0.257	41.3	11.2	11.2
	Blank	5.5	9.50	0.080	0.049	0.051	0.180	30.1		
418,609	Cell	10.3	23.23	0.271	0.289	0.258	0.818	128.1	111.3	34.7
	Blank	4.0	4.18	0.044	0.027	0.026	0.097	16.8		

[a] The corrected integral of absorbance is the product of an integral and the ratio of cell disk weight to blank disk weight.

analogous to H-and-D curves for black-and-white positives (Section III, B). Manipulation of light intensity and/or color temperature of the source will invariably secure an exposure range in which proportionality exists among the peak absorbances of the three dyes.

B. MAGNIFICATION

There should be a direct relationship between the absorption information in a photomicrograph at one magnification and images of the same object at any other magnification, within resolution limits. To test this, a mast cell with cytoplasm stained metachromatically by toluidine blue was photographed at three magnifications. For each magnification, determined by actual measurement in the camera focal plane, the cell image and a contiguous blank area were punched. At the highest magnification, the blank could not be the same size as its cell, the latter occupying most of the field. Table IV summarizes the calculations leading to data which agree rather well with the theoretical linear relation between image chromophore content and the square of the magnification.

C. IMAGE CHROMOPHORE AND EXPOSURE

A key question is whether the image chromophore of a single microscopic object can be measured over a reasonable exposure range. A Feulgen-stained chick erythrocyte nucleus was photographed at 100×

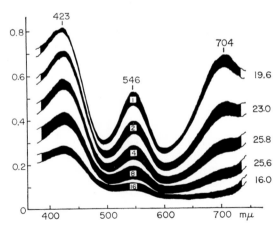

FIG. 12. Relative amounts of Kodachrome II daylight film dyes in five images of a single Feulgen-stained chick erythrocyte nucleus, identical except for exposure time (1–16 seconds). The solid areas are actual differences between the spectra of image and blank solutions. Values of these areas (square centimeters) are shown by large figures at the right. Peak wavelengths of the film dyes, which were extracted in a trypsin-detergent solution, are in millimicrons at the top of the figure.

magnification in exposures of 1–16 seconds. Nonideal conditions existed in the form of strong color background from the beam splitter used when the experiment was performed. Nevertheless, 4- and 8-second exposures gave nearly identical values for the difference between the separately recorded spectra of cell and blank disks (Fig. 12). An exposure range of 3–10 seconds would be acceptable under these conditions.

D. FEULGEN-DNA MEASUREMENT

As a simple Tutorial experiment with the relatively untried Polacolor film, it was decided to measure the Feulgen reaction in a small number of *Vicia faba* nuclei.* The total time for a complete experiment was 2–3 hours, including one hour of "dead time" for extraction. Steps in the procedure were:

(1) Photograph five nuclei in the same field: interphase sisters, anaphase sisters, and a prophase nucleus.

(2) Cut out all nuclei and a blank area with the same punch (9/32-inch nominal diameter, measured area of disk 40 mm²).

(3) Impale disks on wires and place in numbered Vacutainer 2-ml tubes, each containing 1.0 ml DMS. Stopper tightly.

(4) Extract film dyes at 50°–55°C for one hour.

(5) Record the spectrum (350–800 mμ) of the blank solution against DMS in the Bausch & Lomb spectrophotometer, using the "semimicro" cuvettes (1.0-cm path, 0.4-cm width). Similarly record the spectrum of each object solution against the blank solution, directly obtaining "difference spectra." (Alternatively, all solutions can be read against DMS; then the required data are taken from these true spectra by subtracting blank values from corresponding values for each object.)

(6) Using the 535-mμ peak as most stable, record A_{object} minus A_{blank} as a measure of chromophore in the nucleus. (This was done at the Tutorial; absorbances for all other peaks and ΣA were taken later.)

Table V summarizes the data obtained by four Tutorial groups. The mean values obtained are reasonably consistent with expectation, although individual values varied widely. This was partly due to first-time trials of an unfamiliar method by each group and partly due to less than ideal Polacolor prints.

VI. Concluding Remarks

Applications of photographic cytophotometry will generally be identical with those of any other system for measuring absorption in the visible

* *Vicia faba* smears were prepared by Dr. Wolf Prensky, Department of Physiology, Tufts University School of Medicine. I am indebted to Dr. Prensky for his materials and his assistance during the laboratory sessions of the Tutorial.

TABLE V

Vicia faba EXPERIMENT[a]

Stage	No.	462 mμ	535 mμ	571 mμ	625 mμ	681 mμ	ΣA
Interphase sisters	1	0.088	0.084	0.074	0.052	0.057	0.355
		.042	.056	.058	.048	.057	.261
		.073	.061	.057	.040	.066	.297
		.070	.041	.037	.024	.031	.203
		0.068	*0.061*	*0.057*	*0.041*	*0 053*	*0.279*
	2	0.071	0.070	0.066	0.043	0.047	0.297
		.076	.087	.087	.080	.098	.428
		.055	.064	.067	.049	.070	.305
		.051	.036	.035	.011	.000	.133
		0.063	*0.064*	*0.064*	*0.046*	*0.046*	*0.291*
Anaphase sisters	3	0.026	0.031	0.028	0.022	0.030	0.137
		.023	.031	.027	.017	.018	.116
		.034	.012	.013	.006	.016	.081
		.026	.031	.028	.022	.030	137
		0.031	*0.031*	*0.025*	*0.016*	*0.021*	*0.125*
	4	0.055	0.041	0.037	0.020	0.021	0.174
		.025	.035	.034	.032	.037	.163
		.040	.028	.024	.015	.026	.133
		.032	.019	.022	.015	.017	.105
		0.038	*0.031*	*0.030*	*0.021*	*0.025*	*0.143*
Prophase	5	0.088	0.075	0.068	0.047	0.054	0.332
		.050	.074	.070	.054	.072	.320
		.064	.050	.041	.034	.052	.241
		.031	.021	.017	.022	.026	.117
		0.058	*0.055*	*0.049*	*0.039*	*0.051*	*0.253*
Blank	6	0.104	0.069	0.068	0.052	0.044	0.337
		.147	.090	.082	.081	.086	.486
		.163	.117	.104	.088	.071	.543
		.312	.166	.179	.257	.348	1.262
		0.182	*0.111*	*0.108*	*0.120*	*0.137*	*0.657*

[a] Figures in the body of the table are absorbances (and arithmetic means) at the five peak wavelengths of Polacolor film and sums of absorbances at these peaks. Five nuclei and a blank were measured in each of the four experiments recorded here.

spectrum. The only exception to this statement concerns absorption spectra; the photographic method is obviously not suited to the recording of an absorption spectrum of the primary chromophore in the object.

It is possible that the method might be used in problems involving living cells, such as measurement of a natural pigment or uptake of a vital dye. It is difficult to conceive of any other approach, short of television scanning, which would be able to cope with Brownian movement within the cell, much less translatory motion of the entire cell.

At the present time, photographic cytophotometry must endure two major criticisms. It has not been tested exhaustively against a variety of biological materials and it has not been directly compared with any photoelectric procedure. Attempts to fill both of these gaps are now in progress.

Technologically, the method has many good features. It can be simpler than any other method, since only one microscope is required and a single absorbance reading is sufficient data for one cell. It can be faster than any other method; speed is in direct proportion to the number of units that can be photographed at one time. It is theoretically equivalent and probably superior to scanning procedures (14, 20). Its precision has not been defined for biological materials, although the monochrome procedure is more precise than other methods of measuring irregular objects and was found to agree with the two-wavelength spot-measuring technique on a cell-to-cell basis within 2% (20). Versatility of the photographic method is almost entirely a function of magnification, film and disk size, dilution of the film dyes and spectrophotometer cuvette size.

Since reversal film of the Kodachrome type has proven to be an excellent basis for measurement, what is the advantage of Polacolor? Aside from those features appealing to any experimental photographer, summed up in the statement that, "there will be a satisfactory result obtained in a single experiment" (3), there is a special compulsion to make Polacolor work. This unique transfer film is the only device that will place photographic cytophotometry on almost the same basis as a photoelectric procedure in which the final data are achieved at the moment the primary measurement is made or shortly thereafter. It will be recalled that the fundamental reason for turning to ordinary color films instead of monochromes was the fact that they are prepared and processed commercially. Monochromes would be preferable, in fact, if they were available and processed on the same basis as a film like Kodachrome. But the processing delay remains an annoying feature hopefully to be eliminated by further experience with Polacolor.

REFERENCES

1. Allen, R. M., "Photomicrography," 2nd ed. Van Nostrand, Princeton, New Jersey, 1958.
2. Baines, H., "The Science of Photography." Fountain Press, London, 1958.
3. Bird, G. R., and E. S. Emerson, Photographic materials for recording colour and low-light intensity through the microscope. *J. Roy. Microscop. Soc.* **83,** 221–228 (1964).
4. Caspersson, T., Über den chemischen Aufbau der Strukturen des Zellkernes. *Skand. Arch. Physiol.* **73,** Suppl. 8, 1–151 (1936).
5. Caspersson, T., "Cell Growth and Cell Function." Norton, New York, 1950.
6. Caspersson, T. O., and G. Lomakka, Scanning microscopy techniques for high resolution quantitative cytochemistry. *Ann. N.Y. Acad. Sci.* **97,** 449–463 (1962).
6a. Garcia, A. M., and R. Iorio, this volume, pp. 215, 239.
7. Gibson, K. S., Spectrophotometry (200 to 1000 millimicrons). *Natl. Bur. Std. (U.S.), Circ.* **484** (1949).
7a. Hale, A. J., this volume, p. 183.
8. Hiskey, C. F., Absorption spectroscopy. *In* "Physical Techniques in Biological Research" (G. Oster and A. W. Pollister, eds.), Vol. 1, pp. 73–130. Academic Press, New York, 1955.
9. Kelly, J. W., Photographic cytophotometry with a dual microscope. *Science* **138,** 1272–1274 (1962).
10. Kelly, J. W., and L. Carlsson, Protein droplets, especially gelatin, hemoglobin and histone, as microscopic standards for quantitation of cytochemical reactions. *Exptl. Cell Res.* **30,** 106–124 (1963).
11. Kelly, J. W., W. A. Clabaugh, and H. K. Hawkins, Photographic cytophotometry with a dual microscope. II. Microscope assembly and film dye extractions. *J. Histochem. Cytochem.* **12,** 600–607 (1964).
12. Martin, L. C., The light microscope. *In* "Physical Techniques in Biological Research" (G. Oster and A. W. Pollister, eds.), Vol. 1, 325–375. Academic Press, New York, 1955.
13. Mees, C. E. K., "The Theory of the Photographic Process," rev. ed. Macmillan, New York, 1954.
14. Mendelsohn, M. L., The two-wavelength method of microspectrophotometry. III. An extension based on photographic color transparencies. *J. Biophys. Biochem. Cytol.* **4,** 425–431 (1958).
14a. Mendelsohn, M. L., this volume, p. 201.
15. Moses, M. J., Quantitative optical techniques in the study of nuclear chemistry. *Exptl. Cell Res.* Suppl. **2,** 75–94 (1952).
16. Naora, H., Microspectrophotometry in the visible light range. *In* "Handbuch der Histochemie" (W. Graumann and K. Neumann, eds.), Vol. 1, pp. 193–219. Fischer, Stuttgart, 1958.
17. Needham, G. H., "Practical Use of the Microscope." Thomas, Springfield, Illinois, 1958.
18. Niemi, M., Cytophotometry by silver analysis of photomicrographs. Description of a new method and its application to the study of corpuscular hemoglobin. *Acta Anat.* Suppl. **34,** 1–92 (1958).
19. Ornstein, L., The distributional error in microspectrophotometry. *Lab. Invest.* **1,** 250–265 (1952).

20. Ornstein, L., A simple precision photographic technique for cytochemical analysis. Ph.D. Thesis, Part I Columbia University (1957).
21. Patau, K., Absorption microphotometry of irregular-shaped objects. *Chromosoma* **5**, 341–362 (1952).
22. Pollister, A. W., and L. Ornstein, The photometric chemical analysis of cells. *In* "Analytical Cytology." (R. C. Mellors, ed.), 2nd ed., pp. 431–518. McGraw-Hill, New York, 1959.
22a. Rudkin, G. T., this volume, p. 387.
23. Sandritter, W., Ultraviolettmikrospektrophotometrie. *In* "Handbuch der Histochemie" (W. Graumann and K. Neumann, eds.), Vol. 1, pp. 221–338. Fischer, Stuttgart, 1958.
23a. Sandritter, W., this volume, p. 159.
23b. Sandritter, W., G. Kiefer, and W. Rick, this volume, p. 295.
24. Shillaber, C. P., "Photomicrography in Theory and Practice." Wiley, New York, 1944.
25. Swift, H. H., this volume, p. 355.
26. Vickerstaff, T., "The Physical Chemistry of Dyeing," 2nd ed. Wiley, New York, 1954.
27. Walker, P. M. B., and B. M. Richards, Quantitative microscopical techniques for single cells. *In* "The Cell: Biochemistry, Physiology, Morphology" (J. Brachet and A. E. Mirsky, eds.), Vol. 1, pp. 91–139. Academic Press, New York, 1959.

DETERMINATION OF DNA CONTENT BY MICROFLUOROMETRY

Fritz Ruch

DEPARTMENT OF GENERAL BOTANY, SWISS FEDERAL INSTITUTE OF TECHNOLOGY, ZÜRICH, SWITZERLAND

I. Introduction

Microfluorometry has proved very suitable for the quantitative determination of a substance such as DNA in a cell or a cell organelle (*2, 7, 8*). It is more sensitive and, in general, simpler than absorption methods. Measurements are not influenced by uneven distribution of the material. Two-wavelength or scanning methods, as used in absorption measurements, are not necessary since, under proper conditions, the fluorescent light emitted by a substance within an object is proportional only to its amount and independent of its distribution. Errors due to light scattering are much smaller than in absorption photometry.

The apparatus for microfluorometry consists of an ordinary fluorescence microscope combined with a photometer. Measurement of the emitted light must be carried out in a plane corresponding to the exit pupil of the microscope objective. The measuring field is determined by a diaphragm in the image plane. Since the object lies in a dark field in the fluorescence microscope, adjustment of the diaphragm is in general not critical and its opening can usually be larger than the object size. Details of instrumentation for microfluorometry are given by Thaer in this book (*10a*).

For quantitative work, the intensity of the fluorescent light must be proportional to the amount of substance, a condition which is only fulfilled if the absorption of exciting and emitted light is low (Fig. 1). Deviations occur with higher absorption and increase with increasing absorption. It is, therefore, very important that the range of proportionality, that is, the useful measuring range, be checked for each fluorescing substance to be studied.

The sensitivity of microfluorometry depends mainly on the quantum efficiency of the fluorescing material, the excitation intensity of the light source, and the sensitivity of the light receiver. Using the method here described it is, for example, possible to measure the small amounts of DNA in bacteria and fungi.

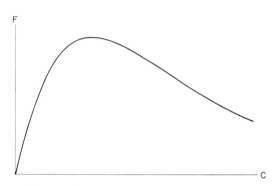

FIG. 1. Dependence of the intensity of fluorescence, F, on the concentration, C, of dissolved material. From Perrin (*6*).

Since fluorometric measurements give *relative values* of substance amount, they can be used to compare the contents of different cells or cellular structures. Absolute DNA values can be obtained if a standard object of known DNA content, for instance, bull sperms, is also measured.

Microfluorometry, like other cytochemical methods, has its limits, and several points must be considered if errors are to be avoided.

II. Staining of DNA

DNA can be stained either with basic fluorochromes or by a modified Feulgen reaction. When choosing the stain, attention must be paid to the fact that proportionality must exist between the intensity of fluorescence and the DNA content. This quantitative relationship can be tested over any desirable DNA range using gelatin or cellulose foils which contain DNA and which can be arranged stepwise in layers (*2*). Test measurements on isolated sperm heads and liver nuclei of the rat are simple and sufficient for most types of work. The average DNA contents of these nuclei are in the ratio 1 : 2 : 4 : 8 (*5*). The preparation of the sperms is described later in this article, and the isolation of liver nuclei results, for example, by Vendrely and Vendrely (*11*).

Many stains fade rapidly on excitation in the fluorescence microscope. This decrease in fluorescence intensity is caused by photodecomposition of the stain and is dependent on the object, the mounting medium, and the intensity of the exciting source. Such stains are hardly suitable for exact measurements.

Berberine sulfate (0.01% in phosphate buffer pH 6.3 or in 50–95% alcohol) was found to be the most suitable of the tested basic fluorochromes. The preparations are placed in the stain solution for 20 minutes, covered with a cover glass, and examined in the stain solution. The range 360–400 nm is used for excitation. Formalin (4%) or alcohol–acetic acid (3 : 1) is suitable for fixation. Berberine sulfate shows very little photodecomposition, the fluorescence intensity remaining constant over a period of excitation of 30 minutes. Berberine sulfate, like other basic stains, colors DNA and RNA (also other acids which may be present). RNA must, therefore, be removed if DNA is to be determined. Ribonuclease can be used for this purpose (for instance, 1 mg in 2 ml

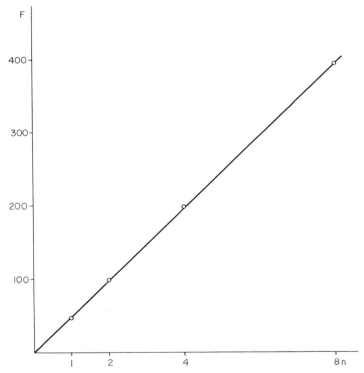

FIG. 2. Liver nuclei and sperms of the rat, stained with berberine sulfate after ribonuclease treatment. Dependence of fluorescence intensity, F, on polyploidy, n. Each point represents a mean value, in arbitrary units, for 20 nuclei. From Bosshard (2).

30% alcohol, 1 hour at 50°C). It is also possible to determine both DNA and RNA separately: the total nucleic acid content is first determined and then the DNA content after RNA extraction. Proportionality exists between fluorescence intensity and DNA content (Fig. 2).

The Feulgen reaction is specific for DNA. The usual application, using fuchsin, is not suitable for fluorescence photometry. Kasten (4) described a number of fluorochromes which can replace fuchsin in the reagent. Bosshard (2) tested these stains for proportionality and found the fluorochrome Auramine O most suitable. Figures 3 and 4 show DNA

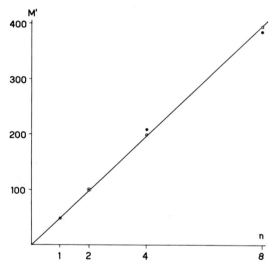

FIG. 3. Liver nuclei and sperms of the rat, stained with Auramine O. Dependence of fluorescence (○) and UV absorption (●) at 265 nm on the polyploidy, n. Each point represents a mean value, in arbitrary units, for 20 nuclei. From Ruch and Bosshard (8).

determinations in sperms and isolated liver nuclei of the rat. The mean values of the DNA contents of the four types of nuclei with increasing polyploidy values lie in a straight line (Fig. 3). Measurements with UV absorption are shown for comparison and are seen to correspond very well with the fluorescence values. Sufficient linearity (within 4%) exists up to the DNA content of a 16-ploid liver nucleus.

As Auramine O is unfortunately not very stable under UV irradiation (Fig. 5), the intensity and time of irradiation have to be as small as possible. (The preparation should therefore be scanned and focused in visible light using phase contrast.) Alternatively, irradiation can be continued until fluorescence has decreased to a more stable value. In this

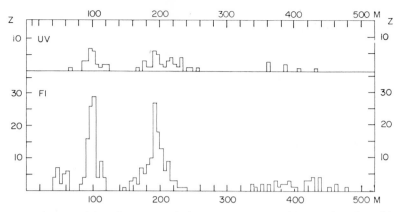

F_IG. 4. Liver nuclei and sperms of the rat. Amounts of DNA (M, in arbitrary units), measured by UV absorption (UV) and microfluorometry with Auramine O (Fl). Z, number of nuclei measured. From Ruch and Bosshard (8).

case the measurement is carried out after a fixed time, for instance, 2 minutes.

These difficulties have, to a large extent, been removed since Ciba (Basle, Switzerland) has supplied us with the stain 2,5-bis-[4'-amino-

$$H_2N-\langle\bigcirc\rangle-\overset{O}{\underset{N}{C}}\diagdown\overset{}{\underset{N}{C}}-\langle\bigcirc\rangle-NH_2$$

(I)

phenyl-(1')] = 1,3,4-oxdiazole (I), which is suitable for the Feulgen reaction and is relatively stable to UV irradiation. The slight bleaching of this stain (Fig. 5) is nearly proportional to the time of UV exposure and has little influence on DNA measurements. The range 360–400 nm is

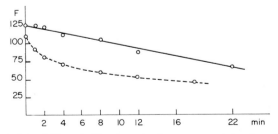

F_IG. 5. Liver nuclei of the rat. Decrease in fluorescence intensity, F, with time of UV irradiation (in minutes) caused by bleaching of the fluorochromes Auramine O (---) and CIBA bisaminophenyl-oxdiazole (—). From Ruch (7).

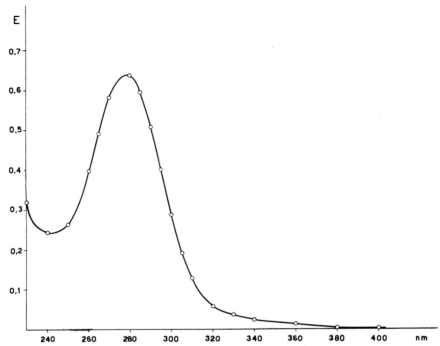

Fig. 6. Spectral extinction (E) of CIBA bisaminophenyl-oxdiazole in solution
(0.003%).

used for excitation. Figure 6 shows the spectral extinction and Fig. 7
the spectral emission of the stain. Since absorption at 260 nm is relatively low, comparative absorption measurements of DNA in stained
preparations are possible with the UV microspectrograph. Use of the
stain increases the extinction readings for DNA by 10%. The possibility
of combined fluorescence and absorption measurements is often advantageous.

We carry out the Feulgen reaction in the following manner:

(1) Fix in formalin 4% ($\frac{1}{2}$–6 hours) or alcohol–acetic acid (3 : 1, $\frac{1}{4}$–3
hours).

(2) Wash in water (10 minutes).

(3) Hydrolyze with HCl (see below for acid concentration and time
of hydrolysis).

(4) Rinse with water (5 minutes).

(5) Stain in freshly prepared stain solution (2 hours). Stain solution:
Mix 10 ml Ciba bis-aminophenyl-oxdiazole solution, 0.01%, in distilled

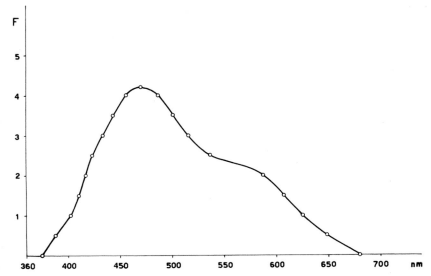

FIG. 7. Fluorescence spectrum of a liver nucleus, stained with CIBA bisamino-phenyl-oxdiazole. Excitation at 366 nm. Kodak Panatomic X film.

water (or 10 ml Auramine O solution, 0.2%), 1 ml of 1 N HCl, and 0.5 ml NaHSO$_3$ solution, 10%; shake and filter.

(6) Wash in sulfite water (3 changes, each for 2 minutes) (sulfite water: 180 ml distilled water; 10 ml of 1 N HCl; 10 ml NaHSO$_3$ solution, 10%).

(7) Wash in water for 10 minutes.

(8) Embed in glycerine.

The preparations can be kept for several days in the refrigerator. Dry preparations can be kept for weeks. For this purpose the samples, after being washed with water, are washed with 50%, 70%, 95%, and absolute alcohol, successively, then dried in a dessicator.

For quantitative determinations it is important that the optimal hydrolysis conditions be maintained. The use of 1 N HCl at 60°C is common, but the use of 6 N HCl at 20°C is often more practical and (with somewhat shorter hydrolysis time) gives the same result.

The optimal time of hydrolysis must be exactly observed. It is best if this is determined for each type of object and fixation. A test of this kind is shown in Fig. 8. The fluorescence intensities of a series of preparations with increasing hydrolysis times (between 5 and 20 minutes) are measured, and thus the time for maximal fluorescence intensity is found. Our experiments showed that, for most materials fixed with formalin or alcohol–acetic acid, the optimal time is 8 minutes if 6 N HCl at 20°C is used and 15 minutes if 1 N HCl at 60° is used.

The time-intensity curves often show two peaks (Fig. 8). This phe-

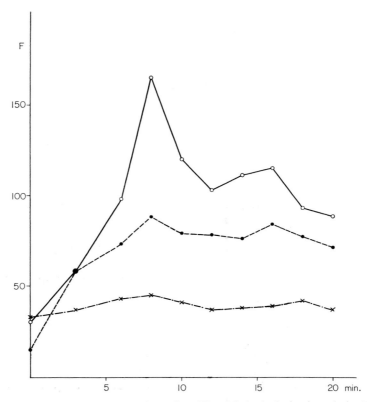

Fig. 8. Changes in fluorescence intensity (F) with hydrolysis time (minutes) for hamster ascites (○), lymphocytes (●), and sperms (×).

nomenon probably results from various DNA complexes. It is not typical of the fluorochrome, but is also present if normal Feulgen staining is carried out using fuchsin (1, 10). If objects with similar types of curves are to be compared, the peak corresponding to the shorter time can be chosen. Caution is required if objects with different types of curves are to be compared and in this case, a supplementary method, for example, a basic fluorochrome such as berberine-sulfate or UV absorption, should be used for checking, and possibly correction, purposes. It seems possible that this difficulty with hydrolysis might be overcome by special treatment of the preparation. Of course more experiments in this direction are necessary.

III. Fixation

When choosing the fixative it is most important to ensure that this neither dissolves any DNA nor influences the fluorescence. Mixtures containing chromic and osmic acids weaken the fluorescence and so are unsuitable. Formalin and mixtures of alcohol and acetic acid or of alcohol, acetic acid, and formalin are especially suitable. All of these mediums have the same time of hydrolysis.

IV. Standard Object

As mentioned above, microfluorometry provides relative values of DNA contents. Absolute values can be obtained only if a standard object of known DNA content is also measured. Morever, such a standard object should always be used if objects on different slides are to be compared, as it is difficult to keep all the optical conditions of the microscope (condenser focusing, for example) constant for each preparation. Bull sperms have a relatively constant DNA content and therefore are good standard objects for DNA determinations. Each slide prepared contains, in addition to the object to be measured, a sample of bull sperms which are stained simultaneously with the object. Since the DNA content of the sperms may vary somewhat from bull to bull, only sperms from one bull should be used. If it is necessary to use further material from another bull, a comparative DNA measurement of the two preparations should be made. The DNA content of bull sperms amounts to 2.9 to 3.4×10^{-12} g (9, 11). If more accurate values are needed for determinations of absolute DNA amounts, the DNA content of the standard preparation must be measured using a biochemical method (11).

We use the following method for preparation of the bull sperm specimens:

(1) Cut the epididymis and shake in 1% citric acid.
(2) Filter through kleenex.
(3) Centrifuge.
(4) Wash quickly with water.
(5) Centrifuge.
(6) Fix in formalin, 4%, or alcohol–acetic acid (3 : 1) 1 hour.
(7) Centrifuge.
(8) Wash quickly in water.

(9) Centrifuge.

(10) Remove water using alcohol. Store in 70% alcohol or dry in desiccator and store.

For use as a standard object, a little of the sperm material is prepared on the slide directly next to the object to be measured. For better adhesion a little albumin can be previously applied to the slide in this position.

V. Optical Factors

1. *Minimal Object Size*

Although the resolving power of the fluorescence microscope is of the same order of magnitude as that of the bright field microscope, it is possible to measure smaller particles with microfluorometry than with microabsorption photometry. For the latter, the minimal object size should be larger than the resolving power (*3*), whereas in microfluorometry the lower limit of the permissible object size is determined only by the amount of light emitted by the particles and by the light sensitivity of the receiver. Care must, however, be taken that the total diffraction pattern of the particle is received by the diaphragm in the image plane.

2. *Object Thickness*

In absorption photometry the object thickness for small or inhomogeneous objects may not substantially exceed the value of the depth of focus. In microfluorometry, on the contrary, the object thickness can be a multiple of the depth of focus. Here, the diaphragm in the image plane must be sufficiently large to receive the total light emitted by the object (to prevent blurred contours, for instance). The upper limit of the permissible object thickness is dependent on the numerical aperture of the objective and amounts to about 10 μm for a numerical aperture of 1.0 and to about 30 μm for a numerical aperture of 0.5. These values are valid for illumination with transmitted light (light or dark field condenser). For illumination with a vertical illuminator, the permissible object thickness is about half as large. However, even in microfluorometry, the preparations used should be as thin as possible since nuclei lying over one another or primary fluorescence (to be discussed below) interferes with the results.

Smear preparations are, as a rule, found to be the most suitable. When microtome sections are used care must above all be taken that partially cut nuclei are not measured. The thickness of the section should, therefore, be 20–30% larger than the maximal nucleus thickness, but if possible not larger than 10 μm.

3. *Numerical Aperture of the Objective*

A fluorescing object behaves optically as self-luminous, that is, as a rule it emits equally in all directions. Depending on its numerical aperture, the objective receives a part of this emitted light. For comparative measurements of various objects the numerical aperture of the objective does not matter. The latter is decisive only for the resolving power, the brightness of the image, and the depth of focus. For most cases an objective with a numerical aperture between 0.95 and 1.1 is the most suitable. Such an objective also allows the use of an immersion dark field condenser. In order to achieve equal light emission in all directions, the refractive index of the embedding medium should be as similar as possible to that of the object itself.

4. *Unspecific Fluorescence*

Fluorescence phenomena which influence the DNA determination can occur in microfluorometry. Thus, it can sometimes be established that in the Feulgen reaction a certain fluorescence of the cell nuclei is present without HCl hydrolysis. This can amount to up to 20% of the DNA fluorescence. Therefore, it is important to measure this DNA-independent fluorescence for each object, using unhydrolyzed preparations and, if necessary, to subtract it from the total fluorescence.

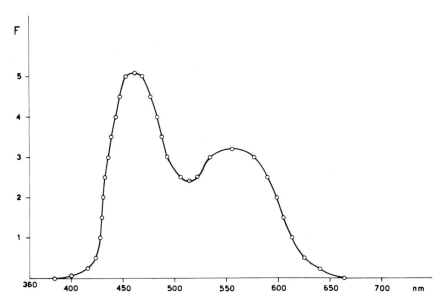

Fig. 9. Primary fluorescence of a liver nucleus, fixed in absolute alcohol. Kodak Panatomic X film.

The interfering fluorescence originates mainly from a certain non-specific action of the stain in the Feulgen reaction. The primary fluorescence of the cells may also play a part here. Thus proteins with cyclic amino acids and nucleic acids show, on excitation in the region of 360 to 400 nm, a weak, bluish fluorescence (Fig. 9), which is stronger after formalin fixation than after alcohol–acetic acid fixation. In thin preparations this primary fluorescence is so small compared with the DNA fluorescence (< 2%) that it can be disregarded. Occasionally other substances in the cell, for example, pigments, show a relatively strong primary fluorescence which can complicate the DNA determination or even make it impossible. In such cases the substances are extracted if possible. A spectral separation of the nonspecific and DNA fluorescence (for instance, by the use of filters) is seldom possible, because most fluorescence spectra are broad and flat.

With higher sensitivity of the photoelectric apparatus, such as is necessary for the determination of very small amounts of DNA, the primary fluorescence of optical parts in the microscope can interfere. This is shown by the fact that light is also registered in the object-free field. The primary fluorescence which is present in the objective to a greater or lesser extent, and the barrier filter can best be suppressed by the use of dark field illumination. Of course, fluorescence-free immerison oil and embedding medium, for example, glycerin, must always be used. As the usual glass slides are seldom fluorescence-free, quartz slides should be used for critical determinations. The influence of primary fluorescence of the optical parts can be reduced by using illuminated fields which are as small as possible (Köhler illumination). If the object-free field, despite all precautions, still shows a certain light intensity, this must be considered in the measurement. This is done most simply by adjusting the galvonometer reading for the field to 0.

VI. Accuracy of the Microfluorometric DNA Determination

No general value for this can be given, as it is dependent on various factors, some of which cannot be measured. The errors in measurement which can be introduced by a suitable apparatus are smaller than the errors which are caused by the object itself. The following factors are the most important: place of preparation; specificity, linearity, and stability of the stain; primary fluorescence of the cell. Since there is no test object with constant, precisely known DNA content at our disposal, a criterion of the measuring accuracy can only be obtained from comparative measurements using other methods, for instance, absorption techniques. Since these methods also have their sources of error, the measuring accuracy can only be relatively determined. Comparative measurements have shown that variations between measurements are not larger for microfluorometry than for UV and Feulgen absorption measurements, the error being within a few percent.

VII. Method of Measurement

An instrument with a stabilized Xenon lamp, such as that described by Thaer in this book (10a), is suitable for microfluorometry.

Work with vertical illumination is especially simple since the illumination is independent of the thickness of the microscope slide. The use of a dark field condenser for transmitted light results in the least background intensity. The latter method is especially siutable for the determination of small amounts of DNA. Care must be taken that the condenser is accurately focused for each preparation. If fluorochromes which show photodecomposition are used, the objects should be irradiated with UV for as short a time as possible. Searching and focusing should, therefore, preferably be carried out in visible light.

Before each measurement, the illumination is adjusted according to Köhler. The field diaphragm in the illumination system is closed until its diameter in the image plane is little greater than the largest dimension of the object. The measuring diaphragm in the image plane of the microscope is then adjusted accordingly. Variable rectangular diaphragms are practical for elongated objects. Usually no filter is necessary in the photometer.

When the microscope is adjusted, the galvonometer reading is regulated to a certain value. If the object is then removed from the measuring field using the mechanical stage, the galvanometer reading should return to 0. If this is not the case (see chapter on nonspecific fluorescence), a 0 correction of the galvanometer should be made. The correction may have to be repeated if the field diaphragms are moved.

The DNA contents of any desirable number of cells of a preparation can now be very quickly determined from their galvanometer readings. It is best if about 10 bull sperms are first measured, then the cells to be determined, and finally 10 bull sperms again. Comparison of the two bull sperm measurements allows the lamp stability to be checked.

If the DNA contents of various preparations (or, for instance, at various time intervals) are to be compared with one another, all measurements must be calculated on the basis of one specific value for bull sperms (in grams or arbitrary units).

The galvanometer readings are proportional to the DNA content and can be plotted in a histogram. The plot is most practical with the DNA contents on the abscissa using a logarithmic scale and the number of measured cells on the ordinate using a linear scale.

REFERENCES

1. Agrell, I., and H. A. Berggvist, Cytochemical evidence for varied DNA complexes in the nuclei of undifferentiated cells. *J. Cell Biol.* **15**, 604–606 (1962).
2. Bosshard, U.; Fluoreszenzmikroskopische Messung des DNS—Gehaltes von Zellkernen. *Z. Wiss. Mikroskopie* **65**, 391–408 (1964).
3. Caspersson, T., "Cell Growth and Cell Function." Norton, New York, 1950.
4. Kasten, F. H., Schiff-type reagents in cytochemistry, 1. Theoretical and practical considerations. *Histochemie* **1**, 466–509 (1959).
5. Leuchtenberger, C., R. Vendrely, and C. Vendrely, A comparison of the content of DNA in isolated animal nuclei by cytochemical and chemical methods. *Proc. Natl. Acad. Sci. U.S.* **37**, 33–38 (1951).
6. Perrin, F., Loi de décroissance du pouvoir fluorescent de la concentration. *Compt. Rend.* **178**, 1978–1980 (1924).
7. Ruch, F., Fluoreszenzphotometrie. *Acta Histochem. Suppl.* **6**, 117–121 (1965).
8. Ruch, F., and U. Bosshard, Photometrische Bestimmung von Stoffmengen im Fluoreszenzmikroskop. *Z. Wiss. Mikroskopie* **65**, 335–341 (1963).
9. Salisburg, G. W., and N. L. Vandemark, "Physiology of Reproduction and Artificial Insemination of Cattle." Freeman, San Francisco, 1961.
10. Sandritter, W., K. Bosselmann, L. Rakow, and K. Jobst, Untersuchungen zur Feulgenreaktion. Die Langzeithydrolyse bei verschiedenen Zelltypen. *Biochim. Biophys. Acta* **91**, 645–647 (1964).
10a. Thaer, A., this volume, p. 409.
11. Vendrely, R., and C. Vendrely, La teneur du noya cellulair en acide desoxyribonucléique a travers les arganes, les individues et les espèces animales. *Experientia* **4**, 434–436 (1948).

GALLOCYANIN CHROME ALUM

Walter Sandritter*, Günter Kiefer,

and

Wirnt Rick

DEPARTMENT OF PATHOLOGY, JUSTUS LIEBIG UNIVERSITY, GIESSEN, GERMANY

I. Introduction

So far only two proved methods are available for the quantitative histochemical detection of nucleic acid in tissue: UV microspectrophotometry (*8, 36*) for both nucleic acids (ribonucleic acid or RNA and deoxyribonucleic acid or DNA), and the Feulgen reaction for DNA (*30*). Both methods have certain disadvantages. Photometry in UV light, for example, is bound to a large, expensive apparatus, and the absorption of proteins may have a disturbing effect (*36*), whereas in the Feulgen reaction the poor reproducibility presents a limiting factor (staining in one step). Therefore, there has been no lack of attempts to make other staining reactions meet the quantitative requirements. In particular, the basic dyes were considered, since these, with the visualization of the phosphate groups of the nucleic acids, would have provided an additional valuable supplement to the other two methods. In our opinion it is certainly an important requirement of quantitative histochemistry that the results of measurements should, as far as possible, be tested by several independent methods.

Since the discovery of nucleic acids by Miescher (*27*), basophilia of the tissue (*5, 11*) has been attributed to a saltlike binding between the phosphate groups and the basic dyestuff (*25, 26*), although other acid tissue components may also enter into the competition. Of all the coloring substances so far examined for a stoichiometric binding with nucleic acids, the dye gallocyanin chrome alum (GC) seemed to be the most suitable (*12*). In comparison with other dyes it was found to have a considerable degree of specificity, since at a pH of 1.64 competition by

* Supported by a grant from the Deutsche Forschungsgemeinschaft.

295

proteins is negligible; on the other hand, the staining was regarded by Becher (*3*) as progressive. Since 1952 (*32, 33, 34*) we have worked with GC and sought to demonstrate the stoichiometry with RNA and DNA in *in vitro* experiments (*10, 37*). *In vitro* experiments have little value if proof of quantitative character has not been established in the tissues.

In working out a color reaction for quantitative histochemical purposes, a large number of investigations is required:

(1) Purity of dyestuff.

(2) Absorption spectrum in solution and in tissue.

(3) Fixation.

(4) Differentiation.

(5) Specificity.

(6) Reproducibility.

(7) Check of endpoint of staining reaction.

(8) Fading of dye.

(9) Lambert–Beer law in tissue (for instance, section thickness, Beer law).

(10) Stoichiometry check with an independent method.

In the present investigations the conditions for a stoichiometric binding between DNA and gallocyanin chrome alum will be tested, and on the basis of cytophotometric measurements it will be shown that in most somatic cell nuclei there is a constant relationship between dye content and DNA quantity.

II. Method

A. DYE SOLUTION AND STAINING

If not otherwise stated, gallocyanin from the Fluka Company was used (Buchs, St. Gallen, Switzerland). The dye was boiled for 10 minutes according to Einarson (*12*) (150 mg gallocyanin, 5 g chrome alum, 100 ml of water); the solution was filtered after boiling and brought to a volume of 100 ml; the pH of the solution was 1.64 (adjustment of pH is made with HCl or NaOH). Only freshly prepared dye solutions were used. The time of staining was 48 hours. The specimen was then washed for 30 minutes in tap water. For removal of the water, 70%, 95%, and absolute alcohol were each used for 5 minutes. Staining of all the preparations was completed in one step (see Section III,B,9). Embedding was in a medium from the Cargille Company (New York), with a refractive index of $n = 1.55$.

B. MATERIAL

Smears were prepared from all the tissues and, in the case of the liver, squashed preparations. Fixation took place after 24 hours of air drying in Carnoy solution (96% alcohol–chloroform–glacial acetic acid, 6 : 3 : 1) for 10 minutes. For the determination of the DNA content, the preparations were pretreated with ribonuclease (Worthington Company) for two hours at 56°C (0.1 mg/ml, pH 6.5 in Sørensen buffer). In the experiments in Section III, B, there was no ribonuclease treatment.

C. Photometry

(a) The measurements of the solutions were made with a spectrophotometer type PMQ II (Zeiss).

(b) The cytophotometric investigations at one wavelength were made on approximately 2400 cells with a device we constructed (*38*). Measuring conditions: 0.35 numerical aperture condenser, ocular 10×; objective oil immersion 100×, 1.25 numerical aperture. Diameter of the measuring point in the microscope, 0.56 μ. Ten to twenty individual measuring points were obtained per cell; the surface was determined planimetrically following photography. Results were expressed in arbitrary units (AU = extinction × area in square microns). The reproducibility was ±3%. Measurements were made outside the absorption maximum of GC at 497 mμ since the extinctions at the maximum (575 mμ) are too high in the case of most objects.

(c) Absorption curves performed on the tissue were made with another cytophotometer of our own construction (Sandritter, unpublished, 1962). The apparatus consists of building units of the PMQ II Zeiss spectrophotometer, in which the cuvette case was replaced by a microscope (condenser, 0.35 numerical aperture; objective Neofluar 100×, 1.25 numerical aperture; ocular 10×; Zeiss Company, Oberkochen). The size of the measuring point was 0.5μ. The microscope is furnished with a fine displacing object table by the Zeiss Company, which makes possible an exact displacement from the measuring point (*I*) to an object-free point in the preparation (*I$_o$*) with an accuracy 0.1μ.

III. Results

A. The Dye

1. *Gallocyanin*

Gallocyanin belongs among the oxazine dyes and is present as a cation even in aqueous solution.

First we had to clarify whether the gallocyanin used as the initial material could be chemically regarded as a uniform substance. According to reports from the Fluka Company, the product contains 87% gallocyanin chlorohydrate, 11.5% crystal water, and 1% ash. For further characterization, elementary analysis was used. After drawing off 9.3%

crystal water and 2.68% sodium chloride as impurities, the following values were obtained: C, found 54%, calculated 53.48%; H, found 3.8%, calculated 3.8%; N, found 8.18%, calculated 8.32%; Cl, found 10.82%, calculated 10.53%. The calculation was based on the formula $C_{15}H_{12}O_5N_2HCl$. Molecular weight was 336.73.

We tested gallocyanin from the Fluka Company, the Gruebler Company, and the Bayer Company. With ascending paper chromatography on No. 2045b Schleicher and Schuell paper in a solvent system (according to Hinrichsen, personal communication, 1962) of pyridine–water–glacial acetic acid–di-n-butyl ether in a ratio of 7 : 3 : 2 : 2 (as running medium the lower phase was used), we found only one component (R_f value = 0.32). If the dye is allowed to stand in glacial acetic acid for 3 days then, as found by Terner and Clark (47), three fractions are found with R_f values of 0.17 (blue-green component), 0.24 (blue component), and 0.35 (violet component). Apparently the dye is altered in a glacial acetic acid solution.

If the Fluka gallocyanin is examined by high-voltage electrophoresis (Wieland and Pfleiderer, 52) in the system formic acid–acetic acid–water in a ratio of 15 : 10 : 75 (Macherey & Nagel paper No. 214, 1600 volts, 75 milliamp, for 3 hours), one finds a broad band slowly migrating toward the negative pole. Thus gallocyanin can be regarded as a homogeneous substance.

2. Gallocyanin Chrome Alum

a. *Metal Complex Binding.* In histological technology the chrome lake of gallocyanin is used (3). For the preparation of the lake, gallocyanin is boiled in a 5% solution of chrome alum for a few minutes. Einarson (12) has worked intensively on the mechanism of lake formation and assumed that there is a complex binding of the chrome to the carboxyl and the hydroxyl group in the *para* position. In addition, side valence compounds are believed to appear on the second hydroxyl group and the bridge oxygen. Thus a monovalent cation would arise. According to Harms (15), on the other hand, the formation of an internal complex salt with one principal and one side valence compound of chromium each to the two hydroxyl groups is to be assumed, since the 5 ring then arising would, for steric reasons, be far more likely (H. Kuhn, personal communication, 1963) than the 4 or 7 ring present according to Einarson's formulation (12). Such 5 rings are also realized in other chrome complexes. According to this, there would be a twofold positively charged GC ion present.

Upon boiling gallocyanin with chrome alum, the chromium(III) ion would be bound with 6 OH_2 or $Cr(H_2O)_6^{3+}$ to the gallocyanin with the removal of water, whereupon the optical properties of the dye would change. Figure 1 shows not only that gallocyanin in a concentration of

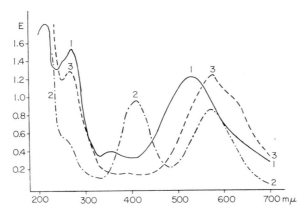

FIG. 1. Absorption spectrum of (1) gallocyanin (0.15%), (2) chrome alum (5%), and (3) gallocyanin chrome alum (1 : 30 diluted).

0.15% shows a different absorption maximum in comparison with color lake (530 mμ), but also that in the formation of lake the extinction co-efficient in the absorption maximum increases 30 times. Color lake has an absorption maximum of 575 mμ. By introduction of chromium, there-fore, a displacement toward the red occurs. Chrome alum shows a rela-tively weak absorption at 400 and 570 mμ. Jacobi and Kuhn (18) have demonstrated a displacement toward red upon transition from symmetri-cal to asymmetrical states of color molecules.

This complex formation between gallocyanin and chrome alum can also be demonstrated in tissues. Gallocyanin (0.5% aqueous solution boiled for 10 minutes, pH 1.65, treated for 48 hours) by itself, for ex-ample, in liver tissue, stains the nuclei and cytoplasm steel gray. Upon subsequent treatment with chrome alum (5% aqueous solution, boiled for 10 minutes and treated for 48 hours) no change in the color occurs. If, on the other hand, the liver tissue is treated in the same way first with chrome alum (no staining) and then with gallocyanin, one obtains a more blue-toned color which is very close to the color of the liver stained with gallocyanin chrome alum.

It is also apparent from this experiment that as a result of the com-plex formation between chrome alum and gallocyanin, new dye proper-ties are developed, and essentially it is the chromium that is responsible for the binding to the nucleic acids.

The significance of the metal complex formation of gallocyanin for the development of the staining and spectroscopic properties of the dye can also be demonstrated with these experiments in which the chromium atom is replaced by other metals (iron or aluminum alum). In comparison with staining using gallocyanin alone, here again, after the complex formation, a different color tone arises. With iron one obtains a more brownish tone, and with aluminum a weaker gray color appears. The spectral curve of gallocyanin aluminum alum, in contrast to GC, has its absorption maximum at 565 mμ and absorbs very strongly below 420 mμ. The gallocyanin iron alum complex has a wide maximum between 560 and 620 mμ.

b. *Purity of the Dye.* Elemental analysis of the GC complex was not possible since the excess chrome alum could not be separated.

If the GC solution used for staining was brought directly onto the paper used for chromatography, then the substance remained at the starting point; apparently the excess of chrome alum prevents chromatographic distribution.

We therefore attempted to isolate the GC complex: 300 ml of the dye solution was evaporated at 40°C in a high vacuum and the residue was boiled with 300 ml of analytically pure methanol in the reflux for 30 minutes. The filtrate was evaporated in a high vacuum at 30°C. Fine, small, violet metal disks were produced, which were readily soluble in water or glacial acetic acid. The absorption maximum of this solution was found to be at 550 mμ and therefore does not correspond to that of the original GC solution. This solution could be analyzed by paper chromatography.

The dye complex obtained under these conditions both in paper chromatography and in high-voltage electrophoresis (experimental conditions as above) only showed one component. In high-voltage electrophoresis, GC migrates 1.7 times more rapidly than gallocyanin.

According to these experiments, the GC complex appears to represent a largely homogeneous substance.

c. *Spectral Properties in Solution and in Tissue.* As shown by Figs. 1 and 2, it can be observed from the absorption curves of GC in solution that there are no crude impurities present.

If GC is bound in the tissue, then, in comparison with the pure solution, there is an increase in absorption in the shorter wavelength (Fig. 2, curve 2). This finding could always be reproduced with our apparatus. In comparison with the absorption maximum at 575 mμ, extinction increases at 470 mμ to its double.

In seeking the causes of this increase in absorption in the shorter wavelengths, one first thinks of sources of error which might have been introduced by the measuring apparatus. A rise in the absorption curve in the short wave region arouses the suspicion that light scattering might play a role. It is well known that scattering of light increases with decreasing wavelengths. We therefore measured thymus lymphocytes in three different cytophotometers, using the Thorell apparatus (Stockholm), the Zeiss Ultramicrospectrograph, and our own apparatus. The course of the curve with each device was equally reproducible and the ratio of E_{575} mμ : E_{470}mμ was always 1 : 0.5.

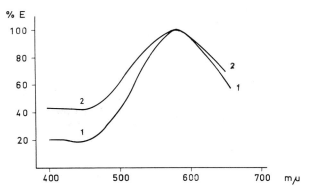

Fig. 2. Absorption curve of gallocyanin chrome alum in solution (1) and in a stained thymus lymphocyte (2).

For this reason alone, the influence of scattered light was improbable. In addition, scattered light was artificially intensified by a change of the refractive index. With an entirely deficient adjustment of the refractive index of the medium to that of the object ($n = 1.56$), that is, embedding in a medium (Cargille) with $n = 1.52$, absorption at 470 mμ increases at the most by 10%. This experiment also shows that scattered light only has a slight influence.

Some experiments with RNA precipitated with GC indicate that apparently the complex salt formation between nucleic acid and GC is responsible for the change in the spectral properties. We have further investigated this connection of complex formation by means of precipitation of GC with sodium acetate. Precipitates of nucleic acid with GC are insoluble. If one uses drastic agents (for example, strong acids) then the spectral properties of the dye change.

If 1 ml of GC solution is added to the same quantity of a 1 M sodium acetate solution, in the course of 24 hours a blue-dyed precipitate will be formed. This process is accelerated by heating to 50°C for 2 hours.

After centrifugation, the sediment is washed several times, each time with 1 ml of 0.05 M sulfuric acid, and the washing is measured. The precipitate is entirely dissolved after five washings.

The photometric measurements show (Fig. 3) that the progressive

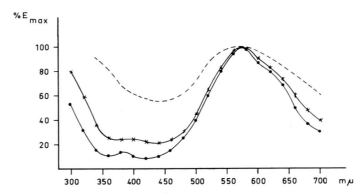

FIG. 3. Absorption curves of gallocyanin chrome alum (lower curve) and different fractions of the washing solution (0.05 M H_2SO_4) of a precipitated sodium acetate gallocyanin chrome alum complex. Middle curve: first washing fraction. Upper curve: fourth washing fraction.

washing of the sodium acetate GC complex, absorption increases sharply below 500 mμ.

The first washing fractions, in contrast to the later ones, consist of unbound GC complex, while the later ones contain predominantly the complex. From this it can be concluded that the complex formation of the dye is responsible for the increased absorption. From the first to the fifth washing fraction the ratio of E_{575} mμ to E_{470} mμ changes from 1 : 0.3 to 1 : 0.66. The pure dye solution has a ratio of 1 : 0.25.

It is apparent from these experiments that the dye, after binding to nucleic acid or acetate, changes its spectral properties. Our experiments give no information as to whether the relative increase of absorption below 500 mμ is brought about by lowering of absorption at the maximum of 575 mμ or whether there is a genuine additional absorption in the short wave region.

B. STAINING CONDITIONS

1. *Influence of Boiling Time upon Staining*

The specifications for the preparation of color lake have been changed from time to time. One finds extremely diverse data with regard to duration of boiling. Einarson (*12*) has given 5 minutes; Stenram (*44*) has boiled the GC solution for 18 hours. We therefore have investigated the influence of long periods of boiling on the color intensity and strength of the color in the solution. After a boiling period of 10 minutes, extinction rises sharply and then remains roughly at the same level. It can be seen from this that within this period of time the formation of the internal complex salt is terminated (Fig. 4). Since no change in the absorption

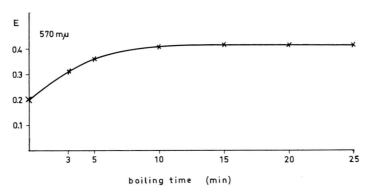

FIG. 4. Relation between boiling time and extinction of a gallocyanin chrome alum solution diluted 1 : 40.

spectrum arises with a boiling time of up to 25 minutes, it may be assumed that no dye association or polymerization takes place.

Similarly the strength of staining of the GC solution increases with longer periods of boiling (44). As is shown by Fig. 5, a rapid increase in

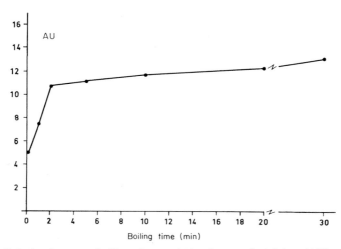

FIG. 5. Relation between boiling time and the degree of staining (AU) of thymus lymphocytes.

the dye content per cell occurs after a period of up to 2 minutes, after which almost a plateau is reached. Comparison between the increased extinction of the color solution and the quantity of the bound dye as a function of the time of boiling shows (Figs. 4 and 5) that the two curves do not reach their maximum simultaneously. The staining properties are essentially fully developed after 2 minutes of boiling. An increase in the dye concentration by boiling for longer than 2 minutes, which is accompanied by an increased extinction, only brings about a slight increase in the color binding. Accordingly, even after a boiling period of 2 minutes, there is a sufficiently large quantity of molecules available for an almost maximal staining.

If one increases the time of boiling of the GC solution to more than 30 minutes, then after 48 hours a change in the spectrum can be detected. Figure 6 (bottom) shows that there is a displacement of the maximum

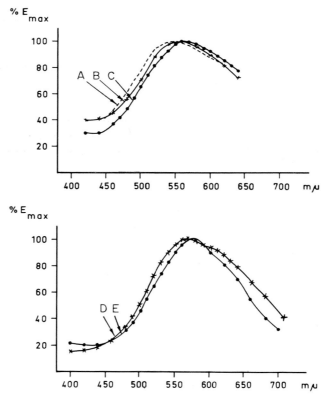

Fig. 6. Absorption spectra. Gallocyanin chrome alum solution: (E) boiled 10 minutes; (D) boiled 48 hours. Thymus lymphocytes after gallocyanin chrome alum staining; (C) solution boiled 10 minutes; (B) solution boiled 48 hours. (A) Tracheal cartilage (human), stained with gallocyanin chrome alum (boiled 10 minutes).

from 575 mμ to 560 mμ. This displacement toward the blue also occurs after staining of cell nuclei with a GC solution boiled for 48 hours.

The absorption maximum of thymus lymphocytes is also displaced by 15 mμ toward the short wave region (Fig. 6, top). It can be seen from these experiments that in GC solutions boiled for a longer time, a red component appears which is connected by Harms (15) to decarboxylation of GC to galloviolet.

2. So-Called Metachromasia

The red-violet component of GC, according to the above experiments, is present particularly distinctly after more prolonged periods of boiling. This red component however, is also present in the GC solution boiled for 10 minutes. Becher (3) [see also Hinrichsen (16), Sandritter (35), Stenram (44)] found that cartilage tissue stains red-violet. Figure 6 (top) shows that in absorption spectra of cartilage tissue, the displacement of the maximum from 575 mμ to 560 mμ also occurs. Thus the same effect appears as in cell nuclei which were stained with GC solution boiled for 48 hours.

With regard to the purity of the dye, it thus appears that even in the solution boiled for 10 minutes, the red component must be present. The deformation of the absorption curve in the tissue (increase of absorption in the short wave region), however, cannot be explained by this means, since the maximal displacement is only slight (Fig. 6).

The red component thus appears to have a strong affinity for acid mucopolysaccharides. In the binding of GC to nucleic acid this component, with a solution boiled for 10 minutes, apparently plays only an insignificant role, since in the spectrum of the cell nuclei no maximal displacement can be demonstrated.

3. Influence of the Age of the Dye Solution

According to Einarson (12) the age of the dye solution also influences the staining. As a guide line it has been found that the dye should not be used for longer than 3 weeks. The aging of the dye solution has no influence upon extinction (right ordinate in Fig. 7). Thymus lymphocytes stained with the same dye solution on different days (Fig. 7) take up less dye from an old solution. The course of this effect is not known. According to these investigations, freshly prepared solution is required for quantitative purposes.

4. Influence of Dye Concentration

From a normally prepared GC solution, lower dye concentrations were prepared by dilution. In addition, a solution was prepared with a double concentration (0.3 g gallocyanin, 10 g chrome alum, and 100 ml water).

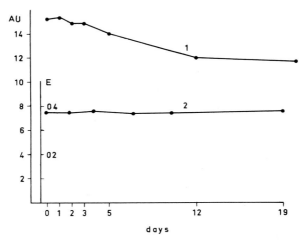

FIG. 7. Influence of the age of staining solution. (1) Results of the measurements on thymus lymphocytes (AU, 497 mμ left ordinate), which were stained with solutions of different ages. (2) Extinction of the staining solution (1 cm cuvette, 570 mμ, 1 : 40 diluted, right ordinate).

All solutions were adjusted to a pH of 1.6. The results of microphotometric measurements distinctly show that the dye content (AU) of the thymus lymphocytes is dependent upon the concentration of the dye in the solution (Fig. 8). Thus, this is not a linear or an exponential dependence; with a semilogarithmic plotting we do not obtain a straight

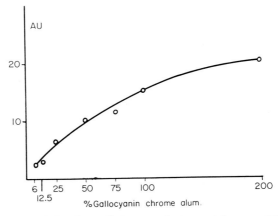

FIG. 8. Dependence of the dyestuff amount that was taken up (thymus lymphocytes, AU, 497 mμ) on the concentration of the staining solution. 100% = normally prepared solution (0.15 g gallocyanin, 5 g chrome alum, 100 ml water).

line. According to this result, it is anticipated that factors that influence the dye concentration of the solution also have a determining effect on the color intensity of the object.

5. Duration of Staining

The time course of a color reaction gives some indications as to the binding mechanism. Experiments with varying durations of staining and measurement of the dye quantity in lymphocytes show that the binding of GC to nucleic acids does not take place as rapidly as might be anticipated with an ionic reaction and that within the usual staining time of 48 hours the final point of the reaction is not quite reached (Fig. 9).

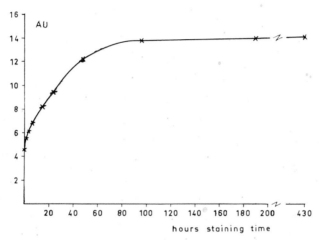

FIG. 9. Relation between the staining time and the dyestuff taken up (AU, 497 mμ) with thymus lymphocytes.

The quantity of dye in the tissue is proportional to the logarithm of the time of staining, since the curve runs straight in the semilogarithmic graph. Thus, color binding follows a Langmuir adsorption isotherm.

6. Influence of the pH of the Dye Solution

Einarson (12) and Stenram (44) have pointed out that with a rising pH of the color solution, the specificity of the solution for nucleic acids is lost. For example, at a pH of 1.6 we observe a very distinct and intensive visualization of the Nissl bodies and at higher pH the remaining cytoplasm is also more intensely stained; at about pH 2.0 the thymus lymphocytes stain a stronger bluish violet. If the uptake of dye by thymus lymphocytes is studied at various pH's (adjustment with NaOH or HCl), the most intensive staining is found at pH 1.6, while below and above this value the uptake of dye becomes distinctly less (Fig. 10). At

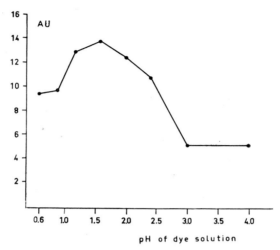

Fig. 10. Relation between pH of the staining solution and bound dyestuff amounts (AU, 497 mμ) with thymus lymphocytes.

pH 5.0, staining is no longer possible, since precipitation of the dye in solution occurs. The supernatant is as clear as water.

The reduction of staining with a rising pH is probably attributable to a repression of the association of the GC molecule so that fewer color ions are available for binding to the phosphate groups of the nucleic acid. At the same time the dissociation of the acid and basic groups of the tissue is probably also altered (cause of the nonspecific staining). Below pH 1.6, the lesser dissociation of the phosphate group of the nucleic acids makes itself felt.

7. Influence of Pretreatment

In earlier experiments it was seen (19) that the quantity of dye bound is to a great extent dependent upon the degree of dissociation of the phosphate groups of nuclear protein. Unfixed calf thymus lymphocytes, after GC staining, showed a dye content of 8.4 AU; after treatment with 2.5% sodium chloride solution the quantity of dye rose to 10.3 AU, and after formaline and alcohol fixation, to 15.7 or 14.1 AU (Table I). Similar conditions were observed after toluidine blue staining. This influence of dissociation is also suggested by the experiments of Mirsky (29) who observed a more intensive binding with crystal violet after removal of histone from cell nuclei.

TABLE I

Relative Dye Contents (AU)

Staining	Object	Untreated	NaCl (2,5%, 2 min)	Formalin (6 hours)	Alcohol (6 hours)
Toluidine blue pH 3.2	Thymus lymphocytes	3.1	6.5	11.4	15
Gallocyanin chrome alum pH 1.64	Thymus lymphocytes	8.4	10.3	15.7	14.1
	Bull sperm	3.9	3.7	4.5	4.5

In further experiments, various objects were subjected to a comparative investigation after formalin and Carnoy fixation without ribonuclease treatment. It was found that in human liver and rat liver there was no difference after treatment with various fixing agents. On the other hand, the values of rat thymus lymphocytes fixed with formalin were 20% higher than those fixed with Carnoy solution. Similar differences were found in erythrocyte nuclei of chickens and *Rana temporaria*.

Paraffin embedding in comparison to the smear preparations, according to our experiments, has no influence on the binding of the dye (Fig. 17).

8. *Influence of Differentiation*

The bond between GC and the nucleic acids is very firm. The nucleic acid–dye complex, even upon treatment with strong acids or bases (*in vitro* experiments with precipitated nucleic acid—dye complexes), cannot by brought into solution. This stable character of the staining is also confirmed by cytophotometric measurements. Figure 11 shows that with

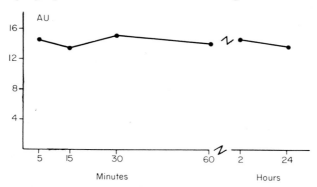

Fig. 11. Dyestuff content of thymus lymphocytes depending on the differentiation in water (497 mμ).

differentiation in water, practically no loss of dye occurs up to 24 hours in thymus lymphocytes. Differentiation in 70% or 96% alcohol also has no influence on the color intensity. The strong affinity of GC for nucleic acids is also shown by the experiments of Schümmelfeder et al. (43) who observed that the acridine orange cation can be displaced by GC.

9. Reproducibility of the Staining

Most of the color reactions, both for quantitative and semiquantitative purposes, are not exactly reproducible. For instance, in the Feulgen reaction the color intensity is dependent upon the time of hydrolysis and the temperature. The staining conditions are easy to control in GC staining, so that good reproducibility is possible. Figure 12 shows the re-

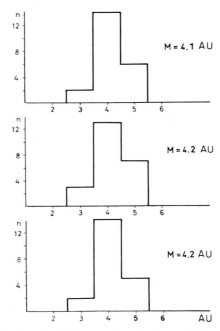

FIG. 12. Reproducibility of gallocyanin chrome alum staining (bull sperm staining on three different days: $n =$ cell number, $M =$ middle value at 497 mμ).

sults of measurements on bull spermatozoa preparations which were fixed at the same time, and stained on three different days, each time with freshly prepared GC solution. The mean values are close to 4.2 AU.

Good reproducibility is only assured when the objects are obtained and fixed at the same time. If the material is removed at various times and the duration of air drying and fixation is varied, then there are divergences in the intensity of staining. The mean dye content of diploid cell nuclei in the present investigations under standard conditions (24-hour air drying, 10-minute Carnoy fixation) was 15 AU. Under different conditions divergences of up to ±3 AU may arise. Nevertheless, the doubling peaks $(2n : 4n : 8n = 2 : 4 : 8)$, which correspond to the ratio of the dye content to the DNA content, are maintained.

10. *Fastness to Light of the Dye*

A quantitative evaluation of the dye content is only possible with photometric methods. But in so doing it must be borne in mind that the light energy streaming in may bring about changes in the absorption properties of the dye. For instance, the absorption of fuchsin in Feulgen-stained cell nuclei is considerably reduced in a strong light ([20]). On the other hand, under the same conditions the extinction of cell nuclei stained with GC remains constant for several days (Fig. 13). The ab-

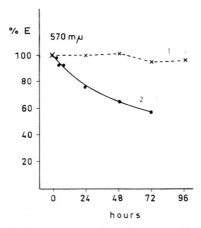

FIG. 13. Change in extinction of liver cell nuclei of rats depending on the duration of radiation in a cytophotometer at 570 mμ: (1) gallocyanin chrome alum staining (ribonuclease treatment); (2) Feulgen reaction.

sorption spectrum does not change either. In these investigations the appropriate point was irradiated without interruption for several days in a microspectrophotometer at a wavelength of 570 mμ (light source, 6-volt, 30-watt, tungsten filament lamp from a PMQ II spectrophotometer of the Zeiss Company). The monochromator aperture of 0.1 mm corresponds to a spectral band width of ±5 mμ. An achromatic condenser with a numerical aperture of 0.32 forms an exit slit of the monochromator with a width of 12 μ in the plane of the object.

C. TESTING OF THE BEER–LAMBERT LAW

A condition for the use of a dye in quantitative histochemistry is the validity of the Beer–Lambert law for the dye solution and the dye bound in the tissue. Lambert's law signifies that extinction rises in proportion to the layer thickness; the same connection is applicable to the concentration (Beer's law). Figure 14 shows the connection between various

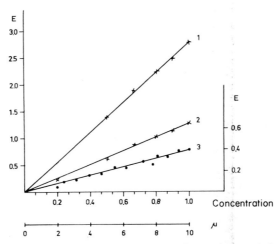

FIG. 14. Validity of the Beer–Lambert law. (1) Dependence of the extinction on the concentration of a gallocyanin chrome alum solution (0.1 cm cuvette, wavelength 570 mμ). The concentration 1.0 represents the undiluted solution. (2) Same relation as for Curve 1 at 497 mμ. (3) Relation between section thickness and extinction in the cytoplasm of liver cells (human, wavelength 570 mμ). Left ordinate and upper abscissa stand for the Curves 1 and 2; right ordinate and lower abscissa for Curve 3.

dye concentrations and the extinction in the solution. The dye, even outside the absorption maximum at 497 mμ, follows the Beer–Lambert law. Most of the cytophotometric measurements were made within this wave region since the extinction of cell nuclei at the absorption maximum is too high and so the possibilities of error become very great (Schwarzschild–Villiger effect).

In the tissue only the dependence upon layer thickness can be tested, since the extinction always represents the unknown magnitude (Lambert law). Sections of the human liver with a homogeneous cytoplasm were measured by photometry within an area of 10 liver cells (about 100 measured points). The layer thickness was determined by the focusing method (51). Figure 14 shows that with increasing layer thickness extinction rises linearly.

Beer's law can only be tested indirectly in tissue. According to Hardy (14), Beer's law is fulfilled when the absorption curves run identically at various dye concentrations. From a total of 15 cell nuclei, with extinctions between 0.1 and 1.22 at 575 mμ, absorption curves were made. Figure 15 gives a selection of these. It can be seen that the absorption

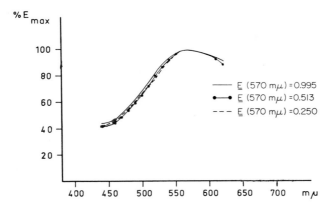

Fig. 15. Testing of the Beer law in the tissue. Cell nuclei of different extinction show the same extinction curves.

curves are identical. This proves that in the tissue Beer's law is also fulfilled.

D. SPECIFICITY OF STAINING

If we begin with the idea that basic dyes with their positive charge groups bind with negative groups in the tissue, then it is anticipated that other acid tissue components will also be stained. The carboxyl groups of proteins, fatty acids, mucopolysaccharides, phosphoproteins, and the phosphate-containing compounds of some of these in the musculature are not stained or are only slightly stained.

The negatively charged groups of proteins at pH 1.64 are, according to our own investigations, not stained. The addition of albumin to a 2.5% RNA solution gives no increase of extinction after placement on filter paper. Serum protein, clupeine, and glutamic acid do not stain on filter paper.

The influence of the reactive groups of proteins on GC staining can also be tested within certain limits by blocking. Acetylation of the amino groups with acetic anhydride in pyridine (for method, see Beneš and Sandritter, 4) does not show a change of intensity of GC staining in ganglionic cells in formalin and Carnoy-fixed spinal marrow of the rat. The Feulgen reaction is also unchanged. The same applies to oxidative deamination of the amino groups with nitric acid. Fast Green staining at pH 8.2 becomes negative. After esterification of the COOH groups with the acid methanol, staining of ganglion cells is diminished. After toluidine blue staining, the cell nuclei and Nissl bodies are completely unstained. The Feulgen reaction is also reduced in intensity. This effect suggests that acidified methanol dissolves at least some of the nucleic acid. This would also explain the reduced GC staining. At the same time, however, upon methylation phosphate groups of the nucleic acid should also be esterified, so that the result would be a negative toluidine blue staining. Since GC still stains, even after esterification, Terner and Clark (47) have assumed that the binding of GC does not take place in the phosphate groups. All experiments so far (see dissociation experiments Section III,B,7.) are against this assumption.

The absence of staining of tissue after trichloracetic acid extraction of nucleic acids (5%, 90°C, 5 minutes) and after treatment with ribonuclease is contrary to the concept of Terner and Clark (47). Thymus lymphocytes (Carnoy fixation), after extraction with trichloracetic acid, show an extinction of 0.02, and liver cells, after ribonuclease treatment, show an extinction of 0.05 (see Sandritter, 41). Pakkenberg (29a) after treating ganglion cells with ribonuclease, found the extinction in the cytoplasm to be the same as in the surrounding brain tissue.

The acid mucopolysaccharides may appear as a further reactive group. These give a pseudometachromatic staining (see above). Fatty acids in most cases were probably dissolved by alcohol treatment or paraffin embedding. However, as is known, often the fatty acids only go into solution after prolonged extraction in heat, so that a test with nucleases is required. The keratohyaline granules of the epidermis are still GC positive after ribonuclease and trichloracetic acid treatment. These are probably acid mucopolysaccharides (7) or lipids (23).

Phosphates should be taken into account, as they appear in musculature, in phosphoproteins, or in metaphasphates (45). *In vitro* experiments show that GC only stains polyphosphates (1% in 10% gelatin), while adenosine monophosphate and adenosine triphosphate cannot be visualized. The gelatins are also unspecifically stained to a slight degree. In tissue experiments the binding of the dye to polyphosphates could also be confirmed. After the addition of GC to a polyphosphate solution, there is immediate precipitation. The degree of the color binding is apparently dependent upon the degree of polymerization of the polyphosphate.

The nonspecific staining of nucleic acid-free structures is dependent upon several factors (boiling time, pH of the dye solution, fixation). Like Stenram (44) we also found, after 24 hours and 48 hours of boiling, an increase in staining, for example, of nerve tissue. Similarly a pH value of over 2.0 increases the staining of brain tissue or connective tissue (*12, 21, 43*). Formalin fixation not only increases the color binding of cell nuclei, but also of nucleic acid-free tissue. Even after ribonuclease treatment there remains a slight stainability of the Nissl bodies after formalin fixation, while after alcohol or Carnoy fixation the Nissl bodies remain unstained.

GC staining, therefore, can be regarded as relatively specific only under certain conditions (alcohol or Carnoy fixation, short boiling period of 10 minutes, pH 1.64) (*35*).

E. RELATIONSHIPS BETWEEN THE DNA CONTENT AND QUANTITY OF DYE

In reply to the question of how far a dye reacts stoichiometrically in the tissue with certain chemical groups, both chemical methods (dye extractions, for example) and cytophotometry can be used. In the present case the situation is particularly favorable, since the DNA content of the cells is fairly accurately known from a great many biochemical and microphotometric works (*48*), therefore, a correlation between the DNA quantity and the dye content of the cell nuclei can easily be made after ribonuclease treatment.

1. Cytophotometric Measurements

As has been described in the chapter on methods, the cell smears were stained after ribonuclease treatment, and the dye content (AU) was determined by cytophotometry. Figures 16 and 17 show that in somatic cell nuclei the dye content (AU) is correlated with the chromosome number and the DNA content. Within a single species or a single organism (human, rat, guinea pig), one finds the typical doubling of the measured values to be parallel with the number of chromosomes $(2n : 4n : 8n = 2 : 4 : 8)$.

The DNA content of diploid cell nuclei is 6×10^{-12} g (*39, 48*). The dye quantity bound corresponds to 15 AU; in tetraploid cells with DNA content of 12×10^{-12} g, one sees a frequency peak of around 30 AU (for octoploid cells with 24×10^{-12} g DNA, the frequency peak is around 60 AU). The histograms show the spread around the mean values using the Feulgen reaction assessed by cytophotometric measurements; in mitotically active tissue such as bull testicles, interdiploid tetraploid measured values are more frequent (cells in the interphase DNA synthesis). Mendelsohn (*24*) found a ratio of the measured values of 2 : 4 : 8 (Swift, *46*) in liver cell nuclei after ribonuclease treatment and GC staining.

A noteworthy fact appears to be that a difference in the non-histone

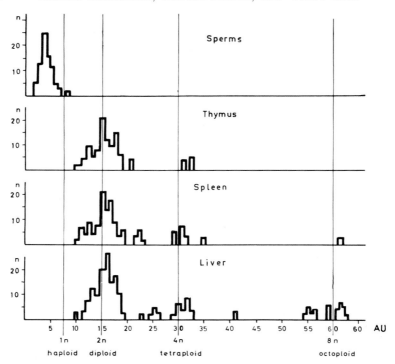

FIG. 16. Graph of the measuring results of different human cell nuclei (ribonuclease treatment, gallocyanin chrome alum staining, n = cell number, AU = extinction × area).

protein content does not influence the binding of the dye. According to Mirsky and Ris (28) and our own investigations (40, 42), thymus lymphocytes only show a very slight quantity of non-histone protein (dry weight 15×10^{-12} g; DNA and histone, 12×10^{-12} g), while liver cell nuclei or other cells with more cytoplasm, with dry weights of cell nuclei between 30 and 50×10^{-12} g, have a higher non-histone protein content. All these types of cells bind the same quantity of dye.

The fasting experiments on rats suggest the same thing and these are accompanied by a loss of dry weight of the liver cell nuclei (17). The binding of the dye remains unaltered (Fig. 17).

A surprising and distinct divergence from this rule is formed by measurements on the spermatozoa of various animals. In all of the cases investigated the dye content of the spermatozoa is lower than could have been anticipated according to the diploid measuring values. In man, bulls, and guinea pigs the measured values are not at 7.5 AU, but between 3 and 5 AU. Maturing stages of the spermatozoa, such as are en-

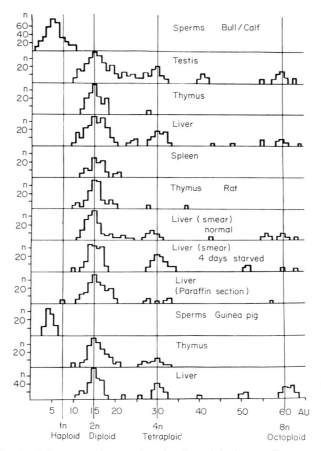

Fig. 17. Graph of the measuring results of cell nuclei of several mammalian cells.

countered in cell smears of bull testicles, on the other hand, show a normal histogram with the usual double series. Peculiarities in the physicochemical state of the spermatozoal DNA, of the binding between DNA and protein, or in the nature and quantity of the protein could be responsible for this reduced color dye binding. This is also indicated by the fact that by increasing the staining temperature (60 degrees, 24 hours) one can achieve a more intensive color binding [see also acid-fast staining of spermatozoa (31)].

A fairly pronounced influence of these factors could also be expected upon comparison of various animal species. We investigated objects whose DNA content was known from our own investigations (39). From the constant dye content of somatic cell nuclei in mammalians, we calculated how much dye should be bound per 1×10^{-12} g DNA = 2.5 AU, and the dye quantity calculated was compared with a measured quantity. Diploid cell nuclei (6×10^{-12} g DNA) bind 15 AU of dye (1×10^{-12} g DNA = 2.5 AU).

Table II shows that in trout erythrocytes and spleen cells there is a

TABLE II

DNA AND RELATIVE DYE CONTENT OF NON-MAMMALIAN NUCLEI

Cell	DNA ($\times 10^{-12}$ g)	Measured (AU)	Calculated[a] (AU)
Mammalian			
Diploid	6	15	—
Trout			
Erythrocytes	5	11	12.5
Spleen	5	11.5	12.5
Chicken			
Sperms	1.5	1.5	3.75
Erythrocytes	3.0	3.0	7.5
Liver	3.0	7.0	7.5

[a] For explanation, see text.

very good agreement between the expected and the measured dye content and also in *Rana temporaria* erythrocytes. Divergences were found in the chicken (and the rooster) and *Bufo viridis*. Here the binding of dye both in spermatozoa and in somatic cell nuclei is distinctly reduced. However, the 1 : 2 ratio of the DNA content between spermatozoa and diploid cells is still quite distinct. In the liver of the chicken, two peaks, 3.5 and 7 AU, are distinctly visible, which can be correlated with diploid and tetraploid cell nuclei.

The results of these measurements show that the dye GC only binds stoichiometrically with the nuclear DNA in certain cases. The non-histone proteins do not enter into competition with the dye. The divergences in various cases (spermatozoa, rooster cell nuclei, *Bufo viridis*) are of the very greatest interest for the problem of the binding between basic proteins and DNA.

2. *Stoichiometric relationship between GC and DNA*

In order to obtain information on the quantitative binding ratios between DNA and GC, one can calculate the molar ratio between phosphate and GC on the basis of cytophotometric measurements and the known DNA content. If in somatic cell nuclei of mammalians it is stipulated that diploid cells bind 15 AU of dye and that the DNA content amounts to 6×10^{-12} g, then one can calculate the quantity of dye per cell nucleus from

$$M = cV,\tag{1}$$

in which c is the molar concentration of the dye and V is the volume of the cell nuclei. Also

$$V = dF,\tag{2}$$

where F is the nuclear surface, d the mean layer thickness;

$$c = E/\epsilon d\tag{3}$$

in which E is the measured extinction, and epsilon is the molar extinction coefficient of the dye solution. From these formulas it then follows that

$$M = EF/\epsilon.\tag{4}$$

By definition, in our cytophotometric measurements, $EF = AU$, in which, upon insertion into Eq. (4), we have to multiply by 10^{-8}, since F has to be expressed in square centimeters. Assuming that 15 AU corresponds to a diploid cell nucleus (6×10^{-12} g DNA), we get $M = 15 \times 10^{-8}/\epsilon$. To calculate the extinction coefficient ϵ, we have to know the quantity of gallocyanin that has actually been dissolved. For this we have evaporated a dye solution prepared in the usual manner after filtration and dried the residue in a vacuum. One hundred milliliters of dye solution yielded 3,881.3 mg dry substance (weighed: 5000 mg chrome alum, 150 mg gallocyanin). Elemental analysis of the residue showed a carbon content of 0.76%. With a C content of gallocyanin (free base) of 60%, accordingly, in 3,881.3 mg of residue there would only be 49.5 mg or 0.165×10^{-3} moles of gallocyanin (that is, 36.9% of the weighed quantity).

A 1-cm cuvette of GC solution at 497 mμ, the wavelength at which we carried out our cytophotometric measurements, had an extinction of 16 (Fig. 1, Curve 3). The molar extinction coefficient E_{497} is then

$$E_{497} = \frac{16}{0.165 \times 10^{-5}} = 9.7 \times 10^{6}.$$

According to Eq. (4) we then get

$$M = \frac{15 \times 10^{-8}}{9.7 \times 10^{6}} = 1.55 \times 10^{-14};$$

that is, 1.55×10^{-14} mole GC is bound per diploid cell nucleus.

If we stipulate a P content of 9.22%, (9) 6×10^{-12} g DNA contains roughly 5.5×10^{-13} g or 1.8×10^{-14} mole of phosphorus. Accordingly, the molar ratio of DNA P to GC is 1 : 0.86, that is, for each phosphate group there are 0.86 dye molecules.

This calculation is based on the assumption that the extinction coefficient at 497 mμ is the same in solution and in tissue. The altered absorption spectrum in the tissue (Fig. 1) would be the result of a lowering of ϵ in the absorption maximum. Conversely, however, it can also be assumed that ϵ_{max} is identical in solution and in tissue. Then one would get an ϵ which would be 43% higher at 497 mμ, that is, an ϵ_{497} of roughly 1.39×10^7. If we assumed this to be so, a diploid cell nucleus would then contain 1.08×10^{-14} mole GC; the molar ratio of DNA P to GC would be 1 : 0.6. A binding ratio P : GC = 1 : 0.6 (2 P for 1 GC) is not very probable, since this would imply that the color binding of GC to DNA could be further intensified by various interventions. We have seen, however, that alcohol fixation by increasing the dye concentration and the dye temperature and prolonging the time of staining does not bring about any appreciable intensification of the staining (within the range of error). The maximal staining has been reached, so that a ratio of 1 : 0.86 (in practice 1 : 1) is far more probable. A ratio of 1 : 1 is theoretically possible, since the GC molecules on the DNA chain have sufficient space available. In addition, it is known concerning other dyes that after binding to a substrate the absorption maximum can be suppressed (26) so that in calculating ϵ, the absorption at 497 mμ can be stipulated to be equal in solution and in tissue.

On the basis of these investigations the following method for a standardized GC staining usable for cytophotometric purposes can be given: Carnoy or alcohol fixation (not longer than 2 hours, smears a maximum of 10 minutes, room temperature). Color solution: 0.15 g gallocyanin (Fluka, Buchs/Gallen, Switzerland) and 5 g chrome alum boiled in 100 ml water for 10 minutes. Filtration. Bring to a final volume of 100 ml of the dye solution, pH 1.64 (if necessary adjust with 1 N HCl). The solution should always be made freshly. Staining: 48 hours at room temperature. Differentiation for any desired length of time in water and rising alcohol.

IV. Discussion

The present investigations show that the binding of dye cations to nucleic acids is dependent upon the most varied factors which must be taken into account for a quantitative color reaction. Under exactly defined conditions, however, reproducible results can be achieved for GC which, with a few exceptions, indicate a stoichiometric combination with DNA.

If from the cytophotometric measurement data we calculate the ratio of P atoms of the nucleic acid to GC molecules, it is found that probably one dye molecule is bound per mononucleotide or P atom.

The opinion prevails (*12, 26*) that there is a binding between the dye cation and the phosphate group. The carboxyl group of the GC molecule at pH 1.64 is not dissociated, so that it cannot enter into competition. The complex-bound chromium atom with two free positive charge groups is to be regarded as the positive charge group of the GC molecule (Fig. 18). The substituted amino group of GC cannot be considered for binding (see above).

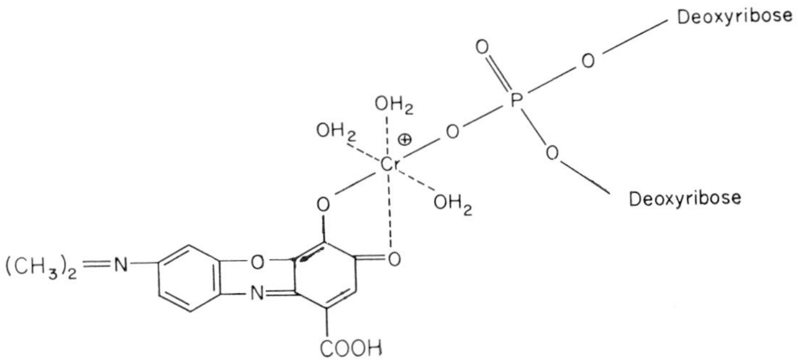

FIG. 18. Suggested equation for the binding of gallocyanin chrome alum to DNA.

How could this binding take place? If we start from the known structure of the DNA molecule (*50*), then the distance between two neighboring P atoms on the polynucleotide chain amounts to about 7 Å. The three 6 rings in the GC molecule are in one plane, so that the diameter vertical to this plane corresponds to that of a carbon atom (3.4 Å). Thus, there is sufficient space to make possible the positioning of one GC molecule per P atom when the molecular plane is vertical to the longitudinal axis of the polynucleotide chain. The binding of the chromium atom to the phosphate group of DNA takes place via an oxygen atom. The space between the two unbound oxygen atoms of the phosphate is 3.5 Å.* With ion radii of the oxygen given as 1.4 Å and of chromium as 0.64 Å, the distance to the second oxygen is too great to allow binding. From this the following picture can be developed for the binding between the phospate of the DNA and the GC molecules (see Fig. 18).

The kinetics of the deposition of dye, represented by the connection between bound quantities of dye and the concentration of dye in solution or duration of staining, follows a Langmuir isotherm. This shows

* Thanks are due to Prof. H. Kuhn, Director of the Physical Chemical Institute of the Landgraf Philipp University of Marburg, for advice on these problems.

that this is a monomeric compound in which the P atoms react successively and independently from one another with the dye (no polymerization). The relatively slow course of the reaction at room temperature, at which the maximum is reached only after 48 hours, and also the more rapid binding at higher temperatures (shortened time of staining) lead to the conclusion that this is a complex-salt binding with nucleic acid. Thus a double chrome-complex-salt binding is present in which both the gallocyanin and the phosphate of the nucleic acids are bound. This chemical compound, as is shown by the solution experiments with strong acids and bases, is extremely stable and thus explains, in contrast to other basic dyes, the progressive character of the staining.

The basic proteins of cell nuclei, which in live cells are bound in the manner of salts to the nucleic acids, do not disturb the color binding in the somatic cell nucleus. Upon fixation or salt treatment of the nuclei there is a dissociation of the nucleoprotein (2), so that phosphate groups are available for the color binding. However, measurements on spermatozoa and cells of chickens and roosters and *Bufo viridis* show that chemical peculiarities of nucleoproteins may prevent maximal dye binding. It can be assumed that the large quantities of basic amino acids, as for example in bull spermatozoa (protamine-like) and rooster spermatozoa (gallin), (13, 29, 49), enter into competition with the dye. Upon maturation of the spermatozoa, the basic amino acid portion increases progressively, so that protamine or protamine-like arginine-rich proteins arise (1, 6) which, according to Lison (22), cause a decreasing basophilia of the nucleoproteins.

Our measurements at various stages of maturity of spermatozoa in bull testicles show that here the early stages still bind the correct quantity of dye and that in spermatozoa the basophilia is reduced. It might be thought in this connection that in addition to the basic proteins the close packing of the DNA molecule in the relatively small spermatozoa might play a role in the reduced staining. The divergences from the constant binding of dye, however, show that the GC staining cannot be used in the same way as the Feulgen reaction for quantitative detection of DNA. At the same time, new and interesting aspects are opened up for the study of the binding condition in a nucleoprotein.

V. Summary

(1)   This paper investigates the degree to which gallocyanin chrome alum binds stoichiometrically with DNA in cell nuclei and thus its limitations in quantitative cytophotometric determinations.

(2)   The dye was examined chromatographically and electrophoreti-

cally for its purity, and the changes in the optical properties were studied after chrome complex formation and binding to nucleic acids.

(3)   By means of a series of investigations (testing of the influence of boiling time, age of the dye solution, dye concentration, duration of staining, pH of the dye solution, fixation, treatment with RNA, and differentiation on the dye binding, fastness to light), the optimal conditions for the preparation of the dye solution and the dying process could be determined.

(4)   The relatively good specificity for the strongly acid phosphate group (sulfate groups stained red, "pseudometachromasia") and the validity of the Beer–Lambert–Bouguer law in tissue and in solution allowed the microphotometric determination of the nucleic acids after staining with gallocyanin chrome alum.

(5)   Cytophotometric measurements on cell nuclei treated with ribonuclease and stained with gallocyanin chrome alum showed that in mammalians the quantity of gallocyanin chrome alum runs parallel with the quantity of DNA or the degrees of ploidy. Divergences from this are found in spermatozoa and erythrocytes containing nuclei in low vertebrates. This may probably be connected with the strongly basic protein components in the cell nuclei.

(6)   The results show that gallocyanin chrome alum staining has certain advantages in comparison with Feulgen staining, for example, the simple staining process and the good reproducibility. The disadvantages of gallocyanin chrome alum staining are principally the lesser specificity for DNA and the influence of pretreatment of the tissue, so that one can only compare preparations treated in exactly the same way with one another.

(7)   Calculation of the gallocyanin chrome alum quantity present in a diploid cell nucleus after RNase treatment allows the conclusion that every phosphate group of the nucleic acid is occupied by one dye molecule.

(8)   From the behavior of the dye upon preparation of the dye solution and staining, it can be deduced that the trivalent chrome complex is bound to the gallocyanin, and upon staining, practically insoluble chrome-double-complex is formed with gallocyanin and nucleic acid. On the basis of the investigations made, the optimal conditions for staining with gallocyanin chrome alum are given.

REFERENCES

1. Alfert, M., Cytochemische Untersuchungen an basischen Kernproteinen während der Gametenbildung, Befruchtung und Entwicklung. "Chemie der Genetik," 9th Mosbacher Colloq., pp. 73–84. Springer, Berlin, 1959.

2. Bayley, P. M., B. N. Preston, and A. R. Peacocke, Thymus deoxyribonucleoprotein. II. Dissociation in sodium chloride solution. *Biochim. Biophys. Acta* **55**, 943–952 (1962).

3. Becher, S., "Untersuchungen über die Echtfärbung der Zellkerne mit künstlichen Beizenfarbstoffen." Bornträger, Berlin, 1921.

4. Beneš, K., and W. Sandritter, Versuche zur histophotometrischen Proteinbestimmung mit der Tetrazonium-Kupplungsreaktion nach Burstone. *Histochemie* **2**, 32–42 (1960).

5. Bethe, A., Die Einwirkung von Säuren und Alkalien auf die Färbung und Färbbarkeit tierischer Gewebe. *Beitr. Chem. Physiol. Pathol.* **6**, 399–425 (1905).

6. Bloch, D. P., and H. Y. C. Hew, Schedule of spermatogenesis in the pulmonate snail *Helix aspersa,* with special reference to histone transition. *J. Biophys. Biochem. Cytol.* **7**, 515–532 (1960).

7. Braun-Falco, O., Über Untersuchungen mit der Hale-PAS-Reaktion (Ritter und Oleson) unter normalen Bedingungen auch bei Erkrankungen des Hautbindegewebes. *Acta Histochem.* **5**, 10–24 (1958).

8. Caspersson, T., "Cell Growth and Cell Function." Norton, New York, 1950.

9. Chargaff, E., Isolation and composition of the deoxypentose nucleic acids and of the corresponding nucleoproteins. *In* "The Nucleic Acids" (E. Chargaff and J. N. Davidson, eds.), Vol. 1, pp. 307–372. Academic Press, New York, 1955.

10. Diefenbach, H., and W. Sandritter, Die quantitative Bindung von Gallocyaninchromalaun an Desoxyribonukleinsäure. *Acta Histochem.* **1**, 55–59 (1954).

11. Ehrlich, P., Beiträge zur Kenntnis der Anilinfärbungen und ihre Anwendung in der mikroskopischen Technik. *Arch. Mikroskop. Anat.* **13**, 263–277 (1877).

12. Einarson, L., On the theory of gallocyanin chromalum staining and its application for quantitative estimation of basophilia. A selective staining of exquisite progressivity. *Acta Pathol. Microbiol. Scand.* **28**, 82–102 (1951).

13. Felix, K., H. Fischer, and A. Krekels, Protamines and nucleoprotamines. *Progr. Biophys. Biophys. Chem.* **6**, 2–23 (1956).

14. Hardy, A. C., as cited in F. H. Kasten, The Feulgen DNA absorption curve *in situ. Histochemie* **1**, 123–150 (1958).

15. Harms, H., "Handbuch der Farbstoffe für die Mikroskopie." Staufen-Verlag, Kamp.-Lintfort, 1957.

16. Hinrichsen, K., Gibt es eine Gallocyanin-Metachromasie? *Acta Histochem.* Suppl. 2, 221–225 (1961).

17. Ito, S., Interferometric dry mass determination of isolated liver nuclei from fasting and fed mice. *Federation Proc.* **15**, 519–520 (1956).

18. Jacobi, H., and H. Kuhn, Richtungen der Übergangsmomente der Absorptionsbanden von Acridin-, Phenazin-, Phenoxazin- und Xanthenfarbstoffen aus Dichroismus und Fluoreszenzpolarisation. *Z. Elektrochem.* **66**, 46–53 (1962).

19. Jobst, K., and W. Sandritter, Über die Beeinflussung der Farbbindung von Toluidinblau und Gallocyaninchromalaun mit Nucleoproteiden (Cytophotometrische Untersuchungen). *Acta Histochem.* **11**, 276–283 (1961).

20. Kasten, F. H., G. Kiefer, and W. Sandritter, Bleaching of Feulgen-stained nuclei and alteration of absorption curve after continuous exposure of visible light in a cytophotometer. *J. Histochem. Cytochem.* **10**, 547–555 (1962).

21. Lagerstedt, S., The quantitative estimation of basophilia through gallocyanin chromalum staining. *Acta Anat.* **5**, 217–223 (1948).

22. Lison, L., Variation de la basophilie pendant la maturation de spermatozoide chez le rat et sa signification histochimique. *Acta Histochem.* **2**, 47–67 (1955).

23. Matoltsy, A. G., and C. Balsamo, as cited in H. G. Goslar, Ein Beitrag zur elektiven Darstellung der Keratine zum histochemischen Verhalten anderer Disulfidverbindungen in der Haut. *Acta Histochem.* **5**, 39–48 (1957).

24. Mendelsohn, M. L., Microspectrophotometry and the cytochemistry of nucleic acids. Doctoral Thesis, Cambridge University (1958).

25. Michaelis, L., "Einführung in die Farbstoffchemie für Histologen." Karger, Berlin, 1902.

26. Michaelis, L., The nature of the interaction of nucleic acids and nuclei with basic dyestuffs. *Cold Spring Harbor Symp. Quant. Biol.* **12**, 131–142 (1947).

27. Miescher, F., "Die histochemischen und physiologischen Arbeiten." Vogel, Leipzig, 1897.

28. Mirsky, A. E., and H. Ris, Variable and constant components of chromosomes. *Nature* **163**, 666–667 (1949).

29. Mirsky, A. E., The composition and structure of isolated chromosomes. *J. Gen. Physiol.* **34**, 475–492 (1951).

29a. Pakkenberg, H., Gallocyanin-chrome alum staining: a quantitative evaluation. *J. Histochem. Cytochem.* **10**, 367–369 (1962).

30. Pollister, A. W., Nucleoproteins of the nucleus. *Exptl. Cell Res.* Suppl. 2, 59–74 (1952).

31. Posaláky, Z., G. Kiefer, and W. Sandritter, Quantitative histochemische Untersuchungen über die säurefeste Anfärbung des Spermienkopfes. *Histochemie* **4**, 312–321 (1964).

32. Sandritter, W., Über den Nukleinsäurestoffwechsel in Plattenepithel- und kleinzelligen Bronchialcarcinomen. *Frankf. Z. Pathol.* **63**, 387–422 (1952).

33. Sandritter, W., Über den Nukleinsäuregehalt in verschiedenen Tumoren. *Frankf. Z. Pathol.* **63**, 422–446 (1952).

34. Sandritter, W., Eine quantitative färberische histochemische Bestimmungsmethode der Nukleinsäuren im Gewebe. *Z. Wiss. Mikroskopie* **61**, 30–37 (1952).

35. Sandritter, W., Die Nachweismethoden der Nukleinsäure. *Z. Wiss. Mikroskopie* **62**, 283–304 (1955).

36. Sandritter, W., UV-Mikrospektrophotometrie. *In* "Handbuch der Histochemie" (W. Graumann and K. Neumann, eds.), Vol. 1, Part I, pp. 220–338. Fischer, Stuttgart, 1958.

37. Sandritter, W., H. Diefenbach, and F. Krantz, Über die quantitative Bindung von Ribonukleinsäure mit Gallocyaninchromalaun. *Experientia* **10**, 210–215 (1954).

38. Sandritter, W., W. Mondorf, H. G. Schiemer, and D. Müller, Beschreibung eines Cytophotometers für sichtbares Licht. *Mikroskopie* **14**, 25-35 (1959).

39. Sandritter, W., D. Müller, and O. Gensecke, UV-mikrospektrophotometrische Messungen des Nukleinsäuregehaltes von Spermien und diploiden Zellen. *Acta Histochem.* **10**, 139–154 (1960).

40. Sandritter, W., D. Müller, and H. G. Schiemer, Über den Nukleinsäuregehalt und das Trockengewicht von haploiden und diploiden Zellen. *Anat. Anz.* **105**, 146–156 (1958).

41. Sandritter, W., G. Pillat, and E. Theiss, Zur Wirkung der Ribonuklease auf Leberzellen. *Exptl. Cell Res.* Suppl. 4, 64–82 (1957).

42. Sandritter, W., H. G. Schiemer, and H. Uhlig, Interferenzmikroskopische Trockengewichtsbestimmungen an Zellen mit haploidem und diploidem Chromosomensatz. *Acta Histochem.* **10**, 155–172 (1960).

43. Schümmelfeder, N., E. Krogh, and K. J. Ebschner, Färbungsanalysen zur Acridinorange-Fluorochromierung. *Histochemie* **1**, 1–28 (1958).

44. Stenram, U., The specifity of the gallocyanin-chromalum stain for nucleic acids as studied by the ribonuclease technique. *Exptl. Cell Res.* **4**, 383–389 (1953).

45. Stich, H., Der Nachweis und das Verhalten von Metaphosphaten in normalen, verdunkelten und Trypaflavin-behandelten Acetabularien. *Z. Naturforsch.* **8b**, 36–45 (1953).

46. Swift, H., Quantitative aspects of nuclear nucleoproteins. *Intern. Rev. Cytol.* **2**, 1–69 (1953).

47. Terner, J. Y., and G. Clark, Gallocyanin chrome alum. I. Technique and specificity. *Stain Technol.* **35**, 167–177, 1960.

48. Vendrely, R., The deoxyribonucleic acid content of the nucleus. "The Nucleic Acids" (E. Chargaff and J. N. Davidson, eds.), Vol. 2, pp. 155–180. Academic Press, New York, 1955.

49. Vendrely, R., A. Knobloch, and C. Vendrely, An attempt of using biochemical methods for cytochemical problems. *Exptl. Cell Res.* Suppl. 4, 279–283 (1957).

50. Watson, J. D., and F. H. C. Crick, Molecular structure of nucleic acids. *Nature* **171**, 737–738 (1953).

51. Weissbach, S., Das Problem der Schnittdickenbestimmung. *Acta Histochem.* **9**, 183–187 (1960).

52. Wieland, T., and G. Pfleiderer, Analytische und mikropräparative Trägerelektrophorese mit höheren Spannungen. *Angew. Chem.* **67**, 257–260 (1955).

CYTOPHOTOMETRY
OF NUCLEIC ACIDS

*Arline D. Deitch**

DEPARTMENT OF MICROBIOLOGY, COLUMBIA UNIVERSITY, NEW YORK, NEW YORK

I. Introduction

This review will be confined to a consideration of three staining procedures that have been used in the quantitative cytophotometric estimation of nucleic acids: the Feulgen reaction, methyl green binding, and methylene blue staining. Each of these staining procedures represents a different chemical approach to obtaining information about the kinds and amounts of nucleic acids to be found in fixed cells. The Feulgen reaction is the best known and best studied of these procedures, and as such it serves as a standard reaction to which the other procedures may be compared. In the Feulgen reaction covalently bonded colored, or *chromophore,* groups become attached to the deoxyribonucleic acid (DNA) molecule as the result of a series of equilibrium reactions. In methyl green binding, on the other hand, electrostatic or saltlike linkages are formed between the basic dye cation and the phosphate groups of (predominantly) DNA. The extent of methyl green binding is determined not only by the amount of DNA present, but also by its state of association with competing protein groups. Since the influence of these competing groups may be largely destroyed, the amount of methyl green binding before and after such treatment provides a sensitive index of the extent of such protein competition. The evidence so far obtained suggests that the competing protein may vary in amount with the metabolic state of the cell. In contrast to this approach, in the methylene blue staining procedure, nucleic acid phosphate groups are saturated by salt linkage to oppositely charged basic dye molecules after the destruction of competing basic protein groups. Since methylene blue binds equally to DNA and

* Supported by Grant No. AI-05703, National Institutes of Health, U.S. Public Health Service, Bethesda, Maryland.

to ribonucleic acid (RNA), and since RNA may be removed quantitatively, amounts of both nucleic acids may be determined by this procedure and RNA : DNA ratios computed for the cell populations being studied.

Thus the use of all three cytophotometric procedures in conjunction with one another may lead to a better knowledge not only of the amounts of nucleic acid present in different cells or cellular regions (nucleolus, nucleus, and cytoplasm), but also of their associations with proteins.

II. The Feulgen Reaction

The Feulgen nucleal reaction for DNA is the cytochemical procedure that has been most used in cytophotometric studies. While it is not possible in this review to cover the information which has been derived from studies using the Feulgen reaction, a few major lines of research should be mentioned. Quantitative use of the Feulgen reaction has helped to establish that the average amount of DNA per chromosome set is constant for animal and plant species, and that replication of DNA is restricted to the interphase (1, 70, 87, 88). Feulgen cytophotometry has been used to determine the extent of polyploidy in mammalian liver and to assess the influence of aging and of various drug, hormonal, and operative treatments upon this polyploidy (5, 30, 37, 38, 87). Other studies of amounts of Feulgen-revealed DNA have shown that aneuploidy and polyploidy occur frequently in various tumor types (6–11, 60, 71, 76–78) and in infection with DNA viruses (17, 19, 61).

The Feulgen reaction depends upon a prior acid hydrolysis of DNA which preferentially removes purines, unmasking the aldehydic function of the deoxyribofuranose sugars to which they were bound (28, 34, 68). The aldehydes thus formed react with a decolorized or leuco Schiff reagent (85), which is converted into its colored form and is bound in situ to the DNA without diffusion (58, 68). Proof that an aldehyde function in necessary for the positive nucleal reaction comes from the observation that aldehyde-coupling reagents block the Feulgen reaction if applied after the acid hydrolysis (35, 53, 58, 59, 63, 92).

The specificity of the Feulgen reaction for DNA is no longer in doubt. The reaction is negative after complete removal of DNA either enzymatically (22) or by extraction of the tissue with hot trichloracetic acid (86). RNA and protein do not give the Feulgen reaction (34, 58), and pretreatment with ribonuclease has no effect on Feulgen intensity (12).

In vitro studies of nucleic acids have shown that the purines of RNA are also susceptible to removal by acid hydrolysis (99), but only the deoxy sugars behave as true aldehydes and hence give the Feulgen reaction. The difference in behavior of the sugar moieties is also the basis for other colorimetric methods for estimating DNA (27). Moreover, it should be remarked that RNA is extracted rapidly from fixed tissue during the acid hydrolysis procedure (*25, 32, 98*), while it is only after a more prolonged hydrolysis that the DNA is also extracted (*vide infra*) (*28, 32, 46, 90*).

The conventional Feulgen hydrolysis has been in 1 N HCl at 60°C. Hydrolysis has also been performed in other concentrations of hydrochloric acid and at lower temperatures (*49, 82, 83*) [see Garcia, Sandritter, this volume]. Other acids have also been used, including perchloric (*29, 103*) and trichloracetic acid (*15, 16*). Using the latter acid, a technique was elaborated in which DNA and histones can be stained and measured in the same cells (*15, 16*). Histones are known to be extractable from fixed tissue with hydrochloric acid, but they are believed to be precipitated and retained in tissue with trichloracetic acid (TCA) (*72*). DNA is then first revealed with a TCA-Feulgen procedure using TCA for hydrolysis, and subsequently the histone is stained by the procedure of Alfert and Geschwind (*3*). The amounts of Feulgen-colored DNA and fast green-stained histone can thus be measured successively in the same cells.

The chemical basis for the recoloration of the Schiff reagent hitherto most frequently cited is that of Wieland and Scheuing (*101*). According to these authors, when sulfurous acid is added to pararosaniline, the decolorized Schiff reagent which results is an amino sulfinic acid derivative of pararosaniline leuco sulfonic acid (I).

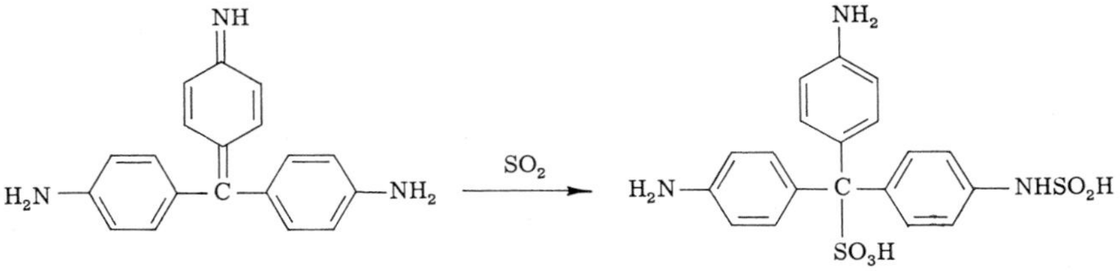

(I)

After two aldehyde groups have been added to this colorless pararosaniline derivative, the sulfonic acid group is released from the central carbon, and the molecule is converted to the magenta-colored quinoid form (II).

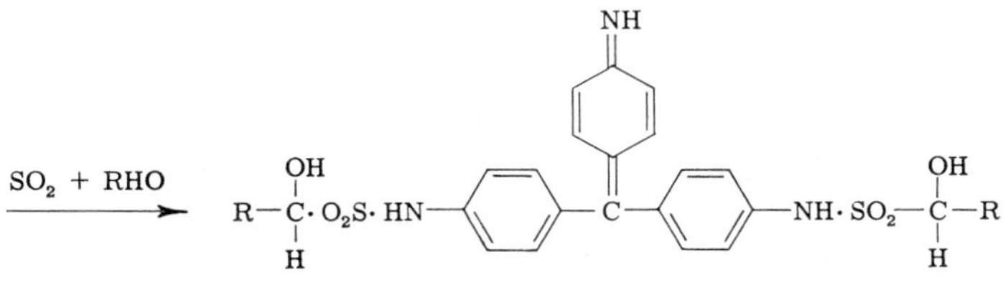

(II)

However, recent studies suggest that the mechanism proposed by Wieland and Scheuing may not be correct and the reaction may be more complex. When a leuco Schiff reagent is combined with formaldehyde, multiple-colored reaction products are found both chromatographically (*13*) and electrophoretically (*47*). As an alternative to Wieland and Scheuing's proposal, it has been suggested that the reaction products of the Schiff reagent with aldehydes are amino alkyl sulfonic acid derivatives of the dye (III) (*43, 48, 64, 81*). Hardonk and van Duijn (*43*)

(III)

have suggested that the multiple reaction products found by Barka and Ornstein may be explained by alkyl sulfonic acid substituents replacing one or more of the six hydrogens of the three primary amines of the pararosaniline molecule. However, Barka and Ornstein noted that tetramethyl pararosaniline, which has only one primary amine with two reactive hydrogens, nonetheless gives four colored Schiff reaction products. It would seem, therefore, that we have not as yet arrived at an adequate chemical explanation of the reaction of the Schiff reagent with aldehydes. It has been pointed out that tissue aldehydes are spatially restricted and can in any case form fewer reaction products, possibly representing only mono- and dialdehyde-substituted Schiff molecules (*44*).

The conventional Schiff reagent is made from basic fuchsin, which is a mixture of pararosaniline and its mono- and dimethyl-substituted congeners (*23*). In recent years many other basic dyes have been proposed as Schiff-type reagents (*52, 53, 66, 67*). The dyes which can be substituted successfully for basic fuchsin are of different chemical types (oxazine, thiazine, triphenylmethane, and so forth), but all have at least one primary amino group (*52, 53, 66*). Although treatment of these dye solutions with sulfurous acid may not necessarily lead to decoloration, the SO_2-containing dye solutions nonetheless act as specific reagents for detection of aldehydes, and aldehyde blockade performed after hydrolysis prevents staining (*53*). A number of these Schiff-type reagents are fluorescent and offer promise in the study of sites where DNA is found in low concentration (*66*) (for instance, in plastids). To date, however, few cytophotometric studies have used dyes other than basic fuchsin in the Schiff reagent (*18, 80*). (However, see Ruch, this volume).

The various formulas that have been proposed for Schiff reagents containing basic fuchsin differ considerably in pH, dye, and SO_2 content (*54, 63*). These factors greatly affect the amount of Feulgen dye found per nucleus (*31, 62, 90*). Even the same reagent batch will vary in these aspects during its useful life, and these variations as well as differences in staining temperature may result in obtaining different mean Feulgen values for similar populations of cells. To compare data from one experiment with another, it is therefore necessary to use an appropriate standard cell system with which to normalize the data.

Caution should be used in the selection of any reference or standard cell type (*100*). The standard cell is preferably one which is not replicating. It should be fixed and handled in a manner identical with the experimental material. Feulgen absorption curves and hydrolysis time curves should be run to determine if the two cell systems behave comparably. It is also desirable that comparison be made with cells of closely similar protein content.

The kind of fixation used influences the rate of liberation of aldehydes during hydrolysis, the rate of breakdown and loss from the tissue of the apurinic nucleic acid derivatives, and the maximum Feulgen intensity achieved (*14, 28, 46, 90*). In general, DNA of tissues fixed in fluids containing chromate or dichromate withstands hydrolysis cleavage and loss longer (30–60 minutes) than that of tissues fixed in alcohol–acetic or formalin (8–16 minutes) (*14, 28, 46*). The maximal Feulgen intensity is, however, greatest after formalin fixation and approximately equal after chromate or alcohol–acetic fixation (*28, 90*).

The size of the tissue block is also a factor in the intensity obtained with the Feulgen reaction. With large blocks there is unequal penetration of the components of the fixative, and dilution and alteration of its contents from the periphery toward the center of the block. The peripheral nuclei have been found to have as much as 30% higher Feulgen values than are found in the more central nuclei of the block (*4, 90*). This is probably due to protein loss from the outer cells during the preparative procedures, since measurement of the Millon reaction for tyrosine residues (*72, 75*) indicates that those nuclei with higher amounts of Feulgen dye have lower Millon values (*90*). Nuclei in frozen sections and sucrose-isolated nuclei give even higher Feulgen amounts than do similar nuclei at the periphery of fixed tissue blocks (*90*) (See Table I). Since nuclear isolation results in loss of nuclear protein, chiefly nonhistone in nature (*73*), it would seem that this protein may be somewhat inhibitory to the Feulgen reaction. Where differences on the order of 10–15% in average Feulgen values are found for two cell types, it is probably desirable to isolate their nuclei and see whether these differences persist.

TABLE I

THE EFFECT OF FIXATIVE PENETRATION ON FEULGEN INTENSITY[a,b]

	Feulgen dye bound	Standard error
Liver (tetraploid nuclei)		
Center of section	6.4	0.05
Edge of section	7.9	0.08
Sucrose homogenate	9.0	0.16
Frozen sections	8.8	0.18
Spermatocytes		
Center of section	8.2	0.08
Edge of section	9.1	0.07
Sucrose homogenate	9.3	0.16

[a] Values in arbitrary units represent means of 15 measurements on formalin-fixed rat nuclei. All tissues were from the same animal.
[b] From Swift (90).

There has not been to date any critical study in animal tissue to determine whether an apurinic acid can be achieved during the Feulgen hydrolysis before cleavage and loss of DNA commences. Studies on plant tissue suggest that the two processes may overlap to a considerable extent with perchloric acid hydrolysis (103) [however, see Savage and Plaut (84)], but there may be a loss of 12% or less of DNA thymine with optimal hydrolysis in 1 N HCl at 60°C (84, 94). In a qualitative study of the Feulgen reaction, Jordanov noted that the high temperature of the hydrolysis bath rather than its acidity may be responsible for loss of Feulgen stainability (49). This author used hydrolysis in 5 N HCl at room temperature and found an extended plateau of Feulgen intensity with hydrolysis time for Carnoy and alcohol–formalin–acetic fixed mouse tissues. Extraction of the optimally hydrolyzed tissue with either water or 5 N HCl at 60°C resulted in a profound loss of Feulgen intensity, while this loss proceeds more slowly with water extraction at room temperature.

When tissues are hydrolyzed for different periods of time, there are differences in their Feulgen absorption curves (Fig. 1) (65, 90). As the hydrolysis time increases, the absorption curve, which has at first a single maximum at about 570–575 mμ, develops an increasing shoulder at 530–550 mμ, until in the overhydrolyzed tissue at 30 minutes, this second absorption maximum is greater in height than the 570-mμ peak. One possible interpretation is that these two chromophores correspond to Schiff reagent molecules substituted with either one or two aldehyde groups. With increasing hydrolysis, one would expect that the number of disubstituted molecules would become larger as vicinal purines are split off and the Schiff reagent becomes bound to two adjacent aldehydes. Alternatively, however, one might postulate that DNA-protein associations are altered during hydrolysis and this is what is being reflected in the changing absorption curve shape. It has been shown that the presence of protein in model systems affects the Feulgen curve shape (Fig. 1)

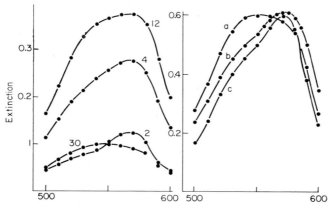

Fig. 1. Absorption curves of Feulgen dye. *Left:* Absorption curves made with microphotometer on single uncut mouse liver interphase nuclei (diameter about 8 μ) fixed in acetic alcohol, showing change in shape with different hydrolysis time in N HCl at 60 degrees. *Right:* (b) Mouse liver nucleus fixed in Sanfelice, 12 minutes hydrolysis. (c) DNA solution (0.35 mg/ml in 1-cm cuvette) hydrolyzed 12 minutes. (a) Same solution but absorbed on 20-μ section of heat-denatured acetic alcohol-fixed egg albumin during 12-minute hydrolysis; the section then stained in Feulgen reagent and measured with a microphotometer. From Swift (*90*).

(*44, 90*). Although the egg albumin is shown here to shift the Feulgen-DNA curve to shorter wavelengths, in the study of Hardonk and van Duijn, bovine serum albumin added to DNA in polyacrylamide films was found to shift the absorption curve toward longer wavelengths (Fig. 2) (*44*). No shift in absorption curve maximum was found for citric acid or sucrose-isolated nuclei with increasing hydrolysis time (*50*). This may be a reflection of the lower protein content of isolated nuclei as compared with those in fixed tissue sections (*73*). As evidence that protein content does not affect the Feulgen reaction, Kasten has noted that pepsin extraction of fixed tissues does not change either the shape of their absorption curves or the amount of Feulgen dye bound per nucleus (*50, 51*). However, it may be that it is necessary to remove the protein from unfixed cells to obtain such effects. Pepsin extraction of unfixed cells has, however, not been studied.

In general, the Feulgen reaction has been found to exhibit a propor-

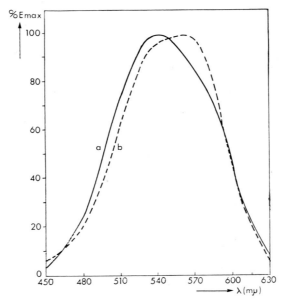

FIG. 2. (a) Feulgen reaction: DNA + polyacrylamide; (b) Feulgen reaction: DNA + bovine serum albumin + polyacrylamide. From Hardonk and van Duijn *(44)*.

tionality to the chromosome number and to the amount of DNA *(77, 96)*. One curious exception has been reported recently by Walker and Richards. These authors found a differential effect of the pH of the Schiff reagent on the amount of Feulgen dye bound in sperm nuclei as compared with liver nuclei (Fig. 3). The pH of the staining solution was found to have little effect upon the amount of Feulgen dye bound by sperm, while the amount of Feulgen dye bound by diploid and tetraploid liver cells doubled as the pH was increased from 1.3 to 2.9. The expected 1 : 2 : 4 ratio of amounts of Feulgen dye per haploid, diploid, and tetraploid nuclei was found only at the lowest pH. At the highest pH used, the ratio was close to 1 : 4 : 8. The authors interpret their results as being due in some way to the markedly different protein associated with DNA in the sperm as compared with that in liver cells, and they caution against the use of sperm cells as a standard for the Feulgen reaction.

III. Methyl Green

The basic dye methyl green, septamethylpararosaniline, has a long history of use in cytology, especially in the mixture of methyl green and

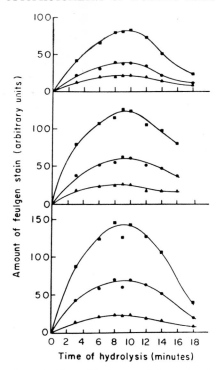

FIG. 3. Differential effect of pH on Feulgen staining at various times of hydrolysis on sperm heads and somatic nuclei (liver) of the mouse. Top, pH 1.3; middle, pH 2.4; bottom pH 2.9; ■ = tetraploid; ● = diploid; ▲ = haploid (sperm). The ratio of tetraploid to diploid nuclei remains constant at 2 : 1, but for the extreme values of pH of staining, the ratio tetraploid : diploid : haploid stain values changes from approximately 4 : 2 : 1 to almost 8 : 4 : 1. From Walker and Richards (*100*).

pyronin of Unna and Pappenheim (*69, 97*). By this procedure nuclei are stained various shades of blue-green to violet, while cytoplasm and nucleoli are stained red. After ribonuclease digestion, Brachet found that chromatin stained green with the methyl green–pyronin mixture, while nucleoli and cytoplasm were unstained. Therefore, he considered the basic dye pyronin to be a specific stain for RNA (*20, 21*). Since Pollister and Leuchtenberger (*74*) found considerable residual pyronin staining in tissue from which nucleic acids had been extracted with trichloracetic acid, they concluded that pyronin stained protein as well as RNA. They noted, however, that methyl green bound specifically and reproducibly to DNA. Ribonuclease pretreatment did not affect the methyl green staining, and no methyl green was bound to tissue after extraction of both nucleic acids.

Unna had observed that pretreatment of tissue sections with hot water markedly decreased the ability of chromatin to stain with methyl green. Pollister and Leuchtenberger, in confirming this observation, found further that this treatment did not lead to lowered Feulgen intensities or to loss of DNA phosphate. They proposed that a physical change in state of the DNA had occurred without change in amount, and they tentatively suggested that this might be a "depolymerization." Kurnick's finding that heating or enzymatic depolymerization of DNA solutions was accompanied by lowered methyl green binding also led him to this conclusion (56, 57). A more recent study of DNA in vitro has shown, however, that only those treatments which destroy the double helical nature of DNA affect its capacity to bind methyl green. Thus, sonic vibration, which depolymerizes DNA without breaking the bihelix, does not affect methyl green binding to DNA, while heat denaturation of DNA, which leads to strand separation ("melting"), results in greatly reduced affinity of DNA for methyl green (79).

Pollister and Leuchtenberger's study was followed by a number of cytochemical studies in which depolymerization of DNA was invoked to explain the lowered methyl green staining of tissues observed after ultraviolet and X-irradiation and in the altered nuclear material of systemic lupus erythematosus (24, 33, 45, 55). Alfert reinvestigated the factors affecting methyl green staining in tissue sections and pointed out that depolymerization might not be an adequate explanation for the reduced methyl green affinity in the situations cited (2). He noted first that methyl green staining was not specific, that is, it was not entirely confined to DNA: The sites of RNA concentration (Nissl bodies and gland cell ergastoplasm, for example) also stained with methyl green. He also noted that the selectivity of staining depended upon the kind of fixative used: After formalin fixation, cytoplasmic RNA may stain strongly with methyl green. Further, he found that much of the loss of methyl green staining occurring after hot water treatment could be restored to sections by blocking protein basic groups by deamination or acetylation. He then suggested that masking of DNA phosphate groups by protein basic groups was at least partially responsible for the lowered methyl green binding observable after heat treatment.

The influence of protein interference on methyl green staining was confirmed in a detailed study of the altered nuclei (L.E. cells and bodies) in systemic lupus erythematosus (S.L.E.) (39–42). These nuclei (usually leukocytes) exposed to serum of patients having S.L.E. are profoundly altered morphologically and tinctorially. The altered nuclear material exhibits lowered methyl green staining relative to its Feulgen values. To explain these findings, depolymerization of DNA had earlier been invoked (*55*). However, Godman and Deitch demonstrated that since acetylation of protein amino groups in this altered nuclear material restored the methyl green values and the Feulgen-methyl green ratio to normal control levels (*39, 42*) (Table II), the change in L.E.

TABLE II

MEAN AMOUNTS OF METHYL GREEN AND FEULGEN DYE BOUND
IN L.E. BODIES DERIVED FROM LYMPHOCYTES[a,b]

	Lymphocytes (20 measured)	L.E. bodies (20 measured)
Methyl green	16.7 ± 0.5	11.9 ± 0.3
Methyl green after acetylation	17.8 ± 0.8	23.1 ± 0.6
Feulgen	19.9 ± 0.4	21.3 ± 0.5
$\dfrac{\text{Postacetylated MeGr}}{\text{MeGr}}$	1.06	1.94
$\dfrac{\text{Feulgen}}{\text{MeGr}}$	1.19	1.79
$\dfrac{\text{MeGr}}{\text{Feulgen}}$ Postacetylated MeGr	1.12	0.92

[a] Measurements of free L.E. bodies in L.E. preparations made from lymphocytes from a patient with chronic lymphatic leukemia.
[b] From Godman and Deitch (*39*).

bodies was due not to depolymerization, but to entry of competing protein, which became linked to DNA. It was shown that considerable amounts of a lysine-rich non-histone protein had in fact entered the altered nuclei and that this serum-derived foreign protein, now known to be antibody globulin, became associated with DNA (*40*), masked DNA phosphate groups, and thus lowered methyl green binding.

A physiological instance in which a non-histone protein blocks methyl green binding to DNA was presented in a study of young rat liver by Bloch and Godman (*16*). These authors stained the same cells successively with methyl green (after ribonuclease pretreatment) and by the Feulgen reaction. They found that if the amounts per cell of these two stains were plotted against each other (Fig. 4), the cells fell into two groups. One group (A) comprised the posttelophase, the DNA-synthesizing, and the preprophase members of the population; these were termed "autosynthetic" and exhibited a proportionality between the amount of methyl green bound and the amount of Feulgen stain. The other group (B), termed "heterosynthetic," comprised cells with the diploid amount of Feulger-stained DNA, but whose DNA showed markedly lower methyl green binding. These cells had prominent nucleoli and large nuclei. The amount of methyl green bound by these cells could be brought to normal values by a prior acetylation of protein basic groups. It was suggested that a non-histone "residual" protein responsible for the mature synthetic functioning of the nucleus is present in greater amount and (or)

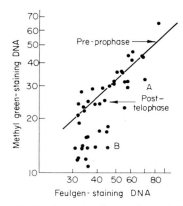

Fig. 4. Comparison of the Feulgen-staining and methyl green-binding capacities of DNA in two types of nuclei in squash preparations of the liver of a young rat; the parallel increase in both stains in the nuclei synthesizing chromosomal material in preparation for division (group A) and the decrease in methyl green binding in a fraction of the nuclei containing the diploid amount of Feulgen-staining DNA (group B) are demonstrated. From Bloch and Godman (16).

closer association to DNA in these heterosynthetic cells and that interference by masking of phosphate groups by this protein is responsible for their decreased staining with methyl green. Extraction and blocking studies were presented to confirm this suggestion.

It would appear from the foregoing that methyl green staining may act as a sensitive measure of the presence in nuclei of a non-histone protein which is closely associated with DNA and whose presence may reflect the metabolic state of the cell.

IV. Methylene Blue

The methylene blue staining procedure (26) was developed to permit measurement of amounts of both RNA and DNA. While azure B has been shown to exhibit specificity of binding to both nucleic acids, marked differences in absorption curve shape are found for RNA and DNA stained with this dye, with RNA being stained metachromatically (36). These differences in absorption curve shape reflect failures in Beer's law and might greatly complicate measurement of RNA : DNA ratios in nuclei where both nucleic acids are undergoing quantitative change. (See however Swith *et al., 91.*) Methylene blue, on the other hand, does not stain RNA metachromatically, and absorption curves taken through nucleoli and cytoplasm are the same shape as those taken through chromatin after removal of RNA (Fig. 5). This difference be-

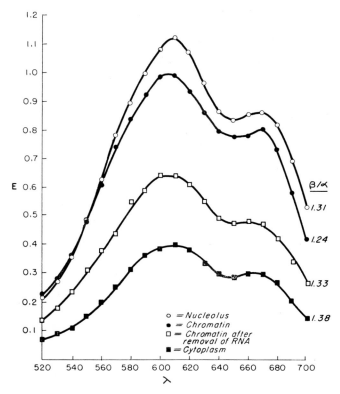

FIG. 5. Representative methylene blue absorption curves taken through different cellular regions of cultured monkey kidney cells. Cells were air-dried, fixed in methanol, and postfixed in formalin, acetylated 18 hours at 45°C, and stained one hour in 2 mg/ml methylene blue. From Deitch (*25*).

tween staining with these two thiazine dyes is related to their chemical structure. While azure B (trimethyl thionine) behaves more metachromatically than methylene blue (tetramethyl thionine) toward RNA, both dyes exhibit metachromasia when bound to such highly electronegative polyanionic chromatropes as sulfate-ester mucopolysaccharides of cartilage matrix or mast cell granules. In contrast to this, the higher homologs of methylene blue such as tetraethyl thionine are not at all metachromatic (*95*).

Tests of models made by mixing various concentrations of RNA or DNA with gelatin show that methylene blue staining at pH 4 follows Beer's law and is stoichiometric for both nucleic acids, while the gelatin is itself unstained (Fig. 6). It is possible then to stain both nucleic acids

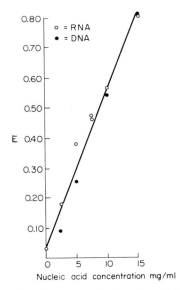

Fig. 6. The effect of varying the concentration of nucleic acid in a gelatin-nucleic acid model. Different concentrations of DNA or RNA were dissolved in gelatin, fixed in alcohol–formalin–acetic acid, and embedded together. Each paraffin section contained a range of nucleic acid concentrations; their extinction values are thus independent of section thickness and can be compared with their known nucleic acid concentrations. From Deitch (25).

in situ and, after measuring the amount bound per nucleus, to extract one nucleic acid, then, after restaining with methylene blue, to remeasure the same nuclei. The extraction procedure adopted in this study was a short hydrolysis in $1N$ HCl at 60°C to remove RNA. Six to ten minutes of such treatment is usually sufficient to remove all RNA without extraction of DNA (84, 94). Hydrolysis in 5 N HCl at room temperature, while not used in this study, should also be tried, since Jordanov using this procedure found complete loss of cytoplasmic and nucleolar basophilia in less than half the time necessary to achieve maximal Feulgen intensity. The use of enzymatic extraction procedures was avoided because of the known resistance of nuclear RNA to RNase extraction (93, 102) and because of the destruction of all nuclear basophilia which may accompany the use of DNase (89).

In order to avoid competitive protein effects, protein basic groups were neutralized by acetylation prior to staining with methylene blue. While this was found, as expected, to enhance methylene blue binding, it did not affect the absorption curve shape. Acetylation was carried out in acetic anhydride at 45° or 60°C. Methylene blue staining reaches a maximum after about 4 hours of acetylation, and there is no further change in the amount of dye bound with increasing time of acetylation. The amount of methylene blue bound is also independent of dye concentration, time of staining, and temperature within wide limits, and of pH from 3.75 to 4.25. Methylene blue staining thus is a progressive procedure that quickly reaches an end point, saturating all available nucleic acid phosphate groups with dye. It should be noted that this does not necessarily mean that all nucleic acid groups can or do take up the dye. The acetylation conditions used are insufficient to block all protein basic groups (26), and it is possible that the remaining basic groups may compete with the dye for nucleic acid sites. In addition, steric hindrance in the tissue also limits dye uptake to an unknown extent.

Comparison was made between chemical values for RNA and DNA and cytophotometric measurements of these substances using methylene

TABLE III

AVERAGE METHYLENE BLUE VALUES FOR ISOLATED HeLa NUCLEI COMPARED WITH THE RATIO OF DNA TO RNA OBTAINED CHEMICALLY[a,b]

Experiment	A Total methylene blue	B Methylene blue after 1 N HCl at 60°C for 6 min.	C = A − B Difference	B/C	Chemical DNA/RNA
1	77.29 ± 0.23	58.39 ± 0.18	18.90	3.09	3.34
2	84.42 ± 3.04	52.57 ± 1.78	31.85	1.65	2.86
3	80.40 ± 2.49	49.92 ± 1.81	30.48	1.64	1.62
4	53.75 ± 1.57	44.75 ± 0.99	9.00	4.97	5.40
5	60.33 ± 1.62	55.61 ± 1.17	4.72	11.78	8.25

[a] In each experiment three bottles of HeLa cells were pooled to make one sample. Nuclei were isolated using 0.1% Tween 80 [From Fisher and Harris (35b)]. Experiments 2 and 3 were replicate experiments made on the same date from two pooled HeLa cell samples. Aliquots of nuclei from each experiment were taken for cytophotometric measurements using the methylene blue procedure after air drying the nuclei, fixing them in methanol, and postfixing them in formalin. RNA determinations were made using an orcinol procedure and DNA by a diphenylamine procedure. (The nuclear isolations and chemical determinations were kindly performed by Dr. Hsiang Ju Lin of the Cell Chemistry Laboratory, Department of Biochemistry, Columbia University.)

[b] From Deitch (25).

blue on the same objects. Nuclei were isolated in the nonionic detergent Tween-80 from cultured HeLa cells, orcinol and diphenylamine procedures were used to obtain average RNA and DNA values, respectively. The ratio of these values was compared with the values for RNA and DNA obtained cytophotometrically (Table III). In general there is good agreement between the two approaches. In this table, Experiments 2 and 3 were duplicate experiments made at the same time on two pooled samples of isolated HeLa nuclei. A low orcinol value (RNA) was obtained for Experiment 2, which caused a discrepancy between the chemical and cytochemical DNA : RNA ratios. The cytophotometric data from the two experiments are, however, in good agreement. These data support the concept that basic dye binding after acetylation can be used to stain RNA and DNA stoichiometrically and also that a short hydrolysis in $1N$ HCl at 60°C is effective in removing chromosomal RNA.

Appendix*

STAINING TECHNIQUES FOR CYTOPHOTOMETRY

I. The Feulgen reaction

    A. Preparation of the Schiff reagent. From Stowell (*86a*).

        (1) Dissolve 0.5 g of basic fuchsin by pouring over it 100 ml of boiled distilled water. Shake thoroughly. Cool to 50°C and filter.

        (2) Add 10 ml of one normal ($1N$) HCl and 2 g of potassium metabisulfite ($K_2S_2O_5$) to the filtrate. Shake, close tightly in a chemically clean bottle, store in the dark for 24 hours.

        (3) Add 0.25 g of neutral activated charcoal, shake for 1 minute, and filter rapidly through coarse filter paper. The clear filtrate is stored in the refrigerator in a tightly closed amber bottle.

    B. Preparation of sulfurous acid bleaches

        (1) 10 ml $1N$ HCl

        (2) 10 ml 10% anhydrous potassium metabisulfite ($K_2S_2O_5$) in distilled water.

        (3) 180 ml distilled water

    The bleach must be made immediately before use. It is used in screw-cap jars, well covered.

    C. Procedure

        (1) The tissue may be fixed in methanol, alcohol–acetic, Carnoy, 10% neutral buffered formalin, alcohol–formalin–acetic acid, or by freeze-dry or freeze-substitution.

---

* This appendix describes staining, extraction, and blocking procedures referred to above and in Cytophotometry of Proteins, pp. 451–468.

(2) Slides are hydrated to water and hydrolyzed in 1N HCl at 60°C for 8 to 16 minutes. The optimal time should be determined for each fixative and cell type used. If many slides are carried into the hydrolysis bath a 1–2 minute rinse in distilled water at 60°C should be added before the acid hydrolysis step to prevent cooling of the HCl.

(3) Chill the slides in cold 1N HCl for 1 minute.

(4) Stain in Schiff reagent for 1 hour at room temperature.

(5) Transfer the slides rapidly into 3 (or more if many slides are being handled) changes of sulfurous acid bleach for a total of 30 minutes.

(6) Rinse the slides for 5 minutes in running tap water followed by distilled water, dehydrate through a graded series of alcohols. Mount from xylene in the index of refraction oil which matches the tissue refractive index as judged with dark field illumination.*

II. TCA–Feulgen followed by alkaline fast green staining for histone. From Bloch and Godman (15).

A. Preparation of TCA Schiff reagent

Dissolve 1 g of basic fuchsin in 200 ml boiling distilled water. Cool to 50°C, add 20 ml of 1N trichloracetic acid (TCA) (mol. wt. = 163). Cool to 25°C, filter, and add 2 g potassium metabisulfite. Shake, let stand for 24 hours. Decolorize by adding 0.5 g activated charcoal for 1 minute. Filter. Store in tightly stoppered amber bottles in the refrigerator.

B. Fixation and staining:

(1) Fix in 10% neutral buffered formalin for 3–6 hours.

(2) Wash overnight in running tap water.

(3) Distilled water rinse.

(4) 1N TCA at room temperature for several minutes.

(5) 15 min (not necessarily optimal time) in 1N TCA at 60°C.

(6) One hour in TCA–Schiff reagent.

(7) Three 5-minute washes in sulfite bleach: 5 ml 10% potassium metabisulfite, 5 ml 1N TCA, 100 ml distilled H_2O.

(8) Wash in tap and distilled water.

(9) Dehydrate in ethyl alcohol, xylene, mount in index of refraction oil.

(10) After measuring the Feulgen reaction, carry out the alkaline fast green reaction (see below) and remeasure the same cells.

* Index of refraction liquids available from R. P. Cargille Labs, Inc., Cedar Grove, N.J.

III. Methyl green
  A. Purification of the dye (from C. Leuchtenberger and A. W.
     Pollister, personal communication, 1948). Methyl green con-
     tains crystal violet as an impurity, which may be removed
     either from the dry dye or the dye solution.
     (1) Shake 10 g of the dry dye thoroughly with 200 ml chloro-
         form and filter under suction. Wash the methyl green on
         the filter paper into a beaker with 400 ml chloroform. Fil-
         ter and rewash with chloroform until the solution shows
         only traces of pink color. Dry the dye in a vacuum desic-
         cator which contains calcium chloride and activated char-
         coal.
     (2) Weigh the dried, purified dye and make up a 1% solution
         in distilled water. (The dye is unstable in the dry form.)
         Store the stock 1% solution in the cold. The stock solu-
         tion may be purified by shaking it with chloroform in a
         separatory funnel. This will prove necessary if it is kept
         longer than a few months.
  B. Solutions: Add 2 parts of 1% stock methyl green solution to 8
     parts of the following solvent:

     | phenol | 0.5 | ml |
     | glycerine | 20 | ml |
     | 95% alcohol | 2.5 | ml |
     | distilled water | 100 | ml |

     The solvent may be kept indefinitely. The pH of the solution
     should be 4.2. The dye solution made up in solvent may be
     kept in the refrigerator for a few days.
  C. Staining procedure: Tissue should be fixed with methanol, Car-
     noy, or by freeze-substitution in alcohol.
     (1) RNA should be removed with RNase or with 1 N HCl at
         60°C for 8–10 minutes.
     (2) Stain slides 45 minutes at 56°C in the dye solution.
     (3) Wash quickly in ice water (few dips).
     (4) Blot gently with filter paper.
     (5) Differentiate in *tert*-butyl alcohol overnight.
     (6) Two changes of xylene; mount in index of refraction oil.
IV. Azure B. From Flax and Himes (*36*).
    Treat methanol, Carnoy, or freeze-substituted tissue with 0.25
    mg/ml azure B at pH 4.0 (e.g., with McIlvaine buffer: 24.6 ml of
    0.1 M citric acid to 15.4 ml of 0.2 M disodium phosphate, or add
    several crystals of potassium acid phthalate to the dye to bring it
    to pH 4.0). Rinse slides in water and leave in the first change of

tert-butanol (without molecular sieve) overnight. Complete dehydration in an additional change of dry *tert*-butanol; xylene;
mount in index of refraction oil.

V. Methylene blue. From Deitch (*25*).

   A. Fixation: Fix tissues in methyl alcohol, alcohol–acetic, formalin, or alcohol–formalin–acetic mixtures or by freeze-substitution in alcohol. If a fixative which does not contain formalin is used, postfix the slides in 10% neutral buffered
   formalin for 10–30 minutes and wash well in running tap
   water.

   B. Removal of RNA: Methylene blue stains both DNA and RNA.
   If a measure of the ratio of nuclear RNA to DNA is wanted,
   the RNA may be removed with 1 N NCl at 60° for 6–10 minutes. This may be done on a separate slide if two populations
   of cells are to be compared. Otherwise proceed through the
   acetylation and staining steps listed below, measure the methylene blue bound per nucleus, then destain the slides in 70%
   alcohol containing 1% trichloracetic acid, extract RNA as
   above, restain, and remeasure the same cells. The slides may
   be mapped to facilitate refinding the same cells.

   C. Acetylate to block competing protein groups for 18–24 hours
   in 100% acetic anhydride at 60°C.

   D. Staining procedure:

      (1) A freshly made (2 or 3 days) solution of methylene blue
      chloride is made up in distilled water at 1 mg/ml. The pH
      should be between 3.8 and 4.0, and it may be adjusted if
      necessary with 0.1 N HCl. Slides are stained for 30–60
      minutes.

      (2) After staining, drain the slides and rinse them in one bath
      of distilled water for 30–60 seconds. Drain well or blot the
      slides lightly and pass them through three 10-minute
      changes of *tert*-butanol in staining jars containing a layer
      of 1/16 inch pellets of Linde molecular sieve type 4A (Un-
      ion Carbide) as a drying agent. Discard the first *tert*-
      butanol when the pellets turn blue or when a blue color
      is seen in the alcohol. Two changes of xylene, 5 minutes
      each. Mount in index of refraction oil to match the tissue
      refractive index.

VI. The alkaline fast green reaction. Modified from Alfert and
   Geschwind (*3*).

      (1) Fix in 10% neutral buffered formalin for 3–6 hours or
      postfix slides of methanol, Carnoy, or freeze-substituted
      tissue in 10% neutral buffered formalin for 10–30 minutes.

(2) Wash overnight.

(3) Remove nucleic acids in freshly made, freshly boiling 5% trichloracetic acid at 90°C for 15–20 minutes.

(4) Rinse slides in cold 5% trichloracetic acid, flood with distilled water washes, follow with several changes of distilled water.

(5) Stain at room temperature for 30 minutes in .1% aqueous solution of fast green FCF made up in 0.005 M phosphate buffer at pH 8.0–8.1 (e.g., dissolve 1 ml of 1% aqueous stock solution of the dye in 9 ml 0.005 M $NaH_2PO_4 \cdot H_2O$, and add several drops of 0.005 M Na_2HPO_4 to bring the pH to 8.0–8.1).

(6) Rinse in several changes of distilled water followed directly by dehydration in 95% ethyl alcohol for 2–5 minutes and two changes of 100% ethyl alcohol 5 minutes each, xylene, and mount in index of refraction oil.

VII. Naphthol yellow S. From Deitch (*25a*).

    A. Fixation: Methanol, acetic–alcohol, Carnoy, or freeze-substitution. Formalin fixation is not suitable. The procedure below is one which has been found to give maximal staining in a shorter time than the one given in the Lab. Invest. reference above.

    B. Stain 30 minutes in 0.1% naphthol yellow S in 1% acetic acid. The stain is stable and may be kept at room temperature. Rinse in 1% acetic acid for 1 minute. Dehydrate in three changes of *tert*-butyl alcohol and two changes of xylene. Mount in index of refraction oil. When naphthol yellow S is used as a counterstain to the Feulgen reaction, it should be used for the shortest time which gives maximal staining intensity (e.g., 30–60 minutes). The intensity of the Feulgen reaction should be checked to see that the naphthol yellow S procedure has not extracted the Feulgen dye.

VIII. The Millon reaction. From Swift and Rasch (*90a*).

    (1) Dissolve 30 g trichloracetic acid in 100 ml distilled water.

    (2) Dissolve 5 g mercuric acetate in the above.

    (3) Divide into two 50-ml portions in two coplin jars; put A at 40°C and B at 30°C.

    (4) Put slides in A for 10 minutes at 40°C.

    (5) Just before using B, add 2.5 ml of 1% $NANO_2$ to the solution, stir well, and transfer slides to B for 40 minutes.

    (6) Three changes of 70% EtOH, 10 minutes each.

    (7) Dehydrate and mount in 1.59 index of refraction oil.

    (8) Measure at 490–500 mμ.

IX. The Sakaguchi reaction from Deitch, A.D. (*25b*).

    (1) Shortly before use prepare:

        4% barium hydroxide (filter just before use).

        1% sodium hypochlorite (prepare by diluting a commercial preparation; freshly obtained "Clorox" was used as a supply of 5% NaOCl).

        1.5% 2,4-dichloro-α-naphthol (Eastman Organic Chemicals No. 3704) in *tert*-butanol.

    (2) Bring the slides to water, using two changes of distilled water. Blot the slides and place them in an empty staining jar.

    (3) Pour 5 parts of the Ba(OH)$_2$ solution, 1 part of NaOCl, and 1 part dichloronaphthol into a flask in succession. Agitate the flask during each addition. Immediately pour the contents of the flask over the slides in the staining jar.

    (4) The reaction is run for 10 minutes at room temperature (22°C).

    (5) The slides are rapidly transferred into 3 changes of tertiary butanol containing 5% tri-N-butylamine (Eastman Organic Chemicals) and then rapidly into 2 changes of xylene containing 5% tri-N-butylamine and then rapidly drained and mounted in 1.580 refractive index oil (R. P. Cargille Co., Cedar Grove, N.J.) containing 10% tri-N-butylamine.

        Move each slide vigorously in the first tertiary butanol for about 5 seconds and then transfer it to the next change of *tert*-butanol. Discard the first *tert*-butanol frequently. Limit the time in the second and third *tert*-butanols and in the two changes of xylene to about 30–60 seconds for each change. Cover the slides well with all reagents and avoid exposure of the tissue to air; otherwise a crust of barium carbonate will form over it. The BaCO$_3$ precipitate which forms on the underside of the slide can be removed with a pledget moistened with dilute acetic or hydrochloric acid.

X. Biebrich scarlet or fast green at acid pH. Stain according to the procedure given for naphthol yellow S in VII. Use 0.1% dye made up in 1% acetic acid.

EXTRACTION AND BLOCKING PROCEDURES FOR CYTOPHOTOMETRY

  I. Nonenzymatic removal of nucleic acids. From Schneider, W.C. (*86*).

  (1) Hydrate slides to water.

(2) Place slides in a freshly made, freshly boiling solution of 5% trichloracetic acid * in a staining jar placed in a water bath. Maintain contents of jar at 85°–90° for 15 minutes in a boiling water bath.

(3) Transfer slides to cold 5% trichloracetic acid.

(4) Flood slides with 70% alcohol; use several changes for a total of 15 minutes.

II. Digestion with deoxyribonuclease

(1) Fixation: freeze-substitution, methanol, Carnoy. Formalin fixation should be avoided.

(2) Deoxyribonuclease: Crystalline DNase: 0.25 mg to 0.5 mg/ml DNase (Worthington Co.) in 0.03 M magnesium sulfate (73 mg $MgSO_4$/100 ml solution). Bring pH to 6.0 with 0.1 N NaOH if necessary. Digest at 37°C for 1–4 hours. The DNase may be made up and frozen in small tubes at dry ice temperatures and stored at −20°C. Used shortly after thawing.

A convenient method of incubation which uses a minimum volume of enzyme to cover the tissue is to use a large Petri dish as a moist chamber. Place several sheets of filter paper thoroughly moistened with distilled water in the bottom of the dish. The slides are blotted dry, placed face up on match stick or glass rod supports, and about 1/2 ml of enzyme placed on the tissue. If the enzyme shows a tendency to flow away, the tissue should be encircled with a glass ring of proper size which is affixed to the surface of the slide (which has been previously wiped dry) with a little silicone grease, vaseline, or paraffin wax. This forms a well into which the solution may be poured. Cover the Petri dish and incubate at 37°C.

III. Digestion with ribonuclease

(1) Fixation: as for deoxyribonuclease. Formalin-containing fixatives may be used.

(2) Ribonuclease. Crystalline RNase (Worthington). Ribonuclease solutions may be frozen (see above for DNase). Concentrations of 0.1 to 0.5 mg/ml are used. Adjust pH with 0.1 N NaOH to pH 6.5. Use moist chamber as for DNase. Incubate at 37°C for 1/2–3 hours.

IV. Acetylation to block lysine amino groups: The slides are brought from 100% alcohol into 100% acetic anhydride at room temperature for 4 to 24 hours. Rinse in several changes of 100% alcohol.

V. Acetylation to block lysine plus arginine: To get complete blockade of arginine, the slides must be methylated in methanolic HCl (q.v.)

* Crystalline trichloracetic acid should be kept refrigerated in a tightly sealed jar.

prior to the acetylation. The slides are then brought from 100% alcohol into 15-ml acetic anhydride + 25-ml pyridine at 80°C for 6 to 24 hours. Check with the Sakaguchi reaction for arginine which should be negative at the end of this procedure.

VI. Methylation in methyl iodide and methanol to block phosphate and carboxyl groups. Modified from Terner (*95a*).

(1) Make up a solution of 12.5% methyl iodide (iodomethane) in dried methanol (v/v) with 1% (w/v) anhydrous sodium carbonate. Place it in a screw cap staining jar over a layer of Linde molecular sieve type 4A (Union Carbide). Seal the jar with tape. Keep the reagent at room temperature for 1–2 hours before use. The methanol should be dried for several days over molecular sieve before being used in the reagent mixture.

(2) The slides are air dried thoroughly before being placed in the methylating mixture. Tape the jar closed to prevent loss of the methyl iodide by evaporation. Methylate at 45°C for 1/2–24 hours, then cool the jar to room temperature. Rinse the slides in three 5-minute changes of 100% methyl or ethyl alcohol. Test the efficacy of the blockade by staining with azure B or methylene blue at pH 6.0. After complete methylation blockade, there will be no binding of these dyes.

VII. See note added in proof, p. 354.

VIII. Histone extraction

Histones may be readily extracted from methanol and freeze-substituted tissue once nucleic acids have been removed. Use the 5% boiling trichloracetic acid extraction described above. Then place the slides in 0.02 N NCl for 1/2–1 hour at room temperature. Check removal of histone with the alkaline fast green procedure.

REFERENCES

1. Alfert, M., A cytochemical study of oögenesis and cleavage in the mouse. *J. Cell. Comp. Physiol.* **36,** 381–409 (1950).
2. Alfert, M., Studies on the basophilia of nucleic acids: the methyl green stainability of nucleic acids. *Biol. Bull.* **103,** 145–156 (1952).
3. Alfert, M., and I. I. Geschwind, A selective staining method for the basic proteins of cell nuclei. *Proc. Natl. Acad. Sci. U.S.* **39,** 991–999 (1953).
4. Alfert, M., and H. Swift, Nuclear DNA constancy: a critical evaluation of some exceptions reported by Lison and Pasteels. *Exptl. Cell Res.* **5,** 455–460 (1953).
5. Alfert, M., and I. I. Geschwind, The development of polysomaty in rat liver. *Exptl. Cell Res.* **15,** 230–270 (1958).

6. Atkin, N. B., and B. M. Richards, Deoxyribonucleic acid in human tumours as measured by microspectrophotometry of Feulgen stain. A comparison of tumours arising at different sites. *Brit. J. Cancer* **10**, 769–786 (1956).

7. Atkin, N. B., B. M. Richards, and A. J. Ross, The deoxyribonucleic acid content of carcinoma of the uterus, an assessment of its possible significance in relation to histopathology. *Brit. J. Cancer* **13**, 773–787 (1959).

8. Atkin, N. B., and A. J. Ross, Polyploidy in human tumours. *Nature* **187**, 579–581 (1960).

9. Bader, S., Distribution of desoxyribose nucleic acid in tumor nuclei. *Proc. Soc. Exptl. Biol. Med.* **82**, 312–315 (1953).

10. Bader, S., A cytochemical study of the stem cell concept in specimens of a human ovarian tumor. *J. Biophys. Biochem. Cytol.* **5**, 219–229 (1959).

11. Bader, S., H. C. Taylor, and E. T. Engle, Deoxyribonucleic acid (DNA) content of human ovarian tumors in relation to histological grading. *Lab. Invest.* **9**, 443–459 (1960).

12. Barka, T., and G. Dallner, The correlation of ultraviolet and Feulgen absorption measured in ascites tumor cells. *J. Histochem. Cytochem.* **7**, 409–415 (1959).

13. Barka, T., and L. Ornstein, Some observations on the reaction of Schiff reagent with aldehydes. *J. Histochem. Cytochem.* **8**, 208–213 (1960).

14. Bauer, H., Die Feulgenische Nuklealfärbung in ihrer Anwendung auf cytologische Untersuchungen. *Z. Zellforsch.* **15**, 225–247 (1932).

15. Bloch, D. P., and G. C. Godman, A microphotometric study of the synthesis of desoxyribonucleic acid and nuclear histone. *J. Biophys. Biochem. Cytol.* **1**, 17–28 (1955).

16. Bloch, D. P., and G. C. Godman, Evidence of differences in the deoxyribonucleoprotein complex of rapidly proliferating and non-dividing cells. *J. Biophysic. Biochem. Cytol.* **1**, 531–550 (1955).

17. Bloch, D. P., and G. C. Godman, A cytological and cytochemical investigation of the development of the viral papilloma of human skin. *J. Exptl. Med.* **105**, 161–176 (1957).

18. Bosshard, U., Fluoreszenzmikroskopische Messung des DNS-Gehaltes von Zellkernen. *Z. Wiss. Mikroskopie* **65**, 391–408 (1964).

19. Boyer, G. S., C. Leuchtenberger, and H. S. Ginsberg, Cytological and cytochemical studies of HeLa cells infected with adenoviruses. *J. Exptl. Med.* **105**, 195–216 (1957).

20. Brachet, J., La détection histochimiques des acides pentosenucléiques. *Compt. Rend. Soc. Biol.* **133**, 88–90 (1940).

21. Brachet, J., La localisation des acides pentosenucléiques dans les tissus animaux et les oeufs d'Amphibiens en voie de développement. *Arch Biol. (Liege)* **53**, 207–257 (1942).

22. Brachet, J., La spécificité de la réaction de Feulgen pour la détection de l'acide thymonucléique. *Experientia* **2**, 142–143 (1946).

23. Conn. H. J., "Biological Stains," 7th ed. Williams & Wilkins, Baltimore, 1961.

24. Devreux, S., M. Johannson, and H. Errera, Affinité du vert de methyl pour l'acide désoxyribonucléique. *Bull. Soc. Chim. Biol.* **33**, 800–805 (1951).

25. Deitch, A. D., A method for the cytophotometric estimation of nucleic acids using methylene blue. *J. Histochem. Cytochem.* **12**, 451–461 (1964).

25a. Deitch, A. D., Microspectrophotometric study of the binding of the anionic dye, naphthol yellow S by tissue sections and by purified proteins. *Lab Invest.* **4**, 324–351 (1955).

25b. Deitch, A. D., An improved Sakaguchi reaction for microspectrophotometric use. *J. Histochem. Cytochem* **9**, 477–483 (1961).

26. Deitch, A. D., and J. Y. Terner, Effect of acetylation on acid dye binding and the Sakaguchi reaction. *J. Histochem. Cytochem.* **13,** 15–16 (1965).
27. Dische, Z., Color reactions of nucleic acid components. *In* "The Nucleic Acids" (E. Chargaff and J. N. Davidson, eds.), Vol. I, pp. 285–305. Academic Press, New York, 1955.
28. Di Stephano, H. S., A cytochemical study of the Feulgen nucleal reaction. *Chromosoma* **3,** 282–301 (1948).
29. Di Stephano, H. S., Feulgen hydrolysis with perchloric acid. *Stain Technol.* **27,** 171–174 (1952).
30. Di Stephano, H. S., H. F. Diermeier, and J. Tepperman, Effects of growth hormone on nucleic acid and protein content of rat liver cells. *Endocrinology* **57,** 158–167 (1955).
31. Elftman, H., A Schiff reagent of calibrated sensitivity. *J. Histochem. Cytochem.* **7,** 93–97 (1959).
32. Ely, J. O., and M. H. Ross, Nucleic acids and the Feulgen reaction. *Anat. Record* **104,** 103–123 (1949).
33. Errera, M., Action des rayons u. v. sur l'affinite du noyau cellulaire pour le vert de méthyl. *Biochim. Biophys. Acta* **7,** 605–606 (1951).
34. Feulgen, R., and H. Rossenbeck, Mikroskopisch-chemischer Nachweis einer Nucleinsäure von Typus der Thymonucleinsäure und die darauf beruhende elektive Färbung von Zellkerzen in mikroskopischen Präparaten. *Z. Physiol. Chem.* **135,** 203–248 (1924).
35. Feulgen, R., and K. Voit, Über den Mechanismus der Nuclealfärbung. II. Mittheilung. Über das Verhalten der Kerne partiell hydrolysierter mikroskopischer Präparate zur fuchsin-schwefligen Säure nach voraufgegangener Behandlung mit Phenylhydrazin. *Z. Physiol. Chem.* **136,** 57–61 (1924).
35a. Fisher, E. R., and R. D. Lillie, The effect of methylation on basophilia. *J. Histochem. Cytochem.* **2,** 81–87 (1954).
35b. Fisher, H. W., and H. Harris, The isolation of nuclei from animal cells in culture. *Proc. Roy. Soc.* B **156,** 521–525 (1962).
36. Flax, M. H., and M. H. Himes, Microspectrophotometric analysis of metachromatic staining of nucleic acids. *Physiol. Zool.* **25,** 297–311 (1952).
37. Geschwind, I. I., M. Alfert, and C. Schooley, Liver regeneration and hepatic polyploidy in the hypophysectomized rat. *Exptl. Cell Res.* **15,** 232–235 (1958).
38. Geschwind, I. I., M. Alfert, and C. Schooley, The effects of thyroxin and growth hormone on liver polyploidy. *Biol. Bull.* **118,** 66–69 (1960).
39. Godman, G. C., and A. D. Deitch, A cytochemical study of the L. E. bodies of systemic lupus erythematosus. I. Nucleic acids. *J. Exptl. Med.* **106,** 575–592 (1957).
40. Godman, G. C., and A. D. Deitch, A cytochemical study of the L. E. bodies of systemic lupus erythematosus. II. Proteins. *J. Exptl. Med.* **106,** 593–606 (1957).
41. Godman, G. C., Pathological changes affecting the nuclear constituents: cytochemical studies. *J. Mt. Sinai Hosp.* **24,** 888–906 (1957).
42. Godman, G. C., A. D. Deitch, and P. Klemperer, The composition of the LE and hematoxylin bodies of systemic lupus erythematosus. *Am. J. Pathol.* **34,** 1–23 (1958).
43. Hardonk, M. J., and P. van Duijn, The mechanism of the Schiff reaction as studied with histochemical model systems. *J. Histochem. Cytochem.* **12,** 748–751 (1964).
44. Hardonk, M. J., and P. van Duijn, Studies on the Feulgen reaction with histochemical model systems. *J. Histochem. Cytochem.* **12,** 758–767 (1964).

45. Harrington, N. J., and R. W. Koza, Effect of x-radiation on the desoxyribonucleic acid and on the size of grasshopper embryonic nuclei. *Biol. Bull.* **101**, 138–150 (1951).

46. Hillary, B. B., Use of the Feulgen reaction in cytology. I. Effect of fixatives on the reaction. *Botan. Gaz.* **101**, 276–309 (1939).

47. Hiraoka, T., Electrophoretic analysis of coloured product produced by Schiff-formaldehyde reaction. *J. Biophys. Biochem. Cytol.* **8**, 286–288 (1960).

48. Hörmann, H. W., W. Grassman, and G. Fries, Über den Mechanismus der Schiffschen Reaktion. *Justus Liebigs Ann. Chem.* **616**, 125–147 (1955).

49. Jordanov, J., On the transition of desoxyribonucleic acid to apurinic acid and the loss of the latter from tissue during Feulgen reaction hydrolysis. *Acta Histochem.* **15**, 135–152 (1963).

50. Kasten, F. H., Stability of the Feulgen-deoxyribonucleic acid absorption curve *in situ* with variation in nuclear protein content and other factors. *J. Histochem. Cytochem.* **4**, 462–470 (1956).

51. Kasten, F. H., The Feulgen-DNA absorption curve *in situ*. *Histochemie* **1**, 123–150 (1958).

52. Kasten, F. H., Additional Schiff-type reagents for use in cytochemistry. *Stain Technol.* **33**, 39–45 (1958).

53. Kasten, F. H., Schiff-type reagents in cytochemistry. I. Theoretical and practical considerations. *Histochemie* **1**, 466–509 (1959).

54. Kasten, F. H., The chemistry of Schiff's reagent. *Intern. Rev. Cytol.* **10**, 1–100 (1960).

55. Klemperer, P. B. Gueft, S. L. Lee, C. Leuchtenberger, and A. W. Pollister, Cytochemical changes of acute lupus erythematosus. *Arch. Pathol.* **49**, 503–516 (1950).

56. Kurnick, N. B., Methyl green-pyronin. I. Basis of selective staining of nucleic acids. *J. Gen. Physiol.* **33**, 243–264 (1950).

57. Kurnick, N. B., and A. E. Mirsky, Methyl green-pyronin. II. Stoichiometry of reaction with nucleic acids. *J. Gen. Physiol.* **33**, 265–274 (1950).

58. Lessler, M. A., The nature and specificity of the Feulgen reaction. *Arch. Biochem. Biophys.* **32**, 42–54 (1951).

59. Lessler, M. A., Specificity in the aldehyde-coupling reactivity of nucleated erythrocytes. *J. Histochem. Cytochem.* **4**, 36–40 (1956).

60. Leuchtenberger, C., R. Leuchtenberger, and A. M. Davis, A microspectrophotometric study of the desoxyribose nucleic acid (DNA) content in cells of normal and malignant human tissues. *Am. J. Pathol.* **30**, 65–85 (1954).

61. Leuchtenberger, C., G. S. Boyer, and J. J. Strain, Quantitative cytochemical investigation on the effect of virus on cells. *Ann. N.Y. Acad. Sci.* **81**, 73-83 (1959).

62. Lodin, Z., J. Müller, and J. Hartman, Basic fuchsin and the Feulgen reaction: significance of the dye for cytophotometric determination of deoxyribonucleic acid in cell nuclei. *J. Histochem. Cytochem.* **11**, 401–408 (1963).

63. Longley, J. B., Effectiveness of Schiff variants in the periodic-Schiff and Feulgen nucleal technics. *Stain Technol.* **27**, 161–169 (1952).

64. Nauman, R. V., P. W. West, T. Tron, and G. C. Gaeke, A spectrophotometric study of the Schiff reaction as applied to the quantitative determination of sulfur dioxide. *Anal. Chem.* **32**, 1307–1311 (1960).

65. Ornstein, L., Discussion following the paper of Kasten. *J. Histochem. Cytochem.* **4**, 442–443 (1956).

66. Ornstein, L., W. Mautner, B. J. Davis, and R. Tamura, New horizons in fluorescence microscopy. *J. Mt. Sinai Hosp.* **24**, 1066–1078 (1957).

67. Ostergren, G., Chromatin stains of Feulgen type involving other dyes than

fuchsin. *Hereditas* **34**, 510–511 (1948).

68. Overend, W. G., and M. Stacey, Mechanism of the Feulgen nucleal reaction. *Nature* **163**, 538–540 (1949).
69. Pappenheim, A., Vergleichende Untersuchungen über die elementare Zusemmensetzung des rothen Knochenmarkes einiger Säugethiere. *Arch. Pathol. Anat. Physiol.* **157**, 19–76 (1899).
70. Patau, K., and H. Swift, The DNA content (Feulgen) of nuclei during mitosis in a root tip of onion. *Chromosoma* **6**, 149–169 (1953).
71. Pearson, A. E. G., and N. B. Atkin, Changes in the deoxyribonucleic acid content of mouse sarcoma 37 cells following serial irradiation. *Nature* **186**, 647–8 (1960).
72. Pollister, A. W., and H. Ris, Nucleoprotein determination in cytological preparations. *Cold Spring Harbor Symp. Quant. Biol.* **12**, 147–154 (1947).
73. Pollister, A. W., and C. Leuchtenberger, The nucleoprotein content of whole nuclei. *Proc. Natl. Acad. Sci.* **35**, 66–71 (1949).
74. Pollister, A. W., and C. Leuchtenberger, The nature of the specificity of methyl green for chromatin. *Proc. Natl. Acad. Sci. U.S.* **35**, 111–116 (1949).
75. Rasch, E., and H. Swift, Microphotometric analysis of the cytochemical Millon reaction. *J. Histochem. Cytochem.* **8**, 4–17 (1960).
76. Richards, B. M., Deoxyribose nucleic acid values in tumour cells with reference to the stem cell theory of tumour growth. *Nature* **175**, 259–262 (1955).
77. Richards, B. M., P. M. B. Walker, and E. M. Deeley, Changes in nuclear DNA in normal and ascites tumor cells. *Ann. N.Y. Acad. Sci.* **63**, 831–848 (1956).
78. Richards, B. M., and N. B. Atkin, DNA content of human tumours: change in uterine tumours during radiotherapy and their response to treatment. *Brit. J. Cancer* **13**, 788–800 (1959).
79. Rosenkranz, H. S., and A. Bendich, On the nature of the deoxyribonucleic acid-methyl green reaction. *J. Biophys. Biochem. Cytol.* **4**, 663–664 (1958).
80. Ruch, F., and U. Bosshard, Photometrische Bestimmung von Stoffmengen in Fluoreszenzmikroskopie. *Z. wiss. Mikroskopie* **56**, 335–341 (1963).
81. Rumpf, P., Recherches physico-chimiques sur la réaction colorée des aldehydes, dite "Réaction de Schiff." *Ann. Chim. (Paris)* [11] **3**, 327–442 (1935).
82. Sandritter, W., and N. Böhm, Atypische Hydrolysekurve bei der Feulgenreaktion von Mäuseascitestumorzellen. *Naturwiss.* **11**, 273 (1964).
83. Sandritter, W. K., K. Jobst, L. Rakow and K. Bosselman, Zur Kinetik der Feulgenreaktion bei verlängerter Hydrolysezeit. Cytophotometrische Messungen in sichtbarem und Ultraviolettlicht. *Histochemie* **4**, 420–437 (1965).
84. Savage, R. E., and W. Plaut, The effect of HCl hydrolysis on the retention of thymidine in DNA. *J. Biophys. Biochem. Cytol.* **4**, 701–706 (1958).
85. Schiff, H., Eine neue Reihe organischer Diamine. *Justus Liebigs Ann. Chem.* **140**, 92–137 (1866).
86. Schneider, W. C., Phosphorus compounds in animal tissue. I. Extraction and estimation of desoxypentose nucleic acid and of pentose nucleic acid. *J. Biol. Chem.* **161**, 293–303 (1945).
86a. Stowell, R., Feulgen reaction for thymonucleic acid. *Stain Technol.* **20**, 45–58 (1945).
87. Swift, H., The deoxyribose nucleic acid content of animal nuclei. *Physiol. Zool.* **23**, 169–198 (1950).
88. Swift, H., The constancy of desoxyribose nucleic acid in plant nuclei. *Proc. Natl. Acad. Sci. U.S.* **36**, 643–654 (1950).
89. Swift, H., Nucleoproteins in the mitotic cycle. *Texas Rept. Biol. Med.* **11**, 755–774 (1953).

90. Swift, H., Cytochemical techniques for nucleic acids. *In* "The Nucleic Acids" (E. Chargaff and J. N. Davidson, eds.) Academic Press, New York, 1955.

90a. Swift, H., and Rasch, Microphotometric analysis of the cytochemical Millon reaction. E., *J. Histochem. Cytochem.* **8**, 4–17 (1960).

91. Swift, H., L. Rebhun, E. Rasch, and J. Woodard, The cytology of nuclear RNA. *In* "Cellular Mechanisms in Differentiation and Growth" (D. Rudnick, ed.), pp. 45–59. Princeton Univ. Press, Princeton, New Jersey, 1956.

92. Tamm, C., and E. Chargaff, Physical and chemical properties of the apurinic acid of calf thymus. *J. Biol. Chem.* **203**, 689–694 (1953).

93. Taylor, J. H., and R. D. McMaster, Autoradiographic and microphotometric studies of desoxyribose nucleic acid during microgametogenesis in *Lillium longiflorum. Chromosoma* **6**, 489–521 (1954).

94. Taylor, J. H., Incorporation of phosphorus-32 into nucleic acids and proteins during microgametogenesis of *Tulbaghia. Am. J. Botany* **45**, 123–131 (1958).

95. Taylor, K. B., The influence of molecular structure of thiazine and oxazine dyes on their metachromatic properties. *Stain Technol.* **36:** 73–83, 1961.

95a. Terner, J. Y., *J. Histochem. Cytochem.* **12**, 504–511 (1964).

96. Tonkelaar, E. M., den, and P. van Duijn, Photographic colorimetry as a quantitative cytochemical method. III. Determination of the absolute amount of DNA in cell nuclei. *Histochemie* **4**, 16–19 (1964).

97. Unna, P. G., "Histochemie der Haut." Deuticke, Leipzig, 1928.

98. Vendrely-Rendavel, C., Substitution de l'acide chlorhydrique à la ribonuclease pour l'étude de la localisation de l'acide ribonucléique au sein des cellules animales. *Compt. Rend. Soc. Biol.* **143**, 294–295 (1949).

99. Vischer, E., and E. Chargaff, The composition of the pentose nucleic acid of yeast and pancreas. *J. Biol. Chem.* **176**, 715–734 (1948).

100. Walker, P. M. B., and B. M. Richards, Quantitative microscopical techniques for single cells. *In* "The Cell" (J. Brachet and A. E. Mirsky, eds.), Vol. I, pp. 91–138. Academic Press, New York, 1959.

101. Wieland, H., and G. Scheuing, Die Fuchsin-Schwefelige Säure und ihre Farbreaktion mit Aldehyden. *Ber.* **54**, 2527–2555 (1921).

102. Woodard, J. E., E. Rasch, and H. Swift, Nucleic acid and protein metabolism during the mitotic cycle in *Vicia faba. J. Biophys. Biochem. Cytol.* **9**, 445–462 (1961).

103. Woods, P. S., A chromatographic study of hydrolysis in the Feulgen nucleal reaction. *J. Biophys. Biochem. Cytol.* **3**, 71–88 (1957).

Note Added in Proof

VII. METHYLATION IN METHANOLIC-HCl. Modified from Fisher and Lillie (*35a*).

Methylation by the methyl iodide procedure given above alkylates amines as well as esterifying phosphate and carboxyl groups (*95a*). Alkylated amines are not susceptible to blockade by acetylation. The following procedure should be used for methylation prior to acetylation (i.e., to block all available lysine and arginine groups):

(1) Mix 99 parts of methanol and 1 part of concentrated hydrochloric acid. Store over Linde molecular sieve for at least a week before using.

(2) Air dry the slides to be treated and methylate them in a well-sealed jar in the methanolic-HCl at 45°–60°C for 1 to 4 hours. Rinse the slides in several changes of methanol.

THE QUANTITATIVE CYTOCHEMISTRY OF RNA

Hewson Swift

WHITMAN LABORATORY, UNIVERSITY OF CHICAGO, CHICAGO, ILLINOIS

I. Introduction

The cytochemical study of RNA possesses its own particular problems, imposed by the biological and biochemical peculiarities of this important group of compounds. RNA, with few known exceptions, is formed in the nucleus as a result of chromosomal activity. As a gene product, it thus behaves very differently from DNA, which is under an entirely different mechanism of cellular control. Thus while DNA undergoes highly specific and quantitatively controlled replication processes, RNA often fluctuates widely in cells undergoing changes in proliferation rates, differentiation, or patterns of protein synthesis. For example, in rat liver regeneration the nucleolar RNA may increase several hundred percent, or in erythrocyte formation RNA falls precipitously from high levels in the hemocytoblast to unmeasurably low levels in the mature red blood cell. Because RNA is a synthetic product of the nucleus, highly sensitive in amount to altered cell states, the demands for RNA quantitation are usually less stringent than for DNA, where accuracy down to the single chromosome level or even below may be required in current research. It is important to remember, then, that with studies on RNA, a high degree of precision in the determination of amounts per cell or organelle has usually not been required. This obviously does not mean, however, that cytochemical or photometric variables can be ignored, particularly where their effects may be nonrandom.

Another property of RNA is its solubility. Since RNA is made in the nucleus and usually has a cytoplasmic site of function, it obviously must migrate in the cell, possibly partly by diffusion but probably also by energy controlled processes (63). There is a continual problem of loss of RNA from cells and tissues during the preparation of material for study. Certain fractions, such as soluble RNA, may be more readily extracted during fixation, staining, and so forth than others. A few special techniques have been employed to minimize such losses, but these are in need of improvement.

In all probability the major problem concerning the cytochemistry of RNA, however, involves an increasing awareness of its chemical diversity. The presence of three distinct classes of RNA is now well established. These fractions, soluble, messenger, and ribosomal RNA, possess quite different structures, are either unbound or bound to very different proteins, and are associated with different aspects of the complex processes of protein synthesis. The separate cytochemical characterization of these three fractions, except in terms of their spatial isolation in the cell, has so far not been generally possible and still remains a major challenge. Also, in addition to these three well-established fractions of RNA, several others have been described. These include a soluble RNA fraction that does not complex with amino acids, of unknown function (98), a nuclear fraction associated with histones (32), and RNA components of mitochondria (82, 83, 93), and chloroplasts (28, 34). In addition to the established functions for RNA, as messenger, in aminoacyl-sRNA, and in the ribosome, these additional as yet poorly characterized fractions may play still other roles, for example as gene suppressors (33) or gene activators (26), or in the specialized protein syntheses associated with the replication of mitochondria and chloroplasts (28).

Cytochemical studies on RNA, as with other components, have as their major aim spatial localization and quantitation. It is thus possible to study separately the RNA associated with cytoplasm, nucleoli, and chromosomes or chromosome regions, in intact cells or tissues. Biochemical methods, although becoming increasingly powerful with advances in the technology of differential centrifugation, usually must of necessity discard cell structure, and the problem of loss of components during the isolation procedure is often acute. Certain kinds of information are thus obtainable only by cytochemical methods, such as the characterization of RNA synthesis at specific regions of the chromosome (27, 70, 81). But the highly important relationship between cytochemical findings and the biochemical identification of the fractions studied is often difficult to establish. Autoradiography, for example, has indicated that nucleoli contain mixed populations of RNA, in terms of the kinetics of precursor incorporation, but there is as yet no agreement on the specific interpretation of this finding in terms of the kind of RNA molecules actually involved (4, 60, 74). The solution of these problems lies in the careful analysis of systems which lend themselves to combined cytochemical and cell fractionation studies. In this way the advantages of both approaches may be utilized, and the findings by either technique may be immeasurably strengthened by support from the other. An excellent example of the combined cytochemical and cell fractionation approach is the work on actinomycin effects both on RNA autoradiographs and on RNA fractions isolated by gradient centrifugation, utilizing HeLa cell cultures (60, 61). It was possible to show that actinomycin concentrations which largely eliminated nucleolar labeling with uridine-H^3 also suppressed the labeling of a 45 S nuclear fraction, and subsequently of the 18 and 28 S ribosome components. This helped to establish the important fact that the nucleolus appears to contain the obligate precursors of ribosomal RNA.

We may thus conclude that in many cytochemical studies on RNA, because of the chemical complexities involved, it is not always clear what is being investigated. But in some cases, such as in descriptive studies of RNA changes with pathogenesis or with development, or in research into diagnostic methods, the lumping together of different RNA fractions and the loss of others from the tissues during preparation may yet provide acceptable data. The bulk of RNA in nucleolus, chromosomes, and cytoplasm is protein bound, and with suitable fixatives may be retained in the cell. It is frequently of interest to know how these more stable RNA-containing components are altered under various experimental conditions. It cannot be overemphasized, however, that wherever possible confirmation of findings should be sought by use of more than one technique, for example, photometry and autoradiography, or either method combined with differential centrifugation and biochemical characterization.

The aspects of RNA cytochemistry discussed here include (1) problems of fixation, (2) dye binding by RNA, (3) extraction and blocking methods, and (4) a brief description of other methods, including ultraviolet absorption and autoradiography. The author has tried to emphasize the reason behind steps in cytochemical preparation and the major variables involved, rather than merely to make recommendations at the formulary level. It is possible to recommend specific steps that can be applied to many current cytological problems, but with any new material, modifications in techniques may have to be made. Also, present methods have their shortcomings and are in need of improvement and further standardization. With some understanding of the variables involved in RNA cytochemistry, the investigator can better adapt the methods available to his particular purposes.

II. Fixation

In the preparation of tissues for RNA analysis, fixation of some sort is usually essential. Fixation obviously makes tissue components more stable for cytochemical study. It denatures and cross-links cell proteins, and thus minimizes the unwanted loss of RNA in staining solutions and other reagents. In addition, fixation removes certain small molecular weight components, which may interfere with UV or autoradiographic determinations, for example, soluble nucleotides and labeled precursors from the unincorporated pool.

In certain cases it is possible to use living cells for ultraviolet studies, and unfixed air-dried, freeze-dried, or freeze-substituted cell cultures or tissue fragments may also be studied directly by ultraviolet or autoradiographic techniques. These special methods are discussed below in the paragraphs on UV absorption and autoradiography. Other techniques almost always involve the use of aqueous reagents. Unfixed tissues in most cases suffer serious extraction damage in aqueous solutions. Thus, even with freeze-dried or freeze-substituted tissues, or air-dried cultures or prints, it is usually necessary to follow dehydration by some kind of fixative. For many tissues, freeze-substitution in methanol, followed by fixation in 80% ethanol at 60°C, seems a useful procedure, but other fixatives such as mercuric chloride, osmium tetroxide, or TCA (trichloracetic acid) added to ethanol have been recommended (6, 24, 30, 95). Direct air-dried tissue imprints, smears, or cell cultures may occasionally be satisfactory, but are best post-fixed with 100% methanol, 10% neutral formalin, or acetic acid–ethanol. The period between drying and fixation may be important, and more uniform results may be obtained if preparations are immediately fixed before being allowed to dry.

Major requirements for fixatives in RNA studies are as follows: (1) They must not extract appreciable amounts of the RNA fractions to be studied. (2) They should interfere as little as possible with the cytochemical reactions. (3) They should allow for specific RNA removal by RNase or acid extraction, and preferably DNA extraction by DNase as well. (4) They should provide adequate tissue morphology. (5) The fixation should be uniform throughout the tissue block.

There is no ideal fixative that fulfills all these requirements. Fixation, like most other aspects of cytochemistry, must involve practical compromises. RNA loss from tissues is a major problem. Soluble RNA as yet has not been adequately localized in cells. It is probably extracted by most aqueous fixatives, such as neutral formalin. It was thought to be retained, for an autoradiographic study, by the use of 5% trichloracetic acid to which had been added 1.37% of lanthanum triacetate (74).

Lanthanum salts have also been added to freeze-dried tissues for ultra-violet studies, to minimize RNA loss (13). Although the addition of lanthanum or similar metal ions may be expected to minimize the diffusion of sRNA, it unfortunately also competes with dye solutions for stainable sites on the molecule (38). Thus it probably cannot be used to preserve sRNA in tissues for staining, but only for UV or autoradiographic studies. In other investigations on the localization of sRNA, freeze-substituted tissues have been used for autoradiography with labeled 5-methyl cytosine as precursor, followed by extraction with cold perchloric acid or ribonuclease (21). A great deal more needs to be done before the localization and sites of synthesis of sRNA are understood. The role of the nucleolus in the methylation of sRNA bases has been indicated for insect salivary glands (8), but research needs to be extended to other tissues. Certain specific sRNA-dye binding reactions have been used for biochemical isolation (97), and these could possibly be adapted for cytochemical study.

Most standard fixatives preserve the majority of protein-bound RNA in cytoplasm, nucleoli, and chromosomes. Strongly acid fixatives, particularly if prolonged, can remove RNA by hydrolysis. Buffer solutions also facilitate extraction. Metal ions, for example, from mercuric or chromic salts, are often used in fixatives, but these may interfere with basic dye binding and also render nuclease extraction difficult or impossible. In general, simple fixatives such as neutral formalin or acetic acid–ethanol provide more uniform fixation than complex mixtures where different components possess different rates of penetration into the tissue block. The time of fixation is also important. Certain fixatives, such as formalin, react slowly with proteins, and therefore more reactive groups are complexed with time (25). A tissue fixed for one hour in neutral formalin or acetic acid–ethanol therefore reacts quite differently to cyto-chemical reactions than one fixed for several days. With formalin, washing time is also important since much, but not all, of the formaldehyde can be removed by water (59).

If nuclease enzymes are to be used, fixation time and temperature are particularly important. In general, short, cold fixation (1 to 2 hours) by acetic acid–ethanol or neutral formalin will facilitate removal of RNA by ribonuclease, or DNA by deoxyribonuclease. It is also true, however, that these shorter times increase the likelihood of unwanted loss of RNA from tissues, for example, in nuclease control treatments or during staining. Longer fixation will reduce the loss of RNA in control tissue, but will also necessitate a more prolonged treatment with the enzyme. For example, Amano (3) recommended long (24 hour) fixation in Carnoy's reagent (ethanol–acetic acid–chloroform) so that RNA loss from tissues was largely prevented. But with tissues fixed for this period, DNase had to be used for 24 hours at 37°C. In tissues fixed for one hour, on the other hand, DNase extraction is usually complete by 1 or 2 hours at 20°C. Thus the same factors, probably associated with completeness of protein denaturation or cross linking, that diminish unwanted RNA loss also necessitate a more prolonged extraction, during which the danger of RNA loss has been increased. The optimal time for fixation and extraction has not been determined, but may be expected to vary for different tissues and different fixatives (*42*). In the examples given here, a short fixation time has generally been favored, and the factors that facilitate RNA loss have been reduced to a minimum; that is, unbuffered solutions of nuclease and dye have been used (*51*), and the time in which tissues are subjected to aqueous solution has been reduced to a minimum.

The process of RNA loss from tissues during preparation can be studied with sections in which RNA has been labeled with P^{32}. Sections can be counted periodically on slides with an end-window counter (*88*). A graph of radioactivity loss in water (nuclease control), probably due to RNA, is shown in Fig. 1. These determinations, made by Taylor and

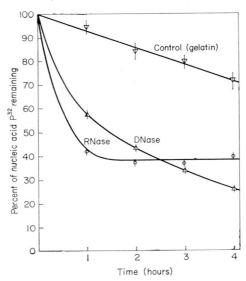

FIG. 1. The loss of nucleic acids during nuclease and control treatments. Nucleic acid amounts were followed in P^{32}-labeled sections of lily anther with an end-window Geiger counter. Note that there is marked loss in label both in DNase (0.01% in 0.005 M MgSO$_4$, with 0.1% gelatin, pH 6.5) and in the aqueous control solution in which the enzyme was absent. The loss in the control and in DNase after 2 or 3 hours is probably due to extraction of RNA. Data of Taylor and McMaster (*88*).

McMaster, also demonstrate RNA loss both during RNase and DNase extraction.

Nonuniformity of fixation may be a real problem in quantitative cytochemistry. Tissue cultures or cell suspensions are usually fixed uniformly, but in any solid tissue, the peripheral cells show differences to most cytochemical reactions from those in the section center. This is probably partly due to extraction of proteins at the periphery during fixation (79). Dilution effects, in which the center of a large tissue block is fixed less completely than the margin are also important, particularly with complex fixatives. They can be minimized by using small tissue blocks or slices with the shortest dimension only 1 or 2 mm. Simple fixatives such as acetic acid–ethanol, Carnoy's reagent, neutral formalin, or glutaraldehyde penetrate well and show moderate uniformity, particularly if the outermost one or two cell layers of the tissue section are excluded from study.

Tissue shrinkage may be important where cell volumes or the relative concentrations of cell components are to be compared. Different fixatives cause different degrees of shrinkage (2). In general the best fixatives for preserving tissue structure, that is, Zenker formol with osmium tetroxide, or Navashin's for plant tissue, may not be suitable for cytochemistry, so that separate blocks often have to be made for cell dimension determination and RNA analysis. Glutaraldehyde (71) seems to be a good fixative both for RNA staining and for preservation of cell morphology. Post-fixation treatments are also important in effecting cell dimensions. Dehydration may produce considerable tissue shrinkage (5, 19), and embedding in certain media (for example, methacrylate) may produce swelling (92). Acid hydrolysis, as for the Feulgen reaction, may also produce tissue shrinkage with a loss in mass of cell components. Where total amounts of dye bound per cell or per nucleus are measured, cell shrinkage may not be important. Where concentration changes are studied, however, this is a serious variable. For example, when a plant root tip is fixed in acetic acid–ethanol, much of the extreme basophilia of the outer cells is a result of differential cell shrinkage; it is much less marked with Navashin's fixation.

To summarize these remarks on fixation, RNA loss from tissues during fixation and subsequent treatments is a major problem, and as yet no adequate method is available for localization of sRNA, except possibly by autoradiography of lanthanum–TCA fixed tissues. Most tissue RNA is protein bound, and the following fixatives have been recommended for their study: freeze-substitution in methanol, followed by fixation in 80% ethanol, or TCA–methanol; fixation of smears, prints, or cell cultures in 100% methanol or 10% neutral formalin; fixation of small tissue blocks in acetic acid–ethanol, Carnoy's, 10% neutral formalin, or 2 to 10% neutral glutaraldehyde. Fixation periods should be short, preferably 1 or 2 hours, usually at 2°–5°C. Treatment in aqueous solutions should be as short as possible to minimize RNA loss, and buffer solutions should be avoided where possible, with pH adjusted by NaOH or HCl.

III. Dye Binding

Basic dye binding, together with autoradiography, probably is the most important and widely used technique for RNA cytochemistry. The dyes most frequently used have been pyronin (10), the thiazins, azure B, toluidine blue, methylene blue (16, 23), and the dye-lake gallocyanin chrome alum (18). Gallocyanin, although it has certain advantages for DNA studies (see the chapter by Sandritter in this volume) stains RNA relatively weakly. Stain intensity can be increased by raising the pH, but this also increases a nonspecific binding to tissue proteins (18, 77). Thus although it has been employed for many important cytochemical studies on RNA (50, 76), it is not recommended for quantitative determinations.

Pyronin has been extremely useful as a general indicator of tissue basophilia, in conjunction with methyl green in the classical Unna–Pappenheim method. Studies on the specificity of methyl green–pyronin have generally supported the fact that under proper conditions the methyl green stains DNA, and the pyronin stains RNA (47, 48, 86). The specificity, however, is clearly dependent on the mixture of the two dyes, one of which, possibly because of steric factors, has a greater affinity for native DNA, and the other for RNA and denatured DNA. When used separately, either stain will combine with both nucleic acids. The affinity of methyl green for DNA is discussed in the chapter by Deitch. Pyronin alone has been used for the cytochemical demonstration of RNA, particularly in conjunction with RNase, by Brachet and collaborators (10, 11). It has not been much used for quantitative studies, possibly in part because pyronin preparations are frequently mixtures of closely related dyes, and problems of reproducibility and even of specificity may be encountered (48).

Most RNA cytophotometry in visible light has utilized thiazin dyes, particularly azure B, following the studies of Flax and Himes (23). Azure B was originally selected by these workers as the thiazin dye showing the maximal metachromatic difference between RNA and DNA. Under the conditions chosen, RNA stains a deep purple color, and DNA a bright blue green. These include a relatively dilute dye solution (0.025%), buffered at pH 4.0, and at elevated temperature. The conditions suitable for the metachromatic differentiation of DNA from RNA, however, are not necessarily those required for quantitative cytochemistry.

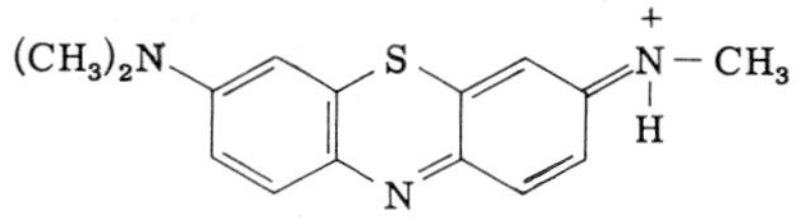

Azure B

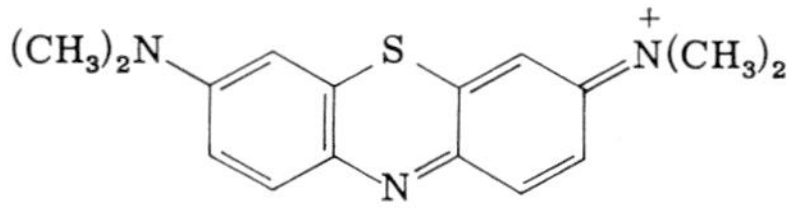

Methylene blue

The staining of fixed tissues with basic dyes is primarily electrostatic in nature, although secondary factors such as steric considerations, bond energies, molecular size, van der Waals attraction, and competition with other charged molecules also may be of importance. Basic dyes are salts of weak bases, and the binding group, or auxochrome, is usually an amino group, which is ionized to $-NH_3^+$ at the pH used for staining. In azure B and methylene blue the amino hydrogens are substituted by methyl groups. When the slide is stained, the dye forms a salt linkage with residues of opposite charge in the tissue. Stainable groups in tissues include the $-PO_3^-$ groups of nucleic acids and the $-COO^-$ groups of the proteins. When mucoproteins are present, the strongly acid $-SO_4^-$ groups of sulfonated polysaccharides and the weaker $-COO^-$ groups of glucuronic acid can also bind the dye. Also, since the dye-tissue interaction is electrostatic, the dye responds to the *total* charge density in the vicinity of stainable components. This means that residues in the tissue of opposite charge are also important, primarily the amino groups of lysine and the guanidyl groups of arginine. The imidazole groups of histidine and terminal amino groups are less numerous and probably less important. These positively charged groups may act in either of two ways: by altering the charge densities of the tissue, and thus affecting dye concentration at the tissue interface, or in the blocking of stainable groups by the formation of nucleic acid–protein salt linkages within the tissue. At least in some cases, nucleic acids occur in living cells attached by such electrostatic linkages between phosphoric acid and basic amino acid residues.

The fundamental requirements, if stains are to be used in quantitative cytochemistry, are obviously to make dye binding specific and stoichiometric. Most basic dyes, at neutral pH, stain DNA, RNA, proteins, and certain polysaccharides. Specificity can be achieved in several ways. (1) The competing substances can be removed from the tissue. For example, RNA staining of chromatin can be studied after the DNA has been extracted with DNase. (2) The staining of proteins by dye linkage with carboxyl groups can be avoided, but nucleic acid staining maintained by using a pH at which carboxyl groups are unionized, but at which the nucleic acid phosphoryl groups are still largely open. There is a narrow area between pH 3.5 and 4.5 where these conditions can be met, but this is a matter of degree, that is, a range where most phosphoryls are ionized and most carboxyls are unionized. (3) The influence of staining or competing groups can be reduced by specific blocking agents. Carboxyl staining may be reduced by methylation or acetylation. Amino and guanidyl groups can also be blocked in a number of ways, most effectively by acetylation or deamination. (4) Certain substances, particularly the sulfonated mucoproteins, such as chondroitin, cannot readily be extracted or their acid groups blocked, but their detection is usually a simple matter. Such substances almost always stain metachromatically with thiazin dyes and are not extractable with nuclease enzymes or acids, whereas RNA is readily removed. They are, of course, also PAS positive, and can often be eliminated as possible sources of confusion merely by their location and morphology (for instance, mucin in goblet cells, chrondroitin in cartilage matrix).

The stoichiometric relation between tissue nucleic acid and dye bound is probably unobtainable in a rigorous sense, but it is approachable in sufficient degree to make thiazin dye binding an essentially accurate method for determination of tissue-bound RNA. Thiazin and many other dyes do not follow Beer's law in solution. There is a gradual shift to the formation of dimers and polymers as the dye solution becomes more concentrated (55). These dimers and polymers are demonstrable as new absorption peaks in the spectral curve of the dye, located at shorter wavelengths. Solutions of azure B thus change in color from light blue to dark blue, to purple and finally to red, as dye concentration is increased. Thus at any one wavelength, the relation between dye concentration and optical density is nonlinear.

It is a fortunate fact, however, that these gradual dye shifts which occur with many dyes in solution usually fail to occur when the dye is bound to a macromolecular substrate. Even though RNA may vary in concentration from extremely dilute in the reticulocyte to highly concentrated in the hemocytoblast, one can show that the shape of the azure B–RNA absorption curve in these different cells remains essentially the same, with the same ratio of monomer, dimer, and polymer peaks (*84*) (Fig. 2). This is apparently because most interaction occurs between

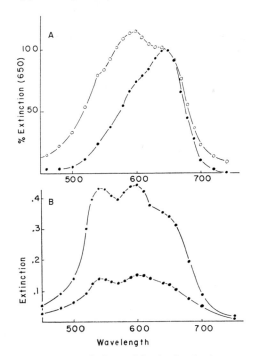

FIG. 2. Photometric tests of Beer's law with the basic dye azure B. (A) DNA staining in two nuclei from the same tissue (*Tradescantia* pollen vegetative and germinative nuclei). The vegetative nucleus (•—•), in which DNA is dilute, shows a prominent α (monomer) peak. In the germinative nucleus (o—o), where DNA is highly concentrated, the β (dimer peak) is most prominent. In such preparations Beer's law does not hold for DNA, and the dye cannot be used for quantitative studies. (B) Cytoplasm from clam (*Spisula*) oocytes. Here azure B–RNA absorption curves are essentially similar for cytoplasm from old (dilute dye) and young (concentrated dye) cells. Beer's law holds, and the dye may appropriately be used for quantitative studies. Data from Swift and Rasch (*84*).

dye molecules bound to the same macromolecule of nucleic acid. The interaction is thus constant whether the nucleic acid is dilute or concentrated, unlike the continuously shifting population of monomers, dimers, and polymers encountered in pure solutions of the dye.

There are some cases, however, where real shifts in the dye absorption curves occur with nucleic acids in stained tissue components. Two such cases have been reported: when chromosomes condense for cell division, the DNA–azure B complex may shift from blue green to blue (*84*) (Fig.

2) ; also, particularly at low pH, where dye binding is weak, absorption curves for nucleolar RNA may differ significantly from absorption curves made on the cytoplasm (*31*). In both these cases, nucleic acid–protein ratios differ at the molecular level. In the condensing chromosome, nucleohistone threads are becoming concentrated, to the exclusion of non-histone protein. In the nucleolus, the RNA is apparently bound to a markedly different protein from that of the ribosomes in the cytoplasm. These variations, which could produce serious deviations from Beer's law, can be obviated by simple remedies. The dye solution can be made more concentrated (0.1%), and the protein "interference" can be mini-mized by amino group removal by deamination or blockage by acetyla-tion (*16, 52*). Both of these treatments increase the amount of dye bound per nucleic acid molecule to the point where saturation or near satura-tion of available binding sites may be obtained. But under these condi-tions there is a good linear relationship between nucleic acid concentra-tion and the concentration of dye bound over the wide limits encountered in tissues. The increase in dye concentration has one ad-verse effect; namely, it may cause noticeable staining of protein carboxyl groups, particularly after amino groups have been removed by deamina-tion. This "background" staining is usually absent, however, if amino groups are acetylated with acetic anhydride (*16*), rather than nitrous acid. This is probably because the acetic anhydride also complexes with and blocks the carboxyl groups of the protein.

At these high concentrations, and with protein interference minimized, the metachromatic difference between DNA and RNA is no longer evi-dent. Deitch (*16*) has pointed out that this may be an advantage, since RNA-DNA ratios may then be obtained by selective removal of one nucleic acid or the other, with photometric determinations made at a single wavelength. An additional advantage in working at high dye con-centrations is that the effect of pH is less important, and thus buffers need not be included in the solution. This can significantly reduce the loss of RNA from tissue sections during the staining procedure, since RNA is readily extracted by salt solutions. Although there is relatively little effect at pH between 3.7 and 4.2, an increasingly large effect is evident even at high dye concentrations when these narrow limits are passed. For this reason, some control of pH, by adjustment with dilute NaOH or HCl, is necessary.

The thiazin dye methylene blue has been preferred by Deitch (*16*) over the closely related azure B, since it was felt the less metachromasy shown by the former dye facilitated direct comparison between DNA and RNA employing photometric determinations at one wavelength, to-gether with specific extraction methods. In our experience, both dyes are equally satisfactory for RNA determinations. Curve shapes for RNA–azure B staining stay essentially the same over wide concentrations of nucleic acid (*23, 39*). Also, there is a good correspondence between amounts of azure B bound and ultraviolet absorption at 2537 Å in the cytoplasm of mouse oocytes, as shown by Flax (*22*). These data are shown in Fig. 3. The linear relation between both RNA and DNA as

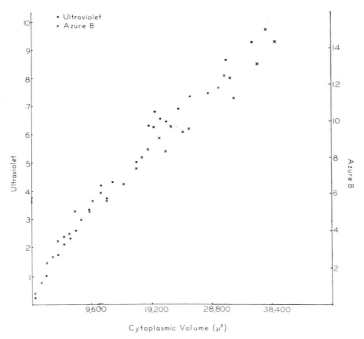

Fig. 3. A comparison of azure B and ultraviolet absorption measurements made on the cytoplasm of mouse ovarian oocytes. Ultraviolet absorption measurements were made at a wavelength of 2537 Å before and after extraction of RNA with trichloracetic acid, and RNA was computed as the difference. Azure B measurements were made at 590 mμ. Data from Flax (*22*).

complexed with gelatin and the amount of methylene blue bound are illustrated in the chapter by Deitch.

We can summarize this section on methods of dye binding as follows: Although several basic dyes, including gallocyanin chrome alum and pyronin, have been used for RNA localization, best results have been obtained with the thiazin dyes azure B and methylene blue, and either of these is recommended. At dilute concentrations (0.025%) azure B stains DNA blue green and RNA purple, and this metachromasy may be helpful for morphological purposes. In some cases, however, particularly for DNA, dye binding may be influenced by protein interference and be nonstoichiometric. These protein effects can be minimized by increasing the dye concentration (to 0.1%), and blocking amino and carboxyl groups with acetic anhydride. Comparison of azure B binding with ultraviolet absorption of cytoplasmic RNA and of methylene blue binding on gelatin-nucleic acid preparations demonstrates that either dye can be used for the determination of RNA *in situ* over the concentration limits found in tissues. Dye binding methods, however, that depend primarily on electrostatic interaction between dye and substrate are probably not capable of the accuracy obtainable with certain covalent interactions, such as the Feulgen reaction. As mentioned above, the fact that RNA variation in tissues is often high also means that the requirements for accuracy in RNA determinations are usually less stringent.

IV. Extraction and Blocking Methods

Extraction methods are important for two reasons: First, the specificity of staining reactions, UV absorption methods, or radioautographs, can be checked by comparing unextracted cells with those from which RNA has selectively been removed. Second, for the determination of RNA in nuclei, it is usually necessary to remove DNA from the tissue. Nucleic acid extraction methods involve either the specific hydrolytic enzyme RNase or DNase, or hydrolysis by acids.

With acid hydrolysis, the RNA is extracted first, and after prolonged treatment the more stable DNA is also removed. It is usually easiest to carry out this extraction on tissue sections. The time of hydrolytic treatment required is strongly dependent on the kind and strength of acid used and the kind of fixation employed for the tissue. With sections from tissue blocks fixed for 1 hour in acetic acid–ethanol, or 10% neutral formalin, extraction of RNA is usually complete in 1 N HCl at 60°C after 6 to 8 minutes (*15, 16, 89*). During this period the DNA in the tissue remains largely intact, although purine bases are removed from DNA molecules. Since purines contribute to the UV absorption of DNA, acid hydrolysis is not acceptable in conjunction with UV studies. With some fixation methods, for example, freeze-substitution followed by ethanol, HCl extraction may also remove other portions of the DNA molecule during the 6- to 8-minute hydrolysis period (*95*). It may also alter staining of the DNA since HCl may remove histones and thus decrease protein interference. Further, if the tissue has been fixed with the DNA still remaining in the native double helical state, basic dye–DNA binding may be altered by the acid denaturation of the DNA. In tissues fixed in acetic acid–ethanol and stained with dilute (0.025%) azure B, for example, HCl treatment causes a change in metachromasy of DNA from blue green to dark blue, probably associated both with partial histone extraction and DNA denaturation.

The adverse effects during acid removal of RNA of partial DNA loss and of some histone protein extraction can be countered by more complete fixation. Formalin fixation practically eliminates DNA extraction during the first 6–8 minutes of HCl hydrolysis and also denatures the histones so that they are not extracted (67). If used together with concentrated (0.1%) azure B or methylene blue, and with protein acetylation, acid hydrolysis in 1 N HCl at 60°C for 6 to 8 minutes affords an adequate method for RNA removal. But since hot acid treatment may extract tissue components, cause shifts in DNA binding by denaturation, and produce tissue shrinkage, it is suggested that this method be used with some caution and comparison be made with extraction by RNase. Acid extraction also causes shifts in tissue refractive index; thus different mounting media may be required for control and acid-treated cells.

Protein extraction during acid removal of RNA may also be reduced by employing acids other than HCl. Perchloric acid (17, 78) and trichloracetic acid (11, 64) have been recommended. Although certain proteins, such as histones, may be less soluble in these acids, criticisms similar to those mentioned above are equally applicable. Some DNA may be extracted during RNA removal (7, 95), alterations in dye-tissue stoichiometry may be produced by DNA denaturation, and some proteins may be extracted. Also, treatment of tissues with trichloracetic acid should be followed by careful washing, since the acid molecules may be bound to proteins, with effects on subsequent staining.

If acid extraction is prolonged beyond the time of RNA extraction, DNA can also be completely removed from tissues. For complete nucleic acid removal, the use of 5% trichloracetic acid has frequently been used, following the technique of Schneider (73). With hydrolysis at 90°C, nucleic acid extraction is complete after 15 minutes in tissues fixed for 1 hour with formalin or acetic acid–ethanol. Where fixation has been prolonged or metallic ions used in the fixative, extraction may take longer. Some RNA basophilia exists in Navashin-fixed plant material even after an hour of extraction, probably because bound chromic ions render the ribonucleoproteins particularly insoluble. Trichloracetic acid extraction is often useful to provide a "blank" tissue section where nucleic acids are absent, for example, in autoradiography. But for photometry, marked shrinkages and refractive index changes are produced and must be considered. Also, phenolic groups of tissue proteins are oxidized, causing shifts in the UV absorption characteristics (66).

Techniques for the selective extraction of RNA and DNA from tissues by the hydrolytic enzymes RNase and DNase are practically indispensable for nucleic acid cytochemistry. The production of unwanted artifacts is usually less than for acid extraction. Nuclease enzymes can provide good tests for the specificity of dye binding, of ultraviolet absorption, and of isotope incorporation in autoradiography. In fact, almost any study involving cytochemical localization of nucleic acid should probably utilize these enzymes for purposes of control.

Several different nuclease preparations have been employed, but the enzymes extracted from beef pancreas (*45, 46*) have been most useful. Both RNase and DNase are commercially available in purified preparations. Some contamination, particularly from proteases, may still be present in certain preparations. RNase may be further purified by boiling enzyme solutions in the presence of ammonium sulfate to remove protease activity (*54*), and DNase by use of electrophoretic separation (*35*). Protease-free preparations are also available commercially. It is advisable to test the activity of enzyme preparations before use. Simple tests of depolymerase activity are available (*35, 49*).

As mentioned above, fixation conditions are extremely important for enzyme digestion. RNase will act rapidly on tissues fixed for one hour in acetic acid–ethanol or cold 10% neutral formalin. Enzyme concentrations of 0.1% will extract all measurable RNA in 1 or 2 hours at 20°C in most tissues. If fixation is prolonged, longer enzyme treatment with temperatures elevated to 37°C may be needed (*3*). Buffer ions alone may extract RNA from tissues, and salt extraction is more rapid at higher pH. Therefore RNase has often been used unbuffered, with the pH adjusted to the acid end of the activity curve at 6.0 or 6.5. Control sections may be treated in water at the same pH. After enzyme digestion, the removal of hydrolyzed fragments of nucleic acid is greatly facilitated by rinsing of sections in 5% trichloracetic acid at 4°–5°C for about 15 minutes (*83*).

If fixation is prolonged or chromic acid or mercuric chloride is used in the fixation, the RNase may work much more slowly and may require elevated temperatures for long periods of time for complete extraction. RNA removal with the fixatives recommended above is usually complete, as determined by a negative orcinol reaction or the loss of labeled RNA in autoradiographs. Certain RNA fractions, however, seem more readily extracted than others. Often RNA in the cytoplasm will be removed before nucleolar or chromosomal RNA. This has been attributed to inhibition of RNase by DNA (*37*), an explanation possibly applicable to chromosomal material, but inadequate to explain the more difficult extractability of nucleolar RNA.

Requirements for DNA extraction by DNase are more exacting. Short fixation in acetic acid–ethanol, freeze-substitution–ethanol, cold 10% formalin, or similar simple treatment is required. Prolonged fixation (more than a few hours), formalin fixation at room temperature, glutaraldehyde, the use of metal ions, all make DNA extraction much more difficult or impossible. This seems to be because of steric interference of the enzyme by bound components of the fixative. In some cases the bound material can be removed, and extraction then becomes possible. For example, formalin fixation at room temperature completely blocks DNase action, but if tissues are treated with hot water (90°C for 15 minutes) much bound formaldehyde is extracted and the enzyme will work (79).

On properly prepared tissues DNase may be used at 20°C in concentrations of 0.02%, adjusted to pH 6.0 or 6.5 with dilute NaOH. Dilute (0.003 M) magnesium sulfate is usually added, since the enzyme requires magnesium ions as a cofactor. More concentrated magnesium ions have been recommended (3), but this facilitates unwanted extraction of RNA. Extraction is usually complete after 1 to 2 hours and in some cases after 15 minutes, particularly with gentle agitation. The enzyme treatment should be followed by additional extraction in 5% trichloracetic acid at 4°–5°C for 15 minutes. Control slides are treated in 0.003 M magnesium sulfate at the same pH, but minus the enzyme. Other controls that may be used involve thermal denaturation of DNase solutions by short heating or enzyme inactivation by addition of zinc ions (58).

Nuclease preparations, if free of proteolytic activity, are moderately stable, and can be used for several series of slides. They should not be allowed to become contaminated with microorganisms for obvious reasons. Enzyme solutions may be kept frozen between periods of use with no apparent loss of activity.

With any new material it is advisable to check nuclease extractions for completeness. Staining reactions (for instance, azure B, methylene blue, the Feulgen reaction) can usually provide good indications of the success of enzyme extractions, but where doubt exists microchemical tests on serial sections or autoradiographs on labeled sections may also be used. The activity of different nuclease enzyme preparations, even when obtained from the same source, may be variable, so that activity tests are helpful in critical work. A few artifacts also may accompany enzymatic extraction, and one needs to be careful of them. Ribonuclease can be quite strongly bound to DNA (96), and thus can inhibit DNA basophilia or increase the ultraviolet absorption of chromatin. It is also possible that DNase may be bound to RNA. Also, during DNA removal by DNase, in some tissues RNA may diffuse in part from its normal position in the tissue and become bound to the basic proteins of the chromatin. Subsequent staining will then indicate an RNase-removable component of the chromatin located at sites formerly occupied by the DNA. This artifact may be eliminated by using gentle agitation and a sufficient volume of enzyme. Also, as stressed above, the continual loss of RNA from tissues during DNase extraction requires that treatments in aqueous media be as short as possible. If it is desired to extract both nucleic acids from a tissue, DNase and RNase can be mixed together in the same solution. The magnesium ions needed for the DNase do not have an adverse effect on RNase.

Blocking agents are important adjuncts to the use of basic dyes, since they can greatly minimize the effects of protein interference. Where both anionic and cationic protein residues can be eliminated from tissues, the dye is able to respond more accurately to the charge densities of the nucleic acid. The two procedures most useful for this purpose are deamination and acetylation. Deamination of protein amino groups by nitrous acid, the Van Slyke reaction, has been used by several workers (1, 52) to increase tissue basophilia. It may be carried out in alcoholic solution to reduce RNA loss. The procedure of Alfert (1) (15% sodium nitrite in 3 parts of 50% ethanol to 1 part glacial acetic acid) is satisfactory. Nitrous acid, in addition to partially removing protein amino groups, also diazotizes the phenolic groups of tyrosine. This produces a yellowish color in tissue proteins, reduces the tyrosine UV absorption at 280 mμ, and produces a new peak at 430 mμ (66).

The acetylation of protein amino groups with 100% acetic anhydride is probably a more satisfactory way to reduce protein interference. RNA loss is usually absent or negligible, and no colored or interfering reactions are produced. Also, the reaction affects both amino and carboxyl groups (36), and thus reduces the effects of negatively charged protein residues on nucleic acid staining (16). Acetylation effects are usually complete after 4 hours in 100% acetic anhydride at 60°C.

In this section on extraction and blocking agents, the importance of nuclease enzymes for providing necessary controls for almost any cytochemical study of nucleic acids has been stressed. If properly used they afford an adequate check on the specificity of stains or of incorporation patterns in autoradiography. They also are essential to the study of chromosomal RNA by either dye binding or ultraviolet absorption through the specific removal of interfering DNA. The most important problems in nuclease digestion studies probably concern variables in the preparation conditions of the tissue and the variable activity of different preparations of the enzymes. Acid extraction with hydrochloric acid for

RNA removal and trichloracetic acid for both nucleic acids may also be used, but cause protein extraction, shrinkage, and refractive index changes as well.

V. Ultraviolet Absorption

Cytochemical determination of nucleic acids by UV absorption, while simple in principle, involves specialized equipment, some of which is described in the chapters by Rudkin and Trapp. A detailed description of these techniques is beyond the scope of this article, and the reader is referred to the above chapters and to reviews on the subject (68, 72, 91).

The investigator may well ask: What information can UV absorption techniques provide that is not more easily obtained by the vastly simpler techniques of staining and visible light photometry? The answers to this question include the following: (1) UV photometry, since it measures the natural absorption of nucleic acid, is more direct. In a few instances it may be applied directly to living cells, but in such cases is only semi-quantitative, since there is no direct way to distinguish absorption due to DNA, RNA, proteins, and scattered light. Also, the wavelengths used are highly injurious to cells, and if more than one or two observations are to be made on any one cell, complex flying-spot television microscopes (9, 56) should be employed to reduce the UV flux. (2) The directness of UV photometry also means that one may investigate soluble components such as sRNA or low molecular weight nucleotides, which may be lost during staining procedures. Lanthanum salts do not interfere with UV absorption, and thus lanthanum-TCA fixation could be employed on fresh smears or cell cultures, together with extraction techniques for removal of sRNA. (3) UV absorption can provide a useful alternate method to check on the results obtained by light microscopy, for example, as additional evidence for the presence of chromosomal RNA (Fig. 4). It may also be used to follow the time course of cytochemical reactions. For example, the Feulgen reaction involves loss of purines, detectable in UV light (7), and in the Millon reaction the formation of tyrosine-mercury complexes can be followed (66). (4) Possibly of greatest interest is the use of UV absorption in the study of experimentally induced changes in the DNA molecule, with the ultimate aim of obtaining cytochemical estimates of base ratios for different parts of the chromosome. Since thermal denaturation of DNA causes an increase in UV absorption and the denaturation temperature is dependent on base ratios, studies on localized increases in chromosome absorption on heating may be possible. Already interesting *in situ* denaturation curves have been obtained with sperm heads (11). Such studies would be impossible with visible light photometry, unless detectable dye shifts were obtained on DNA denaturation. Fluorescent color shifts from yellow-green to orange have been reported for acridine orange bound to DNA (57). It is the author's opinion, however, that except for specific purposes of the kind stated above, ultraviolet absorption studies cannot compete with the relatively simple and more versatile methods of cytophotometry in visible light.

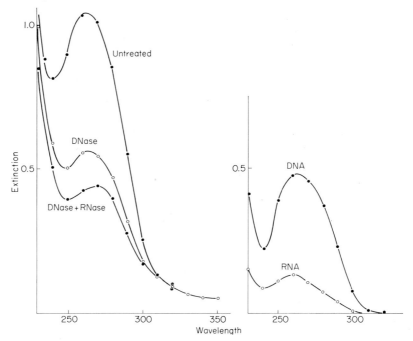

FIG. 4. Determination of RNA and DNA in nuclei of lily tapetal cells by nuclease extraction and ultraviolet absorption. Absorption curves through untreated, DNase-extracted, and DNase-plus-RNase-extracted nuclei are given at the left. At the right are shown the absorption curves for RNA and DNA alone, obtained by subtracting curves from nuclease-treated tissues. Data from Swift (79a).

Simple instrumentation for UV photometry has as major requirements an ultraviolet light source, a good quartz or grating monochromer, and a microscope with quartz or reflecting optics. Absorption levels can be recorded either photographically for later measuring on a densitometer (see chapter by Bloom) or directly from UV-sensitive phototubes, such as the 1P28 photomultiplier. The alignment and focusing of ultraviolet systems, once a difficult problem with light that could not be seen, now is greatly facilitated by use of simple image intensifier tubes, such as the RCA Ultrascope. Good ultraviolet light sources which emit a strong continuous UV spectrum are obtainable, such as the Osram XBO 150W and the Hanovia 510Cl xenon arcs. A number of UV lenses are available such as the Zeiss ultrafluars, Leitz reflecting lenses, or Bausch and Lomb reflecting-refracting lenses. The Zeiss and Bausch and Lomb condensers, objectives, and oculars can be used on standard microscope stands.

Specific problems related to UV photometry are as follows: Nonspecific light loss in cytological preparations may be severe, partly because scatter increases at shorter wavelengths, but also because UV-transparent mounting media that match tissue refractive indexes (RI) (usually RI = 1.565–1.570 for acetic acid–ethanol- or formalin-fixed tissues) are not available. Distilled glycerine (RI = 1.475) is usually used. Its refractive index may be increased by addition of zinc chloride (*41, 69*) or chloral hydrate (*43*), but these can cause extraction of nucleic acids by the mounting medium (*80*). The extent of tissue scatter may be estimated by extrapolation of the scatter curve at 300 to 320 mμ back into the range of nucleic acid absorption, or by use of dark field microscopy (*69*). This extrapolation can only provide rough estimates of scattered light. It is hoped that adequate synthetic mounting media will be developed. Scatter effects are also less when higher numerical aperture objectives are used. In this connection, the numerical aperture 1.25 Zeiss ultrafluar objective is recommended.

Fixation requirements rule out the use of UV-absorbing ions (such as of chromium or mercury). Also, it is probably desirable not to use strongly acid fixatives that may hydrolyze protein phenolic groups, since this causes an elevation and shift in their position (*66*). Also, denaturation of DNA should probably be either absent or complete, since strand separation of DNA molecules produces a 30% increase in UV absorption (*14*). Fixatives producing variable denaturation may thus cause serious errors. At present the effects of fixation on DNA denaturation are not entirely clear and more work needs to be done (*57, 90*).

Specific extraction methods are required to distinguish RNA from DNA within the nucleus and to determine the contribution of protein absorption (Fig. 4). In a few cases, protein absorption may be negligible, since it has, on the average, only about 3 or 4% of the density (per unit mass at 280 mμ) possessed by nucleic acid at 260 mμ. Nuclease enzymes are preferred for nucleic acid extraction, since these have less effect on other tissue components. Acid extraction techniques for RNA may cause serious error by (a) denaturation of DNA, (b) oxidation of phenolic groups, (c) producing increased scatter.

With these variables in mind, it is possible to determine RNA in tissue sections by (a) fixation in 10% neutral formalin, (b) mounting tissues or sections in distilled glycerine between quartz slides and cover slips of the thickness recommended for the condenser and objective used, (c) measuring the optical density of selected areas of the tissue, preferably previously located on a UV micrograph of the material, (d) removal of RNA on the same section, or on a serial section, and remeasuring the same areas to determine the loss in optical density produced by RNase, (e) determination of absorption curve in the 300- to 320-mμ region for the same areas, to correct for light scatter. Although comparatively few careful comparisons have been made between RNA determinations made with UV methods and basic dyes (see Fig. 3), it is probable that greater accuracy is obtainable with visible light, particularly if care is exercised in the staining techniques employed.

VI. Autoradiography

Autoradiography is mentioned here primarily to stress the power of this method in investigations on RNA and to emphasize the value of a combined photometric and autoradiographic approach in cytochemical research. Methods of autoradiography are basically very simple. Many of the problems encountered in the preparation of material are common to other techniques in RNA cytochemistry, as discussed above; namely, fixation methods need to be such that RNA loss is minimized, and yet the RNA also needs to be extractable for control preparations. In addition, however, there are three classes of problems that are specific to autoradiography. (1) There are a large number of variables associated with the kind of precursor to choose, and the concentration and time of treatment. An informed approach to these problems involves the greatest possible understanding of the physiology of the cells and tissues used, of pool sizes, incorporation rates, rates of RNA turnover, and of the rate of loss or metabolic breakdown of the precursor. Such information is often unobtainable, and the investigator is likely with any new material to guess at the proper treatments, and learn from experience. (2) There is a series of problems associated with photographic techniques, namely which emulsion to use, how long to expose the tissues, and techniques of developing and viewing the preparation. (3) Finally, problems of interpretation are equally important. If quantitative estimates of incorporation rates are needed, corrections need to be made for background and self-absorption, and possibly also for image fading. These problems have been discussed in several recent articles, and the reader is referred to them (*12, 20, 44, 62, 65, 87*).

Radioautography obviously adds the needed time dimension to the study of fixed material. Most photometry involves static observations.

The time has probably come in cytochemical studies where merely knowing how much of something is present in a given cell or organelle is in reality not knowing enough. Autoradiography provides information on the rate of precursor incorporation and enables one to distinguish a highly active nucleus from a relatively inactive cytoplasmic inclusion, although they may both contain similar quantities of RNA. It also enables one to see that a single organelle, such as the nucleolus, contains more than one RNA fraction, one that incorporates very rapidly and also loses its label rapidly, and another with a slower rate of incorporation and loss.

It is also true that photometry can be a help to autoradiography. It is important to analyze grain densities in relation to the concentration of underlying nucleic acids, preferably adding corrections for self-absorption, since marked variation in beta-particle path length may occur between the very dense nucleolus and less dense cytoplasm (53). For example, it has recently been stressed (26) that interchromatin areas contain an active RNA fraction, since these show rapid labeling, whereas the more condensed chromatin does not. It is also true, however, that almost all nuclear RNA (except for nucleoli) as shown by staining reactions (85) occurs in the interchromatin areas. The labeling pattern thus does not show two types of RNA, active and less active, with different spatial distributions, but rather a single fraction more concentrated in some portions of the nucleus than others. Another recent paper (75) has emphasized the finding with autoradiographs that certain dense chromosome regions associated with nucleoli probable cannot be responsible for nucleolar RNA production, since they do not label with RNA precursors. Again staining studies could help to elucidate this finding, since they indicate such chromosome regions contain no detectable RNA. Thus autoradiographs fail to distinguish between the absence of RNA within a structure and the presence of an inactive fraction. Staining and labeling preparations together, on the other hand, with proper quantitation of both, can provide a measure both of the amounts of RNA present and its relative specific activity.

Appendix

A few examples are presented here of the application of quantitative estimates of RNA to cytological problems. Details of the photometric methods used are given elsewhere (84).

Figure 5 shows photometric determinations of root tip cells of the bean *Vicia faba*. This material was selected because it made possible an estimate of the stage in interphase of individual cells. Measurements thus

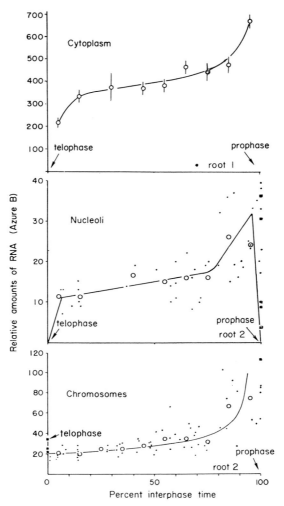

Fig. 5. Estimates of RNA in cytoplasm, nucleoli, and chromosomes of bean nuclei during various stages in interphase growth. Azure B slides were measured by two-wavelength or plug methods. Data from Woodard *et al.* (*94*).

could be plotted against interphase time. Roots were fixed in acetic acid–ethanol. Determinations of total cytoplasmic (plus nuclear) RNA were made on whole cells extracted with DNase, isolated by pectinase, stained with azure B, and measured by the two-wavelength method at 465 and 500 mμ. Nucleolar measurements were made on 4-μ paraffin sections extracted with DNase and stained with azure B. Nucleoli were measured by the plug method at a wavelength of 590 mμ. Nuclear (nonnucleolar) or "chromosomal" RNA was measured on the same sections in areas adjacent to the nucleoli. Both nucleolar and chromosomal RNA were calculated as amount of dye per total nucleolus and nucleus. For further details see Woodard *et al.* (*94*).

In Fig. 6 the amounts of RNA and its incorporation rates are shown

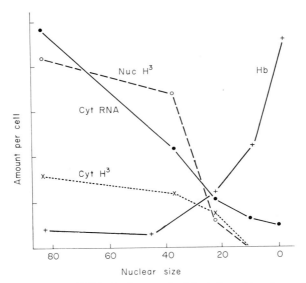

FIG. 6. Measurements on RNA during erythroblast formation in embryo rabbit liver. Cytoplasmic RNA falls rapidly (as determined by azure B), while hemoglobin (determined by its natural heme absorption) increases. Incorporation of cytidine-H³ into the RNA of nucleus and cytoplasm ceases before much of the hemoglobin is synthesized. Nuclear size is expressed as area (μ^2) in prints of cut liver tissue. Autographs are given as grains per μ^2 and are maximal (at 0.42) in the largest nuclei. Cytoplasmic RNA is given in relative units (extinction × area). Data from Grasso *et al.* (*29*).

in forming red blood cells from the liver of 19- to 23-day rabbit embryos. Touch preparations were made on cut liver surfaces fixed in 10% neutral formalin and stained with azure B. Plug measurements were made at 530 mμ on cytoplasmic regions, and the total amount of dye bound was estimated as extinction times area. Hemoglobin estimates were made at the peak absorption of the Soret band, 420 mμ. Methanol fixation was used, since formalin extracted some hemoglobin. Cells were labeled with cytidine-H³, with the injection of 200 microcuries into the placental circulation, and sacrificed 6 hours later. Kodak AR-10 stripping film was used for the autoradiographs.

This study indicated that measurable RNA synthesis had ceased in

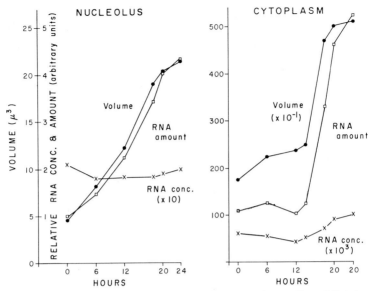

FIG. 7. Amounts of RNA in nucleolus and cytoplasm in rat liver following partial hepatectomy, as determined with azure B. Data from Kleinfeld (unpublished, 1965).

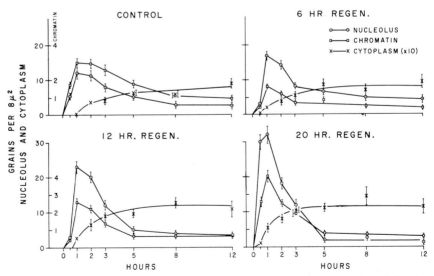

FIG. 8. Incorporation of cytidine-H[3] into various fractions of rat liver following partial hepatectomy. Note the marked increase in early nucleolar labeling at 20 hours, and the more rapid labeling of cytoplasmic RNA. Data of Kleinfeld and von Haam (40).

erythroblast differentiation before most of the hemoglobin was synthesized (29).

Figures 7 and 8 are from a combined photometric and autoradiographic study by Kleinfeld on RNA changes in regenerating rat liver (Kleinfeld and von Haam, 40, and Kleinfeld, unpublished data, 1965). Tissues from 110- to 120-g rats were fixed in acetic acid–ethanol and stained with azure B. Photometric determinations on nucleoli were made with the plug method at a wavelength of 590 mμ. Cytoplasmic RNA was determined on areas 4 μ in diameter or 540 mμ (they may also be measured in larger regions with the two-wavelength method) (84). For autoradiographs, animals were injected with 150 microcuries of cytidine-H^3 and sacrificed at intervals $\frac{1}{2}$ to 12 hours after injection. Sections 3 μ thick were coated with Kodak AR-10 film. Controls included RNase, DNase, and 5% trichloracetic acid at 90°C for 15 minutes.

The photometric data show marked increases in amounts of RNA in nucleolus and cytoplasm. Of considerable interest is the accompanying change in incorporation characteristics of different RNA components. The nucleolar and chromosomal incorporation show the characteristic complex pattern, probably attributable to the presence of both rapidly labeling and slowly labeling RNA fractions. During regeneration the rapid fraction shows a major increase, and the slow nucleolar fraction decreases in activity. Cytoplasmic incorporation also becomes more rapid, and shows detectable label earlier than in the controls.

ACKNOWLEDGMENTS

The author wishes to thank several individuals for their kind permission to reproduce findings in press or published elsewhere. These include Dr. J. Herbert Taylor, Dr. Rachel McMaster-Kaye, Dr. Martin Flax, and Dr. Ruth G. Kleinfeld. Work was aided by grants from the U.S. Public Health Service and the National Science Foundation.

REFERENCES

1. Alfert, M., Studies on the basophilia of nucleic acids: The methyl green stainability of nucleic acids. *Biol. Bull.* **103**, 145–156 (1952).
2. Alfert, M., H. A. Bern, and E. Alfert, Hormonal influence on nuclear synthesis III. On the effects of fixation on nuclear volume. *Z. Wiss. Mikroskopie Mikroskop. Tech.* **62**, 323–326 (1955).
3. Amano, M., Improved techniques for the enzymatic extraction of nucleic acids from tissue sections. *J. Histochem. Cytochem.* **10**, 204–212 (1962).
4. Amano, M., C. P. Leblond, and N. J. Nadler, Radioautographic analysis of nuclear RNA in mouse cells revealing three pools with different turnover times. *Exptl. Cell Res.* **38**, 314–344 (1965).

5. Bahr, G. F., G. Bloom, and U. Fridberg, Volume changes of tissues in physiological fluids during fixation in osmium tetroxide or formaldehyde and during subsequent treatment. *Exptl. Cell Res.* **12**, 342–355 (1957).

6. Barka, T., and P. J. Anderson, "Histochemistry, Theory, Practice, and Bibliography." Harper and Row, New York, 1963.

7. Barka, T., and G. Dallner, The correlation of ultraviolet and Feulgen absorption measurements in ascites tumor cells. *J. Histochem. Cytochem.* **7**, 409–415 (1959).

8. Birnstiel, M. L., J. Jacob, and J. L. Sirlin, Analysis of nucleolar RNA synthesis in dipteran salivary glands. *In* Molecular Cytology Symposium. *Arch Biol.* in press (1965).

9. Bonner, W. A., An ultraviolet microbeam television system. *Ann. N.Y. Acad. Sci.* **97**, 408–411 (1962)

10. Brachet, J., La détection histochimiques des acides pentose nucléiques. *Compt. Rend. Soc. Biol.* **133**, 88–90 (1940).

11. Brachet, J., and J. R. Shaver, The effect of nucleases on cytochemical reactions for amino acids and on staining with acid dyes. *Stain Technol.* **23**, 177–184 (1948).

12. Caro, L. G., High-resolution autoradiography. *Methods Cell Physiol.* **1**, 327–363 (1965).

13. Caspersson, T., Über den chemischen Aufbau der Strukturen des Zellkernes. *Skand. Arch. Physiol.* **73**, Suppl. 8 (1936).

14. Chamberlain, P. J., and P. M. B. Walker, The thermal denaturation of nucleoprotein in boar sperm. *J. Mol. Biol.* **11**, 1–11 (1965).

15. Deane, H. W., The basophilic bodies in hepatic cells. Am. *J. Anat.* **78**, 227–243 (1946).

16. Deitch, A. D., A method for the cytophotometric estimation of nucleic acids using methylene blue. *J. Histochem. Cytochem.* **12**, 451–461 (1964).

17. Di Stefano, H. S., Perchloric acid extraction of ribose nucleic acid from cytological preparations. *Science* **115**, 316–317 (1952).

18. Einarson, L., A method for progressive selective staining of Nissl and nuclear substance in nerve cells. *Am. J. Pathol.* **8**, 295–308 (1932).

19. Fernandez-Moran, H., and J. B. Finean, Electron microscopy and low angle X-ray diffraction studies of the nerve myelin sheath. *J. Biophys. Biochem. Cytol.* **3**, 725–749 (1957).

20. Ficq, A., Autoradiography. *In* "The Cell: Biochemistry, Physiology, Morphology" (J. Brachet and A. E. Mirsky, eds.), Vol. 1, pp. 67–90. Academic Press, New York, 1959.

21. Ficq, A., Localisation d'un acide ribonucléique (RNA) de transfert dans les oocytes d'asteries. *Exptl. Cell Res.* **28**, 543–548 (1962).

22. Flax, M. H., Ribose nucleic acid and protein during oogenesis and early embryonic development in the mouse. Ph.D. Thesis, Columbia University (1952).

23. Flax, M. H., and M. Himes, Microspectrophotometric analysis of metachromatic staining of nucleic acids. *Physiol. Zool.* **25**, 297–311 (1952).

24. Freed, J. J., Desoxyribonucleic acid content of nuclei in tail mesenchyme of *Rana pipiens* embryos. *Nature* **176**, 116 (1955).

25. French, D., and J. T. Edsall, The reactions of formaldehyde with amino acids and proteins. *Advan. Protein Chem.* **2**, 277–335 (1945).

26. Frenster, J. H., Mechanisms of repression and depression within interphase chromatin. *Proc. 16th Ann. Meeting Tissue Culture Assoc.* in press (1966).

27. Gall, J. G., and H. G. Callan, H[3] uridine incorporation in lampbrush chromosomes. *Proc. Natl. Acad. Sci. U.S.* **48**, 562–570 (1962).

28. Gibor, A., and J. Granick, Plastids and mitochondria: Inneritable systems. *Science* **145**, 890–987 (1964).
29. Grasso, J. A., J. W. Woodard, and H. Swift, Cytochemical studies of nucleic acids and proteins in erythrocytic development. *Proc. Natl. Acad. Sci. U.S.* **50**, 134–140 (1963).
30. Hancox, N. M., Experiments on the fundamental effects of freeze-substitution. *Exptl. Cell Ret.* **13**, 263–275 (1957).
31. Himes, M., A quantitative difference in ribonucleoprotein of nucleolus and cytoplasm. *J. Histochem. Cytochem.* **6**, 392 (1958) (Abstract).
32. Huang, R. C., and J. Bonner. Histone-bound RNA, a component of native nucleohistone. *Proc. Natl. Acad. Sci. U.S.* **54**, 960–967 (1965).
33. Jacob, F., and J. Monod, Genetic regulatory mechanisms in the synthesis of proteins. *J. Mol. Biol.* **3**, 318–356 (1961).
34. Jacobson, A. B., H. Swift, and L. Bogorad, Cytochemical studies concerning the distribution of plastids in *Zea mays*. *J. Cell Biol.* **17**, 557–570 (1963).
35. Kalnitsky, G., J. P. Hummel, and C. Dierks, Some factors which affect the enzymatic digestion of ribonucleic acid. *J. Biol. Chem.* **234**, 1512–1516 (1959).
36. Karnovsky, M. J., and G. D. Fasman, A histochemical method for distinguishing between side-chain and terminal (α-acylamido) carboxyl groups of proteins. *J. Biophys. Biochem. Cytol.* **8**, 319–325 (1960).
37. Kaufmann, B. P., M. R. McDonald, H. Gay, N. Okuda, J. M. Pennoyer, and S. Blowney, Organization of the chromosome. *Carnegie Inst. Wash. Yearbook* **47**, 144–153 (1948).
38. Kelley, E. G., Reactions of dyes with cell substances. IV. Quantitative comparison of tissue nuclei and extracted nucleoproteins. *J. Biol. Chem.* **127**, 55–71 (1939).
39. Kleinfeld, R. G., A comparison of nuclear changes in the rat liver during regeneration, thioacetamide treatment, and starvation. Ph.D. Thesis, University of Chicago (1953).
40. Kleinfeld, R. G., and E. von Haam, Nucleic acid metabolism in regenerating rat liver using cytidine H³. *Ann. Histochim.* **7**, 89–96 (1962).
41. Koenig, H., D. Schildkraut, and E. Galler, Nonabsorptive light loss in ultraviolet microspectrophotometry of fixed tissue sections. *J. Histochem. Cytochem.* **1**, 384–385 (1953) (Abstract).
42. Koenig, H., and E. Stahlecker, Further studies on differential extraction of nucleic acids from mammalian nerve cells with perchloric acid. *J. Natl. Cancer Inst.* **12**, 237–238 (1951) (Abstract).
43. Köhler, A., Mikrophotographische Untersuchungen mit ultraviolettem Licht. *Z. Wiss. Mikroskop.* **21**, 273–304 (1904).
44. Koprina, B. M., and C. P. Leblond, Improvements in the coating technique of radioautography. *J. Histochem. Cytochem.* **10**, 269–284 (1962).
45. Kunitz, M., Crystalline ribonuclease. *J. Gen. Physiol.* **24**, 15–32 (1940).
46. Kunitz, M., Crystalline desoxyribonuclease. I. Isolation and general properties, spectrophotometric method for the measurement of desoxyribonuclease activity. *J. Gen. Physiol.* **33**, 349–362 (1950).
47. Kurnick, N. B., Methyl green-pyronin. I. Basis of selective staining of nucleic acids. *J. Gen. Physiol.* **33**, 243–264 (1950).
48. Kurnick, N. B., Histological staining with methyl-green-pyronin, *Stain Technol.* **27**, 233–242 (1952).
49. Kurnick, N. B., Assay of deoxyribonuclease activity. *Methods Biochem. Anal.* **11**, 1–38 (1962).

50. Lagerstedt, S., Cytological studies on the protein metabolism of the liver in rat. *Acta Anat.* Suppl. 9, 1–116 (1949).
51. Lagerstedt, S., The release of ribonucleic acid from Carnoy fixed tissue sections during incubation in McIlvaine's buffer. *Experientia* **12**, 425–426 (1956).
52. Lillie, R. D., Acetylation and nitrosation of tissue amines in histochemistry. *J. Histochem. Cytochem.* **6**, 352–362 (1958).
53. Maurer, W., and E. Primbsch, Grösse der β-Selbstabsorption bei der H^3-Autoradiographic. *Exptl. Cell Res.* **33**, 8–18 (1964).
54. McDonald, M. R., A method for the preparation of "protease-free" crystalline ribonuclease. *J. Gen. Physiol.* **32**, 39–42 (1948).
55. Michaelis, L., The nature of the interaction of nucleic acids and nuclei with basic dye stuffs. *Cold Spring Harbor Symp. Quant. Biol.* **12**, 131–142 (1948).
56. Montgomery, P. O. B., Experimental approaches to nucleolar function. *Exptl. Cell Res.* Suppl. 9, 170–175 (1963).
57. Nash, D., and W. Plaut, On the denaturation of chromosomal DNA *in situ*, *Proc. Natl. Acad. Sci. U.S.* **51**, 731–735 (1964).
58. Nass, S., and M. M. K. Nass, Intramitochondrial fibers with DNA characteristics. II. Enzymatic and other hydrolytic treatments. *J. Cell Biol.* **19**, 613–629 (1963).
59. Pearse, A. G. E., Application of the alkaline tetrazolium reaction to the study of reducing groups in tissue sections. *J. Pathol. Bacteriol.* **67**, 129–136 (1954).
60. Perry, R. P., The cellular sites of synthesis of ribosomal and 4S RNA. *Proc. Natl. Acad. Sci. U.S.* **48**, 2179–2186 (1962).
61. Perry, R. P., Selective effects of actinomycin D on the intracellular distribution of RNA in tissue culture cells. *Exptl. Cell Res.* **29**, 400–406 (1963).
62. Perry, R. P., Quantitative autoradiography. *Methods Cell Physiol.* **1**, 305–326 (1964).
63. Perry, R. P., Role of the nucleolus in ribonucleic acid metabolism and other cellular processes. *Natl. Cancer Inst. Monogr.* **14**, 73–89 (1964).
64. Pollister, A. W., and H. Ris, Nucleoprotein determinations in cytological preparations. *Cold Spring Harbor Symp. Quant. Biol.* **12**, 147–157 (1948).
65. Prescott, D. M., Autoradiography with liquid emulsion, *Methods Cell Physiol.* **1**, 365–370 (1964).
66. Rasch, E., and H. Swift, Microphotometric analysis of the cytochemical Millon reaction. *J. Histochem. Cytochem.* **8**, 4–17 (1959).
67. Rasch, E., and J. W. Woodard, Basic proteins of plant nuclei during normal and pathological cell growth. *J. Biophys. Biochem. Cytol.* **6**, 263–276 (1959).
68. Rudkin, G. T., Cytochemistry in the ultraviolet. *Microchem. J., Symp. Ser.* **1**, 261–276, 1961.
69. Rudkin, G. T., and S. L. Corlette, A photographic method for measuring ultraviolet radiation scattered from microscopic objects. *J. Biophys. Biochem. Cytol.* **3**, 821–825 (1957).
70. Rudkin, G. T., and P. S. Woods, Incorporation of H^3 thymidine into giant chromosomes of *Drosophila* during puff formation. *Proc. Natl. Acad. Sci. U.S.* **45**, 997–1003 (1959).
71. Sabatini, D. D., K. Bensch, and R. J. Barrnett, Cytochemistry and electron microscopy. The preservation of cellular ultrastructure and enzyme activity by aldehyde fixation. *J. Cell Biol.* **17**, 19–58 (1963).
72. Sandritter, W., Ultraviolettmikrospektrophotometrie. *Proc 1st Intern. Congr. Histochem. Cytochem., Paris,* 1960 pp. 33–61. Pergamon Press, Oxford, 1963.
73. Schneider, W. C., Phosphorus compounds in animal tissue. I. Extraction and

estimation of desoxypentose nucleic acid and of pentose nucleic acid. *J. Biol. Chem.* **161**, 293–303 (1945).

74. Sirlin, J. L., J. Jacob, and C. J. Tandler, Transfer of the methyl group of methionine to nucleolar ribonucleic acid. *Biochem. J.* **89**, 447–552, 1963.

75. Sirlin, J. L., C. J. Tandler, and J. Jacob, The relationship between the nucleolus organizer and nucleolar RNA. *Exptl. Cell Res.* **31**, 611–615 (1963).

76. Stenram, U., Changes in the nucleic acid apparatus of the rat liver cell during the appearance of basophilic rods. *Acta Anat.* **22**, 272–277 (1954).

77. Stenram, U., The specificity of gallocyanin-chromalum stain for nucleic acid as studied by ribonuclease technique. *Exptl. Cell Res.* **4**, 383–389 (1953).

78. Sulkin, N. M., and A. Kuntz, Histochemical determination of ribose nucleic acid in vertebrate tissues following extraction with perchloric acid. *Proc. Soc. Exptl. Biol. Med.* **73**, 413–415 (1950).

79. Swift, H., Quantitative aspects of nuclear nucleoproteins. *Intern. Rev. Cytol.* **2**, 1–76 (1953).

79a. Swift, H., Nucleoproteins in the mitotic cycle. *Texas Rept. Biol. Med.* **11**, 755–774 (1953).

80. Swift, H., Cytochemical techniques for nucleic acids. *In* "The Nucleic Acids: Chemistry and Biology" (E. Chargaff and J. N. Davidson, eds.), Vol. 2, pp. 51–92. Academic Press, New York, 1955.

81. Swift, H., Nucleic acids and cell morphology in dipteran salivary glands. *In* "The Molecular Control of Cellular Activity" (J. Allen, ed.), pp. 73–125. McGraw-Hill, New York, 1962.

82. Swift, H., Nucleic acids of mitochondria and chloroplasts. *Am. Naturalist* **99**, 201–227 (1965).

83. Swift, H., B. J. Adams, and K. Larsen, Electron microscope cytochemistry of *Drosophila* salivary glands and *Tetrahymena*. *J. Roy. Microscop. Soc.* **83**, 161–167 (1964).

84. Swift, H., and E. M. Rasch, Microphotometry with visible light. *In* "Physical Techniques in Biological Research" (G. Oster and A. W. Pollister, eds.), Vol. 3, pp. 353–400. Academic Press, New York, 1956.

85. Swift, H., L. Rebhun, E. Rasch, and J. Woodard, The cytology of nuclear RNA. *In* "Cellular Mechanisms in Differentiation and Growth," Growth Symp. No. 14 (D. Rudnick, ed.), pp. 45–59. Princeton Univ. Press, Princeton, New Jersey, 1956.

86. Taft, E. B., The specificity of the methyl green pyronin stain for nucleic acids. *Exptl. Cell Res.* **2**, 312–326 (1951).

87. Taylor, J. H., Autoradiography at the cellular level. *In* "Physical Techniques in Biological Research" (G. Oster and A. W. Pollister, eds.), Vol. 3, pp. 546–577. Academic Press, New York, 1956.

88. Taylor, J. H., and R. D. McMaster, Autoradiographic and microphotometric studies of desoxyribose nucleic acid during microgametogenesis in *Lilium longiflorum*. *Chromosoma* **6**, 489–521 (1954).

89. Vendrely-Rendavel, C., Substitution de l'acide chlorohydrique a la ribonucléase pour l'étude de la localisation de l'acide ribonucléique au sein des cellules animales. *Compt. Rend. Soc. Biol.* **143**, 294–295 (1949).

90. von Borstel, R. C., D. M. Prescott, and F. J. Bollum, Cytochemical localization of primer DNA using DNA polymerase. *J. Cell Biol.* **19**, 72A (1963) (Abstract).

91. Walker, P. M. B., Ultraviolet absorption techniques. *In* "Physical Techniques

in Biological Research" (G. Oster aod A. W. Pollister, eds.), Vol. 3, pp. 402–488. Academic Press, New York, 1956.

92. Ward, R. T., Prevention of polymerization damage in methacrylate embedding media. *J. Histochem. Cytochem.* **6,** 398 (1958) (Abstract).

93. Watson, M. L., and W. G. Aldridge, Selective electron staining of nucleic acids. *J. Histochem. Cytochem.* **12,** 96–103 (1964).

94. Woodard, J. W., E. M. Rasch, and H. Swift, Nucleic acid and protein metabolism during the mitotic cycle in *Vicia faba. J. Biophys. Biochem. Cytol.* **9,** 445–462 (1961).

95. Woods, P. S., Chromatographic study of hydrolysis in the Feulgen nucleal reaction. *J. Biophys. Biochem. Cytol.* **3,** 71–88 (1957).

96. Yotsuyanagi, Y., Mise en évidence au microscope électronique des chromosomes de la levure par une coloration spécifique. *Compt. Rend.* **250,** 1522–1524 (1960).

97. Zamecnik, P. C., M. L. Stephenson, and J. F. Scott, Partial purification of soluble RNA. *Proc. Natl. Acad. Sci. U.S.* **46,** 811–822 (1960).

98. Zamecnik, P. C., M. L. Stephenson, and C. T. Yu, Studies on preparation, fractionation, and degradation of soluble ribonucleic acid. *In* "Protein Biosynthesis," Proc. Symp., Wassenaar, Holland, 1960 (R. J. C. Harris, ed.), pp. 125–131. Academic Press, New York, 1961.

MICROSPECTROPHOTOMETRY
OF CHROMOSOMES

George T. Rudkin*

THE INSTITUTE FOR CANCER RESEARCH, PHILADELPHIA, PENNSYLVANIA

I. Introduction

Chromosomes are important as the centers of control of cell metabolism, control that dictates the range of variation within species and is the only basis for variation between species. They are organized into functional units, separable by simple genetic techniques and divisible by more complex ones. We shall not be concerned with the genetic material of the microorganisms, although the methods described in this chapter have been applied to it (25). It is with the larger, more structured bodies found in higher organisms that we shall be concerned.

The properties of chromosomes that have been investigated by quantitative microspectrophotometry include composition, structure, metabolism, replication, action, and control. We do not propose to discuss them in detail, but shall indicate briefly areas in which contributions have been made. Our primary purpose will be to point out the properties of chromosomes that present special technical difficulties and to outline one of the methods that has been applied to overcome them.

Microspectrophotometric methods are used to detect and measure chemical composition in relation to structure. An ultimate cytogenetic goal is to study both parameters in relation to the activity of individual genetic units, units which carry out single functions. Since a chromosome contains hundreds or thousands of such genes, it is at once clear that ultimately a very high resolving power will be required, unapproachable except in particular cell types. On the other hand, many of the activities of genetic units are coordinated by their organization into chromosomes, and the chromosomes function together as a nucleus so that it is possible

*Supported by Public Health Service Grants No. CA-01613 (to Jack Schultz) and No. CA-06927 and by National Science Foundation Grant No. G-18953.

to approach some questions in diploid cells at the resolving power attainable in the visible and ultraviolet regions of the spectrum.

II. The Material

The technical problems can be illustrated by considering the classical ways in which the chromosomes are manifest in a nucleus. In classical

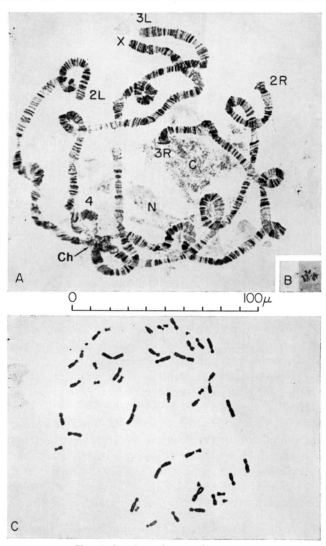

FIG. 1. See legend, opposite page.

interphase cells of diploid or polyploid nuclei, they are in part compacted into "dense chromatin," in part extended into a fine fibrillar network which may appear homogeneous at the resolving power of the light or ultraviolet microscopes. Individual chromosomes are not usually distinguishable. During the process of contraction in the prophase stages of division, the extended portions are coiled up, typically beginning at regular intervals along the chromosome threads to form the chromomeres. At that stage, especially in meiosis, individual chromosomes can often be distinguished and may be identified by their chromomere pattern. The pattern elements are too small for microspectrophotometric measurements to be meaningful except in certain favorable species and for special purposes (24). It is not until metaphase that the methods can be applied in the general case.

The giant polytene chromosomes of the Diptera arise by a process that short-circuits the contraction and separation phases of the chromosome cycle: the kinetochore regions do not separate, and the daughter chromosome strands remain closely paired, resulting in cablelike structures that may have several thousands of times the haploid number of strands. The cross-bands are made up of thousands of chromomeres, all identical in any one band. They are known to be the sites of genetic loci which can be studied individually in active or inactive states. Figure 1 illustrates the degree to which the process increases the diameter, the length, and the internally visible detail of chromomere pattern in the individual chromosomes. The nuclei in these giant cells are functional, in what corresponds to the interphase state of diploid cells.

Fig. 1. All three parts are at the same final magnification, indicated by the scale. (A) Salivary gland chromosomes from a *Drosophila melanogaster* female prepupa. The ends of the six chromosome arms are labeled (R for the right, L for the left arms according to the convention established by the genetic maps). X and 4 have only one conspicuous arm each. The kinetochore regions are fused into a common chromocenter (Ch). The two original chromosomes of each type that were present in the diploid cell from which this nucleus grew are "fused" by intimate somatic pairing. Cytoplasmic material is labeled C, nucleolar material N. (Cooke 6 mm quartz monochromat corrected for 2536A, numerical aperture 0.7; Cooke quartz condenser (dry) stopped down to numerical aperture 0.23; original magnification 533×; 50% acetic acid squash on quartz slide.) (B) Metaphase chromosomes from a *Drosophila melanogaster* female heterozygous for a normal X chromosome and an X chromosome lacking its centric heterochromatic regions. The X chromosomes are at the top, the second chromosomes to the left, the third chromosomes to the right, and the two fourth chromosomes are a pair of tiny dots in the center, probably not visible in the reproduction. (Photomicrographic conditions as in (A); 50% acetic acid squash after pretreatment with hypotonic citrate; ribonuclease treated; see Rudkin, 41.) (C) Metaphase spread of a normal human male; culture of cells from skin; aceto-orcein, air-dried preparation courtesy of Dr. D. A. Hungerford of The Institute for Cancer Research, Philadelphia, Pennsylvania.

For either case, metaphase or giant chromosome, the structural details that can be observed and measured extend to the theoretical limits of resolution and sensitivity of the instruments. Since the delimitation of the chromosome parts to be measured is an essential part of the procedure, the boundaries of the measured area must be known with great precision. A pictorial display is so necessary that only photographic procedures or scanning methods employing other forms of image presentation have been suitable. One of the photographic methods will be described in some detail.

Since the photographic plate is used as a detector for radiation, the procedures here described are applicable to the measurement of a variety of substances that absorb in the ultraviolet or visible regions of the spectrum as well as to mass determination by the absorption of X-rays. Minor modifications of a method for quantitative interference microscopy (4) would serve to adapt it for scanning densitometry. It is equally useful for the measurement of dyes bound to chromosomes by procedures adapted for quantitative work, such as the Feulgen reaction (2, 40). Preparative procedures will be discussed only briefly. Photomicrographic technique is standard, with the extra precaution that special effort should be made to assure even development over the whole surface of the measuring plate (or film). Plates can be adequately handled by a vane moved continuously very close (about 0.05 inch) to its surface; bursts of bubbles of an inert gas through the solution will serve well for either plates or films and has the added advantage that oxygen of the air is excluded from the developer (30, 50).

III. The Photographic Method

A. SCANNING DENSITOMETRY

Caspersson (8) began using a photographic plate as a detector of ultraviolet radiation. The method described here is his original one (Caspersson and Schultz, 11), modified in relatively minor ways. The reader is referred to Mees (30) and Allen (1) for general photographic processes and techniques, and to earlier descriptions of the procedure (32, 37, 38, 44, 49).

The basic instrument is essentially the same for all microspectrophotometric procedures. It consists of an adequate microscope fitted with top quality optical components and illuminated by radiation with as small a range of wavelengths as possible in such manner that each wavelength contributes equally to all points in the image plane. All of the requirements for a microspectrophotometric system [Caspersson (9); Walker (54); Pollister and Ornstein (35)] must be met by the microscope and the specimen before the photomicrograph is taken. From then on the procedures and problems are densitometric and relate to deriving a numerical estimate of absorbance from the information contained in the negative.

The quantitative procedures depend upon a known relationship between the amount of silver on an area of developed negative and the total radiation energy to which the area was exposed. Plate calibration depends upon finding a set of standard relative light intensities to which each plate may be exposed and for each of which a corresponding estimate of deposited silver can be made. Caspersson (8), working in the ultraviolet, controlled photographic processing by exposing a portion of each plate to a standard visible light source through a neutral density wedge and calibrated each batch of plates at each wavelength to be used. Thorell adopted a rotating step sector for calibration at the wavelength of measurement and located it at the image plane of the microscope. His arrangement exacts severe demands: one must have available a clear space in the specimen, so positioned and large enough to accommodate the sector image, and maintain stringent control of the uniformity of the intensity of illumination over the whole field of the microscope. Rudkin et al. (44) exposed a portion of the plate (shielded from the microscope image) separately to radiation from the same source and for the same exposure time as the photomicrograph, also through a rotating logarithmic step sector.

The amount of silver deposited can be estimated by a variety of means, of which the scanning densitometer is most common. Scanning is essential because of variations in shapes and thicknesses of homologous chromosomes or their parts in different nuclei, and a recording instrument is required. Measurements at single "points," so convenient for geometrically regular objects or for estimating concentration, are meaningless here. The absorbance must be integrated over a complete structure, the confines of which are clearly delimited in the densitometer records as well as on the chromosome.

Integration is most conveniently carried out when the response of the measuring instrument is linear with respect to the logarithm of the radiation energy which struck the plate. The calibrating device is used not only to determine that the image on the measuring plate is in the linear part of the response curve, but also to measure the slope of that curve. Caspersson (8), Thorell (49), and Rudkin et al. (44) used the percentage transmission of the plate as the measure of deposited silver. The range of measurable extinction values, about 0.6 units, can be extended if plate density is substituted for transmissivity as a measure (see, for example, Walker, 53, 54), but a logarithmic converter is required in the densitometer or a variable function transformer must be interposed between the densitometer and the recorder (Rudkin *et al. 44*). In either case, care must be taken to keep the measuring spot small enough to avoid distributional error in the *densitometric* measurement, a complica-

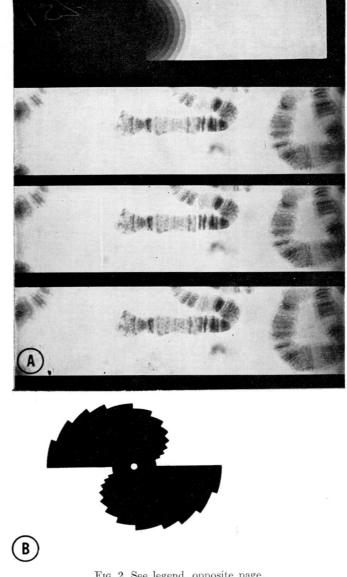

FIG. 2. See legend, opposite page.

tion that does not enter when percentage transmission is the measured variable.

The measurement is straightforward. It is convenient to prepare a print of the measuring plate to the same scale as the densitometer trace, a print that includes reference lines drawn on the back of the plate and on which the paths scanned in the densitometer can be accurately located (see Figs. 2 and 5). The transmissivity of the plate recorded at a spot on a scanned path is proportional to the logarithm of the intensity of radiation at the corresponding point in the microscope field. The difference between the transmissivity for radiation incident on the object, determined at points free from objects (free space), and the transmissivity for radiation which passed through a point in the object is proportional to the absorbance of the object at the point. The area on the densitometer record between the transmissivity along a path in a free space and a path through the object (shaded in Fig. 5) is proportional to the integral of the absorbance of the object over the path scanned, which is, in turn, proportional to the mass of absorbing material in the object in the path scanned. The argument is summarized in the following derivation: For any spot on the plate

$$T_p = -k \log I, \tag{1}$$

so

$$T_{p0} = -k \log I_0 \tag{2}$$

in a free space and

$$T_{pc} = -k \log I_c \tag{3}$$

in the cell where chromophores absorb. Subtracting,

$$T_{pc} - T_{p0} = k \log I_0 - k \log I_c = k \log \frac{I_0}{I_c} = kA. \tag{4}$$

FIG. 2. (A) Contact print of a 4×5 inch negative plate showing the image of the rotating sector and photomicrographs of the free end of chromosome 2R from a salivary gland nucleus of *Drosophila melanogaster*. The three photomicrographs were taken at focal levels 0.5μ apart. The white lines on the center exposure are reference lines drawn on the back of the plate with a pen. The center exposure was in best focus and was used for densitometry. Photography: Cooke glycerine immersion $81\times$ quartz monochromat corrected for 2536A, numerical aperture 1.25; Cooke quartz glycerine immersion condenser, numerical aperture 1.25, stopped down to 0.3; Cooke $10\times$ quartz ocular; final magnification at plate $1535\times$; both sector and photomicrographs exposed by the 257 nm cadmium emission line from a spark gap source (*44*) for the same exposure time (10 sec); Eastman Process plate developed in a developer described by Thorell for 90 seconds at 20°C; agitation by passing a plastic blade back and forth about 0.05 inch (1.25 mm) from the plate approximately once every 2 seconds. (B) A contact shadowgraph of a logarithmic step sector. The sector was rotated in a plane approximately 5 mm from the plate to obtain the image at the top of (A).

For a scan across the plate from spot x_1 to spot x_2,

$$\int_{x_1}^{x_2} (T_{pc} - T_{p0})\, dx = k \int_{x_1}^{x_2} A\, dx. \tag{5}$$

The percentage transmission summed over the length of the scan, given in Eq. (5) and by the shaded area in Fig. 4, has the dimensions of length (of scan) times T_p. If we scan in a series of paths parallel to the x axis, equally spaced Δy apart along the y axis, a scan of length $(x_2 - x_1)$ will represent a sample of the plate $(x_2 - x_1)\, \Delta y$ in area and the integrated percentage transmission for the swath will be given by

$$\int_{x_1}^{x_2} (T_{pc} - T_{p0})\, dx\, \Delta y = T_{Ti}. \tag{6}$$

Summing expressions (6) for adjacent scans from y_1 to y_n results in the percentage transmission integrated over the area of the object,

$$T_T = \sum_{y_1}^{y_n} \int_{x_1}^{x_2} (T_{pc} - T_{p0})\, dx\, \Delta y, \tag{7}$$

which is the value determined from the plate with a scanning densitometer. The absorbance of the object integrated over the scanned area is given by the expression

$$A_T = \sum_{y_1'}^{y_n'} \int_{x_1'}^{x_2'} A\, dx'\, \Delta y', \tag{8}$$

where the primed variables refer to the object space (not to the image space or plate) in the photomicrographic apparatus. From Eq. (4),

$$T_T = \sum_{y_1}^{y_2} \int_{x_1}^{x_2} (T_{pc} - T_{p0})\, dx\, \Delta y = \sum_{y_1}^{y_2} \int_{x_1}^{x_2} kA\, dx\, \Delta y. \tag{9}$$

Combining with Eq. (8) we see that

$$T_T = kA_T m^2, \tag{10}$$

where m is the scale factor (magnification) between the object space and the plate. A_T in the right side of Eq. (10) is related to mass by the absorption coefficient, k', of the chromophore at the wavelength of measurement, expressed as the absorption of unit mass in a unit area, such as picograms per square micron, or

$$A_T = k'M, \tag{11}$$

so

$$T_T = kk'Mm^2, \tag{12}$$

and we have the mass of chromophore in terms of the measured T_T as

$$M = \frac{T_T}{kk'm^2} = A_T/k', \tag{13}$$

where

T_p	= percentage of transmission at a spot on the plate,
T_{p0}	= T_p in the image of a free space,
T_{pc}	= T_p at a spot in the image of the object,
T_{Ti}	= $T_{pc} - T_{p0}$ integrated over one scan,
T_T	= all T_{Ti}'s summed over the scanned area,
I_0	= intensity of radiation passing through a free space in the object plane (and assumed equal to the intensity incident on the object),
I_c	= intensity of radiation which emerged from a spot in the object,
k	= proportionality constant between T_p and I, determined from the image of the calibration system (rotating logarithmic step sector) as described above and in Fig. 3,
A	= absorbance of the object at a spot,
A_T	= A summed for all spots in the scanned area,
x	= distance along a scanned path
y	= distance on the plate perpendicular to scanned paths,
Δy	= distance between centers of scanned paths on the plate,
$x', y', \Delta y'$	= homologs of $x, y, \Delta y$ in the object space of the microscope,
k'	= specific absorptivity of the chromophore in the object at the wavelength at which the photomicrograph was taken (expressed as the absorbance of unit mass per unit area),
M	= mass of chromophore in the object in the scanned area.

If the densitometer reads directly in plate density, D_p, where $D_p = -\log T_p$, then $-D_p$ can be substituted for T_p in the above equations and k will be the experimentally determined relation between $-D_p$ and I, usually called gamma; the measuring procedures would be the same.

The units in which the photometric result [Eq. (13)] is expressed are arbitrary when only relative values are required as, for example, in most measurements of the amount of dye bound by a chromosome. Calibration of the arbitrary units in terms of the amount of chromosomal material to which the dye is bound is difficult, but possible (18, 52).

Measurements made in the absorption bands of naturally occurring material, such as in the ultraviolet bands for the nucleic acids, and expressed in absolute units can theoretically be converted to mass of absorbing material. An essential requirement is that the specific absorptivity of the chromophore as it occurs in the fixed, measured chromosome [k' in Eq. (13)] be known. As a first approximation, we have used the specific absorptivity of DNA in dilute solution for estimating the amounts found in chromosomal regions by microspectrophotometry, an assumption that is justified by good agreement with chemical data where available (*38, 46*). A study of the absorption coefficients of nucleoprotein in concentrations approaching those found in chromosomes would be desirable, but it would be difficult to also take into account possible effects of the physical state of the nucleic acids in specific chromosome regions. It is, for example, possible that change in k' rather than extraction of DNA was responsible for the variability between homologous chromosomes in different nuclei observed by Rudkin *et al.* (*46*).

The overall operation of measuring A_T with the densitometer that produced records in Figs. 3 and 4 (a modified spectroscopist's instrument)

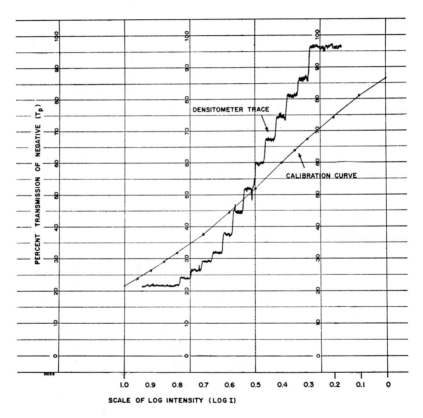

FIG. 3. The staircase-like line is a densitometer trace across the plate shown in Fig. 2A in the region of the sector image. The calibration curve was drawn by plotting the percentage transmission registered for each sector step (*y* axis) at the corresponding value for the logarithm of the relative intensity of radiation transmitted by the step (*x* axis) on an arbitrary scale, taking the logarithm of the incident intensity as 1.0. Scale: 10% transmission = 1 inch in the original. Jarrell-Ash recording microphotometer.

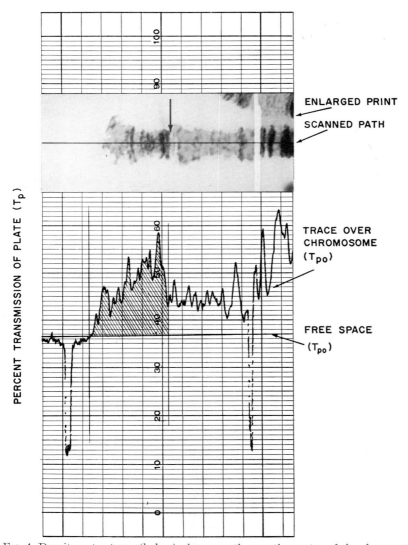

FIG. 4. Densitometer trace (below) along a path near the center of the chromosome in the picture (above). The photograph is the center exposure in Fig. 2 enlarged to the same scale as the densitometer trace. The line labeled FREE SPACE (T_{p0}) was determined from traces beside the chromosome and drawn over the trace shown here. The hatched area represents $\int (T_{pc} - T_{p0})\ dx$ [Eq. (5)] along the chromosome from the tip to a point proximal to a heavy band (arrow). The positions of the ink lines on the plate are easily identified on the densitometer trace. Areas homologous to the hatched area are determined for traces run 0.5 mm apart parallel to the one shown and summed to obtain $\Sigma \int (T_{pc} - T_{p0})\ dx\ \Delta y$ for Eq. (7) (see Rudkin, et al., 44).

is time consuming. The recorder itself is fairly fast (1 second for a full scale deflection of 10 inches), but its speed can be limiting when large, inhomogeneous objects with high contrast are being measured. The magnification factor between the plate and the paper record must be made large enough so that the areas T_{Ti} [Eq. (6) and Fig. 4] are large enough to be measured with reasonable precision; in the densitometer used here, magnification is varied by changing the speed of plate scanning while the recording paper speed remains constant (2 inches per minute). For objects as small as individual bands of *Drosophila* polytene chromosomes or the whole chromosomes of mammalian cells, the plate must be moved quite slowly to obtain areas T_{Ti} of adequate size. It requires, for

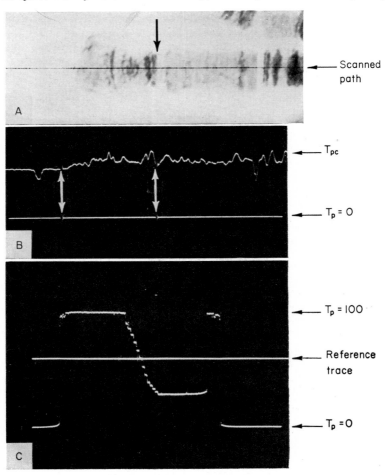

Fig. 5. See legend, opposite page.

example, of the order of 30–40 minutes to scan a human chromosome and another half hour to analyze the records produced when the photographic negative is taken at a magnification of 1000 diameters. A distal portion of a *Rhynchosciara* salivary gland chromosome photographed on a single plate at 750 diameters and demarcated into six regions required about 10 man-hours for the analysis of the records after approximately 3–4 hours of scanning time. Independent re-checking of the data reduction process requires a quarter to half of the original analysis time. A faster densitometer such as, possibly, the Walker type, which was designed for the analysis of photomicrographs, might reduce the time required for scanning by a factor of one quarter to one eighth provided it were equipped with a strip chart (which is available) and did not require frequent changes and adjustment of sheets of recording paper. The time saved would, however, be a much smaller fraction of the total procedure from photography to reduced data.

Engle (*15*) has recently constructed a rapid scanning integrating densitometer in which the photographic plate is scanned once every two seconds by moving it with a saw-tooth motion between a stationary light source and photomultiplier tube. The amplified signals from the photo-

---

Fig. 5. (A) A print from the center exposure in Fig. 2 enlarged to the same scale as the oscilloscope trace in (B). (B) Photograph of the cathode ray oscilloscope tube in the rapid scanning integrating densitometer of Engle (see Engle and H. Rudkin, *15*). The upper trace (T_{pc}) is the profile of a scan along the line shown in the photograph in (A); the vertical displacement is proportional to the output of the photomultiplier tube in the plate-scanning mechanism (T_p). The lower (straight) trace has been set at the "black level" ($T_p = 0$) [see legend to (C)]. The breaks in both traces (arrows) are the marking pips between which integration is performed. The instrument can be ordered to present on a digital voltmeter a number proportional to the area between the trace over the chromosome (T_{pc}) and the black level ($T_p = 0$) between the marker pips. The pips have been set to mark off a chromosomal segment (also marked by the shaded area in Fig. 4). The horizontal reference trace can also be set at the free space level (T_{po}) and the integral between T_{po} and the black level presented on the digital voltmeter. The difference between the two integral voltmeter readings is proportional to $\int(T_{pc} - T_{po})\,dx$ (shaded in Fig. 4). The horizontal sweep of the oscilloscope has been expanded fivefold ($\times 5$). The machine can also be ordered to present the distance between the marker pips in millimeters. (C) Oscilloscope trace across the plate shown in Fig. 2 at the level of the sector image. $T_p = 100$, a clear place on the plate, has been set at 100 volts. $T_p = 0$, the black level shown as the portions of the trace where the photomultiplier tube was darkened by interposition of the plate carriage, has been set at 0 volt. The reference trace, the horizontal line near the center, has been set at the level of one of the steps in the sector. Once it is set, the machine is ordered to present the voltage level (percentage transmission) at the sector step on the digital voltmeter. The plate calibration is completed by determining the voltage level at each step. The horizontal sweep of the oscilloscope has been set at minimal expansion ($\times 1$) so the horizontal scale is 1/5 of that in (B).

multiplier and from a controllable dc reference are presented alternately through a 400 cycle per second chopper to the vertical deflection circuit of an oscilloscope. The horizontal deflection circuit is synchronized with the movement of the plate carriage. The presentation on the face of the oscilloscope is then a trace of percentage transmission of the plate (T_p) against distance (x) superimposed on a horizontal trace at a known dc level (see Fig. 5).

Two marker pips can be set independently at x_1 and x_2 to bracket any chosen portion of the horizontal display (Fig. 5). An electronic integrating circuit can then be switched in to measure (1) the length in millimeters of the scan at the plate between x_1 and x_2; or (2) the integral of T_{pc} between x_1 and x_2; or (3) the integral of T_{p0} between x_1 and x_2, determined from the dc level set at T_{p0}. Integrals, dc levels, or millimeters are read out on a digital voltmeter. Sector calibration is evaluated by reading the dc level at each sector step.

Each scan line must be analyzed separately for work with banded chromosomes. The measurement of isolated objects such as metaphase chromosomes or whole nuclei could be expedited by the addition of a device for automatically moving the plate to successive scanning paths and collecting the sum of the integrals in Eq. (7) over the whole of the object in a single operation.

B. Other Densitometric Procedures

Deposited silver can be estimated in other ways, some of which have been explored, and could be used for the microspectrophotometry of chromosomes. The area densitometer is theoretically applicable to plates so exposed that the percentage transmission of the plate is directly proportional to $-\log I$, as in Eq. (1). The principle of the method and an instrument for its use are described in the chapter by Bahr (3) for plates exposed to electrons and by Carlson (6) for emulsions exposed to X-rays in historadiographic procedures. An attempt to apply the method to plates exposed to light was unsuccessful (16), partly because of the very short range of T_p over which Eq. (1) holds for light as compared with ionizing radiation.

Direct chemical measurement of the silver deposited in a print made from a measurable negative was proposed by Ornstein (33) and applied by Niemi (31) to Feulgen stained nuclei. An alternative is to measure the amount of dye in a "monochrome" print made by a color printing process, used by Ornstein (35) for the measurement of chromosome sets in grasshopper spermatocytes and den Tonkelaar and van Duijn (50, 51) for whole nuclei. The dye is eluted for measurement in a spectrophotometer, a procedure also adopted by Kelly (23) for the measurement of the dyes developed by a reversal process in a color film original. Mendelsohn (*26, 27*) used the two-wavelength method to estimate a single dye developed in a color print of the original negative, a procedure for which a low power optical system was designed.

IV. Direct Measuring Systems

Electronic systems built for the direct measurement of the absorption of radiation by a microscopic specimen have the potential advantage of higher speed and precision than the photographic process can offer. Caspersson's (*10*) microspectrophotometer as improved and modified by Trapp of Zeiss, Oberkochen, is the most precise instrument for the determination of an absorption spectrum, which can be taken at a single spot as small as 0.5 μ in diameter. Ruch (*36*) (see also this volume, p. 281) has placed a spectrograph after the microscope, enabling him to obtain permanent records of spectra on photographic plates. Carlson *et al.* showed that the electronic instrument could be used to measure integrated absorbance of stained metaphase chromosomes. They have also demonstrated that the integrated retardation (see chapters on interference microscopy) of such small objects can be measured in the visible region of the spectrum, accomplished earlier for giant chromosomes (*12*). They had difficulties with interfering substances when they tried to measure DNA by its absorption in the ultraviolet. Rudkin (unpublished results, 1958) compared the photographic method with a direct scanning instrument by measuring the A_T of a portion of a *Rhynchosciara* chromosome at 257 nm by both methods with the following result shown in Table I. The differences are within the errors of the photographic method.

TABLE I

COMPARISON OF PHOTOGRAPHIC AND PHOTOELECTRIC MEASUREMENTS
OF AT IN GIANT CHROMOSOME REGIONS[a]

| Region of chromosome | Method of measurement[b] | | Difference |
	Photographic	Direct electronic[c]	
I	12.4	13.3	7%
II	26.8	28.2	5%
Total	39.2	41.5	6%

[a] Salivary gland, tip of chromosome B, *Rhynchosciara angelae.*

[b] The figures in the body of the table are in absolute units: square microns times absorbance.

[c] Measured with a microspectrophotometer described (and built) by Caspersson.

Scanning systems related to those used for television have been adapted to the microscope for spectrophotometric purposes [Williams (55); Freed and Engle (17); Box and Freund (5); Mendelsohn *et al.* (28, 29)]. The flying-spot system of Freed and Engle, equipped with a device for demarcating an area of any shape within which absorbance is to be integrated (14), should prove most useful for measurements on parts of giant chromosomes at wavelengths from 260 nm through the visible range. Mendelsohn and his collaborators have recorded the output of their scanner in digitalized form on magnetic tape, for the measurement of the gallocyanin chrome alum stain in individual arms of human chromosomes (29). The tape is fed to a large, general purpose digital computer for the rapid reduction of data. Systems such as their CYDAC may allow microspectrophotometric facilities established as auxiliaries to large computer centers to evolve as the most effective means for measurement of the absorption of irregular microscopic objects, including chromosomes and parts thereof.

V. Preparation of Material for Measurement

The fixation and mounting of cells or tissues is one of the most important steps in an investigation, but detailed instructions for general use cannot be given. Different cell types within a species or similar cell types in different species or at different stages of development of a single organism may require quite different treatments in order to preserve their chromosomes in a satisfactory morphological condition, to retain the substances to be measured and to remove interfering substances. A few comments may be helpful.

Chromosome morphology can only be properly observed when the individual chromosomes are extended in the image plane of the microscope, an orientation that is so rare in sectioned material as to make other types of preparation almost mandatory. Smears or squashes of appropriately fixed tissue are methods of choice, and many mammalian cells must be induced to undergo at least one division *in vitro* in order to obtain suitable preparations.

Colchicine arrest of mitosis is routinely used to increase the frequency of metaphases. It may be applied in culture or to whole experimental organisms. One of its effects is to make the chromosomes contract to such an extent that morphological details are obscured, a drawback that is often counteracted by treating the tissue with a hypotonic solution before fixation (19, 21). For a spectrophotometric study it would be necessary to determine the influence of pretreatment on the composition of the chromosomes (46).

The chemical nature of the nucleic acids is such that they are less soluble at low than at high pH. It is necessary, therefore, to fix in an acidic solution early in the preparative procedure in order to maintain morphology and to prevent loss of those macromolecules which have an acidic reaction. Basic substances, notably basic proteins such as the histones, present a special cytological problem which has not yet been completely solved for individual chromosomes (40, 48).

In practice, each new material is a challenge. It is the responsibility of the individual worker to evaluate for himself and to be prepared to demonstrate to others to what extent his methods introduce artifacts, especially by dissolution of measured substances, deposition of interfering substances, failure to extract interfering substances, change in the physical properties of the substances that are preserved on the slide, or by other means.

VI. Applications

A. CHROMOSOME PHYSIOLOGY

The most extensive use of scanning microspectrophotometry has been on the giant, banded chromosomes of the Diptera for which scanning was originally introduced into the photographic procedure (11). It has been employed to study the effect of pairing on the DNA content of homologous chromosome segments (4), disproportionate synthesis of DNA in certain puff regions (45), the relative specific activity of RNA in puffs (combined with autoradiography) (39), the proteins of active and inactive chromosome regions (40, 48), the relationships between chromosome bands, considered to be genetic loci (38, 47), the differential growth of heterochromatin and euchromatin in polytene nuclei (41), the relative mutabilities of different regions within a chromosome (43), and other aspects of the replication and activity of chromosomes and of the genetic units within them.

B. CLINICAL

Studies in the clinical field have been limited to metaphase chromosomes which can be prepared in a state suitable for the analysis of a complete karyotype, that is, to those tissues which can be obtained in culture or as free suspensions containing cells in mitosis. If the investigator should wish to determine only values for whole chromosomes, then a scanning procedure would not be necessary. Methods that are capable of handling isolated objects, such as the two-wavelength method (27), the crushing condenser followed by measurement of the whole chromosome in a single field (13), an area densitometer (3) or one of the dye-coupling methods of densitometry (24) could be equally rapid and may be less costly in instrumentation. However, the demarcation of individual chromosome arms or of other portions within chromosomes is probably best handled by scanning a photograph or scanning the chromosome itself with a pictorial aid such as a photograph or a computer printout for assistance in the identification of morphological landmarks. It may be possible to cut out from prints areas in which silver is to be determined as accurately as those areas can now be defined by scanning. The introduction of a second photographic step may reduce precision which could be restored by replication of the second step at the expense of time and material, but there remains the risk of bias if the demarcation is made solely by visual contrast in a continuous tone print (42).

The first direct application to human chromosomes was a measurement of the difference between the DNA contents of the Ph^1 chromosome characteristic of leukocytes in chronic granulocytic leukemia (46). The characterization of the whole karyotype has begun (29, 42, 46) and should, when completed, serve as a firmer basis for comparison than is at present offered by measurements of length (42). The most serious drawback to general use is the complexity of the instrumentation, its operation, and upkeep.

A most serious problem from the point of view of the routine application of absorption measurements is the preparation of the material discussed above in general terms. Methods in general use only 2 or 3 years ago, adopted because they revealed intrachromosomal detail, extracted varying amounts of ultraviolet absorbing material from different nuclei (46). It will be very important to future work that methods compatible with both the morphological and the chemical pictures be developed. A new method for pretreatment of cells before spreading (20) may be a step in the right direction. Given an adequate method, many problems relating to the physiology and the differentiation of nuclei will be approachable in cells of mammalian origin.

VII. Concluding Remarks

Probably the most important single point to be made after the discussion of a particular technical procedure is that it is only one of many that are available for the solution of a problem. In practice, more than one parameter either is required or is desirable to complete an analysis of a biological phenomenon. The photographic approach to microspectrophotometry has the advantages of being nondestructive to the specimen [although marked changes in DNA can be brought about by irradiation of nuclei by ultraviolet radiation (34, 38)], and of requiring a permanent record in the form of a photographic negative to which one can always return for the extraction of more information. It is applicable to the measurement of absorption of radiation over a wide range of frequencies (9, 12), to the measurement of retardation in interference microscopy (4), and in quantitative polarization microscopy (4, 22). It is compatible with autoradiography and, indeed, may be essential to the proper evaluation of autoradiographic images (39).

REFERENCES

1. Allen, R. M., "Photomicrography," 2nd ed., Van Nostrand, Princeton, New Jersey, 1958.
2. Aronson, J. F., G. T. Rudkin, and J. Schultz, A comparison of giant X chromosomes in male and female *Drosophila melanogaster* by cytophotometry in the ultraviolet. *J. Histochem. Cytochem.* **2**, 458–459 (1954) (Abstract).
3. Bahr, G. F., this volume, p. 137.
4. Bartels, P. H., this volume, p. 93.
5. Box, H. C., and H. G. Freund, Flying-spot microscope adapted for quantitative measurements. *Rev. Sci. Instr.* **30**, 28–30 (1959)
6. Carlson, L., Evaluation of microradiograms for dry weight determination. *Exptl. Cell Res. Suppl.* **4**, 193–196 (1957).
7. Carlson, L., T. Caspersson, G. E. Foley, J. Kudynowski, G. Lomakka, E. Simonsson, and L. Sören, The application of quantitative cytochemical techniques to the study of individual mammalian chromosomes. *Exptl. Cell Res.* **31**, 589–594 (1963).
8. Caspersson, T., Über den chemischen Aufbau der Strukturen des Zellkernes. *Skand. Arch. Physiol.* **73**, Suppl. **8**, 1–151 (1936).
9. Caspersson, T., "Cell Growth and Cell Function." Norton, New York, 1950.
10. Caspersson, T., Quantitative cytochemical methods for the study of cell metabolism. *Experientia* **11**, 45–60 (1955).
11. Caspersson, T., and J. Schultz, Nucleic acid metabolism of the chromosomes in relation to gene reproduction. *Nature* **142**, 294–295 (1938).
12. Caspersson, T., L. Vogt-Köhne, and O. Caspersson, Relations between nucleus and cytoplasm in normal and malignant growth. *In* "Cell Physiology of Neoplasia," 14R Symp. Fundamental Cancer Res., pp. 269–291. Univ. of Texas Press, Austin, Texas, 1960.
13. Davies, H. G., M. H. F. Wilkins, and R. G. H. Boddy, Cell crushing: a technique for greatly reducing errors in microspectrometry. Exptl. Cell Res. **6**, 550–553 (1954).
14. Engle, J. L., and J. J. Freed, Ultraviolet photometry of living cells with a flying spot microscope. In preparation (1965).
15. Engle, J. L., and G. T. Rudkin, A rapid scanning densitometer for integrated absorbancy measurements from photographic negatives. In preparation (1965).
16. Freed, J. J., Personal communication (1956).
17. Freed, J. J., and J. L. Engle, Development of the vibrating-mirror flying spot microscope for ultraviolet spectrophotometry. *Ann. N.Y. Acad. Sci.* **97**, 412–430 (1962).

18. Hardonk, M. J., and P. van Duijn, A quantitative study of the Feulgen reaction with the aid of histochemical model systems. *J. Histochem. Cytochem.* **12**, 752–757 (1964).

19. Hsu, T. C., and C. M. Pomerat, Mammalian chromosomes *in vitro*. II. A method for spreading the chromosomes of cells in tissue culture. *J. Heredity* **44**, 23–29 (1953).

20. Hungerford, D. A., Leukocytes cultured from small inocula of whole blood and the preparation of metaphase chromosomes by treatment with hypotonic KCl. *Stain Technol.* **40**, 333–338 (1965).

21. Hungerford, D. A., and M. Di Berardino, Cytological effects of prefixation treatment. *J. Biophys. Biochem. Cytol.* **4**, 391–400 (1958).

22. Inoue, S., and H. Sato, Arrangement of DNA in living sperm: a biophysical analysis. *Science* **136**, 1122–1124 (1962).

23. Kelly, J. W., this volume, p. 247.

24. Lima-de-Faria, A., Initiation of DNA synthesis at specific segments in the meiotic chromosomes of Melanoplus. *Hereditas* **47**, 674–694 (1961).

25. Malmgren, B., and C.-G. Hedén, Nucleotide metabolism of bacteria and the bacterial nucleus. *Nature* **159**, 577 (1947).

26. Mendelsohn, M. L., The two-wavelength method in microspectrophotometry. Parts I and II. *J. Biophys. Biochem. Cytol.* **4**, 407–414 and 415–424 (1958).

27. Mendelsohn, M. L., this volume, p. 201.

28. Mendelsohn, M. L., W. A. Kolman, B. Perry, and J. M. S. Prewitt, Computer analysis of cell images. *Postgrad. Med.* Bicentennial Med. Educ. Issue, **38**, 567–573 (1965).

29. Mendelsohn, M. L., T. J. Conway, D. A. Hungerford, W. A. Kolman, B. H. Perry, and J. M. S. Prewitt, Computer-oriented analysis of human chromosomes. I. Photometric estimation of DNA content. *Cytogenetics* **5**, in press (1966).

30. Mees, C. E. K., "The Theory of the Photographic Process," rev. ed. Macmillan, New York, 1954.

31. Niemi, M., Cytophotometry by silver analysis of photomicrographs. Description of a new method and its application to the study of corpuscular haemoglobin. *Acta Anat.* **35**, Suppl. 34, 1–92 (1958).

32. Nurnberger, J. I., Ultraviolet microscopy and microspectroscopy. *In* "Analytical Cytology" (R. C. Mellors, ed.), 1st ed., pp. 4/1–4/44 (2nd ed., 1959). McGraw-Hill, New York, 1955.

33. Ornstein, L., The distributional error in microspectrophotometry. *Lab. Invest.* **1**, 250–265 (1952).

34. Pigon, A., and J.-E. Edström, Nucleic acid changes during starvation and encystment in a ciliate (Urostyla). *Exptl. Cell Res.* **16**, 648–656 (1959).

35. Pollister, A. W., and L. Ornstein, The photometric chemical analysis of cells. *In* "Analytical Cytology" (R. C. Mellors, ed.), 2nd ed., pp. 431–518. McGraw-Hill, New York, 1959.

36. Ruch, F., Ein Mikrospektrograph für Absorptionsmessungen im ultra-violetten Licht. *Z. Wiss. Mikroskopie* **64**, 453–468, 1960.

37. Rudkin, G. T., The application of ultraviolet absorbance measurements to problems in cell biology. *IRE Trans. Med. Electron.* **7**, 122–129 (1960).

38. Rudkin, G. T., Cytochemistry in the ultraviolet. *Microchem. J., Symp. Ser.* **1**, 261–276 (1961).

39. Rudkin, G. T., Nucleic acid metabolism in giant chromosomes of *Drosophila melanogaster*. *Ann. Histochim.* Suppl. 2, 77–84 (1962).

40. Rudkin, G. T., The proteins of polytene chromosomes. *In* "The Nucleohistones" (J. Bonner and P. O. P. Ts'o, eds.), pp. 184–192. Holden-Day, San Francisco, California, 1964.

41. Rudkin, G. T., The structure and function of heterochromatin. *In* "Genetics Today" (S. J. Geerts, ed.), pp. 359–374. Pergamon Press, Oxford, 1964.

42. Rudkin, G. T., Photometric measurements of individual metaphase chromosomes. *In* "The Chromosome: Its Function and Structure" (G. Yerganian, ed.), in press, 1965.

43. Rudkin, G. T., The relative mutabilities of DNA in regions of the X chromosome of *Drosophila melanogaster*. *Genetics* **52**, 665–681 (1965).

44. Rudkin, G. T., J. F. Aronson, D. A. Hungerford, and J. Schultz, A comparison of the ultraviolet absorption of haploid and diploid salivary gland chromosomes. *Exptl. Cell Res.* **9**, 193–211 (1955).

45. Rudkin, G. T., and S. L. Corlette, Disproportionate synthesis of DNA in a polytene chromosome region. *Proc. Natl. Acad. Sci. U.S.* **43**, 964–968 (1957).

46. Rudkin, G. T., D. A. Hungerford, and P. C. Nowell, DNA contents of chromosome Ph[1] and chromosome 21 in human chronic granulocytic leukemia. *Science* **144**, 1229–1232 (1964).

47. Schultz, J., and G. T. Rudkin, DNA content in relation to the genetic unit in *Drosophila melanogaster*. *Proc. 10th Intern. Congr. Cell Biol.*, p. 71, L'Expansion Scientifique Française, Paris, 1960.

48. Swift, H., The histones of polytene chromosomes. *In* "The Nucleohistones" (J. Bonner and P. O. P. Ts'o, eds.), pp. 169–183. Holden-Day, San Francisco, California, 1964.

49. Thorell, B., "Studies on the Formation of Cellular Substances During Blood Cell Production." Kimpton, London, 1947.

50. Tonkelaar, E. M. den, and P. van Duijn, Photographic colorimetry as a quantitative cytochemical method. I. Principles and practice of the method. *Histochemie* **4**, 1–9 (1964).

51. Tonkelaar, E. M. den, and P. van Duijn, Photographic colorimetry as a quantitative cytochemical method. II. Determination of relative amounts of DNA in cell nuclei. *Histochemie* **4**, 10–15 (1964).

52. Tonkelaar, E. M. den, and P. van Duijn, Photographic colorimetry as a quantitative cytochemical method. III. Determination of the absolute amount of DNA in cell nuclei. *Histochemie* **4**, 16–19 (1964).

53. Walker, P. M. B., A recording microdensitometer applicable to biological problems. *J. Sci. Instr.* **30**, 162–164 (1953).

54. Walker, P. M. B., Ultraviolet absorption techniques. *In* "Physical Techniques in Biological Research" (G. Oster and A. W. Pollister, eds.), Vol. 3, pp. 401–487. Academic Press, New York, 1956.

55. Williams, G. Z., Direct observation of cellular absorption by ultraviolet television microscopy. *J. Histochem. Cytochem.* **5**, 246–253 (1957).

INSTRUMENTATION
FOR MICROFLUOROMETRY

Andreas A. Thaer

ERNST LEITZ G.M.B.H., WETZLAR, GERMANY

During the past two decades fluorescence microscopy has become one of the most useful microscopic methods in biology and medicine. Its possible applications for the detection and study of primary or secondary fluorescing substances in tissues and single cells are so wide that even a simple enumeration of these applications would be too time consuming. As in the other fields of microscopy, there is a strong tendency to use fluorescence microscopy to obtain quantitative results in addition to qualitative information (1–3, 5–9).

The basic advantages of microfluorometric mass determinations as compared with extinction measurements for the same purpose are mentioned by Ruch in this volume (p. 281). The subject of this contribution is the fundamental requirements of special instrumentation for photoelectric measurement of fluorescence emitted by microscopic objects. Some of the fundamental requirements for microfluorometric instrumentation are already known from fluorescence microscopy. Since good results in microfluorometry require the fulfillment of most of the conditions for fluorescence microscopy, all these conditions will be mentioned here.

Figures 1a and 1b show schematically the normal light path in a fluorescence microscope for transmitted light. Mercury or xenon high-pressure bulbs act as light sources, with high emission in the spectral ranges 350–400 mμ (near UV) and 400–500 mμ (blue-violet), normally used for fluorescence excitation. Excitation filters (or monochromators) select for transmission the spectral range that is required for excitation. Bright field condensers (Fig. 1a) or dark field condensers (Fig. 1b) concentrate the excitation rays on the fluorescing object. The objective forms an image of the fluorescing object as a self-luminous object, whereas all excitation energy is absorbed by the barrier filter.

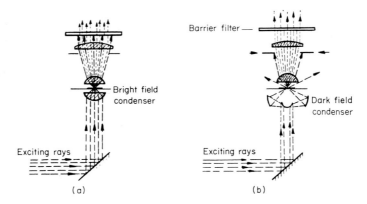

FIG. 1. Light path in a fluorescence microscope with excitation in transmitted light; (a) With bright field condenser; (b) with dark field condenser.

Figures 2a and 2b illustrate the possibility of fluorescence excitation with incident light either by dark field illumination using ring-shaped condensers around the objective (Fig. 2a) or through the objective itself (Fig. 2b) (4).

Excitation with both incident and transmitted light is used for fluorescence microscopy. They may be combined with alternative and even simultaneous illumination and observation of the object with normal

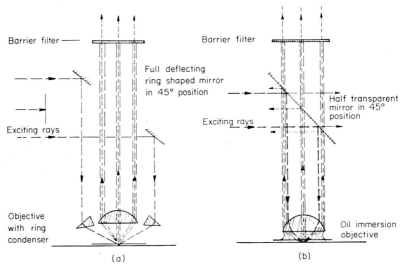

FIG. 2. Light path in a fluorescence microscope with excitation in incident light. (a) Using a dark field illuminator; (b) using a vertical illuminator (bright field).

light (see Figs. 3 and 4), so that the objects can be observed by their fluorescence emission, for instance, after focusing and scanning the preparation with bright field, dark field, or phase contrast observation (4). All of these illumination systems may also be applied to microfluorometry.

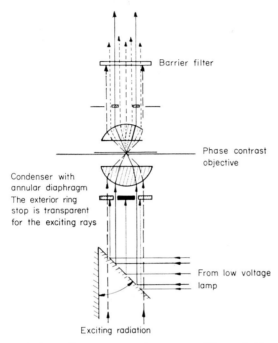

FIG. 3. Light path in a fluorescence microscope with excitation in transmitted light and alternative or simultaneous phase contrast illumination.

In addition to the necessity of sufficient intensity in the spectral range of excitation, microphotometric measurements of fluorescence intensity require a time-stabilized excitation light source. The high-pressure mercury lamps normally used in fluorescence microscopy are very often useless for microfluorometric purposes owing to the spatial instability of their arcs, especially if they are fed with alternating current. Satisfactory spatial stability of the arc is shown by mercury high-pressure burners of the capillary type, for example, the mercury burner ST 75 (only for intensive fluorescence) (Quarzlampen Co., Hanau) or burners with extreme energy output like the type SP 500 (Philips). Time stability of the voltage supply can be obtained in most cases by a good magnetic stabilizer.

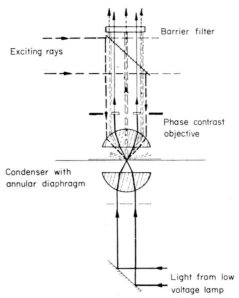

Barrier filter

Exciting rays

Phase contrast
objective

Condenser with
annular diaphragm

Light from low
voltage lamp

Fig. 4. Illuminating system for fluorescence excitation in incident light using a vertical illuminator combined with phase contrast optics for transmitted light (after Grehn and Kornmann, 4).

Compared with the mercury bulbs, the xenon high-pressure lamps have the advantage of a continuous emission spectrum, which is important for the continuous variation of the excitation wavelength range with a monochromator. Recently the xenon high-pressure burners XBO 150 W/1 (Osram), CSX 150 W (Philips), and 901 C-I (Engelhard Hanovia Inc.) have been improved with respect to spatial stability of the arc. Aside from the use of good magnetic stabilizers with sinusoidal output (complete stabilized power supplies obtainable from Sorensen, South Norwalk, Conn.), these burners use direct current, which has a negligible percentage of residual current ripple. The very intensive and relatively small emission spot at the cathode is particularly useful for obtaining high concentration of excitation energy in the object plane using dark field condensers of high numerical aperture. A selection of burners having sufficient stability of the arc still seems to be indispensable.

The choice of the type of excitation light source is, of course, primarily influenced by the necessity of satisfactory fluorescence and therefore excitation intensity in the required spectral excitation range. For excitation in the wavelength range 400–500 mμ, the xenon high-pressure lamp is superior; between 350 and 400 mμ the excitation intensity of both xenon and mercury high-pressure lamps is in the same order of magnitude except for the case in which the absorption maximum of the fluorescing substance is close to the mercury emission line 366 mμ.

On the other hand, with increasing excitation intensity, very often a more and more rapid decrease of fluorescence intensity occurs during radiation. This decrease of fluorescence intensity is caused by photodecomposition of the fluorescing substances and has to be eliminated as much as possible, especially for mass determinations of fluorochromed substances such as DNA (*1, 6, 7, 9*). Therefore, for microfluorometry one should always follow the rule: Reduce the excitation intensity and increase the sensitivity of the photoelectric measuring device as much as possible.

If the concentration, the amount, and the quantum efficiency (for transformation of excitation energy into fluorescence intensity) of the fluorescing material in the measured area are high enough, excitation light sources with lower intensity of the arc (for example, mercury burner ST 75) may also be used with satisfactory results. For excitation in the wavelength range 400–500 mμ under the above-mentioned favorable conditions, even low-voltage incandescent lamps of the quartz iodine type could act as excitation light sources.

Following the illumination principle of Köhler, one should always focus the light source into the entrance pupil of the condenser in order to avoid an inhomogeneous illumination of the object field observed with the microscope, but above all unequal light distribution in the measured area of the object.

Although an aperture diaphragm is not required (unlike the situation of microphotometric extinction measurements, which require an illumination aperture < 0.4), an illumination field diaphragm is very useful for the limitation of the illuminated area around the measuring field for two reasons: (1) to avoid radiation of objects in the vicinity of the object just measured; (2) to reduce light scatter caused by illuminated objects in the surrounding field of the measured area and by all dust particles and inhomogeneities in the light path between illumination field diaphragm and barrier filter.

The spectral range chosen for fluorescence excitation should be selected by the excitation filters as carefully as possible. The exact separation of the transmission curves of excitation filters and barrier filters are of outstanding importance. Otherwise excitation light scattered by the object will contribute to the measured fluorescence intensity. This effect is not necessarily noticeable by visual observation under dark field conditions. If bright field condensers are used the measured background intensity will also increase.

Special attention should be paid to the elimination of the red transmission by the Schott UG filter, widely used for excitation in the spectral range 350–400 mμ, by the Schott Filter BG 38, or a cuvette with copper sulfate solution. Also, the application of interference filters for a narrower spectral band width of the exciting radiation is possible. For normal "interference band filters," however, the transmission curve below 1% transmittance very often is extended relatively far to longer wavelengths. Therefore, despite the lower transmission maxima, interference double band filters (Schott) are preferable.

Monochromators are necessary for the spectral selection of exciting radiation if intensity and spectrum of fluorescence are measured as a function of the excitation wavelength with very narrow spectral bandwidth of the excitation beam. If single monochromators are used, the additional application of excitation filters before or behind the monochromator is recommended for eliminating scattered light of the monochromator in the spectral transmission range of the barrier filter. Generally the exit slit of the monochromator (and consequently its entrance slit and the arc of the used gas discharge lamp) should be imaged into the entrance pupil of the condenser. Only if a very small band width is required for excitation would the "critical" illumination with imaging of the exit slit into the object plane be advantageous.

The application of the most suitable condenser is of considerable importance for obtaining optimal conditions for microfluorometry. The contrast-improving effect of dark field condensers in comparison with bright field condensers is already well known from the microscopic observation of weakly fluorescing objects. As illustrated in Fig. 1b, this effect is based on the fact that the main part of the exciting beam does not enter the objective and therefore cannot cause disturbing background fluorescence by hitting fluorescing components of the objective (fluorite, cement between lenses, and mounting media). Another reason for this improved contrast is that only a very small percentage of the excitation light reaches the barrier filter, which sometimes fluoresces itself owing to the complete absorption of the excitation energy. The result is an almost completely black background, which for microfluorometry means a very low "optical noise level." Another advantage of using dark field condensers is the possibility of using apochromatic objectives, which have higher chromatic correction and a higher numerical aperture than achromatic objectives of the same magnification. The possibilities of alternative illumination with normal transmitted light are restricted, however, to dark field illumination.

If bright field condensers are used, condensers with the highest numerical aperture and good correction should be selected for weakly fluorescing objects, in order to reach the highest possible concentration of excitation energy in the object plane. If there are no problems with respect to sufficient fluorescence intensity for measurement, the main criteria for selection of condensers or even objectives (as condensers) should be freedom from intrinsic fluorescence and sufficient optical quality for forming a sufficiently small image of the illumination field diaphragm in the object plane. Such condensers allow alternative (or even simultaneous) bright field or phase contrast observation (see below). If immersion condensers (for dark field or bright field excitation or illumination) are used, fluorescence-free immersion oil is always preferable.

Compared with normal fluorescence microscopes, a second illumination path for scanning the preparation and for adjusting and focusing the object to be measured in visible light outside of the spectral excitation range is necessary. The photodecomposition of fluorescing substances, which in most cases takes place during the first seconds of radiation, would not allow reproducible and comparable results of microfluorometric measurements if the scanning of the specimen and the focusing procedure of the object were done in fluorescent light. For this reason an easy and rapid conversion from normal illumination to fluorescence excitation is required (see Figs. 5 and 6).

The kind of microscopic observation in normal light made possible by the second illumination path depends on the optical properties of the object and on the available condensers and objectives as well. With a

FIG. 5. Illuminating part of a fluorescence microscope or microfluorometer. Alternative illumination by introducing the exciting beam from the side below the condenser.

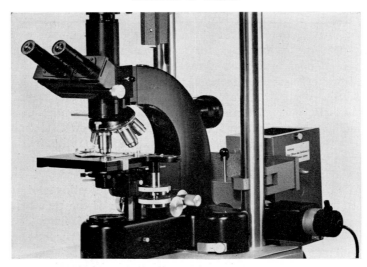

Fɪɢ. 6. Illuminating part of a fluorescence microscope or microfluorometer. Alternative illumination using the normal light path through the microscope base for both the exciting radiation and normal light.

dark field condenser, which creates the optimal conditions for fluorescence microscopy and microfluorometry, only dark field observation with its well known advantages and restrictions is possible. Even object structures with very small differences in refractive indexes as compared with the surrounding medium appear with relatively high contrast; however, the coordination of the fluorescing details with the object structures visible in dark field is sometimes more difficult as compared with bright field or phase contrast observation (see Figs. 7a–7d). Aside from this fact, a bright field condenser becomes necessary if in addition to the measurement of fluorescence intensity an extinction measurement of the same object is desired (for instance, at the spectral extinction maximum of a fluorescent stain in the blue range of the spectrum) (see Figs. 7b, 7d). A microfluorometer with an additional illuminating system for alternative measurements of extinction and fluorescence has been described recently by Prenna (6).

The fluorescence excitation of microscopic objects by incident light is used much less for transparent objects; however, it is the only possibility for fluorescence microscopy of opaque objects. The two different methods of illumination in incident light are demonstrated in Figs. 2a and 2b.

Dark field illumination from above through ring condensers (see Fig. 2a) offers principally the same improvement of contrast for microfluo-

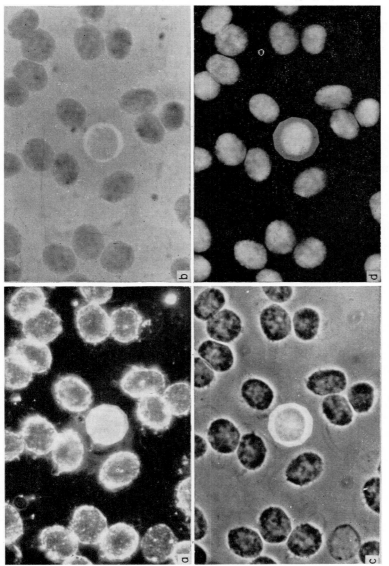

Fig. 7. Fluorochromed nuclei of salamander erythrocytes (preparation made by G. Prenna, Istituto Anatomia Comparata, University of Pavia, Italy). (a) With dark field illumination; (b) with bright field illumination at the spectral absorption peak of the fluorochrome; (c) in phase contrast; (d) in fluorescent light.

rometry as the transmitted dark field illumination. Compared with this type of illumination, however, suitable restriction of the illuminated area by a sufficiently small image of an illumination field diaphragm is not possible. The highest possible numerical aperture of the objective for incident dark field illumination is lower (~ 1.0) than for transmitted dark field illumination. Without these restrictions this type of incident illumination, together with transmitted phase contrast equipment, would give an almost ideal combination for the microfluorometry of transparent objects. But aside from the disadvantages already mentioned, phase contrast objectives with annular condensers for incident dark field illumination are not available on the market.

Good optical conditions for fluorescence excitation can also be obtained with vertical illuminators, used for microscopy of polished sections of metals, ores, and coal (see Fig. 2b). It is easy to understand that this type of fluorescence excitation is most advantageous with objectives of the highest numerical aperture. There is no higher concentration of light on a small object field than by an oil immersion objective with a numerical aperture of 1.3–1.4 and good spherical and chromatic correction. The loss of about 50% of the excitation energy by the semitransparent 45° mirror in the vertical illuminator (see Fig. 2b) is not as critical as it seems. The loss of 50% of the fluorescence intensity by the semitransparent mirror is not offset by the advantage of this system. These losses could be reduced by using 45° deflecting plates with coatings having high reflectance for the spectral excitation range and low reflectance and high transmittance for the fluorescence at longer wavelengths.

Aside from the previously mentioned reasons for the restriction of the illuminated area, the improvement of contrast by reducing the illuminated area in the object plane is especially noticeable.

The focal length for the wavelength range used for excitation and for observation in normal light should be the same or almost the same. Therefore, objectives with sufficient chromatic correction and, if possible, excitation in the blue range of the spectrum are preferred. The thickness of the objects, the fluorescence of which is to be measured quantitatively, should not exceed the focal depth of the objective by much.

The conditions for alternative bright field or phase contrast observation in transmitted light are almost ideal (see Fig. 4) (4). Phase rings in the rear focal plane of the objective cause a further, but negligible, loss of excitation energy.

Slides and cover glasses should, of course, be free from any fluorescence. As an embedding medium purified glycerin, which does not show any fluorescence, is recommended.

If the preparation also contains standards, for instance, bull sperms stained under exactly the same conditions with the same fluorochrome for the microfluorometric determination of DNA (see Ruch, this volume, p. 281), no changes in the excitation conditions in the object plane should occur when the preparation is moved between the two positions in which the fluorescence standards and the objects are located. Such a change in the excitation conditions could be caused by slightly inclined or wedge-shaped slides, if the excitation of fluorescence occurs in transmitted light. With respect to avoiding this error fluorescence excitation in incident light is superior: The focal depth of the objective for image formation also implies the reproducibility of the excitation conditions in the object plane during movement of the preparation with the microscope stage.

The decisive criterion for the selection of the most suitable objective is the highest possible brightness of the fluorescence image (with the lowest possible excitation energy concentration in the object). Since the intensity of fluorescence light from a single object detail picked up by the objective increases by the square of its numerical aperture, this optical property of the objective is the most important one. With very sensitive light-measuring devices now available the lower limit for the brightness of the fluorescing image would be given by the ability of the human eye to identify and focus fluorescing objects at very low light levels. Therefore, for microscopy of weakly fluorescing objects, generally objectives with the highest numerical aperture and the lowest magnification are preferred. For instance, by reducing the linear magnification factor by one half, the fluorescing object details covering 25% of the former area appear brighter by a factor of 4. For the same reason, the final magnification by the eyepiece in the observation tube should be kept as low as possible. In comparison with the brightness in binocular tubes a monocular tube can offer a gain of brightness by a factor of 3–5.

Barrier filters have to meet the same basic requirements as those used in fluorescence microscopy. The accurate measurement of fluorescence intensity with respect to completely blocking the excitation rays and carefully avoiding disturbing intrinsic fluorescence entails greater expense. Modern barrier filters are composed of different filters, including interference coatings on the lower side in order to reduce the spectral part of the excitation rays responsible for the fluorescence of the absorbing part of the barrier filter.

In contrast to extinction measurements of microscopic objects, for microfluorometric measurements the adjustment of the measured area to the area covered by the object itself in most cases is not as important, since the empty surrounding field included in the measured area hardly contributes to the measured light intensity. This advantage, which allows for the use of relatively large diameters of measured area compared with the diameter of the object, takes particular effect with irregularly shaped objects. Of course one should be able to restrict the measured area by variable measuring apertures of circular or rectangular shape if two or more objects are situated very near to each other or if the object detail to be measured is surrounded by other fluorescing parts of the object. For instance, a careful restriction of the measured area to the area of the measured object detail would be necessary if a nucleus stained with a fluorochrome for determination of DNA content (see methods described by Ruch) were surrounded by cytoplasm with relatively strong primary fluorescence.

The photometer attachment with variable and interchangeable measuring diaphragm, shown in Figs. 8 and 10 (Weber, *10*), meets these requirements and offers some additional advantages. The measuring diaphragm is illuminated from above via a swing-out mirror by an ad-

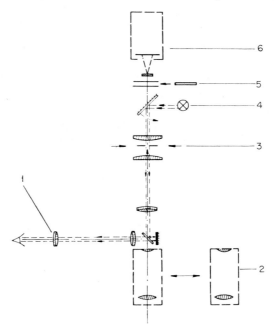

FIG. 8. Light path in the Leitz microphotometer attachment MPV with variable measuring diaphragm (after Weber, *10*). (1) Measuring field observation tube; (2) interchangeable Eyepieces; (3) variable and interchangeable measuring diaphragm; (4) low-voltage lamp and mirror for illumination of measuring aperture; (5) spectral filters; (6) photomultiplier.

ditional small light source and imaged into the monocular observation tube of the photometer attachment. In this way the image of the measuring aperture is superimposed on the microscopic image of the object and indicates exactly the measuring area. The object structure can be seen inside *and* outside the measured area. This is particularly advantageous for searching, focusing, and adjusting the objects to be measured with bright field or dark field illumination and with phase contrast, whereas for the measurement of fluorescence the illuminated field should be restricted to an area not much larger than the measured area. Figure 9 shows some fluorochromed nuclei with the image of the measur-

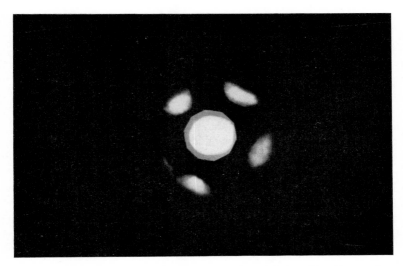

FIG. 9. The microscope image of fluorochromed nuclei (see Fig. 7) superimposed by the image of the measuring aperture. The illumination field diaphragm is partially opened.

ing aperture and of the partially opened illumination field diaphragm.

If a photometer attachment is used with an observation tube between measuring diaphragm and radiation receiver, the surrounding field is covered by the measuring diaphragm. In this case the binocular or monocular tube of the microscope should be used not only for scanning the preparation but also for focusing and adjustment of the selected object to the measured area, after the position of the measured area has been determined and marked by a special graticule used in the eyepiece of the microscope observation tube. Of course exact parfocality of the images in the measuring aperture and in the observation tube is necessary.

The most suitable position for spectral filters is between the observation tube of the photometer attachment and the radiation receiver (see Figs. 8, 11), permitting the observation of the object with unfiltered light. This possibility is especially valuable if the objects, for some reason, must be observed in fluorescent light provided that this would be possible without danger of photodecomposition. Spectral filters are required if the fluorescence intensity is measured in a restricted spectral range of the fluorescence emission. Owing to the necessary high transmittance, only interference filters with band widths that are not too narrow (~ 20 mμ) should be used (for instance, Interference Bandfilters AL or PAL of Schott, Mainz, Germany).

Interference wedge filters, which offer continuous variation of the transmission wavelength, already extend the application of microfluorometric equipment to microspectrofluorometry and consequently to all practical cases in which the measurement of the spectral intensity curve of the fluorescence becomes important. The preferable position for spectral filters between measuring diaphragm and radiation receiver is also suitable for interference wedges owing to the required small diameter of the beam passing through these filters.

For the reproducibility of microphotometric measurements the mode of illumination of the multiplier photocathode is no less important. Photocathodes of multipliers are usually not entirely homogeneous regarding the light sensitivity at different places on the photocathode. In order to attain independence of the illuminated area of the photocathode from the diameter of the measuring aperture and from the light distribution in the measured field, the exit pupil of the light path above the measuring aperture should be imaged onto the photocathode. If no light-scattering devices are used to spread the light on a large area of the photocathode, the small exit pupil should be imaged on the most sensitive spot of the photocathode by moving the multiplier perpendicular to the beam until the highest photocurrent is indicated by the measuring instrument.

Microfluorometric measurements generally require higher sensitivity of the photomultiplier equipment than normal microphotometric extinction measurements of the same measured area. This is particularly true if photodecomposition of the fluorescing substances is to be reduced as much as possible. Multiplier equipment, which is sufficient with respect to sensitivity and signal-to-noise ratio for the application of the plug method or the two-wavelength method in cytophotometry, is not necessarily sensitive enough for microfluorometric purposes. Light fluxes of 10^{-10} lumen should still effect full-scale deflections of the reading instrument; changes of more than $\pm 1\%$ should still be measurable.

The lower limit of optical signals, which can be detected by normal photomultiplier equipment without additional devices for improving the signal-to-noise ratio is given by the noise amplitude of the dark current of the multiplier. This noise amplitude is in the order of magnitude of 10^{-11} amp when, for instance, one of the widely distributed multiplier types RCA 1 P 21 and 1 P 28 is used. It is easy to understand that an optical signal causing a photocurrent of 10^{-11} amp or less is no longer detectable. Therefore the above-mentioned optical signal of 10^{-10} lumen should cause an electrical signal of roughly 100 times this noise level, which means a photocurrent of 10^{-9} amp. Whether this photocurrent is measured by a galvanometer with corresponding sensitivity or a less sensitive reading instrument after amplification is of secondary importance. In order to meet these requirements, multipliers should be

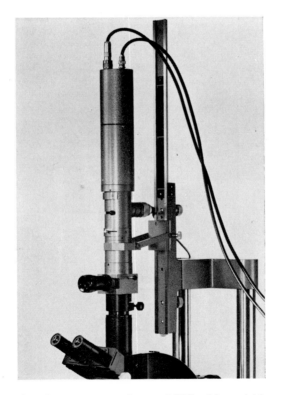

Fig. 10. Leitz microphotometer attachment MPV with variable measuring aperture and multiplier housing (Knott-Electronic, Munich) with EMI Multiplier 6094 A.

carefully selected, since the dark current and the sensitivity for different multipliers of the same type may vary over a range from 1 to 100.

Photomultipliers to satisfy particularly high demands with regard to gain of signal and signal-to-noise ratio are often many times as expensive. Figure 12 shows equipment for microfluorometry with a search unit containing the EMI Multiplier Number 6094 A (Electric and Musical Industries Ltd., England), and an ultrastabilized high-voltage supply (Fa. Knott-Electronic, Munich, Germany). In addition to the high sensitivity and extremely low dark current of the multiplier, the power pack offers long-range stability of the high-voltage supply, which permits longer measuring times.

The above-described basic instrumental requirements have been taken into consideration in the equipment schematically illustrated in Fig. 11

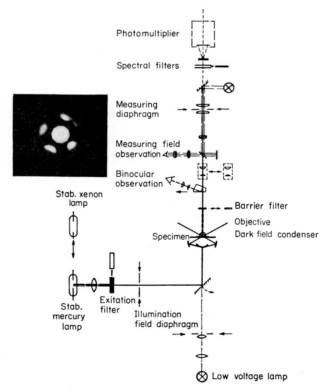

Fig. 11. Optical diagram of Leitz microphotometer MPV equipment for microfluorometry.

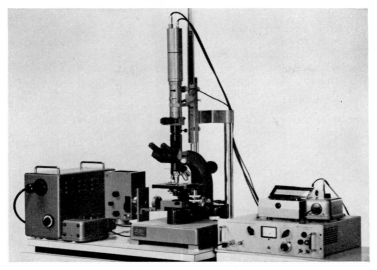

FIG. 12. Equipment for microfluorometry. Leitz Ortholux microscope equipped for fluorescence microscopy, microphotometer attachment MPE, and multiplier search unit with ultrastabilized high-voltage supply (Knott-Electronic, Munich).

and shown in Fig. 12. The building block system of this equipment permits easy and rapid replacement and addition of the different components allowing a versatile adjustment of the equipment to the different purposes of microfluorometry and related fields of application.

REFERENCES

1. Bosshardt, U., Fluoreszenzmikroskopische Messung des DNS-Gehaltes von Zellkernen. Z. Wiss. Mikroskopie Mikroskop. Tech. **65**, 391–408 (1964).
2. Chance, B., Kinetics of enzyme reactions within single cells. Ann. N.Y. Acad. Sci. **97**, Art. 2, 431–448 (1962).
3. Goldman, M., Instrumentation for microfluorometry of stained amoeba. Exptl. Parasitol. **9**, 25–36 (1960).
4. Grehn, J., and H. Kornmann, Kontrastfluoreszenz mit Opakilluminator. Leitz-Mitt. Wiss. Tech. **3**, No. 4, 108–111 (1965).
5. Ornstein, L., New horizons in fluorescence microscopy. J. Mt. Sinai Hosp., N.Y. **24**, No. 6 (1957).
6. Prenna, G., and U. A. Bianchi, Reazioni di Feulgen fluorescenti e loro possibilità citofluorometriche quantitative. 4. Studio del processo di fotodecomposizione e

confronto fra i dati di estinzione a 470 nm e i dati di emissione di fluorescenza nella reazione die Feulgen eseguita con Acriflavina-SO₂. *Riv. Istochim. Norm. Patol.* **10**, 645–666 (1964).

7. Prenna, G., and U. A. Bianchi, Reazioni di Feulgen fluorescenti e loro possibilità citofluorometriche quantitative. 5. Citofotometria quantitativa in fluorescenza ed in assorbimento della reazione di Feulgen con Acriflavina-SO₂. *Riv. Istochim. Norm. Patol.* **10**, 667–676 (1964).

8. Prenna, G., I fenomeni di fotoluminescenza in istochimica. Precisazioni sull'utilizzazione e prospettive di sviluppo. *Biol. Lat.* **17**, 423–452 (1964).

9. Ruch, F., and U. Bosshardt, Photometrische Bestimmung von Stoffmengen im Fluoreszenzmikroskop. *Z. Wiss. Mikroskopie Mikroskop. Tech.* **65**, 335–341 (1963).

10. Weber, K., Das neue Mikroskopphotometer MPV mit variabler Messblende. *Leitz-Mitt. Wiss. Tech.* **3**, No. 4, 103–107 (1965).

INSTRUMENTATION FOR RECORDING
MICROSPECTROPHOTOMETRY

Lothar Trapp

LABORATORY FOR MICROSCOPY, CARL ZEISS, OBERKOCHEN, GERMANY

From an historical point of view, microphotometry originated from UV microscopy. Around the turn of the century August Köhler, the father of the Köhler principle of illumination, built the first UV microscope at Carl Zeiss (10). He used magnesium sparks as a light source and monochromatically corrected quartz objectives. The light source and its current supply were not covered; radiation and chemical by-products were dissipated into the room during operation. It is surprising that working with such equipment was not more dangerous for the operator.

In 1904 Köhler published the first comprehensive paper on photomicrographic investigations in UV light (6). By means of diatoms he proved that resolution was increased when short wavelengths were used for imaging, but in addition he showed the specific UV absorption of cell structures in nonstained specimens. Köhler himself said the following: "An additional feature, which might possibly be even of more importance than this increase in resolution, is the fact that many specimens show varying transmission when exposed to short-wave ultraviolet light. These differences are analogous to those brought about by the large number of methods of staining used in microscopic techniques so far" (6).

About 30 years later Caspersson started his studies on the quantitative determination of nucleic acids in individual cells with the aid of a UV microscope designed by Köhler (2). At that time the light source of the UV microscope, a spark gap between rotary cadmium electrodes, was arranged inside a housing and was optically and acoustically shielded. Harmful vapors were evacuated through tubes (7, 10). Quartz monochromators for the 257 and 275 nm wavelengths were available.

For a number of years the Caspersson method was based on density measurements on UV photomicrographs. Later, photocells and, finally, photomultipliers were used for direct microphotometry (*3*). When, after 1945, Carl Zeiss was again in a position to consider the development of large-scale equipment, work was resumed in the field of ultraviolet microscopy and the development was begun on a modern, registering microphotometer, making use of the experience gained by Caspersson. The result of this work is the UMSP I (*11*) (Fig. 1).

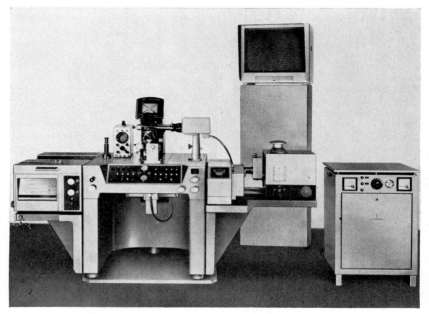

FIG. 1. Zeiss Universal Micro-Spectrophotometer UMSP I.

The principal requirements the instrument had to meet were the following:

(1) Suitability for any wavelength (not just single lines) in the visible spectral range, as well as in the ultraviolet portion that is of interest for biologists.

(2) The possibility of measuring minute specimens photometrically up to the resolving limit of a light microscope.

(3) Point measurement and recording of time curves, specimen curves, and wavelength curves.

(4) Automatic evaluation of specimen scanning.

(5) Convenient operation and the possibility of taking photomicrographs.

At first, development was governed by two problems: to find suitable optical components and to design an ultraprecision scanning stage.

It was necessary for the optics to match the image quality of systems already well known for the visible range and the excellent quartz monochromats in the ultraviolet region. The systems were to be corrected for the range from 240 to 700 nm. The optical components were to offer maximal resolution, that is, numerical apertures appreciably beyond 1.0. Finally, in practical use, they had to differ as little as possible from the standard optics in a microscope. Certain of these requirements—and especially all of them at the same time—seemed impractical using mirror systems. Similarly, experts from all over the world were agreed that a solution with lens systems was not possible either. Köhler reported about less satisfactory results obtained with quartz fluorite achromats (6). Foster and Thiel succeeded in applying the achromats only for a band width of about 10 mm (4).

The first part to be built was a universal objective 100/0.85 (glycerol immersion). Successful investigations were performed and the laboratory set-up fully came up to our expectations. Of course, a still higher numerical aperture was desired. A system of lower power, 32/0.40, as well as UV eyepieces, projectives, UV condensers, and illuminating lenses followed. The image field of these objectives is not flat. In this respect they correspond to our fluorite systems, the Neofluars. We called the objectives "Ultrafluars" and, consequently, any optical component of that degree of correction "Ultrafluar optics". Finally, an Ultrafluar 100/1.25 was added, thus making the optics for the UMSP complete. An Ultrafluar 10/0.20 was recently introduced which represents a dry system offering a long working distance. Table I illustrates the proper-

TABLE I

Zeiss Ultrafluars

Image scale	Numerical aperture	Type of system	Focal length (mm)	Free working distance (mm)	Mech. tube length (mm)	Thickness of quartz cover glass (mm)
10	0.20	Dry	16.4	7.4	160	0.35
32	0.40	Glycerol immersion	6.05	0.45	160	0.35
100	0.85	Glycerol immersion	1.79	0.10	160	0.35
100	1.25	Glycerol immersion	1.77	0.07	160	0.35

ties of the Ultrafluars. Their constructional shape and length, as well as mechanical tube length, correspond to that of our standard microscope optics. The objectives have been corrected for quartz cover glasses of 0.35 mm thickness. That thickness was used to insure that the expensive quartz glasses would not break too easily. They can be used also as specimen slides if the objective serves as condenser. The Ultrafluars are a completely novel type of objective of outstanding performance. Table II illustrates the progress made in the field of Zeiss microscopic optics since the time of Abbe.

TABLE II

Zeiss Microscope Optics

Optical system	Designed by	Available since	Spectral range	Field flatness
Achromat	Abbe	1872	>100 nm, visible	—
Apochromat	Abbe	1886	>200 nm, visible	—
Monochromat	v. Rohr	1904	<10 nm, UV	—
Homal	Boegehold	1923	—	(+)
Planachromat	Boegehold	1936	—	+
Ultrafluar	Habermann	1959	>400 nm, UV and visible	—

The UV condenser 0.8 with iris diaphragm has been computed as a dry system for quartz slides of 0.9 mm thickness. It is a well-known fact in microscopy that changing the specimen with the condenser immersed is rather troublesome.

It is not necessary to say much about the UV projectives. The projective K 10:1 UV has the form of a standard eyepiece and is used for taking photomicrographs on plates 4 × 5 inches; the projective K 3.2 UV is a negative system similar to the former Zeiss Homals and is used for taking photomicrographs on 35 mm film; the projective 100:1 UV is meant only for photometric measurements. All of these systems have been corrected for the ultraviolet and the visible spectral range.

The second problem was the ultraprecision scanning stage to be used for point measurements and automatic scanning of the specimen. Two requirements had to be met in this respect. In carrying out point measurements and displacing the specimen between measured spot and background, one has to relocate the measured spot with a reproducibility better than 0.1 μm. The specimen area to be scanned automatically should correspond to the size of standard cells. Also, it should be possible to rotate the stage in order to check the specimen with regard to dichroism.

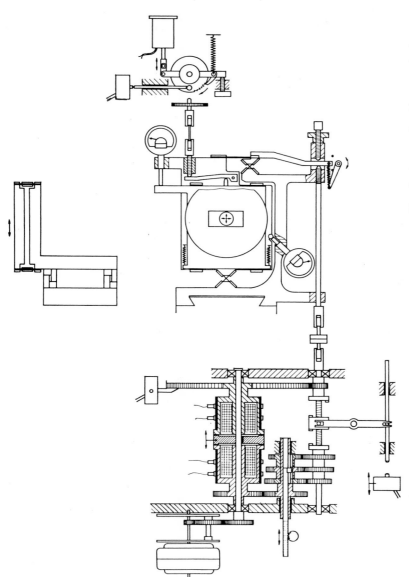

FIG. 2. Schematic diagram of the ultraprecision scanning stage. For further explanation see text.

Brösicke (1) found the following solution (Fig. 2): A lower stage plate is fixed to the clamping holder by means of spring joints. When this plate is moved the specimen follows a circular path which, however, can be considered a straight line over a distance of 500 μm. Another plate has been fastened to the lower plate by four vertically arranged flat springs. The specimen can be displaced at right angles to the previous linear movement over the range of motion of the latter plate, about 100 μm. There is no danger of affecting the state of focusing by this movement. A rotary plate, supported by ball bearings, is mounted on top.

We can now revert to the construction of the UMSP proper (Fig. 3).

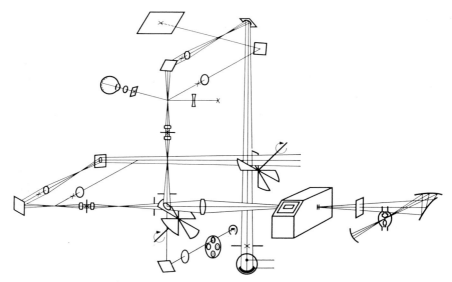

FIG. 3. Schematic diagram of the light path of the UMSP I.

An Osram xenon lamp XBO 450 W is used as the light source. Its radiant intensity is 100 to 1000 times greater than that of a hydrogen lamp (9). Hansen has carried out fundamental investigations on the question of energy in microphotometry (5). The housing of the xenon lamp is equipped with a two-mirror collector and an additional mirror behind the lamp. The radiation emitted by the lamp first passes a heat-protecting filter consisting of a cell filled with water and having quartz windows and a suspended glass filter. The quartz prism monochromator M 4 Q III is arranged behind this heat-protecting filter.

The design of this instrument is based on the two-beam method, using one detector. The diagram of the ray path shows only single lenses, but the UMSP really contains corrected lens systems. The light is divided into two beams, that is, a measuring and a comparison beam, and successively transferred to the detector by two interrupting mirror disks which rotate synchronously. Each of the two light paths contains a field stop and a complete microscopic system. Small circular field stops of different size are available for the measurement, and a field iris diaphragm is used for observation and photomicrography.

The next item arranged in the light path is the microscope condenser; then come the specimen, the objective, and the projective, the latter being placed between two deflecting mirrors. The measured area is limited for both light paths in front of the photomultiplier by one of the measuring diaphragms graded in a geometrical progression. Above the measuring objective the light can be directed undivided in different directions by displacing prisms. The light can follow several possible courses:

(1) It may be sent for observation to either the monocular or the binocular tube. In the course of this procedure ultraviolet microscopic images are rendered visible by forming an intermediate image on a reticle made of fluorescing uranium glass.

(2) As mentioned previously, the light can be directed to the photomultiplier for measurement.

(3) Another possibility is to direct it to the built-in camera with a fixed length for taking photomicrographs on plates (4×5 inches).

(4) In addition, the light can be passed on to an adapter to which a miniature camera, an electronic image converter, or an industrial television set can be connected.

For observation in the visible spectral range, especially for working in phase contrast, an incandescent lamp has been provided in addition to the monochromatic light source.

With respect to the mechanical construction of the equipment, it was not found advisable to use as a basis existing microscope models or components forming part of our production range—except for the monochromator—but instead a special instrument was designed in view of the importance and requirements of the technique. However, for those parts for which special needs might arise, flexibility of the basic arrangement was provided to afford accommodation to these needs.

The central part of the equipment includes the microscopes for the measuring and comparison beams, the radiant field stops, as well as the measuring and phase-contrast diaphragms, the driving and logic elements of the measuring program, the camera for 4×5 inch plates, and the central control desks. The monochromator and the xenon lamp are arranged on a support on the right-hand side, whereas the recorder and, behind it, the signal-processing amplifier and a separate control desk are mounted on the left-hand support. Plesse has reported on the set-up of the electronics concerned (8). A basic principle in the construction of the complete instrument was easy access of any control element from the operating position.

The UMSP permits the following measuring procedures when the recorder is used:

(1) Specimen location and wavelength may remain unchanged during the measurement while only the recorder moves and continuously records the transmission of the specimen concerned; this procedure enables the recording of possible changes in the transmission of the specimen.

(2) The specimen may remain stationary during the measurement, while the wavelength drive of the monochromator moves synchronously with the recorder. This method is identical with the one used for macroscopically recording spectrophotometers. The transmission curve plotted during the measurement is an indication of the chemical properties of the substance measured.

(3) The specimen may be moved during the measurement, but the wavelength remains unchanged. This is the well-known scanning procedure that permits quantitative determinations when inhomogeneous material is being tested. In this case the UMSP plots two curves, the transmission curve referred to above—now as a function of the specimen location—and, in addition, an evaluation curve which indicates the integral of total absorbance. This value is proportional to the amount of substance in the light path during the scanning period.

Sixty years have passed from the first attempts at ultraviolet microscopy until today, and this review has revealed an obvious discrepancy: during the first 30 years experts took little interest in the instrument and as late as 1933 Köhler openly expressed his disappointment (7). Up to that date the design was changed and improved only slightly. Thanks to the impetus given by Caspersson, however, the situation has changed completely. Further development of the equipment and of the methods has greatly advanced and now, 30 years later, there is nothing in the UMSP that resembles the former ultraviolet microscope.

REFERENCES

1. Brösicke, P., Cross-slide table for microscopes. U.S. Patent 3,044,354 (1962).
2. Caspersson, T., Über den chemischen Aufbau der Strukturen des Zellkerns. *Skand. Arch. Physiol.* Suppl. 8, 1–151 (1936).

3. Caspersson, T., G. Lomakka, G. Svensson, and R. Säftström, A versatile ultra-microspectrograph for multiple-line and surface scanning high resolution measurements employing automatized data analysis. *Exptl. Cell Res.* Suppl. 3, 40–51 (1955).

4. Foster, L. V., and E. M. Thiel, An achromatic ultraviolet microscope objective. *J. Opt. Soc. Am.* 38, 689–692 (1948).

5. Hansen, G., Energetische Grenzen der Mikro-Spektralphotometrie. *Zeiss-Mitt.* 2, 117-124 (1961).

6. Köhler, A., Mikrophotographische Untersuchungen mit ultraviolettem Licht. *Z. Wiss. Mikroskopie* 21, 129–165 and 273–304 (1904).

7. Köhler, A., Einige Neuerungen auf dem Gebiet der Mikrophotographie mit ultraviolettem Licht. *Naturwiss.* 21, 165–173 (1933).

8. Plesse, H., Die Elektronik in optischen Instrumenten. *Zeiss-Werkzeitschr.* 41, 51–56 (1961).

9. Reule, A., Strahlungsmessungen an einer Wasserstoff- und einer Xenonlampe. *Zeiss-Mitt.* 2, 355–371 (1962).

10. Zeiss, C., Mikrophotographische Einrichtungen für ultraviolettes Licht. *Druckschr. Mikro* 530 (1937).

11. Zeiss, C., *Universal Micro-Spectrophotometer* UMSP I, Pamphlet No. 40-811/I-e (1964).

INSTRUMENTS AND TECHNIQUES
IN MICRODENSITOMETRY

Abraham Bloom

NATIONAL INSTRUMENTS LABORATORY,
ROCKVILLE, MARYLAND

In this paper two different instruments are described, each of which is somewhat differently designed to make quantitative analyses of light absorption either directly through specimens, or by photographic plates or negatives. The general term to cover this type of analysis is densitometry. The instruments to be discussed are microdensitometers, which are capable of studying areas or specimens of microscopic size. This is accomplished by adding to the instruments a microscope through which the specimen is viewed and measured.

Before proceeding further let us make clear what is meant by the term optical density and explain the reasons that this characteristic is so important in such a wide variety of applications and particularly in fields related to cytology. This is the same characteristic that has been called, in some of the other chapters of this volume, by such names as extinction and absorbance. If one considers a beam of light that passes through an absorbing material, and measures the intensity entering and the intensity leaving, the logarithm of the ratio of input intensity to output intensity is the optical density. For example, if the input is 10 times the output, the optical density is 1.0. If the input is 100 times the output, the optical density is 2.0, and so on.

One might ask the reason for using the logarithm of the ratio rather than the ratio itself. Owing to Beer's law, the concentration of an absorbing material dispersed in an otherwise transparent medium is proportional to the optical density as defined above. It is therefore possible to obtain quantitative measures of the amount of an absorbing material by making measurements of optical density.

The first instrument under discussion is the Joyce Loebl Microdensitometer. This instrument was originally developed by Dr. P. M. B. Walker

(3) then working in the Biophysics Research Unit of the British Medical Research Council at King's College. Its function is to scan a specimen along a preselected line and to plot the variations of optical density of the specimen along that line. (See Fig. 1.)

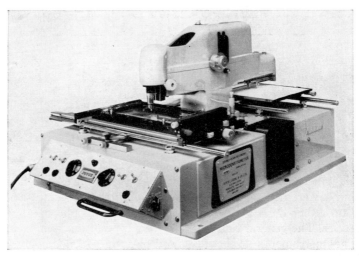

FIG. 1. The Joyce Loebl microdensitometer.

The specimen table moving along the guide rods is linked by a pantograph arrangement to the recording table in the rear. Lever ratios as high as 1000 : 1 are available. Since a recording sheet has 250 mm of useful recording length, specimens ¼ mm in length can be expanded over the whole sheet using the 1000 : 1 ratio arm. Standard ratios available are 1 : 1, 2 : 1, 5 : 1, 10, 20, and 50 : 1. This arrangement, where the recording table and the specimen table are directly linked, is an extremely useful feature because it allows precise measurements of distance on the specimen to be made between any points of interest on the optical density trace produced.

The main part of the instrument is the optical density wedge which is manufactured with a linear variation of optical density from zero to some maximum value. Wedges with ranges to 0.5, 1.0, 2.0, and 3.0 optical density are available as standard (0–4.0 wedges can be made on special order). The instrument splits a single light source into two beams, one passing through the specimen and one through the reference wedge just described. A photomultiplier observes the two beams alternately and if there is any difference in intensity between the two, it signals a servo system to move the reference wedge until its optical density matches that of the specimen. The recording pen that is attached to the reference wedge records the motion of the wedge on the recording sheet. Since this happens continuously as the specimen is scanned, a plot of the optical density variations is obtained.

Figure 2 is a trace through the head of a ram sperm. One picture was taken with a phase contrast microscope, the other with an interference

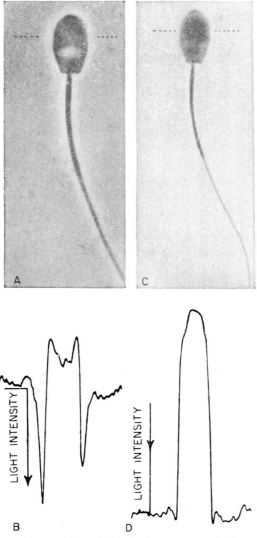

FIG. 2. Densitrometric trace through head of ram sperm. A: Ram sperm by phase contrast. 2300×. B: Microphotometer record of distribution of light intensity along line in A. C: Ram sperm by interference contrast. 2300×. D: Microphotometer trace of distribution of light intensity along line in C. Unlike phase contrast, interference contrast correctly depicts variations in optical path.

microscope. Note how the microdensitometer trace reproduces the halo effect on the phase contrast microscope, as well as the dip in the center which is not shown with the interference microscope.

Figure 3 is a trace through a muscle fibril showing the optical density variations along the length of the fibril.

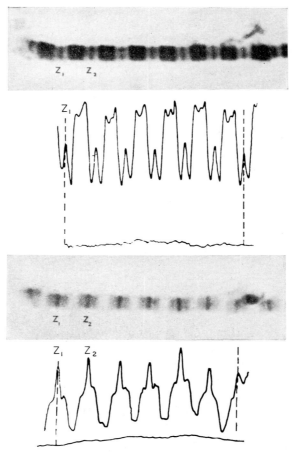

Fig. 3. Densitrometric trace through muscle fibril.

In many applications, a typical example being the study of the structure of complex molecules like DNA by X-ray diffraction, it is necessary to feed the information from the curves into a computer for processing. Computer attachments have been developed which can place the optical density information, as well as the position on the specimen, directly on punched cards, paper tape, or magnetic tape. Where simpler problems are involved, an integrator attachment is available which enables the operator to get direct integration of the area under any curve in the record.

A great deal of interest has been shown in the past year in two other attachments for this instrument. One is an automatic interval stepper unit which can be programmed so that after the completion of a scan of the specimen along a given line, the specimen table is made to index and begin another scan along an adjacent parallel line. After completion of a whole set of scans of the entire specimen the instrument automatically shuts off. An attachment to give isodensity profiles of the specimen works in conjunction with the stepper attachment to scan the entire specimen and to plot the variations in optical density in such a manner as to make it a simple procedure to draw isodensity profiles of the specimen.

Figure 4 shows an isodensity plot which is typical of the kind of pat-

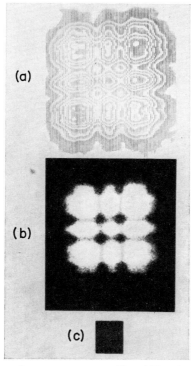

FIG. 4. Isodensity plot of square aperture. The diffraction pattern of the square aperture has been photographed slightly out of focus. The width of the original negative image is ½ mm, and the slit size is 10 μ × 10 μ. Note smearing of the grain in the microdensitometer plot. (Increasing film density is blank—dots–dash in this presentation.) See text for explanation of (a), (b), and (c).

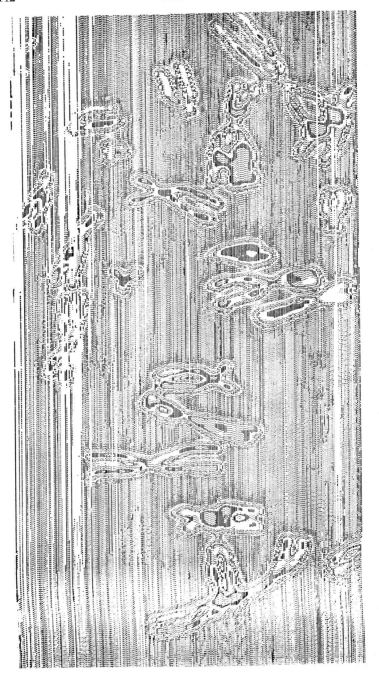

Fig. 5. Isodensity plot of chromosomes.

tern obtained with this attachment. The pattern (a) was obtained by scanning (c) and shows the diffraction pattern of a square aperture, so tiny on the original 35-mm frame that an arrow is required to show its position. Figure 4b is a photographic enlargement of 4c.

In Fig. 5 one sees an isodensity plot of a number of chromosomes. Note the variations in size and shape, and the definite internal structure that is visible. Next (Fig. 6), we take one of the chromosomes and scan it

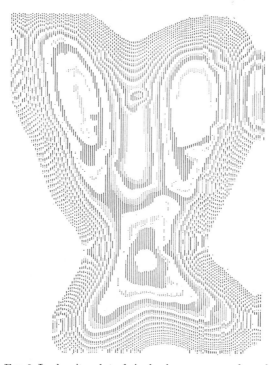

Fig. 6. Isodensity plot of single chromosome enlarged.

alone, simultaneously increasing the magnification. Notice the sharp delineation of structure and the possibilities inherent in this type of plot to produce a maximum of useful information.

The second instrument, the Barr & Stroud Integrating Microdensitometer, was developed by Dr. E. M. Deeley (1) of the Wheatstone Physics Laboratory, King's College, and a paper describing its theory and operation was first published in the *British Journal of Scientific Instruments* in July 1955.

This microdensitometer is designed to solve a different kind of problem. Suppose that one wishes to determine the total quantity of an absorbing material present in a particular specimen. We saw previously that the concentration of absorbing material is proportional to the optical density of the absorber. The concentration times the volume will give the total amount of this material. But this simple relation can be used only if the optical density is uniformly distributed through the specimen. The problems of nonuniform distribution have been thoroughly covered in this volume (see Garcia and Iorio, Hale, and Mendelsohn). If the distribution is nonuniform, it is necessary to break up the specimen into smaller pieces having essentially uniform optical density, and then to add up all the information obtained in this manner. This process is what mathematicians call integration and for this reason the instrument is called an integrating microdensitometer. (See Fig. 7.)

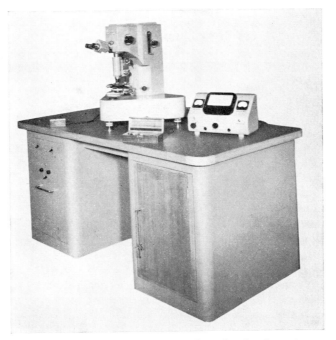

Fig. 7. The Barr & Stroud integrating microdensitometer.

A tungsten lamp is used as a light source, and the beam passes through a graded spectrum filter which allows the selection of any wavelength from 4000 to 7000 Å. The light then passes through the specimen, which is mounted on a regular microscope stage. An optical system attached to the microscope projects an enlarged image (up to 1000 times) in the plane of a mechanical scanning system. The function of the scanner is to serially scan the specimen image and to allow light to pass to the photo-multiplier in small amounts. It has been pointed out that the graded spectrum filter has a broad band width. If narrower band widths are required, the graded spectrum filter has a position for white light to pass directly through. A sharper filter can then be placed in a filter holder provided under the condenser.

The electronic circuits, housed in the left-hand drawer of the console, take the signal from the photomultiplier tube, compute the optical density from it, and store this in an integrating circuit which proceeds to add up the total of all the bits as they are scanned.

In using the instrument, one first finds a clear area around the specimen and scans this. This reading, presented on a large meter, can be adjusted to approximately zero by using a variable neutral density filter in series with the beam, allowing more and more light through, until the integrated reading is zero. The area to be scanned is then moved into view and its integrated reading obtained. The difference between the two readings is a measure of the quantity of absorbing matter in the specimen.

This procedure is in some ways similar to that used in operating a spectrophotometer, where first a reference is used and then the sample to be measured. There are other similarities, too. The instrument incorpo-rates the equivalent of a monochromator, and because it can be set up to make simple optical density measurements without scanning or inte-grating, it can be used as a microspectrophotometer.

As an illustration of the work that has been done with the Barr & Stroud, we can report on two applications at the National Institute of Health in Bethesda, Maryland. (2, 4). First, results of the work done in the Ophthalmology Branch were published as a paper titled Influence of Myleran on Cell Proliferation (4). Myleran is a drug used in the treat-

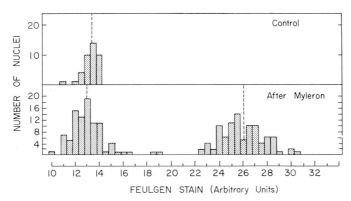

Fig. 8. DNA content of epithelial cells.

ment of leukemia, and in some cases has been found to cause cataracts of the eye as a side effect. In order to study the mechanism of the action of this drug, Myleran was administered to a group of rats, while another group was kept as controls. After a period, the animals treated with Myleran showed the formation of giant cells not present in the untreated animals. Figure 8 shows the results of measurements made on the DNA content of the epithelium cells, using the Barr & Stroud Microdensitometer. Note how clear the results are: the control group shows a distribution peaked at 12.9, while those treated with the drug have two peaks, one at 12.9, the other at 26. These results give strong evidence that Myleran allows the cell process to proceed to the point of doubling its chromosome content, but inhibits the final division into two cells, so that giant cells with double DNA content are produced.

The second application is the work done in Dr. George G. Glenner's laboratory at the National Institutes of Health (2). For a long time there has been disagreement between the biochemists and the histochemists regarding the action of certain enzymes. The biochemists have isolated enzymes from tissue and have determined the behavior of the enzymes outside the body. Tests then made by histochemists to check the behavior of these enzymes in tissue have not given the same results. Working on the theory that the enzymes bound in the tissue might be

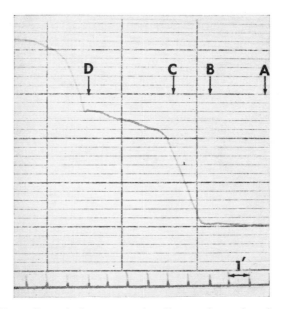

FIG. 9. Record of enzyme action. See text for explanation.

different from the ones studied by the biochemists, that is, that the latter are only those which can be most easily freed from the tissues, Dr. Glenner's group (2) succeeded in isolating some of the bound enzymes and determined their chemical activity. It was found that certain substances would inhibit the activity of the enzyme while others could make it recover that activity. The final test was to make a study of the enzyme in the tissue and show how it reacted to the same inhibiting and activating agents.

For this test the Barr & Stroud was set up to act as a microspectrophotometer, as mentioned earlier. No integration was used, but the total absorbance of the material inside the tissue was observed. A recorder was connected to the meter readout so that a record could be made, and changes over a period of time observed. A special device had to be fitted to the microscope stage so that the specimen could be kept at constant temperature and subjected to various agents as required. Figure 9 shows the results of the tests. Time proceeds here from right to left. The region from A to B represents washout and temperature equilibration. No change in optical density of the sample occurs during this period. At B, substrate is added, which in effect reacts with the enzyme and dyes the tissue. We note that from B to C an increase in optical density takes place. At C inhibitor is added. Note the slowing down of the enzyme activity. At D an activating agent, in this case cobalt, is added. Note the sharp rise in activity that takes place. Here the microdensitometer functioned in a rather unconventional way, and in effect was used not only as a microspectrophotometer but as a kinetic reaction monitor.

REFERENCES

1. E. M. Deeley, An integrating microdensitometer for biological cells. *J. Sci. Instr.* **32,** 263 (1955).
2. Felgenhauer, K. and G. G. Glenner, Quantitation of tissue-bond renal aminopeptitase by a microdensitometric technique. *J. Histochem. Cytochem.* **14** (1), 53 (1966).
3. Walker, P. M. B., and H. B. Yates, *Proc. Roy. Soc.* **B140,** 274 (1952).
4. Influence of Myleran on cell proliferation. *Invest. Ophthalmol.* **3** (1964).

Part III

METHODS FOR THE QUANTITATIVE ASSAY OF PROTEINS, POLYSACCHARIDES, AND LIPIDS

CYTOPHOTOMETRY OF PROTEINS

Arline D. Deitch*

DEPARTMENT OF MICROBIOLOGY, COLUMBIA UNIVERSITY, NEW YORK, NEW YORK

I. Introduction

The principal procedures that have been used for the quantitative cytophotometric estimation of cellular proteins are, first, the specific color reactions for amino acid residues such as the Millon reaction for tyrosine and the Sakaguchi reaction for arginine; second, acid dye binding to the basic amino acids, lysine, arginine, and histidine; and, third, a group of procedures for the detection of proteins of high isoelectric point, the histones and protamines. This review will consider each of these procedures in turn.

II. The Millon Reaction

The Millon reaction is one of the oldest protein spot tests, and it has been used fairly frequently in cytophotometric studies (1, 6, 8, 20, 33, 38, 53, 54, 56, 57, 76, 77). In this procedure, nitrous acid and mercuric ions attack tyrosine and tryptophan residues to form nitrosomercurial derivatives of these amino acids. Both tyrosine and tryptophan give compounds with this procedure that absorb ultraviolet light, but only tyrosine gives a colored reaction product with a maximal absorption at 500 mμ. It is this absorption of visible light that has usually been measured, and the Millon reaction is therefore generally considered to be a specific procedure for estimating tyrosine residues. The amount of Millon-revealed tyrosine has been used as a rough measure of the amount of cellular protein.

The early Millon procedures were carried out in strongly acidic mixtures containing sulfuric acid and mercuric sulfate. Histones are known

* Supported by Grant No. AI-05708-VR, National Institutes of Health, U.S. Public Health Service, Bethesda, Maryland.

451

to be soluble in this reagent (*46*) and to be extractable from tissue by mineral acids (*15, 47*). A Millon procedure using sulfuric acid would, therefore, measure only non-histone protein. Trichloracetic acid (TCA), on the other hand, is believed to precipitate histones and prevent their extraction from fixed tissue. Pollister and Ris therefore proposed a Millon reagent in which sulfuric acid is replaced by trichloracetic acid to measure total nuclear proteins, that is, both histone and non-histone protein (*53*). These authors further proposed that the sulfuric acid Millon be used after hot trichloracetic acid extraction of nucleic acids (*61*) to measure non-histone protein. They used both the total protein and non-histone protein procedures to study the nature of the nucleolar proteins of maize (Fig. 1). Since the same range and distribution of extinction

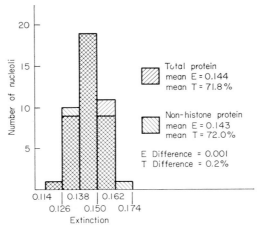

Fɪɢ. 1. Superimposed histograms of extinction values of two equal samples (40 cells) of sections of nucleoli of pollen mother cells of maize. The thickness of each nucleolus was measured, and the extinction values were corrected to a common thickness of 3 μ. Thus the extinction differences are presumably due only to variations in the amount of protein. The double-hatched blocks are regions of overlap of the histograms for total protein and for protein treated with sulfuric acid–divalent mercury reagent. Susa fixative. From Pollister and Ris (*53*).

values (that is, absorbance) were found using both procedures, it was concluded that the nucleolar protein was chiefly non-histone in nature. If histone had been a major component, it would have been extracted, resulting in lower extinction values after the sulfuric acid Millon procedure as compared with the TCA-Millon techniques.

Rasch and Swift made an intensive study of the Millon reaction and correlated the natural absorption of proteins at 280 mμ (due to tyrosine and tryptophan residues) with the amount of Millon chromophore obtained in various cell types and in model proteins. They concluded that it is not possible to achieve an accurate calibration of the Millon reaction in this way owing to several variables affecting both the ultraviolet absorption of proteins and the Millon chromophore. They noted the existence of several competitive reactions occurring during the course of the Millon reaction, such as oxidative degradation of tyrosine and the production of nitroso and diazo compounds. In general, however, a fair correlation was found between ultraviolet absorption and formation of the Millon chromophore (Fig. 2). In more recent years the Millon reaction

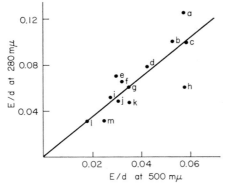

FIG. 2. Correlation between natural ultraviolet absorption of proteins and intensity of the Millon reaction. (a) *Triturus* (newt) liver nucleus, fixed in 1 : 3 acetic acid–absolute ethanol. (b) Mouse skeletal muscle, fixed in 10% neutral formalin. (c) White human hair, unfixed. (d) Mouse smooth muscle (small intestine), fixed in acetic–alcohol. (e) *Spisula* oocyte cytoplasm, fixed in acetic–alcohol. (f) *Triturus* liver cytoplasm, fixed in acetic–alcohol. (g) Lily tapetal nucleus, fixed in acetic–alcohol. (h) Silk thread, unfixed. (i) Lily tapetal cytoplasm, fixed in acetic–alcohol. (j) Egg albumin, heat denatured and subsequently fixed in 10% neutral formalin. (k) Onion root nucleus fixed in acetic–alcohol. (l) Egg albumin, heat denatured and subsequently fixed in acetic–alcohol. (m) Egg albumin, fixed in acetic–alcohol.

Natural protein absorption at 280 mμ is expressed as E/d, where d is section thickness in microns. Specimens were mounted in glycerine–chloral hydrate or glycerine–zinc chloride mixtures to minimize nonspecific light loss due to scatter. In tissue sections, interfering absorption due to nucleic acids was removed by treating preparations with ribonuclease (points e,f,i), deoxyribonuclease and ribonuclease (points a and g), or by extraction in hot 5% trichloracetic acid (point k). Millon intensity at 500 mμ is also expressed as extinction per micron section thickness (E/d). Preparations were mounted in oil of proper refractive index and corrected for diazo absorption where appropriate. Section thickness was determined directly at a magnification of 1400× on section folds adjacent to measured areas.

The line drawn represents the linear regression of ultraviolet measurements on Millon measurements. The sample standard error of ultraviolet data, estimated from Millon data, is 0.0052 E/d units. Since the average value of ultraviolet measurements is 0.0671 E/d units, there is a 7.7% standard error implied for estimates of protein by the Millon reaction as used here. From Rasch and Swift (57).

has fallen into some disuse, probably because of the relatively low absorbance of its chromophore, the inaccuracies of its stoichiometry as discussed by Rasch and Swift, and also because of the advent of the interference microscope which provides an alternative procedure for estimation of total protein mass.

III. The Sakaguchi Reaction

The Sakaguchi reaction is a highly specific colorimetric procedure for arginine in which α-naphthol (58) or hydroxyquinoline (59) is coupled with a hypohalite [either hypochlorite (58) or hypobromite (74)] to the guanidyl group of arginine in the presence of a high concentration of an alkali. The colored product is supposed to be a quinoneimine (12). In earlier histochemical procedures (9, 10, 22, 62, 69, 73), the alkali used was sodium or potassium hydroxide and the reaction was very destructive to tissue sections. Perhaps for this reason and because of the relatively low intensity of its colored product it has been used fairly infrequently in microspectrophotometric studies (19, 33, 36, 39, 40, 41, 56). McLeish et al. (39) substituted 2,4-dichloro-α-naphthol for α-naphthol in the reagent mixture and achieved a more intense red color. In order to prevent the reaction product from fading, they found it necessary to mount their

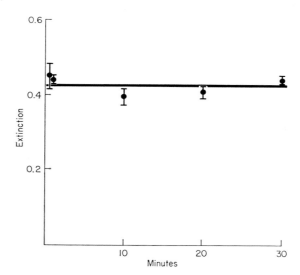

Fig. 3. Effect of length of time in the Sakaguchi reagent on the intensity of color produced in the cytoplasm of megakaryocytes found in sections of newborn rat liver fixed in acetic–alcohol. From Deitch (28).

preparations without dehydration in a mixture of glycerol and sodium hydroxide. The two cell types studied by them were observed to exhibit unequal fading within the first few days after preparation of the slides.

This writer (28) undertook a study of the Sakaguchi reaction using 2,4-dichloro-α-naphthol, but substituting barium hydroxide for sodium hydroxide as the alkali. Even saturated solutions of barium hydroxide do not destroy tissue structure, nor does this alkaline treatment cause the loss of sections from slides, which commonly occurs when either sodium or potassium hydroxide is used in histochemical procedures (52). It proved possible with a modified Sakaguchi reagent (28) to achieve intensely colored preparations which stain rapidly in the reagent to an end point (Fig. 3). By adding a tertiary amine (tri-N-butylamine) to the dehydrating and mounting media, preparations were obtained which did not fade (Fig. 4) and in which one could match the tissue index of refraction to prevent nonspecific light losses in cytophotometric measurements. As a check on the stoichiometry of the reaction, cytophotometric measurements were carried out on two cell types for which chemical measurements of amounts of arginine are available (70). Good agreement was obtained between the ratio of amounts of arginine for bull sperm and for trout sperm as determined cytophotometrically and chemically (Table I).

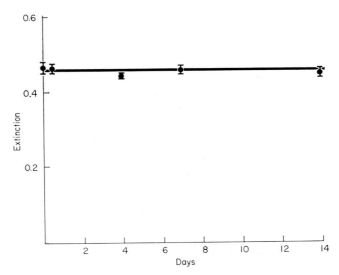

FIG. 4. Check on the fading of a Sakaguchi-stained slide. Intensities of megakaryocyte cytoplasm measured on one slide and remeasured at various times after the reaction. From Deitch (28).

TABLE I

MICROSPECTROPHOTOMETRIC ESTIMATION OF THE AMOUNT
OF ARGININE IN SPERM BY THE SAKAGUCHI REACTION[a]

	Amount per cell (in arbitrary units)
Bull sperm	4.99 ± 0.07
Trout sperm (*Salmo faria*)	3.71 ± 0.04
$\dfrac{\text{Arginine per bull sperm}}{\text{Arginine per trout sperm}}$	1.35
Ratio from Vendrely and Vendrely (70) by chemical Sakaguchi procedure.	1.44

[a] From Deitch (*28*).

IV. Acid Dye Binding

The predominant mechanism of staining proteins by acid dyes is electrostatic bonding of the dye anions to the available cationic groups of proteins (*23, 27, 32, 42*). The latter are the ε-amino groups of lysine and hydroxylysine, the guanidyl groups of arginine, the imidazole groups of histidine, and the relatively infrequent free terminal α-amino groups. The extent to which an anionic dye will bind to these cationic groups is limited by a number of factors, including the pH of the staining solution, the concentration of the dye and its affinity for protein, the effect of the fixative, the availability of the protein basic groups to the dye, the nature of the solvent ions, and the ionic strength of the staining solution (*63*).

In a cytophotometric study of acid dye binding (*27*), the following conditions were postulated as necessary to achieve stoichiometric staining of protein:

(1) The dye chosen must have strong affinity for the protein basic groups.

(2) The dye concentration should be high.

(3) The pH of staining should be sufficiently acid to prevent inhibition of dye binding by carboxyl ion competition and to allow maximal dissociation of the dibasic amino acid residues.

(4) The dye solvent should be of low ionic strength in order to prevent competition of solvent ions at the protein binding sites, but it should have some buffering capacity.

(5) The dye molecule should be small for ready diffusibility and for close approach to the binding sites within the protein molecule.

The dye chosen for study was naphthol yellow S, the dipotassium salt of flavianic acid (I).

(I)

This dye has a long history of use in the precipitation and estimation of the basic amino acids, for which it has strong affinity (*37, 64, 65, 71, 72*). A further factor influencing the choice of this yellow dye for cytophotometric investigations was the desire to use it as a counterstain to the Feulgen reaction in order to permit estimation of both protein and DNA in the same nuclei. The absorption curves of the Feulgen and flavianic acid chromophores are sufficiently separated so that there is usually no overlap at their absorption maxima (Fig. 5).

Dye binding with naphthol yellow S was found to reach a maximum largely independent of dye concentration and staining time. Hydrolysis in 1 N HCl for the Feulgen reaction causes about a 10% decrease of naphthol yellow S staining, probably as a result of extraction of some histone during the acid hydrolysis, while DNase or hot trichloracetic acid pretreatment on the other hand causes a 20–30% increase in dye binding, indicating that DNA may mask some of the protein basic groups and prevent them from staining (Table II). A mild acetylation procedure,

TABLE II

Effect of Removing Nucleic Acid on Naphthol
Yellow S Staining of Salamander
(*Triturus viredescens*) Liver Nuclei[a]

Pretreatment	Extinction
None	0.998 ± .031
Feulgen nucleal reaction	0.923 ± .028
1 N HCl at 60°C for 8 minutes	0.879 ± .023
Ribonuclease	0.992 ± .058
Deoxyribonuclease	1.247 ± .058
RNase and DNase	1.289 ± .039
Hot trichloracetic acid	1.171 ± .046

[a] Each figure represents the mean of 15 extinction measurements at 435 mμ. From Deitch (*27*).

having amino groups as its primary site of attack (*51*), reduces flavianic acid binding to albumin and casein models by about 45% and 60% respectively (*27*). This percentage reduction in staining is approximately

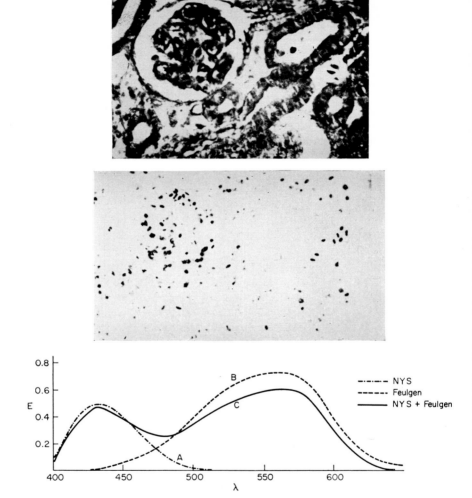

FIG. 5. Carnoy-fixed salamander (*Necturus*) kidney section stained with a Feulgen-naphthol yellow S procedure and photographed with violet light (top) and green light (middle) to show the distribution of protein and DNA as revealed by this double staining procedure.

Bottom: (A) Absorption curve of salamander liver cytoplasm stained with the naphthol yellow S procedure. (B) Absorption curve of salamander liver nucleus stained with the Feulgen reaction. (C) Absorption curve of salamander liver nucleus stained with the Feulgen reaction and counterstained with the naphthol yellow S procedure. From Deitch (*27*).

proportional to the lysine fraction of the total dibasic amino acids (that is, lysine to lysine + arginine + histidine residues) of these purified proteins (24). This was taken as evidence that mild acetylation blocks lysine basic groups and that the dye binds stoichiometrically to the dibasic amino acid residues of proteins (27). Naphthol yellow S has been used fairly frequently in various cytophotometric studies (27, 30, 33, 34, 43, 44, 75–77).

Recently this writer and J. Y. Terner returned to an exploration of acid dye binding and protein blocking and unmasking procedures (30, 68). These studies were aided by the development of a reproducible protein model of known amino acid content. The model protein system consisted of paraffin sections of heat-coagulated, Carnoy-fixed egg albumin, cut at constant microtome speed. An amino acid analysis of an aliquot of this protein is shown in Table III.

TABLE III

BASIC AMINO ACID COMPOSITION OF OVALBUMIN[a]

	Moles	Total (%)
Lysine	0.252	49.4
Arginine	0.178	34.9
Histidine	0.080	15.7
Total	0.510	100

[a] The protein sample used was a 2× recrystallized sample from Nutritional Biochemical Co. A short column amino acid analysis was performed on a Technicon Autoanalyzer. No hydroxylysine was found.

Staining of the albumin model was carried out in 10-fold dilution of three anionic dyes, naphthol yellow S, fast green FCF, and Biebrich scarlet (Table IV). Although staining proceeded to an end point with all three dyes, it is evident that, of them, naphthol yellow S has the greatest affinity for protein basic groups: With one hour of staining, the same staining intensity was reached for a 100-fold dilution of naphthol

TABLE IV

EFFECT OF DYE CONCENTRATION ON DYE BINDING (EXTINCTIONS)[a]

Dye (%)	Staining time (hours)	Naphthol yellow S	Fast green	Biebrich scarlet
1	1	0.944	0.864	0.964
0.1	1	0.918	0.834	0.972
0.01	1	0.933	0.484	0.364
0.001	1	0.268	0.063	0.044
0.001	24	0.924	0.738	0.865

[a] Ovalbumin sections, Carnoy fixed, stained with different concentrations of anionic dyes made up in 1% acetic acid (pH 2.78), rinsed 1 minute in 1% acetic acid, and dehydrated in *tert*-butanol.

yellow S as in the 1% solution of the dye, while it was achieved for only a 10-fold dilution of the other two dyes. With 24 hours of staining, independence of dye concentration was extended to a 1000-fold dilution for naphthol yellow S but not, however, for the other two dyes (*30*). Acid dye binding was found to be reproducible and independent of variation in staining and rinsing time (*29*). When methanol-fixed lymphocytes were stained in 0.1% fast green in 1% acetic acid, the amount of dye bound per cell was found to be independent of staining time from 10 minutes to 1 hour, and of time in a 1% acetic acid rinse from 30 seconds to 15 minutes.

The effect of acetylation was reinvestigated on sections of the albumin model. If acetylation is carried out in pure acetic anhydride at 5° or 25°C, the various histochemical procedures for the detection of amines such as the ninhydrin-Schiff (*11*) and the chloramine T–Schiff procedure (*21*) are rendered negative (*30*). This mild acetylation procedure does not, however, affect the intensity of the Sakaguchi reaction for arginine. Acetylation as described above results in a 49% decrease in naphthol yellow S binding as compared with control values (Fig. 6). This percentage decrease corresponds to the lysine fraction of the basic amino acids of the albumin model (Table III). It was thus possible to confirm the suggestion made earlier (*27*) that acid dye binding is stoichiometric for the dibasic amino acid residues and that it is possible to effect a specific acetylation blockade of amino groups without attacking guanidyl or imidazole groups. The possibility is thus open to characterize proteins in specific cellular sites by determining their lysine fraction by the difference between measurements of naphthol yellow S bound before and after acetylation in acetic anhydride at room temperature.

Another procedure that has been used to destroy amino groups is deamination by nitrous acid (*2*, *49*). The primary site of attack of this procedure is the amino group, but the guanidyl group is also susceptible to attack (*51*). When albumin model slides are stained with the naphthol yellow S and Sakaguchi procedures and cytophotometric measurements made, it has been found that deamination of guanidyl groups commences before all amino groups have been destroyed. Deamination, therefore, is not as desirable a protein blocking procedure as acetylation in effecting a specific amino blockade.

More vigorous acetylation conditions will block all amino groups and a variable fraction of guanidyl groups as well. Such procedures as acetylation in 100% acetic anhydride at 60° or 80°C, or in a 3 : 5 mixture of acetic anhydride in pyridine or collidine at these temperatures, result in a 60–75% decrease in naphthol yellow S staining from control values and in some reduction of Sakaguchi intensity. An intensive attempt to block all guanidyl groups succeeded only if carboxyl groups were first blocked by methylation in methanolic–HCl (*29a, 31, 66*) prior to acetylation in the pyridine mixture at 80°C (*29a, 30, 68*). After these successive pretreat-

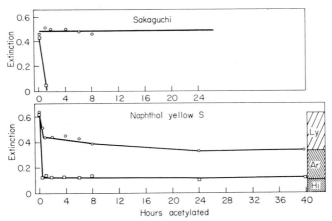

Fig. 6. The effect of acetylation after methylation on acid dye binding and the Sakaguchi reaction: Methylation for 2 hours in methanolic–HCl (99 : 1) at 60°C. ○, Acetylation in 100% acetic anhydride at 25°C; □, acetylation in acetic anhydride and pyridine (3 : 5) at 80°C. To the right, the fractional lysine, arginine, and histidine composition of the albumin model are shown on the same scale as the extinction values for naphthol yellow S binding. Methylation causes a rise in naphthol yellow S binding over control values, but prior methylation does not affect the percentage decrease in acid dye binding from control values found with acetylation in 100% acetic anhydride at room temperature. Prior methylation is required to cause a complete abolition of the Sakaguchi reaction and decrease of acid dye binding to a level which indicates that only histidine is staining. Ovalbumin sections, Carnoy fixed.

ments, acid dye binding is reduced to about 16% of control values (Fig. 6), which compares well with the histidine fraction of the basic amino acids (Table III). The Sakaguchi reaction is entirely negative after pretreatment first with methylation and then vigorous acetylation (Fig. 6).

The resistance to acetylation of some guanidyl groups and their susceptibility to attack after prior methylation suggest that some guanidyl groups may be strongly linked to carboxyl groups, perhaps in the form of intramolecular salts (67). Methylation pretreatment causes a rise in acid dye binding over control values; there is, however, no difference between methylated and unmethylated albumin sections in the percentage reduction of acid dye binding caused by a mild acetylation in 100% acetic anhydride at 25°C. The Sakaguchi reaction intensity is also unaffected by methylation followed by mild acetylation (Fig. 6).

The residual acid dye binding which occurs when staining is performed after first methylating carboxyl groups, and then acetylating lysine and arginine residues, consists of acid dye binding to histidine (Fig. 6, Table III). This then may be considered to be a specific method for the detection and quantitative cytophotometric estimation of this amino acid (68). The imidazole ring of histidine is not susceptible to attack by conventional acylating agents (50a). However, pretreatment with a new and more vigorous agent, trifluoracetic anhydride, used at 60°C for 48 hours, was found to abolish all tissue acidophilia (30). The blockade of histidine staining achieved by this treatment may, however, be the result of cleavage and loss of the imidazole ring rather than of its acetylation (50a).

V. Methods for Histones and Protamines

A number of procedures for the staining of basic proteins that depend upon their high isoelectric points have been proposed. Of these, the best known is the first of its type, the alkaline fast green procedure of Alfert and Geschwind (3) which has been used extensively in cytophotometric studies (1, 4–8, 14–19, 25, 26, 33, 34, 45, 50, 55, 56, 60). In this empirical procedure, tissues are fixed in formalin, nucleic acids are extracted with hot trichloracetic acid (61), and staining is performed with 0.1% fast green FCF at pH 8.0–8.1. The staining reaction is usually restricted to nuclei and follows the same distribution in appearance as Feulgen-revealed DNA (14). A positive reaction is also given by sites of concentration of basic cytoplasmic proteins such as the eosinophilic granules of leukocytes and by the cytoplasm of cells rich in ergastoplasm, such as plasma cells. Alfert and Geschwind noted that protamine, histone, lysozyme, and cytochrome C droplets dried on filter paper and fixed with formalin were all able to stain with fast green at pH 8. Of these, only histone and protamine would be found in nuclei, and it was subsequently shown that protamine is extracted by the trichloracetic acid hydrolysis used to remove DNA (7). The amount of staining at pH 8 is considered to reflect the net positive charge of the protein being stained (that is, the excess of basic over acidic amino acids) rather than the total amount of basic amino acid residues in the protein (3). In a further investigation of model proteins, Bloch and Godman (14) found that an inhibition of fast green staining at pH 8 occurs when proteins with high dicarboxylic amino acid content, such as casein or pepsin, are added to histone droplets. Thus alkaline fast green staining does not merely reflect changes in amounts or in the relative basicity of histone; it may also be affected by masking of the dibasic amino acid residues of histone by the dicarboxylic acid residues of adjacent non-histone protein.

The Feulgen–fast green ratio of many cell types has frequently been found to be constant, even during replication of DNA or during different metabolic states (1, 3, 5, 6, 14, 56).

The actual numbers assigned to such a ratio will, of course, depend upon the wavelengths chosen for the measurement of the two chromophores. In Alfert's data, this ratio was expressed as being between 1.5 and 2.0 for a number of normal cell types (3, 4). However, in degenerating pyknotic nuclei and in heteropyknotic nucleated erythrocytes, higher amounts of alkaline fast green staining occur, depressing the Feulgen–fast green ratio to 0.60–0.65 (3, 4). It is possible that the higher amounts of fast green found in these cells may be a reflection of the lower than normal amounts of non-histone protein found in pyknotic cells and in heteropyknotic erythrocytes (4, 38, 48).

An alteration of the Feulgen–fast green ratio in the other direction, toward an increase in the ratio due to decreased alkaline fast green binding as compared with the intensity of the Feulgen reaction, was reported by Bloch and Godman in their study of the liver cells of young rats (15). That portion of the cell population constituting the post-telophase, the DNA-synthesizing, and the preprophase members (autosynthetic cells) exhibited proportionality between Feulgen and fast green values (Fig. 7). These cells have also been found to have proportional Feulgen and methyl green values (see Fig. 4, "Cytophotometry of Nucleic Acids," this volume, p. 338). On the other hand, the heterosynthetic cells (diploid cells with large nuclei and prominent nucleoli) had depressed fast green binding, as well as lowered methyl green staining (Fig. 7). The Feulgen–fast green ratio for these cells is thus higher than in normal cells. A non-histone nuclear protein was shown to be present in the heterosynthetic cells in greater amounts than in the autosynthetic cells and to contribute to the observed decrease in methyl green binding. It was considered possible that the decreased binding of Fast Green also resulted from a similar type of inhibition (*15*).

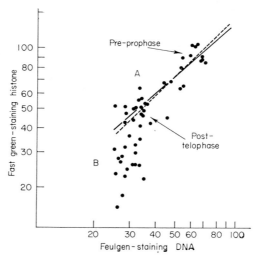

FIG. 7. Comparison of the Feulgen staining of DNA and the Fast Green binding of histone in the two types of nuclei of a rat liver preparation. Among the cells involved in the duplication of chromosomal material, there is an approximately proportional increase in the DNA and the histone as shown by the two types of stain. A fraction of the cells containing the diploid amount of DNA show a decreased capacity for Fast Green staining of histone. Compare this figure with Fig. 4 in the chapter "Cytophotometry of Nucleic Acids," p. 338. From Bloch and Godman (*15*).

While the variations in alkaline Fast Green binding reported above may reflect actual changes in amounts of an inhibitory non-histone protein, this would be difficult to establish. Bloch and Hew (*17*) noted that with the alkaline Fast Green procedure, "a decrease in staining may be attributed to an actual decrease in histone, masking of basic groups of the histones, decrease in the basicity of histone, the latter either by changes in the relative ratios of strongly basic arginine to the less strongly basic lysine, or to an increase in the acid residues, glutamic and aspartic acid."

The need for an alternative cytophotometric procedure for the quantitative estimation of histone is therefore evident. It would be particularly desirable if the amounts of histones as estimated by this method were not subject to competitive masking effects of anionic groups. The author has proposed such a method (*29*). Although this work is still in progress, it may be pertinent to consider the approach in broad outline. It depends upon the measurement of acid dye binding to the dibasic amino acid residues at an acid pH before and after extraction of histones. The amount of histone is estimated as the difference between these two measurements. The inhibitory effect of tissue anionic groups may be overcome by extraction of nucleic acids and (or) methylation (*29a, 67*) to block all phosphate and carboxyl groups. These procedures essentially convert proteins into polycations, which are readily stained to an end point with acid dyes. It is possible, using such a method, not only to estimate amounts of histone and non-histone protein per cell, but also to assess the extent of carboxyl blockade in the histone and non-histone fractions by making a comparison of staining values obtained for methylated and nonmethylated tissue.

The other histochemical procedures which have been proposed for the revelation of basic proteins, including the ammoniacal silver procedure of Black and Ansley (*13*), the picric acid–eosin and the picric acid–bromphenol blue procedures of Bloch and Hew (*16, 17*) must be considered as essentially qualitative procedures for the detection of different basic protein moieties (lysine-rich and arginine-rich histones and protamines), and so are not germane to this discussion.

VI. Cytophotometric Staining Procedures

The staining, extraction, and blocking procedures referred to above may be found outlined in appendix to "Cytophotometry of Nucleic Acids," pp. 342–349, this volume.

REFERENCES

1. Alfert, M., and H. A. Bern, Hormonal influence on nuclear synthesis. I. Estrogen and uterine gland nuclei. *Proc. Natl. Acad. Sci. U.S.* **37**, 202–205 (1951).
2. Alfert, M., Studies on basophilia of nucleic acids: The methyl green stainability of nucleic acids. *Biol. Bull.* **103**, 145–156 (1952).
3. Alfert, M., and I. I. Geschwind, A selective staining method for the basic proteins of cell nuclei. *Proc. Natl. Acad. Sci. U.S.* **39**, 991–999 (1953).
4. Alfert, M., Changes in the staining capacity of nuclear components during cell degeneration. *Biol. Bull.* **100**, 1–12 (1955).
5. Alfert, M., Quantitative cytochemical studies on patterns of nuclear growth. *Proc. Symp. Fine Structure Cells, Leiden, 1954,* pp. 157–163. Nordhoff, Groningen, 1955.
6. Alfert, M., H. A. Bern, and R. H. Kahn, Hormonal influence on nuclear synthesis. IV. Karyometric and microspectrophotometric studies of rat thyroid nuclei in different functional states. *Acta Anat.* **23**, 185–205 (1956).
7. Alfert, M., Chemical differentiation of nuclear proteins during spermatogenesis in the salmon. *J. Biophys. Biochem. Cytol.* **2**, 109–114 (1956).
8. Ansley, H. R., A cytological and cytophotometric study of alternative pathways of meiosis in the house centipede *Scutigera forceps* (Rafinesque). *Chromosoma* **6**, 656–695 (1954).
9. Baker, J. R., The structure and chemical composition of the Golgi element. *Quart. J. Microscop. Sci.* **85**, 1–72 (1944).
10. Baker, J. R., The histochemical recognition of certain guanidine derivatives. *Quart. J. Microscop. Sci.* **88**, 115–121 (1947).
11. Barka, T., and P. J. Anderson, "Histochemistry." Harper (Hoeber), N.Y., 1963.

12. Bhattacharya, K. R., Partial characterization of the colored product of the Sakaguchi reaction. *Ann. Biochem. Exptl. Med. (Calcutta)* **20**, 93–96 (1960).

13. Black, M. M., and H. R. Ansley, Histone staining with ammoniacal silver. *Science* **143**, 693–695 (1943).

14. Bloch, D. P., and G. C. Godman, A microphotometric study of the synthesis of desoxyribonucleic acid and nuclear histone. *J. Biophys. Biochem. Cytol.* **1**, 17–28 (1955).

15. Bloch, D. P., and G. C. Godman, Evidence of differences in the desoxyribonucleoprotein complex of rapidly proliferating and non-dividing cells. *J. Biophys. Biochem. Cytol.* **1**, 531–550 (1955).

16. Bloch, D. P., and H. C. Y. Hew, Schedule of spermatogenesis in the pulmonate snail *Helix aspersa* with special reference to histone transition. *J. Biophys. Biochem. Cytol.* **7**, 515–532 (1960).

17. Bloch, D. P., and H. C. Y. Hew, Changes in nuclear histones during fertilization and early embryonic development in the pulmonate snail, *Helix aspersa. J. Biophys. Biochem. Cytol.* **8**, 69–81 (1960).

18. Bloch, D. P., Symposium: Synthetic processes in the cell nucleus. I. Histone synthesis in non-replicating chromosomes. *J. Histochem. Cytochem.* **10**, 137–144 (1962).

19. Bloch, D. P., and S. D. Brack, Evidence for the cytoplasmic synthesis of nuclear histone during spermiogenesis in the grasshopper *Chortophaga viridifasciata* (De Geer) *J. Cell Biol.* **22**, 327–340 (1964).

20. Bryan, J. H. D., DNA-protein relations during microsporogenesis of *Tradescantia. Chromosoma* **4**, 369–392 (1951).

21. Burstone, M. S., An evaluation of histochemical methods for protein groups. *J. Histochem. Cytochem.* **3**, 32–49 (1955).

22. Carver, M. J., F. C. Brown, and L. E. Thomas, An arginine histochemical method using Sakaguchi's new reagent. *Stain Technol.* **28**, 89–91 (1953).

23. Chapman, L. M., D. M. Greenberg, and G. L. A. Schmidt, Studies on the nature of the combination between certain acid dyes and proteins. *J. Biol. Chem.* **72**, 707–729 (1927).

24. Cohn, E. J., and J. T. Edsall, "Proteins, Amino Acids and Peptides," p. 354. Reinhold, New York, 1943.

25. Das, C. C., B. P. Kaufman, and H. Gay, Histone protein transition in *Drosophila melanogaster.* I. Changes during spermatogenesis. *Exptl. Cell Res.* **35**, 507–514 (1964).

26. Das, C. C., B. P. Kaufman, H. Gay, Histone protein transition in *Drosophila melanogaster.* II. Changes during early embryonic development. *J. Cell Biol.* **23**, 423–430 (1964).

27. Deitch, A. D., Microspectrophotometric study of the binding of the anionic dye, naphthol yellow S by tissue sections and by purified proteins. *Lab. Invest.* **4**, 324–351 (1955).

28. Deitch, A. D., An improved Sakaguchi reaction for microspectrophotometric use. *J. Histochem. Cytochem.* **9**, 477–483 (1961).

29. Deitch, A. D., A cytophotometric method for the estimation of histone and non-histone protein. *J. Histochem. Cytochem.* **13**, 17–18 (1965).

29a. Deitch, A. D., this volume, pp. 327–354.

30. Deitch, A. D., and J. Y. Terner, Effect of acetylation on acid dye binding and the Sakaguchi reaction. *J. Histochem. Cytochem.* **13**, 15–16 (1965).

31. Fisher, E. R., and R. D. Lillie, The effect of methylation on basophilia. *J. Histochem. Cytochem.* **2**, 81–87 (1954).

32. Fraenkel-Conrat, H. L., and M. Cooper, The use of dyes for the determination of acid and basic groups in proteins. *J. Biol. Chem.* **154**, 239–246 (1944).

33. Godman, G. C., and A. D. Deitch, A cytochemical study of the L. E. bodies of systemic lupus erythematosus. II. Proteins. *J. Exptl. Med.* **106**, 593–606 (1957).

34. Godman, G. C., A. D. Deitch and P. Klemperer, The composition of the L. E. and hematoxylin bodies of systemic lupus erythematosus. *Am. J. Pathol.* **34**, 1–23 (1958).

35. Hofman, K., Imidazole and its derivatives. Part I. *In* "The Chemistry of Heterocyclic Compounds" (A. Weissberger, ed.), Vol. 6, p. 446. Wiley (Interscience), New York, 1953.

36. Hoover, C. R., and L. E. Thomas, Microspectrophotometric studies of the Feulgen and arginine histochemical reactions. *Proc. Histochem. Soc. J. Natl. Cancer Inst.* **12**, 219, 1951.

37. Kossel, A., and R. E. Gross, Über die Darstellung und quantitative Bestimmung des Arginins. *Z. Physiol. Chem.* **135**, 167–174 (1924).

38. Leuchtenberger, C., A cytochemical study of pycnotic nuclear degeneration. *Chromosoma* **3**, 449–473 (1950).

39. McLeish, J., L. G. E. Bell, L. F. LaCour, and J. Chayen, The quantitative cytochemical estimation of arginine. *Exptl. Cell Res.* **12**, 120–125 (1957).

40. McLeish, J., and H. S. A. Sheratt, The use of the Sakaguchi reaction for the quantitative determination of combined arginine. *Exptl. Cell Res.* **14**, 625–628 (1958).

41. McLeish, J., Comparative microphotometric studies of DNA and arginine in plant nuclei. *Chromosoma* **10**, 686–710 (1959).

42. Mathews, A., A contribution to the chemistry of cytological staining. *Am. J. Physiol.* **1**, 445–454 (1898).

43. Meek, E. S., The cytochemical estimation of protein using Naphthol Yellow S and combined measurement of deoxyribonucleic acid. *J. Histochem. Cytochem.* **10**, 564–567 (1962).

44. Meek, E. S., Quantitative cytochemical analysis of protein and deoxyribonucleic acid in ascites tumour cells. *Brit. J. Cancer* **16**, 157–162 (1962).

45. Meek, E. S., A quantitative cytochemical study of chromosomal basic protein in static and proliferative cell populations. *Exptl. Cell Res.* **33**, 355–359 (1964).

46. Mirsky, A. E., and A. W. Pollister, Chromosin, a desoxyribose nucleoprotein complex of the cell nucleus. *J. Gen. Physiol.* **30**, 117–148 (1946).

47. Mirsky, A. E., and H. Ris, Chemical composition of isolated chromosomes. *J. Gen. Physiol.* **31**, 7–18 (1947).

48. Mirsky, A. E., and H. Ris, The composition and structure of isolated chromosomes. *J. Gen. Physiol.* **34**, 475–492 (1951).

49. Monné, L., and D. B. Slautterback, The disappearance of protoplasmic acidophilia upon deamination. *Arkiv Zool.* [2] **1**, 455–462 (1950).

50. Moore, B. C., Histones and differentiation. *Proc. Natl. Acad. Sci. U.S.* **50**, 1018–1026 (1963).

50a. Morton, A. A., "The Chemistry of Heterocyclic Compounds," page 402. McGraw-Hill, New York, 1946.

51. Olcott, H. S., and H. L. Fraenkel-Conrat, Specific group reagents for proteins. *Chem. Rev.* **41**, 151–197 (1947).

52. Ornstein, L., Unpublished observations (1951).

53. Pollister, A. W., and H. Ris, Nucleoprotein determination in cytological preparations. *Cold Spring Harbor Symp. Quant. Biol.* **12**, 147–157 (1947).

54. Pollister, A. W., and C. Leuchtenberger, The nucleoprotein content of whole nuclei. *Proc. Natl. Acad. Sci. U.S.* **35**, 66–71 (1949).

55. Posalaky, Z., G. Kiefer, and W. Sandritter, Quantitative histochemische Untersuchungen über die säurefeste Anfärbung des Spermienkopfes. *Histochemie* **4**, 312–321 (1964).

56. Rasch, E., and J. W. Woodard, Basic proteins of plant nuclei during normal and pathological growth. *J. Biophys. Biochem. Cytol.* **6**, 263–276 (1959).

57. Rasch, E., and H. Swift, Microphotometric analysis of the cytochemical Millon reaction. *J. Histochem. Cytochem.* **8**, 4–17 (1960).

58. Sakaguchi, S., Über eine neue Farbenreaktion von Protein und Arginin. *J. Biochem.* (*Tokyo*) **5**, 25–31 (1925).

59. Sakaguchi, S., A new method for the colorimetric determination of arginine. *J. Biochem.* (*Tokyo*) **37**, 231–236 (1950).

60. Sandritter, W., and D. Kleinhans, Über das Trockengewicht, den DNS- und Histonproteingehalt von menschlichen Tumoren. *Z. Krebsforsch* **66**, 333–348 (1964).

61. Schneider, W. C., Phosphorus compounds in animal tissues I. Extraction and estimation of desoxypentose nucleic acid and of pentose nucleic acid. *J. Biol. Chem.* **161**, 293–303 (1945).

62. Serra, J. A., Eine neue histochemische Reaktion—die Reaktion des Arginins. *Naturwiss.* **32**, 46–47 (1944).

63. Singer, M., Factors which control the staining of tissue sections with acid and basic dyes. *Intern. Rev. Cytol.* **1**, 211–255 (1952).

64. Stein, W. H., and S. Moore, The use of specific precipitants in the amino acid analysis of proteins. *Ann. N.Y. Acad. Sci.* **47**, 95–118 (1946–1947).

65. Steinhardt, J., Participation of anions in the combination of proteins with acids. *Ann. N.Y. Acad. Sci.* **41**, 287–320 (1941).

66. Terner, J. Y., and G. Clark, Alkylation of amines: a study of methylation and its effect on amines. *J. Histochem. Cytochem.* **8**, 184–188 (1960).

67. Terner, J. Y., Histochemical alkylation: A study of methyl iodide and its effect on tissues. *J. Histochem. Cytochem.* **12**, 504–511 (1964).

68. Terner, J. Y., and A. D. Deitch, In preparation (1966).

69. Thomas, L. E., A histochemical test for arginine-rich protein. *J. Cellular Comp. Physiol.* **28**, 145–158 (1946).

70. Vendrely, R., and Vendrely, C., Arginine and deoxyribonucleic acid content of erythrocyte nuclei and sperms of some species of fishes. *Nature* **172**, 30–31 (1953).

71. Vickery, H. B., A useful compound of histidine. *J. Biol. Chem.* **71**, 303–307 (1926).

72. Vickery, H. B., The determination of arginine by means of flavianic acid. *J. Biol. Chem.* **132**, 325–342 (1940).

73. Warren, T. N., and J. F. A. McManus, A Sakaguchi tube test for arginine applied to histochemistry. *J. Natl. Cancer Inst.* **12**, 223 (1951).

74. Weber, C. J., A modification of Sakaguchi's reaction for the quantitative determination of arginine. *J. Biol. Chem.* **86**, 217–222 (1930).

75. Welsh, R. M., and K. Resch, Application of Naphthol Yellow S cytophotometry in deoxyribonucleic acid and protein determinations on larval material of *D. melanogaster*. *J. Histochem. Cytochem.* **11**, 675–691 (1963).

76. Woodard, J., Intracellular amounts of nucleic acids and protein during pollen grain growth in *Tradescantia*. *J. Biophys. Biochem. Cytol.* **4**, 383–390 (1958).

77. Woodard, J., B. Gelber, and H. Swift, Nucleoprotein changes during the mitotic cycle in *Paramecium aurelia*. *Exptl. Cell Res.* **23**, 258–264 (1961).

INTRODUCTION TO THE CYTOCHEMISTRY OF SULFHYDRYL AND DISULFIDE GROUPS

G. F. Bahr*

BIOPHYSICS BRANCH, ARMED FORCES INSTITUTE OF PATHOLOGY, WASHINGTON, D.C.

Practically all sulfur in cells and tissues occurs as sulfhydryl (—SH), disulfide (—S—S—), methionic (—S—CH$_3$), and sulfate (—SO$_3$) groups. While the divalent sulfur in sulfhydryl, disulfide, and methionine groups is a typical constituent of the majority of proteins, the fully oxidized sulfur in sulfate groups is found as an important constituent of the ground substance and mucus. Quantitatively less significant amounts of two- and six-valent sulfur are present in many of the small molecules of cells and body fluids that are most active biologically.

Quantitative cytochemistry has several methods at hand of studying the sulfurous compounds in cells. These methods reveal, with few exceptions, the localization of groups that, by virtue of being bound to major molecular structures, have survived extraction in histological fixing and dehydrating fluids. The smaller sulfur-containing molecules are lost in the preparation and staining procedures. One speaks, consequently, of the histochemistry or cytochemistry of protein-bound sulfhydryl and disulfide groups.

Determination of total amounts of sulfur may at times be desirable for purposes of judging the ratio of sulfur occurring in one of the specific groups mentioned above to total sulfur present. Usually standard chemical methods are limited by the low concentration of sulfur in tissues, which rarely exceeds 2%. The method of Engström (15) and Lindström (22) using the characteristic absorption of certain wavelengths of soft X-rays provides better resolution in terms of tissue areas than microchemistry. Again, however, the low concentration of sulfur prohibits rational cytochemical work with X-rays on a subcellular or cellular level.

* Supported by the American Cancer Society, Grant No. P-259D.

The use of radioactively marked sulfur is the method of choice for the study of methionine, while both radioactivity and stains can be successfully employed in the study of sulfate groups (20).

This chapter will deal with two cytochemical methods for the estimation of relative and total amounts of sulfhydryl and disulfide groups that have been shown to be specific and reproducible as well as practical for cytophotometry.

I. Biological Significance of —SH and —S—S— Groups

In the course of this introduction to the quantitative cytochemistry of sulfhydryls and disulfides, it appears appropriate to discuss in brief some of the major biological functions that are ascribed to these groups. These functions can be separated roughly under the following headings:

(a) Structure.
(b) On-off switching of specific biological activity.
(c) Participation in the reduction-oxidation balance of cells.

This arbitrary separation considers only the most prominent among several functions that a sulfhydryl or a disulfide group may display at the particular place in a cell or tissue. A change in activity with respect to *one* function will usually affect the *other* functions as well.

Keratin in hair and horn, structures rich in sulfur, provide the best example of intermolecular and intramolecular disulfides that are essential in maintaining structure. Chemical breaking of the disulfide bonds leads to the dissolution of the tertiary structure of the protein. The keratin softens, swells, and loses its tensile strength. Less conspicuous, but probably more complex reversible structural changes involving sulfhydryls and disulfides are certain to occur at the subcellular level, that is, in the fibers of the mitotic spindle (24) and very likely in cytoplasmic microtubules. The transformation of one form of clotted fibrin into another is ascribed to rapid sulfhydryl interchanges following in principle the reactions represented in Fig. 1 (18). These changes are often initiated and mediated by small mounts of sulfhydryl. Thus only one or two equivalents of titratable sulfhydryl per 100,000 g of protein are involved in the transformation of fibrin-i into fibrin-s (23). Jensen (18) and Klotz et al. (21) have suggested that sulfhydryl interchanges (Fig. 1) could furnish a means of electron transport in oxidation-reduction reactions, especially in systems that appear to transfer energy over a distance. Jensen pointed out that most disulfide groups in native proteins are either sterically hindered or otherwse unreactive; that is, the twisting protein molecule keeps certain groups "inside" of its meshwork, so that some disruption of

protein structure is necessary to make them available for reaction. Without this restriction, disulfide reactions could proceed indiscriminately in
living organisms, and chaos would ensue. Steric hindrance is also a likely
means by which the rates of certain processes, such as the production of
fully polymerized keratin in epithelial cells from smaller units like

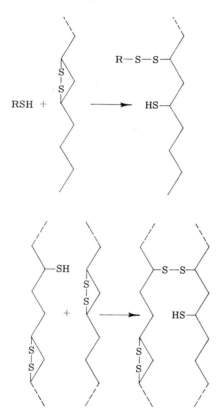

FIG. 1. Sulfhydryl–disulfide interchange in proteins. From Jensen, (18).

tonofibrils, are controlled. The rate of aging of the gel of the lens of the
eye may thus be determined. Sulfhydryl interchanges are not confined to
sulfhydryl–disulfide groups but may involve other chemical groups as well.
A most intriguing scheme to account for the sliding motion of muscle
fibrils in the Huxley–Hanson model of muscle action has been given by
Weber (Fig. 2). Sulfhydryl groups and possible disulfide groups have
been found by Riley and Lehninger to be active in maintaining mito-
chondrial volume. Swelling and contraction of rat liver mitochondria may
be induced by compounds containing thiol and disulfide.

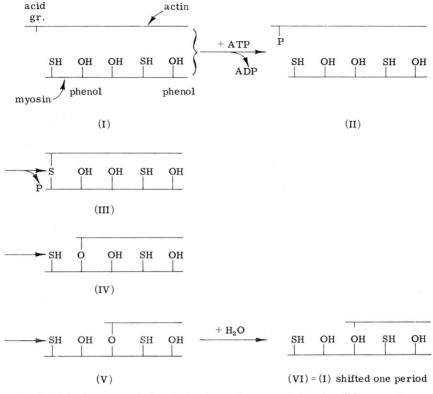

Fig. 2. Weber's proposed chemical scheme to account for the sliding motion assumed in the Huxley–Hanson theory of muscle contraction. From Weber (*30*).

As sulfhydryl–disulfide interchanges may affect the structure of tissues visually or microscopically, so may the specific physiological performance of molecules depend on their structural integrity maintained by disulfide bonds. One of the outstanding examples of this role became known when the detailed structure of insulin was elucidated (Fig. 3). Oxytocin and the related vasopressive cystine-containing peptide hormones are biologically inactivated when the disulfide is reduced to sulfhydryl and activated if the disulfide is reestablished by oxidation (*12, 13*). In this instance, and in others, the sulfhydryl–disulfide interchange can be looked upon as a physiological "on-off" switch. Many enzymes are known to be dependent on sulfhydryl (*7*). They are inactivated when their sulfhydryl group or groups are blocked, and activated again by reagents restoring the sulfhydryl. Thus sulfhydryl–disulfide reactions function as one of the regulatory mechanisms of enzyme activity.

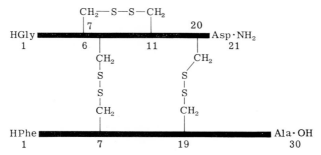

Fig. 3. Outline of the structure of insulin, showing the intrapeptide- and inter-peptide-chain disulfide linkages. The numbers refer to the sequence of residues. From Low and Edsall (*23a*).

Finally, sulfhydryl and disulfide groups constitute an oxidation-reduction system according to

$$2 \text{—SH} + 2 \oplus \rightleftarrows \text{—S—S—} + 2 \text{ H}^+$$

which is of fundamental moment in the regulation of cellular respiration.

Since the work of Barron and collaborators (*8, 9*) and the studies of Eldjarn and Pihl (*14*), involvement of sulfhydryl groups has figured prominently in explanations of the damaging effects of ionizing radiation on living cells, as well as of protection therefrom. For a recent reappraisal of this concept see the review by Ord and Stocken (*26*).

The cytochemist can make only reasonable *assumptions* as with which functional type of sulfhydryl or disulfide groups he may be dealing. These assumptions will be based on *a priori* knowledge of the functions of the respective tissue and possibly the functions of its constituent cells. Thus it appears reasonable to consider most of the sulfhydryl and disulfide found in a keratinizing epithelium as reflecting the production of keratin. Different levels of concentration of sulfhydryl in kidney cells may be more difficult to interpret. It is fair to say, however, that a high sulfhydryl content in a nonkeratinizing cell reflects high metabolic activity, with participation of many enzymes. Levels are high in dividing cells and in cells synthesizing protein. It is not surprising, therefore, that high concentrations of sulfhydryl are found in cells having high concentrations of ribonucleic acid (*3, 25*).

II. General Technical Considerations of Cytochemistry of Sulfhydryls and Disulfides

The cytochemical methods for the demonstration and measurement of sulfhydryl and disulfide groups are based on the reactivity of the sulfhydryl groups only. Disulfide groups must, therefore, be reduced to sulfhydryl groups. One thus has a means at hand of distinguishing sulfhydryl groups quantitatively from disulfide groups, in that only the sulfhydryls are determined at first. After reduction of the disulfides, both are determined together as sulfhydryls; the difference from the primary sulfhydryl determination then yields the amount of disulfides. Depending on the type of reduction used, one disulfide will render either two sulfhydryls or one sulhydryl and one nonreactive group. By blocking or eliminating sulfhydryls prior to reducing the disulfides one can, theoretically, determine the latter directly.

Aside from considerations of biological variations in the reactivity of sulfhydryl groups, which are primarily a consequence of their "accessibility" to the cytochemical detector and of the tertiary structure of the protein producing steric hindrance, processing of the tissue introduces additional variables in total amounts of detectable sulfhydryl. In most instances, preparation, fixation, and staining procedures aim at the preservation and detection of all sulfhydryl groups present. This aim is seldom reached. Degrees of reactivity of sulfhydryl groups to various reagents remain, even in severely denatured proteins.

Little has so far been reported on exploration of the biological information that could be derived from the differentiated reactivities of sulfhydryl groups in cells (3, 28).

Denaturation probably leads to some disulfide formation, but—more important—exposure of the reactive sulfhydryl makes them susceptible to auto-oxidation during processing. Therefore, every precaution should be taken to protect the sulfhydryl groups from being inadvertently lost in the processing of the tissue. The specimen should never be exposed to air after it has been fixed but should be transferred from liquid to liquid as quickly as possible. If it is stored for any length of time, it is advisable to purge the medium with pure nitrogen and store it under this or another inert gas. Interference of impurities in solvents and reagents with sulfhydryl visualization has been recognized by Bennett and Watts in a thoroughly critical discussion of the parameters of cytochemical demonstration of sulfhydryl groups with mercury orange. Their complete list of possibly interfering substances is valid for work with sulfhydryls in general and is therefore given here *in extenso*.

Four types of impurities have been recognized and are to be avoided. First, heavy-metal impurities are often found as contaminants in organic solvents obtained through commercial channels, in water, or in reagents such as trichloracetic acid. Recognition of this important source of loss of —SH groups has led to precautions designed to free all solvents and reagents of even traces of heavy metals before permitting contact with tissue destined for sulfhydryl cytochemistry. Trichloracetic acid was distilled *in vacuo*. Water and organic solvents were carefully distilled and, in many instances, further purified by passage through sulfonic acid ion-exchange resin columns, or slurried with a sulfonic acid ion-exchange resin. Use of metal instruments for handling tissue has been avoided or reduced to a minimum, with precautions to use clean, uncorroded instruments. Volatile heavy-metal compounds such as tetraethyl lead and osmium tetroxide have been kept entirely away from the refrigerator and containers used for the work. Diphenylthiocarbazone was used as a reagent for detecting traces of heavy metals in solvents. Second, peroxides have been detected as impurities in some of the solvents used, particularly some of the alcohols. Since peroxides can oxidize —SH groups, an accurate titration of total sulfhydryl cannot be expected in their presence; therefore, solvents used for —SH work should be free of peroxides.

Third, mercaptans or hydrogen sulfide present as an impurity in the solvent can interfere with the reaction by competing with tissue thiols for the available sulfhydryl reagent. In the absence of sulfhydryl reagent, thiols or hydrogen sulfide can convert tissue disulfide groups to sulfhydryl. For these reasons, mercaptans and H_2S impurities in solvents must be avoided if accurate measurement of tissue —SH is desired.

Fourth, acids can interfere with the binding of mercury orange by driving the equilibrium of Eq. (1) in the reverse direction. The equilibrium constants are such that substantial amounts of acid are necessary in order to make this reversal appreciable. Trace amounts of acid, therefore, are of no concern. Concentrations above 0.1 to 1 N might begin to have an effect.

Although the four types of impurities mentioned here are especially important in quantitative cytochemical work involving thiols, they must be avoided also if reliable results are to be achieved in a qualitative way.

III. Methods for Quantitative Cytochemical Determination of Sulfhydryl Groups

A. MERCURY ORANGE

Aryl and alkyl mercuric halides react with sulfhydryl groups according to the equation

$$\underset{\text{thiol}}{\text{R—SH}} + \underset{\substack{\text{organic} \\ \text{mercurial}}}{\text{X—Hg—R}'} \rightleftarrows \underset{\text{mercaptide}}{\text{R—S—Hg—R}'} + \text{H}^+ + \text{X}^-, \tag{1}$$

a reaction first used by Hellermann and collaborators (*17*) in a study of sulfhydryls in egg albumin. These authors employed *p*-chloromercuribenzoate according to the equation protein-SH + Cl—Hg—⟨benzene ring⟩—COOH ⇌

protein-SH—Hg—⟨benzene ring⟩—COOH + H^+ + Cl^+ (2)

Bennett and Yphantis (*11*) synthesized a red compound, 1-(4-chloromer-cury-phenylazo)-naphthol-2 or mercury orange, which earlier had been called red sulfhydryl reagent (RSR), for the specific purpose of applying it as a reagent for sulfhydryls. The mechanism of the reaction follows

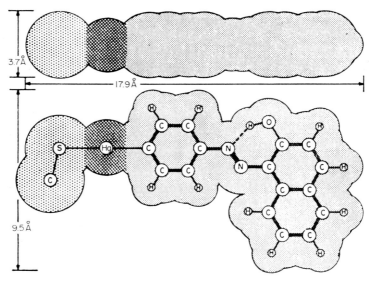

Fig. 4. Diagram of probable molecular shape and dimensions of a mercury orange mercaptide. The upper figure shows the molecule as seen on edge. The lower figure represents it in plain view. The limits of the molecule are meant to represent the limits of the van der Waals radii of its constituent atoms. The relative thickness of the lines connecting various atoms in the lower figure is intended to represent roughly the number of electrons implicated in the bond. The dotted line between the naphtholic hydrogen and an azo nitrogen represents a hydrogen bond. The three types of shadings (from right to left) are meant to imply that the molecule has a colored portion, a dense portion, and a portion that was part of the original thiol. From Bennett and Watts, (*10*), p. 324.

Eqs. (1) and (2) and is illustrated in Fig. 4, in which an estimate of the molecular dimensions and the relationship of the constituting atoms is also depicted. Its spectral characteristics are illustrated in Fig. 5. There is a rather broad peak in the visible region, which shows some variation

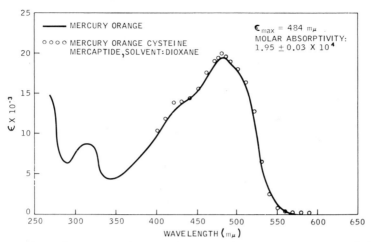

Fig. 5. Absorption spectrophotometric curves for mercury orange and for its cysteine mercaptide. Note that the absorption curve of cysteine mercaptide of mercury orange resembles closely that of mercury orange itself in the visible range. After Bennett and Watts (10), 325.

of ϵ_{max} and λ_{max} for various organic solvents. A mounted specimen, however, renders an absorption curve that coincides for all practical purposes with the absorption curve of the dye proper (10) (Fig. 5).

Mercury orange is one of the most critically tested cytochemical means for the visualization and quantitative determination of sulfhydryl groups. It has been discussed in detail by Bennett and Watts and is described in standard textbooks of histochemistry (4, 27). The fact that the reagent has only recently become available commercially explains why this highly specific, obviously easy method has not yet had widespread application. This is regrettable not only because there is still a very limited number of truly quantitative staining procedures for the cytochemist, but also because application of two quantitative sulfhydryl methods, based on different reaction principles, multiplies rather than merely adds to the information about the distribution and function of sulfhydryl and disulfide groups in cells. On the assumption that the supply of the reagent will continue, the following staining procedure, essentially as recommended by Barka and Anderson, is given.

Fixation: One per cent trichloracetic acid in 80% ethanol, at 4°C, overnight. Since trichloracetic acid has been found to preserve and reveal sulfhydryl groups excellently, but often maintains tissue structure poorly, the alternative fixatives such as Carnoy solution, alcohol, dimethylformamide, or freeze-substitution may be tried (10).

Dehydration (after aqueous fixation): In graded alcohols, acetone, dioxane, or dimethylformamide.

Embedding: If required, in paraffin, celloidin, Carbowax, or esterwax.

Staining: Dehydrated smears, imprints, or deparaffinized tissue sections 5- to 8-μ thick are directly transferred to a solution of mercury orange* in toluene (2×10^{-5} M, about 1 mg/100 ml) (*20*), or they are submersed in a saturated solution of the mercury reagent in absolute ethanol (about 3 mg/100 ml), previously diluted with distilled water to a final concentration of 80% ethanol (*23*). This solution may be buffered to pH 8.0 (*19*).

The slides remain for at least 24 hours in the staining solution, after which they are washed for 1 to 2 minutes in two changes of absolute ethanol, briefly treated with xylene, and mounted in a medium matching the refractive index of the specimen. For most proteins this will require an index of about 1.54 to 1.56 (*10*).

Care should be taken not to dilute the mounting medium with an excess of xylene still on the slide, since this would lower the desired refractivity of the mounting medium.

B. DIHYDROXY-DINAPHTHYL DISULFIDE (DDD)

The interaction of sulfhydryls with disulfide groups, according to the equation

$$\text{R—SH} + \underset{\text{disulfide}}{\text{R'—S—S—R''}} \underset{\text{thiol}}{\rightleftarrows} \text{R—S—S—R'} + \text{HS—R''}, \qquad (3)$$

in which R, R', and R'' are aryl or alkyl moieties, constitutes the most specific reaction of sulfhydryls. This has been taken by Barrnett and Seligman as the base for a highly specific visualization of protein-bound sulfhydryl groups. The authors synthesized 2,2'-dihydroxy-6,6'-dinaphthyl disulfide for this purpose. The reagent, conveniently called DDD, is used as illustrated in Eq. (4).*

(I)   (4)

*Available from K and K Laboratories, 121 Express Street, Plainview, New York.

Fast Black K

(II)   (4)

DDD reacts with thiols of protein (Eq. (4), I) by exchanging hydrogen. The disulfide reagent is split. One half of it attaches to the protein; the other half is reduced to 2-hydroxy-6-naphthyl sulfide, which is subsequently extracted with ether, together with any remaining DDD. The reaction is reversible and therefore readily influenced by mass action (*6*).

The colorless, protein-bound naphthol is converted in a second procedural step (Eq. (4), II) into a colored azo dye by a number of diazotized compounds. Equation (4) illustrates the coupling with diazotized 4-amino- 3,6-dimethoxy 4-nitroazobenzene* (*2*, *3*). The original procedure of Barrnett and Seligman (*5*) prescribed the use of tetrazotized diorthoanisidine, a compound having two active diazo groups. It produces a blue color when both groups react with the protein-bound naphthol (dicoupling) and a red color when only one diazo group reacts (monocoupling). Since the development of two colors unnecessarily complicates the quantitative cytochemical evaluation of sulfhydryl, several monocouplers have been proposed (*3*, *6*, *29*), of which this author prefers the fast black salt K illustrated in Eq. (4), because it marks the sites of specific naphthol fixation by a comparatively deep blue. As with all diazo couplers, there is a nonspecific reaction of the diazo group with tissue components other than naphthol bound with the protein sulfhydryl, yield-

*Available from Roboz Surgical Instrument Company, 810 18th Street, N.W., Washington 6, D.C.

ing a light red nonspecific background coloration. Pearse suggests that such nonspecific coloring may result from diazonium reactions with histidine and tyrosine residues. Extensive series of blocking and model experiments confirming the theoretical specificity of the approach have been carried out by both the original authors (*3, 29*) and further users, some of whom modified the method.

Fixation: One percent trichloracetic acid in 80% ethanol, at 4°C overnight, for pieces of tissue of about 1-cm³ volume. Smears and imprints are sufficiently fixed after 10 minutes. Other fixatives mentioned for the mercury orange method also appear suitable.

Dehydration: From aqueous fixatives, in graded alcohols, acetone.

Embedding: In paraffin or other media listed with the mercury orange method.

Staining: Tissue sections 5- to 8-μ thick are deparaffinized in xylene and brought through alcohol to distilled water. Slides are incubated in a coplin jar for 60 minutes at 50° to 60°C in the reagent solution freshly prepared by the following formula: Dissolve 25 mg DDD in 15-ml ethanol and add 35-ml veronal-acetate buffer, pH 8.5. Shake the mixture. Varying with each batch, there is usually an undissolved portion of DDD or contaminant, giving the solution a somewhat milky appearance. Let coplin jar cool to room temperature after incubation (10 minutes); rinse slides in distilled water. Rinse in two changes of 0.01% acetic acid, which transforms the sodium salts of both reagent and reaction products into free naphthol, the uncoupled part of which is now soluble in organic solvents. Wash in two changes of ethanol and one change of absolute ether for 5 minutes each. Rinse in ethanol and in distilled water. Transfer sections to coplin jar containing phosphate buffer at pH 7.0. Sprinkle the dry diazo powder of fast black salt K evenly on top of buffer. Do not use more than 0.5 to about 1 mg per milliliter of buffer and shake gently for 5 to 10 minutes. Rinse in distilled water, dehydrate in alcohol or acetone, and mount in refractive index medium between 1.54 to 1.56, for quantitative work.

Other diazo couplers may require a different pH. Barka and Anderson have listed pH from 7.6 to 7.8 for fast blue B, fast blue RR, or fast red RC. Personal experience (*2*) has shown that fast black salt K produces maximal absorption at pH 6.8 when reacted with DDD *in vitro*. In thin sections maximum coloration is developed at pH 7.2. A pH of 7.0 has been chosen because the reddish background stain is weakest and the specific coloration for sulfhydryls is strongest (*2, 3*).

Spectral characteristics: The reaction product of DDD with fast black K exhibits a broad maximum of 590 mμ (Fig. 6), which is little influenced by variations of pH (*3*). In tissue sections, absorptions at shorter wave-

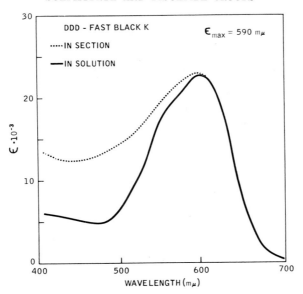

FIG. 6. Absorption curve of the reaction product of DDD and fast black K in buffer (solid line) and of protein-bound DDD/2 with fast black K (broken line). Unspecific reactions of fast black K with tissue components produce a weak red stain, which is responsible for increased absorption at shorter wavelengths. λ_{max} is identical for the specific reaction in both solution and in tissue.

lengths than ϵ_{max} are elevated because of the added absorption from unspecific reactions of the diazonium salt with tissue components, ϵ_{max} of which is found in the red component at 490 mμ (3). Since there is no significant overlapping of the absorption of this red component with the specific absorption, however, the wavelength of 590 mμ can safely be used for quantitative purposes.

IV. The Methods for Quantitative Cytochemical Determination of Disulfide Groups

A. GENERAL TECHNICAL REMARKS

In this introductory chapter only those methods for the study of disulfide groups that may be useful in quantitative cytochemistry will be considered. This discussion will be restricted to *reduction* procedures, that is, the transformation of disulfides, —S—S—, into sulfhydryls, —SH. Methods are available (27) as yet untested quantitatively, by which one aims to *oxidize* sulfhydryls and disulfides alike, producing sulfuric acid groups, —SO$_3$H. Basic dyes such as the ones discussed by Kelly may then be used for quantitative staining of the acid groups.

The quantitative reduction of disulfides is subject to variations because of the variable resistance of disulfides to the reagents employed and because of the degree of denaturation of different proteins by various fixatives. Usually, after having attempted to reduce all disulfide, one must be content with considerably less morphological preservation than one sees with a method for sulfhydryl alone. It should also be kept in mind that breakage of disulfide bonds tends to increase loss of protein from the specimen.

A number of methods of reducing disulfide groups have been described and are listed in textbooks and reviews on the subject (3, 4, 27). A reducing agent should be chosen that produces a maximal amount of sulfhydryl in reducing —S—S— groups, but preserves the morphological features to a reasonable degree. In this respect potassium cyanide and ammonium sulfite are unsuitable, since only one —SH is produced per disulfide group. The reducing reagent most often used is sodium thioglycollate. Next, personal experience has shown BAL (British anti-lewisite, which is dodecyl mercaptan) to be a very satisfactory reducer. Since on the one hand the reducer has to be applied in a rather alkaline milieu, progressive morphological destruction takes place. Reduction is, on the other hand, a slow process, requiring either prolonged exposure to the reagent or elevated temperatures. These effects, working in the opposite direction from our cytochemical aims, make it necessary to test our object for optimal conditions. A series of incubations at room and elevated temperatures will quickly reveal the time required to reach the point of maximal reduction (color development), while the morphological features of our particular object are still reasonably well preserved.

B. METHOD OF REDUCTION

Essentially, according to Teiger, Farah, and Di Stefano, deparaffinized sections are treated for 2 hours (smears a shorter time) at 50°C with 0.5-M BAL (or thioglycollic acid) in ethanol in which 0.4% potassium hydroxide has been dissolved. If sections show a tendency to be lost during the incubation, they may be protected by dipping the slide in 0.2% celloidin dissolved in ether–ethanol, 1 : 1, or by 0.2% Parlodion in amyl acetate. Remove and air-dry. A thin coat of cellulose nitrate now covers and holds the specimen. This measure should be taken only if necessary, since it tends to decrease the number of detectable sulfhydryl groups. After incubation wash in three changes of distilled water containing 1% acetic acid for 5 to 10 minutes, followed by a 5-minute wash in distilled water only. Stain for —SH with one of the above-described methods.

V. Blocking of Sulfhydryl Groups

There are many reagents that block or destroy sulfhydryl groups, making it easier to lose them in preparation and staining procedures not carefully controlled than to preserve them. Most of the specific blocking agents react reversibly with sulfhydryl groups and may, to a varying extent, be replaced by a sulfhydryl reagent used later, such as mercury orange or DDD. If only proof of a negative reaction of the sulfhydryl reagent is required, this theoretical reversibility appears, however, to be negligible with the series of blocking agents recommended by Bennett and Watts (10) and the N-substituted maleimides (16). The effectiveness of either one of these in maintaining the block through the reduction procedure for disulfides is questionable. Although there is no report on measurements or on serious experimentation in this respect, one must assume that the sulfhydryl of the reducing reagent will compete for the blocking agents, such as iodoacetamide, iodoacetate, or N-ethyl-maleimide, and remove them. Sulfhydryl that has been converted to disulfide by mild oxidants will, of course, be reduced again. Alternatively, one could oxidize sulfhydryl to the sexivalent sulfuric acid stage with peracetic or performic acid. It is known, however, that extensive reaction with these acids proceeds until all disulfides are oxidized too (27). Considering these uncertainties in any approach to the exclusive determination of disulfides by blocking or eliminating them, it appears safer to determine disulfide as the difference between amounts of primary sulfhydryls and the total amount of sulfhydryls after production of secondary sulfhydryls through reduction of disulfides.

VI. Handling of Material for the Determination of Sulfhydryls and Disulfides

A. SMEARS, IMPRINTS, SINGLE CELLS FROM TISSUE CULTURE

Smears or imprints should be fixed immediately. Drying should be avoided. Slides carrying tissue culture cells should be freed from adherent culture medium by a brief wash in saline or Ringer's solution.

If a value for disulfide is desired and the cell population is rather uniform (lymphocytes, fibroblasts), two parallel slides are used—one for determining free reactive (primary) sulfhydryl groups, the other for determining total sulfhydryl after reduction of disulfides. A sufficient number of microspectrophotometric measurements (about 100) will then render the amount of disulfides as the difference of average primary sulfhydryl content per cell from the first slide *versus* the simultaneously determined sum of average primary and secondary sulfhydryls per cell from the second slide.

If one wishes to correlate —SH and —S—S— within one cell, it is necessary to measure the —SH content in the selected cells first and mark these values on survey photographs of the preparation. The mounting medium is then removed by soaking the slide in xylene or benzene until the cover slip can easily be removed. This requires up to several hours, depending on the size of cover slip used. Care should be taken not to dislodge any of the cells in removing the cover slip. The specimen is then washed in two additional changes of xylene, rehydrated through graded alcohol, and incubated in the reducing medium for previously determined optimal time (*vide supra*). After appropriate washing, it is allowed to react with one of the two sulfhydryl reagents, whereupon the preparation is again mounted in the medium of chosen refractive index. The photographic map of the preparation will now permit remeasurement of the given cell for total, primary, and secondary sulfhydryls. Since it is usually difficult to discern the rather weakly colored objects offering few morphological hallmarks for recognition, one may digress from the rule of strictly matching the refractive index of the mounting medium with that of the cell. A difference of about 0.004 (preferably to the lower side) will facilitate recognition in a good phase-contrast system or dark field illumination.

Preparations containing single cells offer an opportunity to correlate the absolute amount of sulfhydryls found in a cell with the total dry mass of the cell. By submersion in xylene, as previously described, the mounting medium and the cover slip are removed and the slide is carried through graded alcohols into distilled water for interference microscopic measurements. Only through correlation of this type can information be gained about true increases in sulfhydryl activity for a given amount of protein. All other increases must *prima facie* be interpreted (for non-keratinizing cells) as increased concentrations of protein.

B. Tissue

If the objective of the study is a comparison of different cells in the same tissue, one section containing these cells will suffice. Experience has shown that most routinely used microtomes produce sections of sufficient evenness for quantitative purposes (*1*). When dealing with material requiring separate pieces of tissue originating from different areas of an organ, or when comparison of experimental effects with normal levels of sulfhydryl is desired, it is necessary to embed the pieces of tissue close to each other in one paraffin block and to section them together.

This assures that the thickness of the layers of the two (or more) objects is sufficiently comparable for quantitative determination of relative concentrations. Absolute values, which would require knowledge of the absolute thickness of the section, are seldom biologically significant enough to justify the effort, not to mention imminent considerations of possible losses and morphological displacements encountered in the processing of the specimen. Correlation of sulfhydryl values with total protein faces the notorious difficulties of interference microscopy in work with sections. In a semiquantitative fashion, however, information can be obtained as to how much of an observed increase in sulfhydryl is simply the consequence of protein accumulation by comparing the distribution of sulfhydryls with the distribution of dry mass.

VII. Conclusions

The reactivity of the sulfhydryl group of cellular proteins sets it apart from other reactive groups of proteins. It is the group most likely to be affected, for example, by changes in the ionic milieu of the cell sap; by the actions of radiant energy, including heat; and by the actions of drugs and poisons. The sulfhydryl group thus is useful to the cytochemist as a very sensitive indicator of the function of the cellular machinery, especially if the measurements can be correlated to the dry mass of the cell. Carefully conducted reduction of disulfides will enhance considerably the information on the "activity state" of the protein.

On first sight one may be disappointed by the low absorptivities or the low "contrast" of both sulfhydryl stains recommended here, as compared with many histochemical stains. On the contrary, for cytophotometry this is an advantage and reflects only the small amounts of sulfhydryl that can be sensitively detected.

The biological significance of quantitative information on sulfhydryls and disulfides is limited by the fact that only protein-bound groups are assayed and that one determines them without discrimination as to the type of protein involved. The relative ease with which the mercury orange method in particular can be applied, however, indicates that sulfhydryl determinations can be a most valuable adjunct in studies of cellular biology.

REFERENCES

1. Bahr, G. F., Techniques for judging the quality of paraffin sections to be used in microspectrophotometry. *Mikroskopie* **10**, 13–18 (1955) (in German).
2. Bahr, G. F., Changes in liver cell elements during stimulated protein synthesis. *Acta Radiol.* Suppl. 147 (1957).

3. Bahr, G. F., and G. Moberger, Histochemical methods for the demonstration of sulfhydryl groups in normal tissues and malignant tumors. *Acta Pathol. Microbiol. Scand.* **42**, 109–132 (1958).

4. Barka, T., and P. J. Anderson, "Histochemistry." Harper (Hoeber), New York, 1963.

5. Barrnett, R. J., and A. M. Seligman, Demonstration of protein-bound sulfhydryl and disulfide groups by two new histochemical methods. *J. Natl. Cancer Inst.* **13**, 215–216 (1952).

6. Barrnett, R. J., and A. M. Seligman, Histochemical experiments on sulfhydryls and disulfides. *In* "Glutathione," Proc. Symp., Ridgefield, Conn., 1953 (S. P. Colowick *et al.*, eds.), pp. 89–102. Academic Press, New York, 1954.

7. Barron, E. S. G., The effect of ionizing radiations on systems of biological importance. *Ann. N.Y. Acad. Sci.* **59**, 574–594 (1955).

8. Barron, E. S. G., S. Dickman, J. A. Muntz, and T. P. Singer, Studies on the mechanism of action of ionizing radiations. *J. Gen. Physiol.* **32**, 537–594 (1949).

9. Barron, E. S. G., and S. Dickman, Studies on the mechanism of action of ionizing radiations; inhibition of sulfhydryl enzymes by alpha, beta, and gamma rays. *J. Gen. Physiol.* **32**, 595–605 (1949).

10. Bennett, H. S., and R. M. Watts, The cytochemical demonstration and measurement of sulfhydryl groups by azo-aryl mercaptide coupling, with special reference to mercury orange. *In* "General Cytochemical Methods. (J. F. Danielli, ed.), Vol. 1, pp. 317–374. Academic Press, New York, 1958.

11. Bennett, H. S., and D. A. Yphantis, 1-(4-Chloromercuriphenylazo)-naphthol-2. *J. Am. Chem. Soc.* **70**, 3522 (1948).

12. du Vigneaud, V., "A Trail of Research in Sulfur Chemistry and Metabolism." Cornell Univ. Press, Ithaca, New York, 1952.

13. du Vigneaud, V., Hormones of the posterior pituitary gland: Oxytocin and vasopressin. Harvey Lectures **50**, 1–26 (1956).

14. Eldjarn, L., and A. Pihl, Mechanisms of protective and sensitizing action. *In* "Mechanisms in Radiobiology" (M. Errera and A. Forssberg, eds.), pp. 231–296. Academic Press, New York, 1960.

15. Engström, A., Quantitative micro- and histochemical elementary analysis by Roentgen absorption spectrography. *Acta Radiol. Suppl.* 63 (1946).

16. Friedmann, E., D. H. Marrian, and I. Simon-Reuss, Antimitotic action of maleimide and related substances. *Brit. J. Pharmacol.* **4**, 105–108 (1949).

17. Hellerman, L., M. E. Perkins, and W. M. Clark, Urease activity as influenced by oxidation and reduction. *Proc. Natl. Acad. Sci. U.S.* **19**, 855–867 (1933).

18. Jensen, E. V., Sulfhydryl-disulfide interchange. *Science* **130**, 1319–1323 (1959).

19. Kawamura, N., Cytochemical and quantitative study of protein-bound sulfhydryl and disulfide groups in eggs of arbacia during the first cleavage. *Exptl. Cell Res.* **20**, 127–138 (1960).

20. Kelly, J. W., This volume, p. 489.

21. Klotz, I. M., J. Ayers, J. Y. C. Ho, M. G. Horowitz, and R. E. Heiney, Interaction of proteins with disulfide compounds: some implications for electron transport in proteins. *J. Am. Chem. Soc.* **80**, 2132–2141 (1958).

22. Lindström, B., Roentgen absorption spectrophotometry in quantitative cytochemistry. *Acta Radiol.* Suppl. 125 (1955).

23. Lorand, L., A. Jacobsen, and L. E. Fuchs, *In* "Sulfur in Proteins," Proc. Symp., Falmouth, Mass., 1958 (R. Benesch *et al.*, eds.) p. 109. Academic Press, New York, 1959.

23a. Low, B. W., and J. T. Edsall, *In* "Currents in Biochemical Research" (D. E. Green, ed.), p. 379. Wiley (Interscience), New York, 1956.

24. Mazia, D., SH and growth. *In* "Glutathione," Proc. Symp., Ridgefield, Conn., 1953 (S. P. Colowick *et al.*, eds.), pp. 209–228. Academic Press, New York, 1954.

25. Müller, W., G. Moberger, and G. F. Bahr, Occurrence and distribution of sulfhydryl groups in brain tumors. *Naturwiss.* **45,** 64 (1958).

26. Ord, M. G., and L. A. Stocken, Biochemical effects of x-irradiation and the sulfhydryl hypothesis: a re-appraisal. *Nature* **200,** 136–138 (1963).

27. Pearse, A. G. E., "Histochemistry," 2nd ed. Little, Brown, Boston, Massachusetts, 1960.

28. Riley, M. V., and A. L. Lehninger, Changes in sulfhydryl groups of rat liver mitochondria during swelling and contraction. *J. Biol. Chem.* **239,** 2083–2089 (1964).

29. Teiger, D. G., A. Farah, and H. S. Di Stefano, Cytophotometric determination of protein-bound disulfide groups. *J. Histochem. Cytochem.* **5,** 403–407 (1957).

30. Weber, H. H., "The Motility of Muscle and Cells." Harvard Univ. Press, Cambridge, Massachusetts, 1958.

Selected References from the Sulfhydryl Literature

Bäckström, S., Studies on sulfhydryl-containing substances in sea urchin embryos of various developmental trends. *Exptl. Cell Res.* **16,** 165–173 (1959).

Cafruny, E. J., H. S. Di Stefano, and A. Farah, A cytophotometric determination of protein-bound sulfhydryl groups. *J. Histochem. Cytochem.* **3,** 354–359, 1955.

Caspersson, O., and L. Révész, Cytochemical measurement of protein sulfhydryls in cell lines of different radiosensitivity. *Nature* **199,** 153–155 (1963).

Ellman, G. L., Tissue sulfhydryl groups. *Arch. Biochem. Biophys.* **82,** 70–77 (1959).

Ernst, H., and U. Hagen, Untersuchungen über die Verteilung und Reaktionsfähigkeit von Sulfhydrylgruppen in der tierischen Zelle. *Z. Naturforsch.* **14b,** 104–110 (1959).

Hyde, B. B., An evaluation of the Barrnett-Seligman procedure when used to determine changes in the ratio of nuclear protein-bound disulfide to sulfhydryl groups during mitosis. *J. Histochem. Cytochem.* **9,** 640–646 (1961).

Ogura, R., J. M. Knox, and A. C. Griffin, Quantitative studies of epidermal sulfhydryl. *J. Invest. Dermatol.* **36,** 29–35 (1961).

Sakai, H., Studies on sulfhydryl groups during cell division of sea urchin egg. I and II. *J. Biophys. Biochem. Cytol.* **8,** 603–607 and 609–615 (1960).

Scaife, J. F., The role of thiol groups in the development of radiation damage in thymocytes and Ehrlich ascites carcinoma cells. *Can. J. Biochem. Physiol.* **42,** 1717–1727 (1964).

Wiman, L. G., A study on protein-bound sulfhydryl groups in pulmonary cytodiagnosis. Thesis, University of Uppsala (1964); published by Almquist & Wiksell, Stockholm.

QUANTITATIVE CYTOCHEMISTRY OF ACID MUCOPOLYSACCHARIDES

John W. Kelly*

DEPARTMENT OF ANATOMY,
TUFTS UNIVERSITY SCHOOL OF MEDICINE,
BOSTON, MASSACHUSETTS

A truly small number of investigations qualify under the title of this chapter, even if it were seriously considered that there is any fundamental difference between cytochemistry and histochemistry. The number is further restricted by the decision to discuss only *visualizing* methods which offer some reasonable chemical basis for quantitative study. Some reference to the qualitative background for this subject in morphological observations, physiology, and chemistry may be useful. Compounds that are not acid mucopolysaccharides (AMP)—neutral MP, proteins, lipopolysaccharides, or glycolipids—will be mentioned when it is appropriate to clarify certain reactions. Specific methodology will not be given, since that is clearly available elsewhere.

I. The Mucinous Substances

Mucopolysaccharides are significant components of the ill-defined group of "mucinous substances." These substances were originally characterized partly by a small set of empirical staining reactions and partly by physiological and physical properties as more or less viscid secretions of remarkable water-binding capacity. Several recent symposia have dealt with many aspects of these raw substrates as they are found in their three major habitats: intracellular (48), extracellular in connective tissues (19), and as typical epithelial secretions (28). Quintarelli (50) gives an excellent historical review of concepts and terminology relating to

* Acknowledgment is made to the National Institutes of Health for grants RG-7058, AM-06071, AM-08939, and HTS-5338, which supported various aspects of certain original investigations mentioned in this paper.

mucinous substances. It seems acceptable to call the secretion of an epithelium, regardless of germ-layer origin, a mucus. The secretion of mesodermal cells, generally accumulated as an intercellular amorphous component of connective tissue, is a mucin. Pseudomucin is a pathological term for mucin of atypical staining reactions, which may reflect a paucity of AMP and predominance of protein. None of these terms has the slightest chemical meaning. "Mucoid" has been used to mean "mucin," but should be dropped from general usage, since it has been given a more restricted biochemical meaning by some authors (for example, orosomucoid of blood, ovomucoid).

Few normal examples of strictly intracellular AMP can be given, except for the mucus precursors and mast cell or basophil cytoplasmic granules. In Hurler's disease (gargoylism) cells of the liver, kidney, spleen, and occasionally other organs accumulate one or both types of the AMP species found in the urine (40). It is even possible that an MP component, sialic acid, is to be found in cells as a component of the endoplasmic reticulum membranes (18). This is not surprising, since AMP is definitely a component of many cell membranes with which the endoplasmic reticulum often shows continuity. Not only cell membranes, but also the so-called "extraneous coats" of cells, such as bacterial capsules and egg jelly coats, contain AMP in abundance (31, 44). Even if markedly attenuated on most cells, the special name "glycocalyx" has been suggested for generalization of the extraneous coats (5).

Extracellular AMP is the general rule. In higher animals, it forms part of the connective tissue ground substance and organic matrix of bone and cartilage and is localized in rather pure states in such sites as vitreous body, nucleus pulposus, and Wharton's jelly. Corresponding substances in higher plants are the pectins and gums, and in lower plants the slime layers.

II. Chemistry of Acid Mucopolysaccharides

Chemical terminology is far from stabilized, indicating a rapidly expanding field with many gaps remaining in structural knowledge of even the most familiar compounds (12). Dorfman's recent definitions are accepted here (18).

"Mucopolysaccharides" (MP) are "high molecular weight heteropolysaccharides of the general class found in connective tissues, e.g., hyaluronic acid." A "mucopolysaccharide-protein complex" is MP bound "by apparent covalent links to proteins." Others have used "mucoprotein" for such complexes. "Mucoprotein" is a protein bearing small side chains of carbohydrate. These have been called "glycoproteins," although that term has also been used more loosely to describe various proteins containing carbohydrate.

The hallmark of any mucopolysaccharide (MP) is a hexosamine. In addition, the MP may contain hexuronic acid (not conclusively demonstrated in epithelial secretions), hexose, sulfuric acid, and, in mucus MP, sialic acid and/or fucose. Some of these characteristic components are

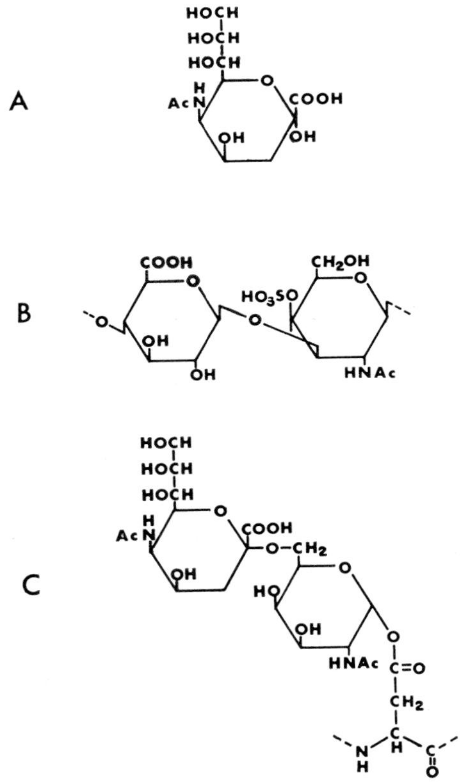

FIG. 1. Representative structural components of acid mucopolysaccharides. (A) N-Acetylneuraminic acid (an iduronic acid). (B) Repeating disaccharide unit of chondroitinsulfuric acid with D-glucuronic acid and N-acetyl-D-galacturonic acid. (C) Example of "mucoprotein" linkage (ovine submaxillary gland), showing aspartyl group of protein attached to N-acetylgalactosamine and N-acetylneuraminic acid. From Clark and Grant (12) and Gottschalk (23).

shown in Fig. 1. It has even been proposed that the mucopolysaccharides be renamed "glyosaminoglycans" as a class (29). Table I is a summary of the best known mucopolysaccharides.

TABLE I

ACID MUCOPOLYSACCHARIDES OF CONNECTIVE TISSUE[a]

Name	Hexosamine	Hexuronic acid	Sulfate
Hyaluronic acid	Glucosamine	Glucuronic[b]	0
Keratosulfate	Glucosamine	(Galactose)	1
Heparin monosulfate (heparitin sulfate)	Glucosamine	Glucuronic, iduronic	1
Heparin	Glucosamine	Glucuronic, iduronic	2½
Chondroitin	Galactosamine	Glucuronic	0
Chondroitin sulfate A	Galactosamine	Glucuronic	1
Chondroitin sulfate B (β-heparin)	Galactosamine	Iduronic	1
Chondroitin sulfate C	Galactosamine	Glucuronic	1

[a] After Dorfman (18).
[b] No acid component.

III. Qualitative Histochemistry and Cytochemistry

A general background for this section, including specific methods and excellent bibliographies, may be obtained from two leading source books on histochemistry (2, 49) and from various review or survey articles on mucinous substances and mucopolysaccharides (3, 13, 14, 24, 25, 43, 62).

All methods for visualizing AMP fall into three categories: binding of oppositely charged color ions to anionic groups in the AMP, incorporation of radioisotopes into newly forming AMP, and binding of fluorescent antibodies to AMP. The first of these is also basic to almost any method of AMP "fixation," a step so important that there really can be no quantitative cytochemistry without some agreement on a limited number of modern fixing procedures and total abandonment of the empirical heritage.

IV. Fixation

Like carbohydrates generally, the "fixation" of AMP is atypical, since these compounds are not susceptible to those physical or chemical agents which tend to denature proteins. In fact, ordinary fixing agents are only useful when the mucinous substance has a high protein content. The somewhat conflicting views of Curran (13, 14) and Szirmai (64) on the admissibility of older fixation methods for AMP are instructive. The principles of AMP "fixation," when not entirely dependent on associated protein, are as follows:

(1) Use of dehydrating agents, such as ethanol or acetone, and avoid-

ance of subsequent exposure to aqueous media. The dehydration is best performed in the cold, from ice-cold to $-20°C$. One might call this merely "retention" of AMP, since there is no assurance some AMP will not again resolubilize.

(2) Immobilization by freezing, preferably at liquid nitrogen temperatures, with subsequent dehydration of the frozen material. Freeze-drying or freeze-substitution in bulk have been used. Freeze-substitution of cryostat sections offers perhaps the greatest promise here. Ordinary cryostat or frozen sections have been used for some work; it must be recognized that thawing damage cannot be avoided.

(3) Heavy metals (basic lead acetate, barium hydroxide, lead nitrate, calcium acetate) have been used in aqueous or alcoholic solutions to take advantage of the precipitating action of the cations on the AMP anion groups. These methods are troublesome and only fair, unless they are applied in some form of freeze-substitution.

(4) Precipitation of the AMP by one of the quaternary ammonium compounds (for example, cetylpyridinium chloride) has been applied with great success, especially in combination with formaldehyde to accomplish simultaneous protein fixation (*35, 68, 71*). These "fixing" methods are essentially the same as applications of the quaternary ammonium detergents for blocking reactions (see below).

(5) Szirmai (*64*) has applied certain cationic dyes as fixatives for AMP, on the logical basis that the dyes are so highly selective and energetic in their binding to anionic groups. It can only be advantageous to have fixation and staining take place simultaneously. The method was best applied to cryostat sections.

V. Visualization

A. Methods Depending on AMP Anionic Groups

Under ordinary conditions, many cationic or "basic" dyes will bind to one or both types of anionic or "acidic" groups of AMP, the carboxyl group, $-COO^-$, or the sulfuric acid ester group, $-OSO_3^-$. This so-called "basophilia" is not an all-or-none affair, however, since many factors—notably hydrogen ion concentration (pH), electrolyte content (ionic strength), and organic solvent content (dielectric constant) of the staining bath—will influence the binding of dye to substrate (*58, 69*). It has become more and more evident that this binding is stoichiometric, that is, under carefully controlled and specified conditions, both cationic and anionic dyes are bound to certain substrates in fixed proportions. This is an absolute requirement for any quantitation based on dyes. Metallic cations should be bound to AMP in the same manner as dyes, with less steric specificity.

I. *Cationic Dyes*

Given the initial and somewhat selective binding of dye to AMP, it is possible to distinguish three types of staining methods characterized partly by optical behavior of the dyes and partly by pH regulation of the staining bath. Optical "behavior" here refers to whether the dye is orthochromatic or metachromatic (*6, 32, 33, 53*) in its reactions and whether either type is then notably fluorescent (*66*).

a. *Alcian Blue*. This is an orthochromatic, nonfluorescent, copper phthalocyanine dye apparently binding to AMP through its isothiouronium groups (*56*). Staining is usually conducted in a bath of pH 2.5 (*47*). It is generally held today that Alcian blue detects carboxyl groups and is inconsistent, at least, in reactions with sulfated AMP.

b. *Astrablau* (*Astra Blue*). Similar to Alcian blue, this dye is usually used in a staining bath of pH 0.2 to detect only sulfate ester groups of mast cells, basophils, cartilage, and some types of mucus (*9*), not as a substitute for Alcian blue at pH 2.5 (*2*).

c. *Toluidine Blue or Azure A*. These dyes are strongly metachromatic members of the thiazine family, yielding striking color shifts from blue to red in the presence of AMP, especially sulfated AMP. They are not usefully fluorescent. No fixed pH values have been set by general agreement for the staining bath; both dyes have been used in the pH 1–5 range generally. Metachromatic shades (reddish) are roughly dependent on the electronegativity of the various substrates. In general, it may still be stated that the order of decreasing effectiveness in eliciting the metachromatic reaction from a suitable dye is sulfate > carboxyl > phosphoryl. Even the nucleic acids, therefore, will show a violet shade intermediate between the orthochromatic and metachromatic states.

d. *Acridine Orange*. Called AO in its application as a diagnostic stain in cancer cytology, acridine orange is an extremely efficient fluorochrome with striking metachromatic properties (*7, 8*). Its diagnostic value depends upon the ready distinction between yellow-green fluorescence with DNA in contrast to orange-red fluorescence with RNA. It is not ordinarily considered to be a stain for AMP, yet its extreme fluorescence metachromasy, a flame red color, is seen in mast cells, basophils, and cartilage matrix.

Atabrine has served as a nonmetachromatic fluorochrome for mucin detection (*14*). Acriflavine has similarly been used to detect the cerebroside sulfuric acid ester (CSAE) seen in neurons in "metachromatic leukoencephalopathy" or diffuse cerebral sclerosis (*26*).

II. *Metallic Cations*

a. *Colloidal Iron (Hale Reaction)*. Dialyzed ferric hydroxide or ammonium ferric glycerate is applied to sections, the excess washed away, and the section is then exposed to potassium ferrocyanide. Sites of anionic groups, especially AMP, are revealed by the resulting Prussian blue reaction. Mowry (*47*) has discussed the details of this method, pointing out that it is important to distinguish between the "outmoded Hale stain or procedure and the more enduring and important Hale reaction." Selectivity for particular anionic groups is not claimed.

b. *Bi-Col Method*. Wolman combined the Hale reaction and a colloidal gold treatment at low pH to distinguish strongly and weakly acidic MP. Pearse (*49*) has discussed the method, concluding that while sharp color distinctions are met (blue versus red-brown), the specificity of the colloidal gold portion of the reaction is probably low. The method has not been widely used.

c. *Barium Rhodizonate Method*. Stempien (*63*) proposed the detection of sulfated AMP by treating sections first with barium chloride, followed by sodium rhodizonate to yield the red barium rhodizonate at sites of sulfate. The method correlated well with radioautography and metachromatic staining, with certain exceptions.

B. METHODS DEPENDING ON AMP ANTIGENICITY

Kent (*39*) has described the application of fluorescent antibodies to salivary gland mucus, blood group substances, and *Cryptococcus* capsules. Apparently, both carboxyl and hydroxyl groups of the antigens are involved in reactions with antibody. Sialic acid is essential for the salivary gland reaction, but probably not for the blood group substance reaction.

Evans and Kent (*20*) also described a method which, while having no immunological specificity, may fittingly be described here. Basic polysaccharides from *Aspergillus* are conjugated with fluorescein isothiocyanate. These polysaccharides, composed of galactosamine and *N*-acetylgalactosamine, then bind to tissue AMP in essentially the same manner as a basic dye. They may be considered colorless polycations acting simply as carriers for the fluorescent label. Deacetylated chitin has also been used in the same manner. Results with both types of basic polysaccharides are similar to Alcian blue staining.

C. METHODS DEPENDING ON AMP INCORPORATION OF RADIOISOTOPES

General radioautographic techniques have been reviewed by Fitzgerald (*21*). The use of $S^{35}O_4$ has been thoroughly validated as the absolute criterion for detection of sulfated AMP, against which all other methods must be judged (3). In comparative studies, however, the metachromatic reactions generally correlate well with S^{35} localizations.

D. Auxiliary Methods

An auxiliary method means one that involves manipulation of factors other than the major visualizing procedure, in order to increase the latter's specificity. Strictly speaking, this is exactly what one does to make Astrablau, for example, a specific test for sulfated AMP by adjusting the pH to 0.2. It is desired here to draw attention to very general methods of modifying coloring reactions, as a distinct class in the histo- or cytochemical approach.

1. Blocking and Unblocking

Organic chemists have for years possessed techniques for reversibly or irreversibly "covering" one reactive group in a molecule while some other group reacts. For example, in Sørenson formol titration, formaldehyde is used to suppress amino-group basicity and allow protein-bound carboxyl groups to be directly titrated. This is, incidentally, the reason for the well-known action of a formaldehyde fixative in enhancing basophilia: a relative excess of free carboxyl groups remains to bind cationic dyes. Van Slyke deamination is an example of what the cytochemist calls an irreversible "blocking" reaction.

a. *Esterification.* Methylation with acid methanol destroys reactivity of both carboxyl and sulfate ester groups. Carboxyl groups are restored by mild saponification with potassium hydroxide or by oxidation with permanganate. Sulfate groups are destroyed, however, by methanolysis.

Acetylation apparently blocks only carboxyl groups, leaving sulfate groups unaffected (45). Deacetylation restores the metachromasy of most MP's except those containing sialic acid.

b. *Quaternary Ammonium Complexing.* A special group of blocking-unblocking methods has arisen out of Scott's biochemical system for fractionating and purifying tissue polyanions (54). The system depends upon precipitating complexes formed between polyanions and a large number of quarternary ammonium detergents (QN^+), such as cetylpyridinium chloride. These complexes are resolubilized by addition of electrolytes such as NaCl or $MgCl_2$. However, the concentration of any electrolyte required to dissolve a given complex is directly proportional to the electronegativity of the polyanions. In a mixed precipitate, say, of hyaluronic acid, chondroitin sulfate, and heparin, the progressive addition of a salt will solubilize first the weakest AMP, hyaluronic acid, then chondroitin-sulfate, and finally heparin.

Scott's method was first used cytochemically by Bloom and Kelly (9) in the simple blocking of Astrablau staining of mast cells by prior application of cetylpyridinium chloride to sections. There have now been several developments of the basic idea for cytochemical and histochemical purposes: selective extraction (35) involved blocking of all AMP in sections by one treatment with QN^+, then the unblocking of different groups by three selected concentrations of salt. In all sections, the unblocked AMP was visualized by metachromatic staining with toluidine blue.

Zugibe (70) treated sections with QN^+ and then complexed the tissue-bound QN^+ with ferric thiocyanate to yield water-soluble reddish products at sites of AMP. Complexes were formed in the presence of different amounts of electrolyte. Zugibe's work followed his own earlier applications of QN^+ compounds as AMP "fixatives," as well as those of Williams and Jackson (68, 71).

Saunders (51) used the fluorescent dye acridine orange as a direct blocking-visualizing agent for AMP, in the presence of sodium chloride or after prior blocking with QN^+.

It was mentioned above that Szirmai (64) suggested the direct "fixation" and simultaneous staining of AMP with favorable cationic dyes. This has been done successfully with toluidine blue (65) and Alcian blue (55). For theoretical reasons, these applications and the fluorescence method of Saunders (51) are the most elegant histochemical variations on Scott's biochemical system. Nothing is gained by fixing first with a colorless cation and then replacing that with a second colored cation if the latter may be applied directly.

2. Extractions

In this context, an extraction is the more or less selective removal of AMP from sections by nonenzymatic reagents, such as acids, alkalis, or neutral salts. This has not been widely used in AMP cytochemistry, although in discussing the procedure as applied to nucleic acids, Atkinson (1) has pointed out that the presence of extractable AMP may interfere with interpretations of the nucleic acid observations.

3. Enzyme Digestions

Mucases have often been applied to sections for the selective removal of AMP species or groups. Such enzymes have generally been hyaluronidase, neuraminidase (sialidase), β-glucuronidase, and pectinase (14). Zugibe (70) used two adaptive enzymes from Flavobacterium which would hydrolyze (a) heparin, heparitin sulfate, hyaluronic acid, and the chondroitin sulfates except CSA-B or (b) all of these except heparin and heparitin sulfate. In conjunction with testicular and streptococcal hyaluronidase, Zugibe applied the adaptive enzymes to detect individual AMP by fractional reduction of staining. A little-known "heparinase" has been used histochemically (27).

A reverse side of the coin exists here. There has been recognized for some time a so-called "masking" effect in which the protein moiety competes with cationic dye for anionic binding sites on the AMP molecule. In vitro and in situ studies have shown that suppression of AMP staining, which can be total, is reversed by prior digestion of the material with some proteolytic enzyme (14, 33). Benditt and French (4) have shown that the application of any enzyme to a tissue section can simulate natural masking of AMP (or any tissue polyanion) if the enzyme itself is bound to the negative groups of a substrate which it does not digest and remove. It is also possible that the binding of dye by one polyanion, for example RNA, can mask the binding by AMP. Such an effect has been shown for the metachromatic staining of egg extraneous coats and tissue mast cells (32, 34).

4. Chromotrope Formation

It is possible to modify certain groups in some compounds so that they assume properties of AMP. The useful change is usually restricted to formation of anionic groups, which give the compound new basophilic and usually metachromatic reactivity; this process is sometimes called "chromotrope formation."

Usually tissues are treated with a sulfating agent such as sulfuric acid in ether (41, 46). Hydroxyl groups are thus converted to ester sulfate groups. Most substances which are PAS-positive will, therefore, be susceptible to this type of alteration. There are, however, some interesting discrepancies between the two reactions which deserve further investigation (37).

Other reactions are less commonly used. Oxidation of keratinous elements with permanganate, peracetic acid, or bromine apparently converts cystine disulfide bonds into sulfonic groups, which are strongly acidic as in cysteic acid. There is an excellent cytochemical test for insulin in the islets of Langerhans depending upon this type of oxidation followed by metachromatic staining with a special dye, pseudoisocyanine (52). Phosphorylation of hydroxyl groups forms chromotropes which are approximately as basophilic as the nucleic acids, or even as metachromatic as some sulfuric acid esters (42).

VI. Quantitative Cytochemistry

The purposes of quantitation of AMP in cells and tissues may range from the simple desire to replace the unreliable plus-minus system of subjective ranking of microscopic preparations to more sophisticated measurements of intracellular components according to the amount of dye they bind. While it is highly desirable to employ methods that approach the intact cells or tissues directly through the microscope, there are useful methods of lesser resolution which measure "bound dye" by its uptake from a bath or its extraction after binding.

The reader should see Shugar's (57) article on general problems in quantitating any staining reaction. The only direct reference on quantitation of AMP reactions is that of Szirmai (64). "It is possible that most of the stains which have been used by histologists during the last hundred years could be made the basis of a quantitative cytochemical technique, in the sense that under controlled conditions a suitable measuring instrument would give reproducible results. In fact, very few have been so used, and of these, none commands universal confidence" (67). This statement is especially true for AMP cytochemistry, there being no more than a dozen investigations that might be called quantitative. Most of these studies could be considered as depending upon applications of physical chemistry (58) to tissue sections, since none has been based upon organic reactions which tend to display greater "specificity." It has been stated that the essence of dye reactions is such that we can only establish certain physicochemical parameters to define limits where staining will or will not occur (17).

A. SPECTRAL STUDIES

Microspectrophotometric studies usually begin with knowledge of dye spectra in the bound state in cells and tissues. Flax and Himes (22) examined some AMP-containing materials in their extensive study of metachromatic staining of RNA with azure A. For our purposes, there were two extremely important results. First, it was emphasized that in *any* stained object, the measured spectra are those of bound dye only, while in typical solution experiments with dye and substrate, the spectra are sums of bound and unbound dye. Second, it was shown that even a metachromatic dye, characterized by extreme spectral instability in solution, may obey the Bouguer–Beer law in sections. Spectra of toluidine blue bound to cartilage and mucus were examined by Kelly (33), illustrating adherence of this dye to the Bouguer–Lambert law. Carnes and Forker (11) also made spectral studies of toluidine blue and crystal violet with cartilage and amyloid.

B. MICROSPECTROPHOTOMETRIC DYE-BINDING STUDIES

After some familiarity with dye spectra is gained, the goal is usually to measure the amount of dye bound per unit mass of substrate or dye bound by an entire cell under various conditions.

Mast cells from rat peritoneal fluid have been investigated with a metachromatic dye, toluidine blue (*34*), using dye bound per cell and the degree of metachromasy as criteria. Technical aspects of the staining process were investigated, some comparisons made between metachromasy in solution and in cells, and the order of amounts of toluidine blue bound per cell calculated (about 3×10^{-14} mole/cell or 0.06M average concentration). Preliminary remarks were made on synthesis of the metachromatic components of the cytoplasm and effects of cortisone and thyrotropic hormone on these components.

An essentially nonmetachromatic dye, Astrablau, was used in a separate study of the rat mast cells (*9*). The remarkable spectral stability of this dye and uniformity of dye binding in different cell preparations when staining is carried out at pH 0.2 permit this dye to be strongly recommended for quantitative studies. A lens-cuvette (*38*), first used for examining the metachromatic spectra of toluidine blue in saturated solutions, was also used to support the Astrablau measurements.

Carnes and Forker (*11*) conducted a most interesting set of experiments designed to make some distinctions between metachromatic staining of cartilage and amyloid. Using a microspectrophotometer, they compared the binding of both substrates with toluidine blue and with crystal violet, metachromatic dyes from two different families, whose mechanisms of staining are apparently different for unknown reasons. Variables used were ionic strength, or effective electrolyte concentration, and dielectric constant, or solvent effect compared with that of water. They also investigated the kinetics of staining by these dyes.

From the early dye-binding experiments of Pischinger, Dempsey and others (*16, 58*) developed the basophilia extinction method, using methylene blue especially, to obtain "signature curves" of various tissue polyanions, including AMP. These may be viewed as titration curves of anionic groups over a pH range, the general result being that cationic dye binding is systematically depressed as the pH of staining is lowered. The "extinction" of staining—a most unfortunate choice of terms—is best measured photometrically, though even visual end points are useful here. Singer (*59, 60*) and his co-workers investigated the effect of pH and ionic strength on metachromatic staining of fibrin and various tissue fibrinoids.

C. Biochemical and Ultramicrochemical Studies

There are investigations which attempt to bridge the gap between accepted chemical methods for AMP and cytochemical methods. Joel *et al.* (*30*) studied aging of cartilage in this way, comparing uronic acid, hexosamine, and hexose determinations with the Hale colloidal iron and PAS methods. Within the stated limits of the methods, there was good agreement between chemical and histochemical tests. It is common practice in histochemistry to use smears or filter paper preparations of various purified AMP, or solutions of the same compounds, as "models" for studying cytochemical reactions (10, 15). These are usually qualitative and at best semiquantitative, but have been of great value to cytochemists. Quantitative applications of these models are discussed in relation to their use for protein cytochemistry (36).

Correlation of biochemical and histochemical analyses of mucinous substances in the cock's comb, both aspects being quantitative, was made by Szirmai and Balazs (65). More recently, Szirmai (64) applied Scott's methods (cf. Section V, D, 1, b) quantitatively to microgram amounts of cartilage in the form of oriented sections.

VII. Summary

The mucinous substances or *mucosubstances* (61) are reviewed briefly, with remarks on their chemical nature. Methods for their identification and localization in cells and tissues, especially those of possible quantitative application, are outlined. These methods depend chiefly upon the following functions of acid mucopolysaccharides: (a) content, nature, and spacing of anionic groups, (b) antigenicity, and (c) incorporation of radioisotopes. Some auxiliary procedures for increasing specificity of the basic methods are given. A relatively small number of quantitative investigations have been made on acid mucopolysaccharides, usually depending upon photometric assay of dye binding or direct microchemical measurement of the bound dye.

REFERENCES

1. Atkinson, W. B., Differentiation of nucleic acids and acid mucopolysaccharides in histologic sections by selective extraction with acids. *Science* **116**, 303–305 (1952).
2. Barka, T., and P. J. Anderson, "Histochemistry: Theory, Practice, and Bibliography." Harper (Hoeber), New York, 1963.
3. Bélanger, L. F., Comparisons between different histochemical and histophysical techniques as applied to mucus-secreting cells. *Ann. N.Y. Acad. Sci.* **106**, 364–378 (1963).
4. Benditt, E. P., and J. E. French, Histochemistry of connective tissue. I. The use of enzymes as specific histochemical reagents. *J. Histochem. Cytochem.* **1**, 315–320 (1953).
5. Bennett, H. S., Morphological aspects of extracellular polysaccharides. *J. Histochem. Cytochem.* **11**, 14–23 (1963).

6. Bergeron, J. A., and M. Singer, Metachromasy: An experimental and theoretical re-evaluation. *J. Biophys. Biochem. Cytol.* **4**, 433–457 (1958).

7. Bertalanffy, F. D., Diagnostic reliability of the acridine orange fluorescence microscope method for cytodiagnosis of cancer. *Cancer Res.* **21**, 422–426 (1961).

8. Bertalanffy, L. von, and I. Bickis, Identification of cytoplasmic basophilia (ribonucleic acid) by fluorescence microscopy. *J. Histochem. Cytochem.* **4**, 481–493 (1956).

9. Bloom, G., and J. W. Kelly, The copper phthalocyanin dye "Astrablau" and its staining properties, especially the staining of mast cells. *Histochemie* **2**, 48–57 (1960).

10. Braden, A. W. H., The reactions of isolated mucopolysaccharides to several histochemical tests. *Stain Technol.* **30**, 19–26 (1955).

11. Carnes, W. H., and B. R. Forker, Metachromasy of amyloid. A spectrophotometric study with particular reference to the dye-chromotrope bond. *Lab. Invest.* **5**, 21–43 (1956).

12. Clark, F., and J. K. Grant (eds.), "The Biochemistry of Mucopolysaccharides of Connective Tissue." Cambridge Univ. Press, London and New York, 1961.

13. Curran, R. C., The histological demonstration of connective-tissue mucopolysaccharides. *In* "The Biochemistry of Mucopolysaccharides of Connective Tissue" (F. Clark and J. K. Grant, eds.), pp. 24–38. Cambridge Univ. Press, London and New York, 1961.

14. Curran, R. C., The histochemistry of mucopolysaccharides. *Intern. Rev. Cytol.* **17**, 149–212 (1964).

15. Davies, D. V., Specificity of staining methods for mucopolysaccharides of the hyaluronic acid type. *Stain Technol.* **27**, 65–70 (1952).

16. Dempsey, E. W., H. Bunting, M. Singer, and G. B. Wislocki, The dye-binding capacity and other chemohistological properties of mammalian mucopolysaccharides. *Anat. Record* **98**, 417–429 (1947).

17. Dempsey, E. W., J. D. Vial, R. V. Lucas, Jr., and A. I. Lansing, Characterization of the reaction between orcein and the elastic fibers of the ligamentum nuchae of the horse. *Anat. Record* **113**, 197–214 (1952).

18. Dorfman, A., Polysaccharides of connective tissue. *J. Histochem. Cytochem.* **11**, 2–13 (1963).

19. Doyle, W. L. (ed.), Histochemistry of extracellular substances (Symposium). *J. Histochem. Cytochem.* **11**, 2–39 (1963).

20. Evans, E. E., and S. P. Kent, The use of basic polysaccharides in histochemistry and cytochemistry: IV. Precipitation and agglutination of biological materials. *J. Histochem. Cytochem.* **10**, 24–28 (1962).

21. Fitzgerald, P. J., Autoradiography in cytology. *In* "Analytical Cytology" (R. C. Mellors, ed.), 2nd ed., pp. 381–429. McGraw-Hill, New York, 1959.

22. Flax, M. H., and M. H. Himes, Microspectrophotometric analysis of metachromatic staining of nucleic acids. *Physiol. Zool.* **25**, 297–311 (1952).

23. Gottschalk, A., The basic structure of glycoproteins and problems of their chemical and physicochemical analysis. *Ann. N.Y. Acad. Sci.* **106**, 168–176 (1963).

24. Hale, A. J., Histochemistry of polysaccharides. *Intern. Rev. Cytol.* **6**, 193–263 (1957).

25. Hashim, S., A survey of histochemical methods used for the identification of polysaccharides and their derivatives. *Acta Anat.* **16**, 355–366 (1952).

26. Holländer, H., A staining method for cerebroside-sulfuric esters in brain tissue. *J. Histochem. Cytochem.* **11**, 118–119 (1963).

27. Isidor, P., Étude sur la caractérisation histologique et histochimique de l'héparine. *Bull. Microscop. Appl. (Paris)* [2] **4**, 41–44 (1954).

28. Jakowska, S. (ed.), Mucous secretions (Symposium). *Ann. N.Y. Acad. Sci.* **106**, 157–809 (1963).

29. Jeanloz, R. W., The nomenclature of mucopolysaccharides. *Arthritis Rheumat.* **3**, 233–237 (1960).

30. Joel, W., Y. F. Masters, and M. R. Shetlar, Comparison of histochemical and biochemical methods for the polysaccharides of cartilage. *J. Histochem. Cytochem.* **4**, 476–478 (1956).

31. Kelly, J. W., Metachromasy in the eggs of fifteen lower animals. *Protoplasma* **43**, 329–346 (1954).

32. Kelly, J. W., The metachromatic reaction. *Protoplasmatologia* **II-D-2**, 1–98 (1956).

33. Kelly, J. W., The use of metachromasy in histology, cytology and histochemistry. *Acta Histochem.* Suppl. 1, 85–102 (1958).

34. Kelly, J. W., and G. Bloom, A quantitative spectrophotometric study of the mast cell. *Exptl. Cell Res.* **16**, 538–564 (1959).

35. Kelly, J. W., G. D. Bloom, and J. E. Scott, Quaternary ammonium compounds in connective tissue histochemistry. I. Selective unblocking. *J. Histochem. Cytochem.* **11**, 791–798 (1963).

36. Kelly, J. W., and L. Carlson, Protein droplets, especially gelatin, hemoglobin and histone, as microscopic standards for quantitation of cytochemical reactions. *Exptl. Cell Res.* **30**, 106–124 (1963).

37. Kelly, J. W., P. N. Morgan, and N. Saini, Detection of tissue fungi by sulfation and metachromatic staining. *AMA Arch. Pathol.* **73**, 70–73 (1962).

38. Kelly, J. W., and G. Svennson, Absorption measurement with a lens-cuvette in saturated solutions of a metachromatic dye. *J. Phys. Chem.* **62**, 1076–1079 (1958).

39. Kent, S. P., A study of mucins in tissue sections by the fluorescent antibody technique. III. The specificity of antibody to salivary gland mucins and the effect of chemical alterations of mucins on the specificity of the antibody. *Ann. N.Y. Acad. Sci.* **106**, 389–401 (1963).

40. Kobayashi, N., Acid mucopolysaccharide granules in the gomerular epithelium in gargoylism. *Am. J. Pathol.* **35**, 591–605 (1959).

41. Kramer, H., and G. M. Windrum, Sulphation techniques in histochemistry with special reference to metachromasia. *J. Histochem. Cytochem.* **2**, 196–208 (1954).

42. Landing, B. H., and H. E. Hall, Phosphorylation as a histochemical procedure. *J. Histochem. Cytochem.* **4**, 41–46 (1956).

43. Lillie, R. D., Studies on the histochemistry of normal and pathological mucins in man and in laboratory animals. *Bull. Intern. Assoc. Med. Museums* **29**, 1–53 (1949).

44. Lippman, M., A proposed role for mucopolysaccharides in the initiation and control of cell division. *Trans. N.Y. Acad. Sci.* [2] **27**, 342–360 (1965).

45. Materozzi, G., Acetylation blockade of the chromotropy and basophilia of various histologic substrates. *J. Histochem. Cytochem.* **11**, 59–61 (1963).

46. Mowry, R. W., Observations on the use of sulfuric acid in ether for the sulfation of hydroxyl groups in tissue sections. *J. Histochem. Cytochem.* **6**, 82–83 (1958).

47. Mowry, R. W., The special value of methods that color both acidic and vicinal hydroxyl groups in the histochemical study of mucins. *Ann. N.Y. Acad. Sci.* **106**, 402–423 (1963).

48. Padawer, J. (ed.), Mast cells and basophils. *Ann. N.Y. Acad. Sci.* **103**, 1–492 (1963).

49. Pearse, A. G. E., "Histochemistry, Theoretical and Applied," 2nd ed. Little, Brown, Boston, Massachusetts, 1960.

50. Quintarelli, G., Histochemical identification of salivary mucins. *Ann. N.Y. Acad. Sci.* **106**, 339–363 (1963).

51. Saunders, A. M., Histochemical identification of acid mucopolysaccharides with acridine orange. *J. Histochem. Cytochem.* **12**, 164–170 (1964).

52. Schiebler, T. H., and S. Schiessler, Über den Nachweis von Insulin mit den metachromatisch reagierenden Pseudoisocyaninen. *Histochemie* **1**, 445–465 1959.

53. Schubert, M., and D. Hamerman, Metachromasia: Chemical theory and histochemical use. *J. Histochem. Cytochem.* **4**, 159–189 (1956).

54. Scott, J. E., Aliphatic ammonium salts in the assay of acidic polysaccharides from tissues. *Meth. Biochem. Anal.* **8**, 145–197 (1960).

55. Scott, J. E., Personal communication (1966).

56. Scott, J. E., G. Quintarelli, and M. C. Dellovo, The chemical and histochemical properties of Alcian blue. I. The mechanism of Alcian blue staining. *Histochemie* **4**, 73–85 (1964).

57. Shugar, D., Quantitative staining in histo- and cytochemistry. *Progr. Biophys. Biophys. Chem.* **12**, 153–210 (1962).

58. Singer, M., Factors which control the staining of tissue sections with acid and basic dyes. *Intern. Rev. Cytol.* **1**, 211–255 (1952).

59. Singer, M., and P. R. Morrison, The influence of pH, dye, and salt concentration on the dye binding of modified and unmodified fibrin. *J. Biol. Chem.* **175**, 133–145 (1948).

60. Singer, M., and G. B. Wislocki, The affinity of syncytium, fibrin and fibrinoid of the human placenta for acid and basic dyes under controlled conditions of staining. *Anat. Record* **102**, 175–194 (1948).

61. Spicer, S. S., The use of various cationic agents in histochemical differentiation of mucopolysaccharides. *Am. J. Clin. Pathol.* **36**, 393–407 (1961).

62. Spicer, S. S., Histochemical differentiation of mammalian mucopolysaccharides. *Ann. N.Y. Acad. Sci.* **106**, 379–388 (1963).

63. Stempien, M. F., Jr., The use of a barium chloride-sodium rhodizonate technique for the histochemical localization of some sulphated acid mucopolysaccharides. *J. Histochem. Cytochem.* **11**, 478–481 (1963).

64. Szirmai, J. A., Quantitative approaches in the histochemistry of mucopolysaccharides. *J. Histochem. Cytochem.* **11**, 24–34 (1963).

65. Szirmai, J. A., and E. A. Balazs, Metachromasia and the quantitative determination of dyebinding. *Acta Histochem.* Suppl. 1, 56–79 (1958).

66. Vassar, P. S., and C. F. A. Culling, Fluorescent staining, with special reference to amyloid and connective tissues. *AMA Arch. Pathol.* **68**, 487–498 (1959).

67. Walker, P. M. B., and B. M. Richards, Quantitative microscopical techniques for single cells. *In* "The Cell: Biochemistry, Physiology, Morphology" (J. Brachet and A. E. Mirsky, eds.), Vol. 1, pp. 91–139. Academic Press, New York, 1959.

68. Williams, G., and D. S. Jackson, Two organic fixatives for acid mucopolysaccharides. *Stain Technol.* **31**, 189–191 (1956).
69. Wilson, J. W., Basophilic components of the cytoplasm (Intro. to Symp. on Basophilic Components of the Cytoplasm). *J. Histochem. Cytochem.* **2**, 317–321, (1954).
70. Zugibe, F. T., Mucopolysaccharides of the arterial wall. *J. Histochem. Cytochem.* **11**, 35–39 (1963).
71. Zugibe, F. T., K. D. Brown, and J. H. Last, A new technique for the simultaneous demonstration of lipid and acid polysaccharides on the same tissue section. *J. Histochem. Cytochem.* **7**, 101–106 (1959).

POLARIZATION OPTICAL ANALYSIS OF LIPID-CONTAINING STRUCTURES WITH WEAK BIREFRINGENCE

H. P. Missmahl

DEPARTMENT OF MEDICINE,
UNIVERSITY OF TÜBINGEN, TÜBINGEN, GERMANY

Analyses of myelin sheets and of light-sensitive cells with the polarizing microscope made possible the explanation of these ultrastructures long before the electron microscope was used. With the polarizing microscope, it could be shown that in these objects protein lamellae alternate with oriented lipids in a fashion similar to that in the membranes of erythrocytes. As a result, a fine structural map could be outlined which applies also to other structures, for example, to the endoplasmic reticulum and to the mitochondria (10, 11, 12).

Several years ago we demonstrated that lipids can also occur as oriented deposits in fibrillar structures (5, 6). At this time it was known that the fibers of reticulin connective tissue are birefringent. The opposing opinion expressed by a few (3) can be explained by the small retardation of birefringence of these fibers. It is usually smaller than 10 nm. This weak birefringence can only be detected by using a polarization microscope of excellent quality. The optical lenses must be free from strain birefringence.

We reported earlier a simple method which enables one to test the lenses of the polarizing microscope. One needs only a histological section of an amyloid-containing organ that is Congo red stained. In this specimen, the amyloid shows a green anomalous polarizing color. This green color remains the same if one turns the stage of a polarizing microscope. A change from deep green to yellow shows that the lenses have a strain birefringence; a change from deep green to red, that the polarizer and analyzer are not mutually perpendicular. Furthermore, one needs an elliptical compensator (Brace-Köhler compensator) for the detection of weak birefringence. This tool enables one to find birefringent structures with a retardation of 1 nm. One has only to place the compensator in the compensator slot of the microscope and turn the plate of the compensator clockwise and counterclockwise from one of the zero positions. The weak birefringent structures not detectable without the compensator will be brightened and darkened, and therefore visible. At the same time the optical sign of the birefringence can be determined and a measurement of the retardation of birefringence taken. The gypsum plate red of first order and the Berek compensator are not useful to determine the retardation and optical sign of weak birefringence.

Reticulin fibers in histological sections that are mounted in water or from which the water has been removed by alcohol have a positive sign of birefringence with respect to the length of the fibers. This positive sign of birefringence changes to a negative one if a frozen section of formalin-fixed organs is imbibed with glycerol (Figs. 1 and 2). This glycerol reac-

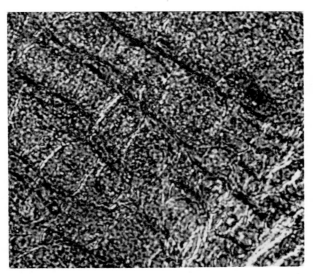

Fig. 1. Mouse liver. Frozen section mounted in water. Compensation with elliptical compensator. The reticulin fibers in the walls of sinusoids have the same optical sign of birefringence as the collagen fibers in the bottom right-hand corner of the figure.

tion of reticulin fibers means a specific polarization optical method of demonstrating reticulin fibers.

This author is unaware of any other substance that has the same effect on reticulin fibers. The glycerol reaction of reticulin fibers also enables us to determine the lipids of the fibers and their oriented ultrastructural arrangement. This can be confirmed by the following examinations, which

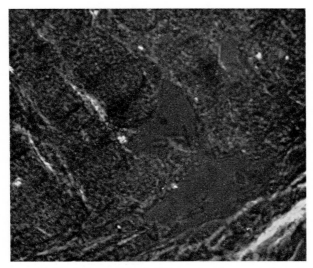

Fig. 2. The same field of view as Fig. 1. The section is mounted in glycerine. Compensation with elliptical compensator. The optical signs of birefringence of reticulin and collagen fibers are different.

are typical of a polarizing optical analysis for structures of weak birefringence.

I. Extraction of Reticulin Fibers
with Alcohol, Acetone, and Other Lipid Solvents

Frozen sections of organs with reticulin fibers (adrenal glands, spleens, kidneys) were incubated for different lengths of time in lipid solvents.

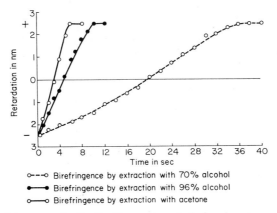

o---o Birefringence by extraction with 70% alcohol
●——● Birefringence by extraction with 96% alcohol
o——o Birefringence by extraction with acetone

Fig. 3. Birefringence of reticulin fibers using alcohol and acetone as solvents.

Following this, sections were mounted in glycerol, and both optical sign and retardation of birefringence were determined in the reticulin fibers. Using this method for alcohol and acetone, we obtained the results shown in Fig. 3. From this graph it can be seen that the negative birefringence of reticulin fibers mounted in glycerol disappears as a function of the time of the action of the solvents and on their concentration. This shows that the negative birefringence of these fibers mounted in glycerol is produced by lipids.

II. Imbibition Test on Reticulin Fibers with Substances of Different Refractive Indices

For the imbibition test, birefringent structures are impregnated with substances of different refractive indexes, and each time retardation and sign of birefringence are determined. Graphs from which the form and intrinsic birefringence of the subject can be determined are obtained by this method. This is because form birefringence can be found in structures in which two substances with differing refractive indices are arranged in an oriented manner. The particles of these structures must be small in comparison with the wavelength of light. In the oriented structures, the particles of the two different substances must alternate. In addition, it must be possible to imbibe one of the two substances with the imbibition fluids. The greater the difference between the two refractive indices, the stronger will be the form birefringence. When they both have the same refractive index, form birefringence disappears. This means that the intrinsic birefringence of the object can be measured at this point.

Since part of the birefringence of the reticulin fibers is produced by a substance which can be extracted by lipid solvents, we had to look for suitable imbibition fluids. Only mixtures of water and glycerol were found useful. Any refractive index between 1.33 and 1.45 can be obtained by mixing water and glycerol in the appropriate ratios. The measurements of the imbibition test on reticulin fibers before and after extraction by acetone are demonstrated in Fig. 4. From this graph it can be seen that retardation and optical sign of the birefringent reticulin fibers change during imbibition with mixtures of water and glycerol of different refractive indices. The optical sign in water is positive and the retardation is relatively high. The retardation of birefringence becomes smaller with increasing refractive indices of the imbibition fluids. With a refractive index of 1.37, the optical sign of birefringence changes. With further increase of the refractive index of the imbibed fluid, the retardation of birefringence with a negative optical sign increases. We could not determine the ascending part of the imbibition curve because we could not find

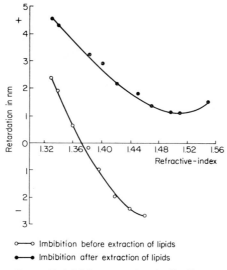

o——o Imbibition before extraction of lipids
●——● Imbibition after extraction of lipids

FIG. 4. Imbibition test of reticulin fibers.

a suitable fluid which had a refractive index of more than 1.45. The imbibition curve of reticulin fibers after extraction with acetone corresponds to that of collagen fibers.

III. Determination of the Melting Point

For this purpose histological sections with reticulin fibers were heated on a specially equipped heating stage of a microscope. At the same time the birefringence was observed. The negative birefringence of the reticulin fibers mounted in glycerol disappears between 55° and 60°C.

As a result of these polarization optical analyses the following conclusions can be drawn: the reticulin fibers after extraction with a lipid solvent have a positive intrinsic and a positive form birefringence. They react to polarized light as do collagen fibers. This means that reticulin fibers have also a fibrillar structure. The imbibition curve obtained by using mixtures of water and glycerol shows, in addition to the birefringence of the fibrillar structures within the reticulin fibers, the existence of additional birefringence of a second substance which is arranged in an oriented manner in or on the fibrils. The second substance produces positive form and negative intrinsic birefringence of the reticulin fibers with respect to their length. Since the melting point of the substance in the reticulin fibers is between 55° and 60°C, and since this substance can be extracted by a lipid solvent, one can be certain that it is composed of

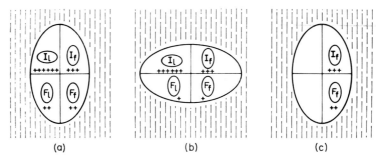

Fig. 5. The birefringence of reticulin fibers demonstrated by index ellipses. (a) Without extraction of lipids; sections mounted in water. (b) Without extraction of lipids; sections mounted in glycerine. (c) After extraction of lipids; sections mounted in water or caedax. I_l = intrinsic birefringence of lipids. F_l = form birefringence of lipids; I_f = intrinsic birefringence of fibers; F_f = form birefringence of fibers.

lipids. Figure 5 shows in the form of index ellipses the combination of various birefringences that can be determined in reticulin fibers.

The intrinsic birefringence of the lipids acts negatively with respect to the length of the reticulin fibers. We therefore can conclude that the long axis of the lipid molecules must be oriented perpendicular to the reticulin fibers. The positive form birefringence with respect to the length of the reticulin fibers which is produced by these lipids proves again that the lipids are arranged in an oriented manner.

The form birefringence of the lipids and the fibrils of the reticulin fibers is very much weakened by mounting the histological sections in glycerol. The strong intrinsic birefringence of the lipids predominates over both the intrinsic birefringence and the remaining form birefringence of the reticulin fibers and gives these fibers negative birefringence with respect to their length, as was demonstrated.

Windrum et al. (13) published their chemical results about reticulin fibers a short time after we had reported that they contain lipids; their report confirmed our findings. Our findings in Gaucher's cells show that similar polarizing optical analyses are also possible in cells (9).

In 1914, Anitschkow (1) found fibrillar structures in these cells. His results were confirmed by electron microscopy (4). In microscopic preparations of Gaucher's cells, cells with structures arranged in the form of a meshwork are found with the polarization microscope. On these structures, lipids are deposited in an oriented manner. In addition, cells are found which show lipid deposits in a crystalloid form. Figure 6 shows a Gaucher's cell of the liver between crossed polars in which the structures forming a meshwork contain lipids.

These structures give positive birefringence with respect to their length

FIG. 6. A Gaucher's cell with net-forming, lipid-containing structures. Frozen section unstained. Human liver. Polarization microscope between crossed polars.

when they are mounted in water or after treatment of the histological sections with alcohol. Mounting in glycerol without pretreatment with lipid solvents leads to the reversal of the optical sign of this birefringence, that is, the structures become negatively birefringent with respect to their length. Figure 7 shows the retardation of the birefringence of these intra-

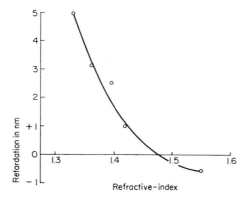

FIG. 7. Imbibition test of Gaucher's cells with net-forming structures.

cellular fibrils after imbibition with mixtures of water and glycerol or with anise oil. This curve shows that the lipids of these cells are arranged in an oriented manner perpendicular to the intracellular fibrils in the same way as those in the reticulin fibers.

The polarization microscope makes possible not only an analysis of lipids arranged in an oriented manner in or on fibrils, but also a measurement of the relative content of the lipids in fibers. The negative birefringence found in preparations mounted in glycerol becomes stronger with increasing lipid content of the fibrils. When one measures the positive birefringence of a fiber mounted in water and afterward the negative birefringence of a fiber mounted in glycerol, a factor can be obtained from these measurements. We use the formula $(a + b)/a$ for its calculation, where a is the retardation in nanometers of the positive birefringence of the fibers mounted in water, and b the retardation in nanometers of fibers mounted in glycerol. The optical sign of birefringence is not a mathematical one. It only means the relation of the active refractive indices in the object. The two retardations are therefore written in the formula as absolute values without taking into consideration the optical signs.

The factor for the normal reticulin fiber in the kidney of the mouse is 2.08 ± 0.63. This value becomes higher for increased amounts of lipids in the fiber and lower for decreased amounts. Using this factor, we were able to demonstrate that the reticulin fibers in liver, spleen, and kidney lost lipids when cortisone was given (7). We also found that the reticulin fibers of these organs lose lipids before the beginning of secondary amyloidosis. The amyloid can only be deposited on these fibers when lipids have been removed from them ($2, 8$).

IV. Summary

A polarization optical analysis has the following characteristics: (1) Determination of the optical sign and the retardation of the given birefringence. (2) Observation of changes of the birefringence using a fluid which extracts some substance from the object. (3) Determination of intrinsic and form birefringence using the imbibition test.

From this analysis one can draw conclusions about the ultrastructure of a given object and, as has been shown for the reticulin fibers, about the amount and the chemical nature of its constituent material. It is important to point out that examinations by these means are possible only with an excellent polarization microscope. An ordinary light microscope which only has a polarizer and an analyzer is not a polarization microscope.

REFERENCES

1. Anitschkow, N., Über experimentell erzeugte Ablagerungen von anisotropen Substanzen in der Milz und im Knochenmark. *Beitr. Pathol. Anat.* **57**, 201–222 (1914).
2. Heller, H., H. P. Missmahl, E. Sohar, and J. Gafni, Amyloidosis: Its differentiation into perireticulin and peri-collagen types. *J. Pathol. Bacteriol.* **88**, 15–34 (1964).

3. Kramer, H., and K. Little, The nature of reticulin. *In* "Nature and Structure of Collagen" (J. T. Randall, ed.), pp. 33–43. Butterworth, London and Washington, D.C., 1953.

4. Marsh, De Q. B., and J. Kautz, The submicroscopic morphology of Gaucher's cells. *Blood* **12**, 324–335 (1957).

5. Missmahl, H. P., Spezifischer polarisationsoptischer Nachweis reticulärer Fasern. *Z. Wiss. Mikroskopie* **62**, 234–236 (1955).

6. Missmahl, H. P., Doppelbrechung der reticulären Fasern und sich hieraus ergebender Nachweis von gerichtet eingelagerten Lipoiden in die reticuläre Faser. *Z. Zellforsch.* **45**, 612–619 (1957).

7. Missmahl, H. P., Experimentelle und klinische Beobachtungen über wechselnden Lipoidgehalt reticulärer Fasern in Leber, Milz und Niere. *Klin. Wochschr.* **36**, 29–34 (1958).

8. Missmahl, H. P., and M. Hartwig, Polarisationsoptische Untersuchungen an der Amyloidsubstanz. *Arch. Pathol. Anat. Physiol.* **324**, 489–508 (1953).

9. Missmahl, H. P., and W. Kübler, Polarisationsoptische Untersuchungen an Gaucher-Zellen. *Frankf. Z. Pathol.* **72**, 190–193 (1961).

10. Schmidt, W. J., Die Doppelbrechung der Markscheide osmierter Nervenfasern. *Z. Mikroskopie* **52**, 158–165 (1935).

11. Schmidt, W. J., Doppelbrechung von Karyoplasma, Cytoplasma und Metaplasma. *Protoplasma-Monogr.* **11** (1937).

12. Schmidt, W. J., Polarisationsoptische Analyse eines Eiweisslipoidsystems, erläutert am Aussenglied der Sehzellen. *Kolloid-Z.* **85**, 137–148 (1938).

13. Windrum, G. M., P. W. Kent, and J. E. Eastone, The constitution of human renal reticulin. *Brit. J. Exptl. Pathol.* **36**, 49–59 (1955).

Part IV

OPTICAL METHODS FOR THE ANALYSIS OF ORIENTATION OF BIOLOGICAL STRUCTURES

PRINCIPLES OF POLARIZED LIGHT

Peter H. Bartels

LABORATORY FOR APPLIED AND THEORETICAL MICROSCOPY,
E. LEITZ, INC.,
NEW YORK, NEW YORK

I. Principle of Analysis

Polarizing microscopes are extremely sensitive and accurate measuring instruments which can be used to analyze the submicroscopic morphology of biological materials. The principle of such an analysis follows these lines of argument: Any structural anisometry in a specimen must cause corresponding differences of the optical properties, in particular, differences in optical density or refractive index. Structural anisometry must, therefore, be accompanied by optical anisotropy. The optical anisotropy of the specimen structure will introduce typical changes in the state of polarization of transilluminating light. The nature of these changes will be discussed in simple terms in the main part of the present paper. Measurement of these changes then permits conclusions as to the optical anisotropy that caused them. With the optical anisotropy known, the structural anisometry follows.

The practical operation of a polarizing microscope is relatively simple. The interpretation of specimen behavior requires some knowledge of the principles of polarized light. It is not necessary, however, to have a thorough knowledge of crystal optics in order to use the method with success. The required notions can be derived quite independently and only to the extent that they are needed.

II. Light Polarization

The propagation of light takes place in the form of electromagnetic waves. The word "wave" implies a periodical process. For the present purpose it is sufficient to consider only the periodical changes of the strength of the electrical field. This may be indicated by an arrow (see

Fig. 1), called the "electric vector." Vectors are used to describe quantities which have not only a magnitude, but also a direction. The magnitude is expressed by the length of the vector. In the case of the electric vector of

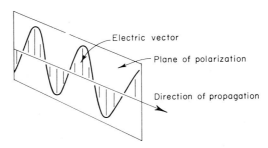

FIG. 1. Schematic drawing representing electrical field of a light wave.

a light wave, this changes periodically. Its direction is perpendicular to the direction of propagation of the light wave: light is a transversal wave. The oscillation takes place in a certain plane which is called the plane of vibration, or polarization. Light waves always have a certain plane of vibration and a certain state of polarization, for example, linear, elliptical or circular, as will be explained later.

In a beam of light which comes from a light source, the planes of vibration may assume all orientations, and the light may have all states of polarization. Natural light is statistically unpolarized. What is meant specifically by the expression "polarized light" is a beam of light in which the planes of vibration of all light waves are parallel to each other and where the state of polarization is uniform for all light waves (see Fig. 2).

FIG. 2. Schematic drawing of cross section of a beam of "natural light" on the left, and of "polarized light" on the right. The state of polarization here was assumed to be linear in all cases; normally there could also be elliptically or circularly polarized light. The light on the left is "statistically unpolarized," as it comes from a light source.

Light with a uniform state of polarization can be obtained from a normal beam of light by sending it through a polarizer or, more generally, a "polar."

III. Polars

A polar is an element that will transmit only light with the one plane of vibration that corresponds to the polar's own plane of vibration. All light entering a polar will immediately be split into two components: one parallel to the polar's plane of vibration, the other perpendicular to the polar's plane of vibration. The first is transmitted, and the second is eliminated (see Fig. 3). There are two types of polars, filter polars and

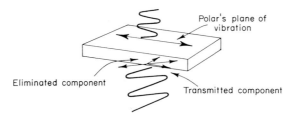

Fig. 3. The polar only transmits light that oscillates in its own plane of vibration.

prism polars. Filter polars consist of thin sheets of plastic material that have been oriented by stretching and have been stained with dichroic substances. All these dichroic particles are embedded in an oriented manner. A dichroic substance, a dye, for example (see Fig. 4), has coefficients

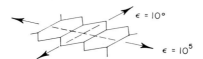

Fig. 4. Schematic drawing of dichroic dye particle. High absorption is observed for light oscillating in one plane and practically no absorption in a perpendicular plane.

of absorption that depend upon the plane of polarization of the light. In one direction the dye molecule absorbs very little; in a perpendicular direction the coefficient of absorption may be very high. Filter polarizers eliminate all light not parallel to their own plane of vibration by absorption. This means that high light intensities may overheat and damage the filter, but filter polars have the advantage of not restricting the condenser aperture. Perfected to a high degree, filter polarizers may give extinction ratios of 100,000 : 1. An important requirement is neutrality. The extinction ratio of a filter polarizer should be independent of the wavelength. Prism polarizers (Fig. 5) may give higher extinction ratios. They normally consist of calcite prisms cut with a certain orienta-

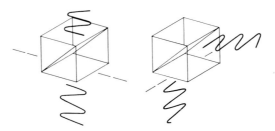

FIG. 5. Principle of a prism polar. On the left the light has a plane of polarization such that it is fully transmitted; on the right, it is totally reflected out of the system and not transmitted.

tion to the calcite crystal axis and cemented together in such a fashion that for light of one plane of polarization they act like a plane glass plate. For light with a plane of polarization perpendicular to the first mentioned one, they act as a totally reflecting surface.

IV. Polarizing Microscope

A polarizing microscope is principally a microscope similar to any other one, but equipped with some special optics and accessories. (See Fig. 6.) The first essential component is a polar, which is mounted below

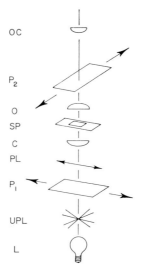

FIG. 6. Principal components of a polarizing microscope and their arrangement: L, light source; UPL, unpolarized light; P_1, first polar, polarizer; PL, linearly polarized light; C, condenser, strain-free; SP, specimen; O, objective, strain-free; P_2, second polar, crossed to the first one, analyzer; OC, ocular.

the condenser. This polar is called the polarizer. The light is statistically unpolarized as it comes from the light source. After it has passed the polarizer, it is linearly polarized. The specimen is illuminated with linearly polarized light. Above the objective a second polar is mounted. The plane of vibration of this second polar is crossed to the plane of vibration of the polarizer under the condenser. When there is no specimen in the object plane, the light coming from the polarizer will have no component in the direction of this second, crossed polar. The field of view will appear completely dark, or extinguished. The reason for this arrangement of "crossed polars" becomes apparent when one considers what kind of information about the specimen one wants to obtain from a study under the polarizing microscope. The principal question is this: Does the specimen in any way influence the state of polarization of the trans-illuminating light? If the specimen in no way changes the state of polarization of the linearly polarized, illuminating light, no light will pass the second polar and the field will remain extinguished. But, if the specimen does change the state of polarization in the very least, the light will necessarily obtain a component in the direction of the second polar. The specimen will then appear bright on a dark background. Since the second polar is used to analyze the influence of the specimen, it is called the analyzer.

Any such influence upon the state of polarization of the illuminating light must, of course, come from the specimen, and the specimen only. The optics in condenser and objective must, therefore, be "strain-free." Strain in optics introduces optical inhomogeneities which would brighten the field, reduce the extinction ratio, and introduce errors.

V. Birefringence

Principally there exist two different kinds of materials. First, there are materials that do not influence the state of polarization of light. These materials are called isotropic. They are optically homogeneous, have only one refractive index, and no direction of preference whatsoever. Isotropic materials cannot, of course, be analyzed in a polarizing microscope. They will remain extinguished at all orientations. One can find out nothing more about them than that they are isotropic.

Materials that do influence the state of polarization of the illuminating light are called anisotropic. They have two or three refractive indexes in different directions of space and have preferred directions, which are called optic axes. Since they change the state of polarization of the il-luminating light, they will give it a component in the direction of the plane of vibration of the analyzer, and will thus appear bright on the extinguished background.

Anisotropic materials are also called "birefringent," which refers to the fact that not one, but two different refractive indexes are effective. The linearly polarized, illuminating light will split up into two components which oscillate in the two directions of the two refractive indexes, perpendicular to each other (see Fig. 9).

The influence that a birefringent specimen will take upon the state of polarization will depend upon a number of factors. Among others, these are the difference between the two effective refractive indexes, the geometric specimen thickness, and the orientation of the specimen with respect to the polarizer's plane of vibration.

A birefringent specimen placed upon the microscope stage will, however, not appear bright at all orientations. Instead, upon rotation of the microscope stage it will pass through four positions of extinction and four positions of maximal brightness. The explanation for this behavior is as follows (see Fig. 7).

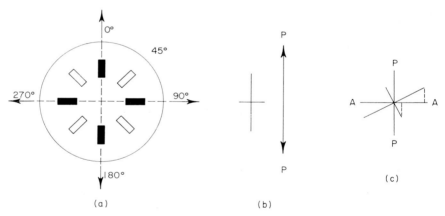

(a)   (b)

FIG. 7. (a) The four positions of full extinction and the four diagonal positions of maximal brightness through which a birefringent specimen will pass during a full rotation of the microscope stage. (b) Of the two effective indexes in the specimen, one is parallel to the direction of the polarizer P–P. The specimen therefore seems to have only this one refractive index and remains extinguished. (c) The diagonal position is indicated, with both effective indexes having components in direction of P–P and, of course, A–A, the direction of the analyzer.

The two directions in which the birefringent specimen offers different refractive indexes are perpendicular to each other. In those orientations where the direction of one of them is parallel to the plane of vibration of the polarizer, the other will offer no component. In this position the specimen seems to have only the one refractive index and will appear extinguished. In a position 90° from this, the other refractive index direction will be parallel to the plane of vibration of the polarizer, and the first will offer no component. So here will be another position of extinction. A rotation by 180° will repeat the first position, rotation by 270° the second. But in any position exactly 45° from a position of extinction, the specimen will appear in maximal brightness. In this position both directions will contribute with their maximal components in respect to both the crossed polarizer and the analyzer.

VI. Operation of Polarizing Microscope

The first step in the operation of a polarizing microscope is to cross analyzer and polarizer, so that the field appears at maximal extinction. The specimen is placed on the stage; then is slowly rotated. A birefringent specimen will go through four positions of extinction. One of them is selected as a reference position. It tells how the directions of the two effective refractive indexes are oriented with respect to the physical shape of the specimen (Fig. 8). From this position of extinction the stage

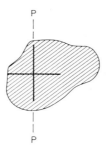

Fig. 8. The position of extinction reveals the orientation of the direction of the two effective refractive indexes with respect to the physical shape of the specimen structure.

is rotated by exactly 45°. The specimen will then appear in maximal brightness. This is the position in which all further measurements are carried out, and to which all further theoretical discussions apply.

VII. Relative Sign of Birefringence

To determine the "relative sign" of the birefringence or to find out which of the two effective refractive indexes is the larger and which is the smaller one, a comparison plate is used. This is usually known as "gypsum plate," "Red I" order plate, full waveplate, or "sensitive tint" plate. The comparison plate consists of an oriented plane parallel piece of gypsum, ground and polished to a certain thickness so that its aniso-tropic effect will produce the polarization color "Red I" over the whole field when the plate is inserted in the diagonal tube slot above the ob-jective.

The meaning and the origin of the polarization colors will be further discussed below. Here it will be sufficient to say that with increasing effect of the specimen upon the state of polarization of the transillu-minating light, a sequence of typical "polarization colors" become visible, and "Red I" is a very distinctive and easily recognized polarization color. The orientation of the two effective indexes in the comparison plate is, of course, known and indicated on its mount. The direction of the "slow ray" is usually called γ; this is the direction of the higher refractive index.

When the higher index of the comparison plate runs parallel to the higher index in the specimen, the effects will add up and a "higher polarization color" will result, for example, a brilliant blue. When, how-ever, the higher indexes of comparison plate and specimen are crossed, their effects will subtract, and a polarization color lower than "Red I" will result, for example, a bright yellow. One also speaks of "additive position" and "subtractive position."

Once one has thus established which of the two effective indexes has the higher value, one can make a statement about its orientation with respect to the specimen structure under examination.

In the case of a filament, when the higher index runs parallel to the long extension, one would call the "relative sign of the birefringence" positive with respect to the filament. In the case of a lamella, one might refer the relative sign of the birefringence to the orthogonal on the plane of the lamella; on a hollow tubular structure and also when spherical structures are involved one might refer it to the radius. The relative sign of the birefringence is not necessarily identical with the absolute sign.

VIII. Principle of Compensation

The next logical step in the examination of the material would be to measure the difference between the two effective indexes. This is done by means of compensators, which are inserted in the tube slot after the specimen has been brought into an exact 45°, or diagonal, position. The compensator control knob is then operated until the specimen detail, or more exactly, the one spot in the specimen detail which is compensated, appears extinguished. The specimen influence has thus been "compensated," and it remains to read the difference between the two compensator settings at the start and at the point of compensation.

IX. Optic Path Difference and State of Polarization

To explain what physically occurs and how the specimen really affects the transilluminating light, one should start with a simple model. For the time being the use of monochromatic light will be assumed.

Linearly polarized light comes from the polarizer. In the birefringent specimen it splits into two components, which oscillate in two directions at right angles to each other and each at 45° with respect to the polarizer. For each of the two components the specimen has a different refractive index, denoted as n_0 and n_e in Fig. 9. Optical path is defined as the prod-

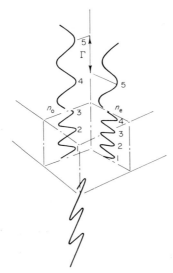

Fig. 9. The transilluminating light is split in the birefringent, diagonally oriented specimen into two components. Two different refractive indexes are effective for these two components; they will thus suffer a relative shift, or a "retardation." A count of wave crests makes the comparison easier.

uct of geometric thickness times refractive index. Through a specimen of a given geometric thickness d, one component will travel the optical path dn_0, the other dn_e.

In a specimen of higher optical density than air, both will be slowed down, but one will be slowed down more than the other. This optic path difference will lead to a change in relative position, or a "phase difference" between the components.

The total phase difference will depend upon two factors, the geometric thickness of the specimen and the refractive index difference in the two directions, or the birefringence. If the phase difference, or retardation, is called Γ, one arrives at the equation $\Gamma = d(n_e - n_o)$. This optical path difference is also called the retardation because it retards one wave relative to the other and leads to a phase difference, as can be seen from Fig. 9.

One can measure such phase differences either in fractions of a wavelength, for instance, $\lambda/30$, or one can express it in a corresponding number of millimicrons; $\lambda/30$ would be 18 mμ for monochromatic light of 540 mμ. One may also express it in degrees (Fig. 10), since one wavelength

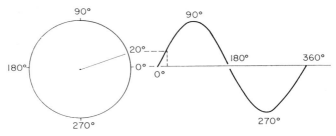

FIG. 10. The phases of the periodical wave process on the right can be described as fractions of a complete cycle and then expressed in degrees.

or 540 mμ could be described as a complete cycle of a vibration, corresponding to 360°; $\lambda/30$ in this description would correspond to a phase difference of 20°. As the transilluminating light emerges from the specimen, the following conditions persist. There are two linearly polarized vibrations, which are polarized in two directions at right angles to each other and which have a phase difference. They will be superposed on each other and lead to a resultant vibration. One must now ask what will happen when two such vibrations are superposed. For this consideration the trace of each vibration is drawn, as indicated by the thick line in Fig. 11a.

A complete cycle of a periodical process may be described in degrees as 360°. A fraction of such a cycle, or its "phase," can also be described in degrees, as shown in Fig. 10. The phases of the linear vibrations as shown in Fig. 11a are shown in Fig. 11b.

First, some special cases will be discussed. The first assumption will be that the two vibrations have no phase difference. They start at the same moment, and reach their turning point at 90° at the same time; both pass the 180° point at the same time, which coincides with the 0° point, only they pass in a reverse direction. The two vibrations are "in

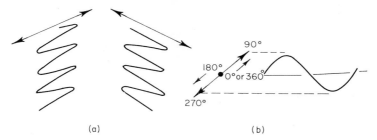

(a)   (b)

Fig. 11. To examine what happens when two linearly polarized waves are super-posed, it is more practical to look at their traces, here indicated (a) as the two thick lines on top. The trace is the line that the wave would draw in a plane perpendicular to the direction of propagation or the "head-on" view of the sche-matically drawn wave. (b) The phases of the periodical vibration are transferred to the trace.

phase." The resulting vibration can be derived strictly from a paral-lelogram of forces. It will be a linear vibration which always is exactly between the two components.

The next case would be a phase difference of 360°. Since after 360° a full cycle is completed, the same conditions exist as if there were no phase difference, and the same linear resultant is obtained (Fig. 12a).

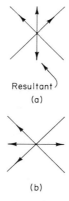

Resultant
(a)

(b)

Fig. 12. Superposition of two vibrations, here indicated by their traces, which are linearly polarized and at right angles to each other. (a) No phase difference, or phase difference 360°, 720°, and so on. (b) Phase difference of a half cycle, or 180°.

A phase difference of 180° or half a wavelength means that when one vibration starts as before, the other starts from the same point, but in the direction toward the 270° turning point. The resultant vibration will again be linear, but its plane of polarization will be rotated by 90° from the ones obtained from zero or a 360° phase difference (Fig. 12b).

If there exists a 90° phase difference between the two vibrations, one vibration just passes through the starting point (zero), as represented by the central point in Fig. 13(a), when the other is at a turning point, as indicated by the four peripheral points in Fig. 13(a). The first will,

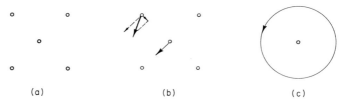

(a)   (b)   (c)

FIG. 13. Construction of resulting vibration from superposition of two linearly polarized vibrations with 90° phase difference. See text for explanation of (a), (b), and (c).

when in the center at this instant, make no contribution to the resultant, and with the second vibration being at the same instant at one of the turning points, this already yields four points of the resulting vibration. If one considers the situation a moment later [Fig. 13(b)], one vibration has just passed the turning point and moves toward the center, while the other has moved away from the center. If the resultant is then constructed and this procedure is repeated for each succeeding instant, one arrives at the complete resulting vibration, which is circular, as shown in Fig. 13(c). A 90° phase difference between the two components leads to circularly polarized light. This is what a lambda-quarter plate, or quarter-wave plate, does. Thus the resulting vibration has been found for five special cases: a linear resultant for the phase difference 0°, a circular vibration for the phase difference 90°, and again a linear vibration for the phase difference 180°, this time with its plane of polarization rotated. Then at 270° a case corresponding to the 90° phase difference results, and again a circular vibration is obtained.

For all other phase differences one would obtain elliptically polarized light. In fact, elliptical polarization is the general case for which the

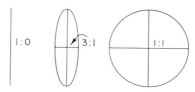

FIG. 14. Trace of a resulting vibration: on the left a linear vibration, in the center elliptical, and on the right circular. The first and the last actually are border cases of the general case of elliptical state of polarization.

linear polarization and the circular polarization are special cases. An ellipse is characterized by the ratio of its two axes, which might be, for example, 3 : 1. A circle could be considered as a special ellipse with an axis ratio of 1 : 1, and a linear polarization as an ellipse with an axis

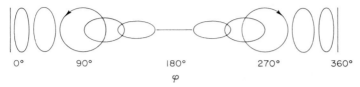

FIG. 15. Ellipticity of light emerging from a birefringent specimen as a function of the phase difference introduced by the specimen.

ratio 1 : 0 (see Fig. 14). So, if one asks for the state of polarization of light emerging from a specimen which introduces increasing phase differences, one can observe (see Fig. 15) that lack of a phase difference means the specimen has either no birefringence or the geometrical thickness zero. The light will pass through as it came from the polarizer

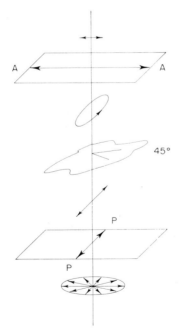

FIG. 16. A birefringent specimen in diagonal position imparts an ellipticity to the transilluminating light. The analyzer will only transmit that component which is parallel to its plane of vibration.

(linearly polarized), will have no component in the direction of the analyzer, and will be completely extinguished. As the specimen begins to introduce a small phase difference, the emerging light will have a very slender elliptical polarization with the long axis parallel to the polarizer and with a small component in the direction of the analyzer. As the phase difference increases, the ellipse will grow broader, until at a 90° phase difference circularly polarized light is obtained. Then the ellipses will have a reversed axis ratio, with the long axis parallel to the analyzer. The ellipse will become flatter and flatter, until at a 180° phase difference a linear vibration is obtained which is parallel to the analyzer. Phase differences larger than 180° lead to elliptical vibrations again, with a reverse sense of rotation, until at 270° a circular vibration results, which with further increased phase differences finally becomes a linear vibration again. Whatever the state of polarization of the light emerging from the specimen—linear, elliptical, or circular—the analyzer will transmit only the component parallel to its own plane of vibration (see Fig. 16).

X. Measurements with Compensators

If the state of polarization of the light emerging from the specimen is analyzed, one can exactly calculate the phase difference which it has introduced, and thus measure its birefringence. The method of measuring is that of compensation. A compensator is made of birefringent material which gives, depending upon its orientation, certain ellipticities to the light passing through it. These ellipticities can be varied by either tilting or rotating the compensator in order to give different orientations. A compensator drum permits an exact reading of its orientation, which corresponds to a certain ellipticity. The compensator is adjusted so that it introduces just the same ellipticity that the specimen has introduced, but in a reverse sense. It will thus exactly eliminate the specimen influence and give back to the illuminating light that linear state of polarization which it had before it passed the specimen. This means that it will no longer have a component in the direction of the analyzer, and the specimen will appear extinguished, though now in a 45° position. The compensator drum can be directly calibrated in phase difference, or path difference.

The compensator reading directly yields a value of Γ, from which one can obtain the effective birefringence by dividing by the geometric thickness d: $\Gamma/d = (n_e - n_0)$.

There are different types of compensators. The most widely used are the Berek compensator, the Senarmont method of compensation, and the Brace–Koehler compensator. These are distinguished from each other by the measuring range which they cover, and one obtains more accurate results when a compensator is chosen that covers a range not much greater than the specimen birefringence demands.

The Berek compensator consists of a calcite plate cut with respect to its optic axis so that it acts like a plane glass plate when left in a horizontal position. Tilting this plate lets one index become less and less effective, so that with increasing tilt angle an increasing anisotropy is produced. The standard Berek compensator covers retardations of up to four wavelengths (chosen from the green center of the spectrum) or around 2200-mμ optic path difference. To give a numerical example, such a retardation would mean, in a 10-μ section, a birefringence as follows:

$$\Gamma = d(n_e - n_0),$$
$$2200 \ m\mu = 10,000 \ m\mu \times (n_e - n_0),$$
$$0.22 = difference \ in \ refractive \ indexes.$$

The accuracy of the Berek compensator is approximately 2 mμ at the low end of its measuring range.

The Senarmont method employs a monochromatic green filter and a quarter-wave plate inserted in subparallel position (not the usual $\lambda/4$ plate) below the analyzer. The superposition of the elliptically polarized light coming from the specimen and the circular polarization introduced by the quarter-wave plate leads to a linear vibration again. However, the plane of vibration of this resulting linear vibration is rotated, and the amount of rotation is a direct function of the ellipticity of the light coming from the specimen. To measure, therefore, one simply rotates the analyzer until the specimen appears dark. The retardation is a direct function of the angle of necessary analyzer rotation. The measuring range of this inexpensive and elegant method is approximately 550-mμ optical path difference.

The Brace–Koehler compensator is used for very small retardations. It consists of a very thin Mica plate and will, upon rotation of this plate in its mount, compensate up to the birefringence of the plate, usually up to 1/10, 1/20, or 1/30 of a wavelength. Under favorable conditions, optical path differences of as little as 0.5 mμ, or 5 Å, can be measured with such a compensator. This, in a 10 μ-thick specimen, corresponds to a difference of refractive indexes of only 0.00005.

XI. Polarization Colors

It remains to explain the polarization colors. From now on a polychromatic "white" light source will be assumed. A specimen of a certain geometric thickness and birefringence is assumed to be in the position of maximal brightness, or at 45° position. For one wavelength out of the continuous spectrum the condition for a path difference of exactly one wavelength, or a phase difference of 360°, will then certainly be fulfilled.

A path difference of exactly one, or a multiple of one wavelength, means a resultant vibration for light of this specific wavelength which is linear and has the same orientation as the light which comes from the polarizer. This means that its plane of polarization is crossed to the plane of vibration of the analyzer, and that light of this wavelength will not be transmitted. For all other wavelengths not a linear, but an elliptical state of polarization will prevail, so all other wavelengths will be transmitted.

This is, then, how polarization colors originate: From the full spectrum of the light source which gives the impression "white light," one spectral region is missing. Assuming that the path difference is 550 mμ, the green light will have gone through a complete cycle of ellipticity, and arrive at the analyzer linearly polarized. It will not be transmitted. Red, yellow, and blue light, however, are transmitted, and these together give the impression of purple. So if one sees purple detail in the specimen one knows that the path difference in the specimen must be exactly 550 mμ. If the analyzer is rotated by 90° and thus made parallel to the polarizer, one should then see the green, and the green light only. In a polarizing microscope with crossed polarizer and analyzer, one always sees the complementary colors to the missing wavelengths. A thicker specimen might just fulfill the condition of a path difference of, for example, three wavelengths of green light. This would make a total path difference of 1650 mμ, which at the same time, however, would mean that two wavelengths of red light of 825 mμ wavelength each would be extinguished.

Consequently the polarization color for this path difference is different, since red light of a certain wavelength is now also missing from the full spectrum. In fact, each path difference is indicated by a typical polarization color. The polarization colors are divided into "orders," according to units of green wavelengths.

The first order appears for path differences from 0 to 550 mμ. The second-order colors appear for path differences from 550 to 1100 mμ, and so on. The polarization colors of the higher orders become fainter, until very high path differences again lead to a white polarization color. This white is called "white of higher order," in contrast to the grayish-white polarization color of very small path differences, which is called white of the first order.

XII. Indicatrix

For the interpretation of the measured values, a brief explanation of some terms used in the analysis of structures in polarized light is necessary. An understanding of specimen behavior in polarized light will be much easier if one completely ignores the actual physical shape of the specimen and rather directs his attention to the orientation of the optical characteristics. The physical shape, for instance, of a specimen structure in a thin section is in many cases a complete product of chance, depending entirely upon how one happened to cut the section. What is typical for this structure, however, is its optical constants, and one must look for their values and orientation. So the behavior of a given detail during manipulation under the polarizing microscope is not described in terms of its physical orientation, but in terms of the orientation of its optical determinatives. To give an example: the examination is started by rotating the structure into a position of extinction. Then one knows that one of its two effective refractive indexes runs parallel to the polarizer, the other parallel to the analyzer. The actual physical position of the structure at this position is unimportant.

The optical behavior of detail under the polarizing microscope is described by means of a geometrical symbol, called the indicatrix. The indicatrix is a three-dimensional model which exactly represents the optical properties of any given material or structure. This indicatrix is imagined to be inscribed in the structure under study and to describe the behavior of the structure in terms of indicatrix orientation. Only the cross section of the indicatrix is effective. This cross section will generally have the shape of an ellipse and is called the index ellipse. For use as indicatrixes one had to invent symbols which describe the behavior and represent the optical properties of various materials. Isotropic materials show the same behavior under the polarizing microscope at all orientations. They always appear in the same way—they remain extinguished. Furthermore, they are optically homogeneous and have the same refractive index in all directions of space. The appropriate symbol for them is a sphere. Regardless of from what angle or from which direction one looks at a sphere, its cross section will always remain a circle. The radius of the sphere represents the refractive index, which is the same in all directions of space—a sphere with a large radius is chosen as an indicatrix for isotropic materials with a high refractive index, and a sphere with a small radius as indicatrix for materials with a small refractive index. There is no preferred direction, no optical axis.

Now consider anisotropic materials, first those with two refractive indexes. These have one preferred direction, or optical axis, and are also called uniaxial materials. One of the two refractive indexes in uniaxial materials is always equally effective and always has the same value, regardless of the orientation of the indicatrix. This refractive index is called the ordinary refractive index n_0. The other refractive index is different from the ordinary one and is called the extraordinary refractive index n_e. It becomes more or less effective, depending on the orientation of the indicatrix with respect to the optical axis of the microscope. Assuming that the extraordinary refractive index is larger than the ordinary one, the indicatrix then has the shape of an ellipsoid of revolution, the long axis of which represents the extraordinary refractive index n_e; and the short axis, the ordinary refractive index n_0. The former index will be effective to its full value when the long axis of this ellipsoid of revolution is oriented exactly in the plane of the microscope stage and

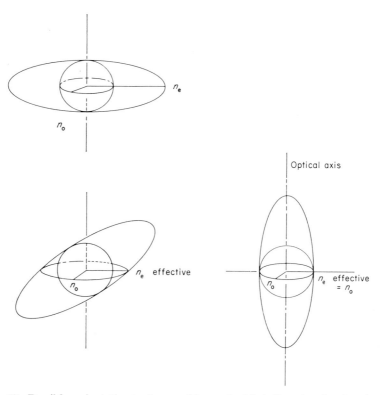

FIG. 17. Possible orientations of a positive uniaxial indicatrix, showing how n_e varies in its effective value.

is therefore perpendicular to the optical axis of the microscope. If, however, the indicatrix includes an angle with the microscope axis, the index
ellipse will have a smaller axis ratio. Finally, when the direction of n_e
and the optical axis of the microscope coincide, the cross section of the
indicatrix has become a circle, and n_e has assumed its smallest value, the
same as n_0. In this position the material seems to be isotropic, and this
preferred direction is called an optical axis. One must, of course, know
how much of the extraordinary refractive index is effective to calculate
the true or principal birefringence of a material. This is shown in Fig. 17.
Materials in which n_e is larger than n_0 are called positive birefringent.
The indicatrix has the shape of a cigar. Other uniaxial materials have
an n_e which is smaller than n_0. The indicatrix then has a lenticular shape,
and the birefringence is called negative.

Materials with three different refractive indexes in the three directions
of space have two optical axes and are called biaxial. The indicatrix is
no longer a body of revolution, but a general ellipsoid (see Fig. 18). The

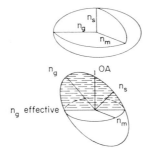

FIG. 18. Indicatrix of biaxial material, with the three indexes n_g, n_m, and n_s. When
it is tilted around n_m, there are two positions where the effectiveness of n_g is reduced to just the value of n_m. Looking down these directions the effective index
ellipse is a circle. Under these two tilt angles, one is looking down the two optical
axes of the material.

index ellipse will, with two exceptions, always be an ellipse with two
effective refractive indexes. Suppose there are three refractive indexes,
all different from each other. If the indicatrix is now tilted in such a
fashion that the largest refractive index is not fully effective, but only
with a smaller value, then there must be one position in which the
largest refractive index is just as effective as the medium one. The index
ellipse in this case is a circle; the material appears to be isotropic, and
for this direction there exists an optical axis. Such a tilt around the
direction of the medium refractive index can, of course, be carried out
either in one or in the other direction, so that a second optical axis

appears under a symmetrical tilting angle on the other side. Both optical axes are in the plane of the largest and the smallest refractive index.

The true shape and orientation of the indicatrix can be obtained by determining the relative sign of the birefringence on a number of principal sections through the specimen and by measuring the index ellipse on these sections. The indicatrix fully describes the optical anisotropy of the specimen. To make the transition from an indicatrix to a description of how submicroscopic elements may be arranged in an anisometric manner, one must consider that several factors contribute to the optical anisotropy.

The measured birefringence is always a total birefringence. To this, two factors contribute. One is a material characteristic, and this is called the intrinsic birefringence. The other is a textural influence, and its contribution is called form birefringence. Intrinsic and form birefringence may add up or they may partially compensate each other when they have opposite signs. It is possible by the technique of imbibition analysis to separate these two contributing factors.

The application of these useful techniques to biological materials has been discussed extensively by Bennett, Schmidt, and Frey-Wyssling.

GENERAL REFERENCES

Bennett, H. S., The Microscopical Investigation of Biological Materials in Polarized Light, p. 591. McClung, *In* "Handbook of microscopical technique," 3rd ed. New York, Hoeber, 1950.

Frey-Wyssling, A., "Submicroscopic Morphology of Protoplasm and Its Derivatives," Elsevier, Amsterdam and New York, 1948.

Schmidt, W. J., Instrumente und Methoden zur mikroskopischen Untersuchung optisch anisotroper Materialien mit Ausschluss der Kristalle. *In* "Handbuch der Mikroskopie in der Technik" (H. Freund, ed.), pp. 147–315. Umschau-Verlag, Frankfurt, 1957.

BIREFRINGENCE AND DICHROISM
OF DYES AND THEIR SIGNIFICANCE
IN THE DETECTION
OF ORIENTED STRUCTURES

H. P. Missmahl

DEPARTMENT OF MEDICINE,
UNIVERSITY OF TÜBINGEN,
TÜBINGEN, GERMANY

Tissues and cellular structures on which birefringent and dichroic dyes are deposited with a certain orientation show the combined optical effects of all the participating dye particles. The double refraction and dichroism of such stained tissues are very strong and easily observable under polarizing microscopes.

Such oriented deposits of dyes occur naturally or are produced by staining tissues with appropriate dyes. Among naturally stained objects we find the blue chitin of the fresh-water mite (Hydrachnidae) (17), the oriented embedding of iron oxide on the surface of the teeth of reptiles and fishes (14, 16), and the feathers of some birds (13, 17, 18). Examples of enhanced birefringence or artificially produced dichroism are mitochondria (10), gliafibrils (19), plant fibers (20), and amyloid (2–6). Thus, oriented deposits of dyes have been demonstrated in widely differing structures.

The basic units of these structures are oriented, which means that these tissues or cellular structures should exhibit birefringence even without dyes. However, usually this double refraction is so weak that it can be demonstrated only with difficulty, if at all. A typical example is the birefringence of the granules of basophilic leukocytes (8, 9), which can be observed only after supravital staining with toluidine blue.

The oriented deposition of dyes on the tissues usually enables one to observe the fine structure with a polarizing microscope and demonstrates the arrangement of the basic units. For such work one must know the exact optical properties of these dyes.

There are two ways in which a polarizing microscope can be utilized for these investigations:

(1) *The demonstration and optical analysis of birefringence:* The object is observed between crossed polars. This means that the planes of polarization of the polarizer and analyzer are mutually perpendicular (1, 11, 12, 15).

(2) *The demonstration and optical analysis of dichroism:* The object is placed above the polarizer and observed without analyzer.

Double refraction, or birefringence, means that the periodic variations which compose light occur in two mutually perpendicular planes. The velocity of light differs in these two planes, and one of the rays is retarded. Naturally we also observe a different index of refraction for each of the two rays. A birefringent material is said to be dichroic if it absorbs one of the polarized rays more strongly than the other; owing to the different absorption for different planes of light vibrations, the material appears to vary in color when observed in different directions. Table I

TABLE I

EXAMPLES OF BIREFRINGENT AND DICHROITIC DYES

Acridine orange	Methyl violet
Amido Black 10B	Nile blue
Congo red	Orange G
Cresyl violet	Ponceau 2R
Crystal violet	Rivanol
Evans blue	Sirius red
Janus green B	Sudan Black B
Methylene blue	Toluidine blue
Methyl orange	Trypan blue

shows some birefringent and dichroic dyes which are suitable for such investigations.

In this chapter the optical properties of Congo red and toluidine blue will be shown, and some generally applicable rules will be derived from these examples.

Congo red is easily deposited on amyloid in histological sections (2–6). Amyloid is a substance of fibrous structures which is deposited along fibers of connective tissues as the result of certain diseases or hereditary trends. Amyloid stained with Congo red appears green if observed between crossed polars. Clockwise rotation of the elliptic compensator intensifies this green color. Counter-clockwise rotation of the compensator causes a yellow appearance.

In order to observe dichroism one places the object above the polarizer, not using the analyzer. The object is therefore illuminated by plane polarized light. If the plane of polarization of white light is parallel to the long axis of the dye particles, Congo red appears deep red. This color changes to light red if the plane of polarization is perpendicular to the long axis. It is possible to observe all these phenomena by simply smearing Congo red on microscope slides (4). A few drops of the dye solution are put on a slide and dried by smearing with a glass rod. The optical properties of Congo red can also be demonstrated by means of flow birefringence (20).

How are these color changes brought about?

a. *The appearance of the anomalous polarization color.* The green polarization color can be explained, like all other birefringent and dichroic color phenomena, on a physical basis. To do this one measures the path differences of the double refraction in monochromatic light of different wavelengths.

For Congo red the curve in Fig. 1 is obtained. Congo red is a strong

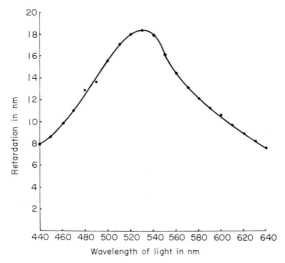

FIG. 1. Congo red. Dispersion of birefringence.

double refractor in green light, but only weakly so in red and blue. The direction of this double refraction is positive with respect to the long axis of the dye molecule.

In histological sections and in cells there is a thin layer of dye; only the birefringence of green light is observed. The polarization color is therefore green. The absorption of the green light can only be observed in thick layers. With an increase in thickness, the color changes first to yellow, then to red. Such colors should be called anomalous polarization colors; terms such as "dichroism between crossed polars" or "metachromasia" sometimes used in the literature are incorrect.

b. *Changes in the anomalous colors of polarization of Congo red by compensation.* Rotation of the elliptic compensator during illumination with white light first compensates the weak birefringence of red and blue light. The weak components of red and blue light which accompany the green anomalous color are thereby extinguished. This causes the intensification of the anomalous green light of clockwise rotation of the compensator. Counterclockwise rotation of the compensator does not cancel the double refraction of the embedded Congo red, but brightens the field of view, thus enhancing the intensity of the white light. This causes an increasing yellow color upon counterclockwise rotation.

c. *Dichroism of Congo red.* The dichroism of a dye can be measured with a polarization microscope by a method devised by Wälchli (20). First the coefficient K is measured, which expresses the dependence of the absorption on the planes of polarization of the light in the object. Then the object is illuminated with polarized light and placed so that the plane of polarization is first parallel with the plane of polarization of the ordinary ray in the object. Next the apparatus is rotated so that the plane of polarization of the incident light becomes parallel with the plane of polarization of the extraordinary ray in the object. In both cases the absorption is measured.

In the case of Congo red, Wälchli found, and we have confirmed, the

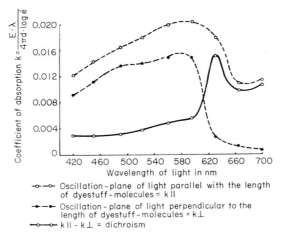

FIG. 2. Congo red. Dichroism measured as absorption of light in the two oscillation planes. After Wälchli (20).

curves exhibited in Fig. 2. These curves show that Congo red absorbs green light very strongly if it is parallel with the length of its molecules and weakly if it is perpendicular to it.

The dichroism of this dye is strongest in green light. This again accounts for the fact that thin layers of oriented particles of Congo red have a green anomalous color of polarization. One plane of polarization of particles of Congo red is quite transparent to green light.

Several observations can be made using this understanding of the optical phenomena of Congo red–dyed amyloid.

The green color of polarization proves that the dye particles are oriented. Such an orientation is only possible if the ultrastructure of the object is oriented. All structures which show anomalous colors of polarization, whether naturally or as a result of staining, must be composed of oriented units. In the case of amyloid we know that it is a fibrous structure and exhibits positive intrinsic birefringence and form birefringence by itself.

Once the optical properties are known, one can find the direction of the main axis of the dye particles by rotating the compensator. This can then be confirmed by observing the dichroism. From the direction of the dye particles one can determine the direction of the basic units of the ultrastructure on which the dye was deposited. In amyloid the particles are deposited parallel to the length of the fibers. It is now possible to establish the direction of amyloid fibers in all histological slides dyed with Congo red. This method next enabled us to detect otherwise undetectable minute foci of pathological deposits of amyloid in connective tissue.

The second example concerns toluidine blue. This dye enabled us recently to prove the birefringence of the granules of basophilic leukocytes. We incubated 1.6 ml of blood citrated with 0.4 ml of sodium citrate solution for 10 minutes with 0.2 ml of a 5% solution of toluidine blue. By this method the basophilic granules acquire an anomalous color of polarization, which is varied by rotation of the elliptic compensator (9).

If citrated blood is incubated for 1 hour with toluidine blue (8), small birefringent particles are observed in the protoplasm of the leukocytes. The structure of these particles is also explained by optical analyses of toluidine blue. The dispersion, that is, variation of birefringence with wavelength, and the dichroism of toluidine blue are determined after deposition on amyloid and slide smears (7). The dispersion curve of the double refraction of this dye differs very much from that of Congo red (Fig. 3). Toluidine blue is positively birefringent with respect to the main axis of the particles for wavelengths between 420 and 510 nm. Light of longer wavelengths shows negative birefringence. Negative bire-

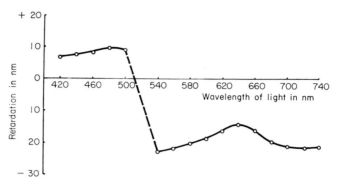

FIG. 3. Toluidine blue. Dispersion of birefringence.

fringence does not mean absence of double refraction, but that the refractive index of the ordinary ray is larger than that of the extraordinary ray.

The yellow-red anomalous color of polarization of thin layers of toluidine blue is due to the fact that its birefringence is maximal at longer wavelengths. Undercompensation cancels the weak birefringence of blue light, and an intensification of the red anomalous color of polarization is observed. Counterclockwise compensation cancels the birefringence of the red light, and the anomalous color of polarization becomes yellow.

The dichroism of this dye is easily observable: Oriented deposits of toluidine blue are placed in the path of the polarizer and illuminated with

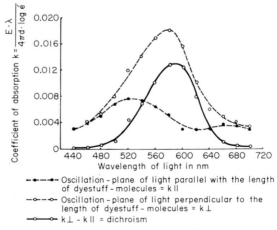

FIG. 4. Toluidine blue. Dichroism measured as absorption of light in the two oscillation planes.

blue and red light so that the plane of polarization of the incident light is parallel with the length of the dye particles. Rotation of the object by 90° shows that the dichroism of this dye is strong in red and weak in blue light (7). The curve in Fig. 4 shows the values of dichroism observed in toluidine blue.

How can the oriented deposition of toluidine blue aid in elucidating the ultrastructure of basophilic leukocytes?

Upon clockwise compensation all negative quadrants of the granules turn red and all positive quadrants turn green. We call the upper right and lower left quadrants positive. This corresponds to negative crosses of polarization and shows that the dye particles are arranged in circles in these granules.

The birefringence of these cellular structures also proves that the external and internal parts are of similar construction.

The axis of the crosses of polarization in the basophilic granules is not parallel with the planes of polarization of the polarizer and analyzer. This means that these granulues are not spheres, but rather ellipsoids.

The small birefringent particles in the protoplasm of the leukocytes mentioned above were also analyzed optically. They proved to be spheres and to consist of concentric shells. In this case the axis of the crosses of polarization is parallel with the planes of polarization of the polarizer and the analyzer.

In Table II are summarized the optical properties of several dyes we investigated, including the dyes already mentioned.

TABLE II

Strength of Dichroism[a] and Maximum of Birefringence[b] of a Few Dyes

Wavelength (nm)	Congo red	Methylene blue	Crystal violet	Methyl violet	Toluidine blue	Evans blue
460	ϕ	ϕ	ϕ	ϕ	ϕ	ϕ
500	+	+	+	ϕ	+	ϕ
540	++	+	+	+	+	+
580	+	++	++	++	+	++
620	ϕ	++	ϕ	ϕ	++	++
Maximum of birefringence	520–560	580–620	500–560	540–580	520–620	580–620

[a] ϕ = No dichroism; + = weak dichroism, ++ = strong distinct dichroism.
[b] Measured in nm.

The following conclusions concerning the optical behavior of thin layers of oriented deposits of birefringent and dichroic dyes in polarized light can be derived from this discussion:

(1) Oriented deposits of birefringent and dichroic dye particles show strong birefringence and pronounced dichroism.

(2) The birefringence of these dyes varies markedly with varying wavelengths of incident light; hence their anomalous colors of polarization.

(3) The anomalous colors of polarization of thin layers of such dyes correspond to the wavelengths for which the birefringence is strongest.

(4) In thick oriented layers of birefringent and dichroic dyes the specific absorption is superimposed on the anomalous color of polarization.

(5) Maximal dichroism occurs in birefringent and dichroic dyes at wavelengths which exhibit strongest birefringence.

(6) Changes of the anomalous color of polarization by use of the elliptic compensator help to elucidate the arrangement and position of the dye particles.

(7) Oriented deposits of birefringent and dichroic dyes enable one to determine the specific ultrastructures in tissues or cellular structures even if their size is near the limit of the resolution of optical microscopes.

(8) The appearance of anomalous colors of polarization in stained tissues or cellular structures proves that the dye is deposited in an oriented manner.

(9) The optical analysis under polarized light of oriented deposits of dyes helps determine the ultrastructure of the object in which these dyes are embedded.

REFERENCES

1. Bennett, H. S., Microscopical investigation of biological materials with polarized light. In "Handbook of Microscopic Technique" (R. McClung Jones, ed.), 3rd ed., pp. 591–677. Harper (Hoeber), New York, 1950.
2. Diezel, P. B. and A. Pfleidener, Histochemische und polarisationsoptische Untersuchungen am Amyloid. Arch. Pathol. Anat. Physiol. 332, 552–567 (1959).
3. Heller, H. H., H. P. Missmahl, E. Sohar, and J. Gafni, Amyloidosis: Its differentiation into perireticulin and pericollagen types. J. Pathol. Bacteriol. 88, 15–34 (1964).
4. Missmahl, H. P., Polarisationsoptischer Beitrag zur Kongorotfärbung des Amyloid. Z. Wiss. Mikroskopie 63, 133–139 (1957).
5. Missmahl, H. P., Welche Beziehungen bestehen zwischen den verschiedenen Formen der Amyloidose und den Bindegewebsfasern? Verhandl. Deut. Ges. Inn. Med. 65, 439–442 (1959).
6. Missmahl, H. P., Die Beeinflussung des polarisierten Lichtes durch die Amyloidsubstanz. Ann. Histochim. Suppl. 2, 225–234 (1962).

7. Missmahl, H. P., Metachromasie durch gerichtete Zusammenlagerung von Farbstoffteilchen, erläutert am optischen Verhalten des Toluidinblau. *Histochemie* **3**, 396–412 (1964).

8. Missmahl, H. P., Nachweis von doppelbrechenden Strukturen im Protoplasma der Leukozyten des peripheren Blutes nach Supravitalfärbung mit Toluidinblau beim Menschen. *Klin. Wochschr.* **42**, 750–751 (1964).

9. Missmahl, H. P., Der feinstrukturelle Aufbau der Granula basophiler Leukozyten des menschlichen Blutes. *Blut* **12**, 159–163 (1966).

10. Pfeiffer, H. H., Birefringence and Janus green dichroism of mitochondria in tissue culture cells. *Symp. Fine Structure Cells, 1954, Leyden*, p. 77–81. Noordhoff, Grøningen, 1955.

11. Schmidt, W. J., Dichroitische Färbung pflanzlicher und tierischer Gewebe. *In* "Handbuch der biologischen Arbeitsmethoden" (E. Abderhalden, ed.), Vol. V, Part 2, pp. 1835–1924. Springer, Berlin, 1931.

12. Schmidt, W. J., "Wie erforscht man den submikroskopischen Bau von Zellen und Geweben?" W. Schmitz, Giessen, 1950.

13. Schmidt, W. J., Polarisationsoptik und Farberscheinungen der lipochromführenden Federäste von *Xipholena lamellipennis. Z. Zellforsch. Mikroskop. Anat.* **45**, 152–175 (1956).

14. Schmidt, W. J., Natürliche Färbung von Reptilien- und Fischzähnen durch Eisenoxyd. *Zool. Anz.* **161**, 168–178 (1958).

15. Schmidt, W. J., Instrumente und Methoden zur mikroskopischen Untersuchung optisch anisotroper Materialien mit Ausschluss der Kristalle. *In* "Handbuch der Mikroskopie in der Technik" (H. Freund, ed.), pp. 149–315. Umschau-Verlag, Frankfurt, 1956.

16. Schmidt, W. J., Über orientierte Einlagerung von Eisenoxyd in die Fibrillenröhrchen des Zahnbeins. *Histochemie* **1**, 247–250 (1959).

17. Schmidt, W. J., Histologische Untersuchungen an Papageienfedern mit gelbem eigenfluoreszeierendem Pigment. *Z. Zellforsch. Mikroskop. Anat.* **55**, 469–485 (1961).

18. Schmidt, W. J., and H. Ruska, Über das schillernde Federmelanin bei *Heliangelus* und *Lophophorus. Z. Zellforsch. Mikroskop. Anat.* **57**, 1–36 (1962).

19. Der Färbedichroismus der Gliafibrillen. *Histochemie* **3**, 257–268 (1963).

20. Wälchli, O., Beitrag zur Kenntnis des Anbaues der Zellulose. *Schweiz. Arch. Angew. Wiss. u. Technik* **11**, 129–138, 181–189, 216–222, and 241–246 (1954).

DICHROISM AND DIFLUORESCENCE

Fritz Ruch

DEPARTMENT OF GENERAL BOTANY,
SWISS FEDERAL INSTITUTE OF TECHNOLOGY,
ZÜRICH, SWITZERLAND

Dichroism and difluorescence studies provide information on the submicroscopic or molecular structure of anisotropic biological objects and, in contrast to related studies using birefringence, can be specific for a certain substance. This substance must, of course, show either light absorption or fluorescence. These properties may be obtained by the use of staining reactions but the interpretation of the result then becomes difficult.

Only a few compounds in a cell (for instance, pigments) show absorption in the visible spectral range and are available for dichroism investigations. On the other hand, several compounds (such as proteins, nucleic acids, lignin) absorb in the UV range and may show dichroism. Illumination with UV causes many compounds in the cell to emit fluorescent light in the visible or the UV range. However, the intensity of the emitted light is very low in some cases, and special highly sensitive equipment is then needed for difluorescence analysis.

The methods for dichroism and difluorescence can be explained using a few examples. Because of their relative simplicity two plant objects are first considered.

I. Chloroplasts

Chloroplasts show birefringence, dichroism, and difluorescence in visible light (6, 7). The lamelliform chloroplasts of the algae *Mongeotia* are most suitable for polarization studies.

Living chloroplasts in water show dichroism (7). This effect can be measured with a microscope photometer equipped with a revolving analyzer, a tungsten or zirconium lamp, and a monochromator. Figure 1

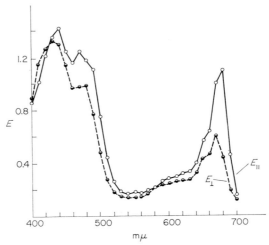

Fig. 1. Dichroism of a living chloroplast of *Mongeotia* (Ruch, 7). *E*, extinction for a plane of vibration parallel ($E_{||}$) and normal ($E_{\perp}$) to the chloroplast.

shows the absorption of polarized light with planes of vibration parallel and normal to the chloroplast. Absorption is mainly due to the chlorophyll and carotinoid content of the chloroplast. Dichroism is highest in red light and absorption highest for light with a plane of vibration parallel to the chloroplast. The dichroism may be due to intrinsic dichroism, form dichroism, or a mixture of both. Intrinsic dichroism appears if the absorbing molecules are oriented, whereas form dichroism gives evidence of a regular submicroscopic structure (lamellar or small rodlike composite bodies).

It is possible to distinguish the two types of dichroism by imbibition experiments. Form dichroism depends on the refractive index of the imbibition liquid, while intrinsic dichroism is not influenced by this factor. If the chloroplasts, fixed by freeze drying or with formalin, are embedded in liquids of increasing refractive index, the dichroism is lowered. In Fig. 2 the dichroism in glycerol ($n_D = 1.47$) is shown. The experiments indicate that the living chloroplasts exhibit mainly form dichroism due to their submicroscopic lamellar structure. (The lamellae can easily be demonstrated with the electron microscope.) Since only a relatively low intrinsic dichroism is observed, the absorbing chlorophyll and carotinoid molecules cannot be oriented parallel as is often supposed.

Similar results are obtained from difluorescence investigations (7). If illuminated with UV or blue light, chloroplasts emit red fluorescent light which, for living algae, is partially polarized. The degree of polarization can be measured using a sensitive device with a Savart quartz plate and

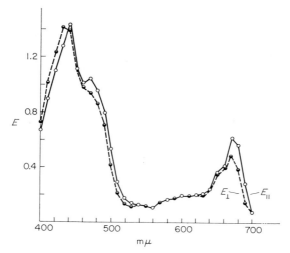

Fig. 2. Dichroism of a chloroplast of *Mongeotia*, fixed with formalin and embedded in glycerol (Ruch, 7). E, $E_{||}$, and $E_{\perp}$ as in Fig. 1.

a compensator. The degree of polarization decreases considerably after fixation and imbibition in glycerol, indicating that the difluorescence of the chloroplast is mainly an effect of form anisotropy, similar to that of dichroism. Compared to dichroism, difluorescence is more sensitive and has the added advantage of being specific for chlorophyll.

II. Lignified Cell Walls

More detailed investigations of dichroism and difluorescence have been made with lignified plant fibers and tracheids (2–4). For these relatively simple objects it was possible to check the optical anisotropy by calculations using Wiener's formula. The lignin in the cell wall shows light absorption in the UV, with a maximum at 280 mμ. The dichroism is measured using a special UV microscope fitted with a rotating analyzer, compensator, and photoelectric measuring device (5).

In Fig. 3 the results of imbibition experiments with spruce tracheids are shown (2). Dichroism is expressed as the quotient $E_{||}/E_{\perp}$. The slopes of the curves prove a form effect and the curves tend toward 1 (no dichroism) with increasing refractive index. In Fig. 4 the calculated Wiener curves for various lignin and cellulose contents are shown. The curves for lignin contents ($\delta_1 = 0.25 \ -0.35$) comparable to those of spruce tracheids correspond very well with the experimental findings. It must be concluded that the UV dichroism of this cell wall is pure form

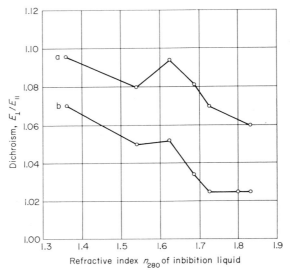

Fig. 3. UV dichroism of spruce tracheids at a wavelength of 280 mμ: (a) on radial wall; (b) on tangential wall (Frey, 2).

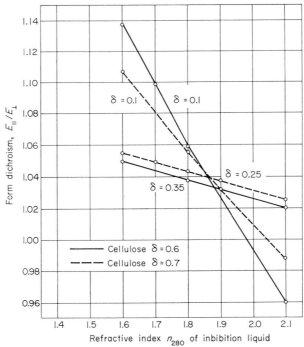

Fig. 4. Theoretical Wiener curves of form dichroism, calculated for n_{280} (Frey, 2).

dichroism due to the submicroscopic rodlike composite body. Lignin, in contrast to cellulose, must be in an amorphous state in the cell wall.

The same conclusions can be drawn from difluorescence investigations

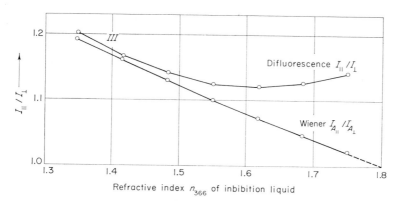

Fig. 5. Comparison of experimental difluorescence $I_{||}I/_{\perp}$ of jute fiber with calculated values according to Wiener (Hengartner, 4).

(4). Figure 5 shows the experimental and theoretical curves. The former is slightly bent. The reason for this deviation is not known.

III. DNA

The specific absorption of this substance in the UV enables the determination of its molecular orientation in biological specimens by dichroism measurements. The method was first used by Caspersson (1). Oriented DNA in fibers or sheets possesses intrinsic dichroism. Absorption is greatest for a plane of vibration of light normal to the molecular direction and smallest for a plane parallel to it (Fig. 6). The dichroic ratio depends on the water content of the preparation. The ratio reaches a maximal value of 4.6 for 90% water content (5, 8). Using this value it is possible to determine the degree of DNA orientation in cell nuclei. High degrees of orientation are found in elongated sperm heads. In ordinary nuclei little or no DNA dichroism could be established. This is also valid for most chromosomes. However, measurable effects may be found in salivary gland chromosomes (6). As the effects depend on fixation, interpretation is difficult. More detailed investigations with this method are likely to be of value for further chromosome studies.

In addition to the brief review of dichroism and difluorescence, the influence of optical anisotropy on ordinary absorption and fluorescence measurements is commented on as follows: It has been suggested that

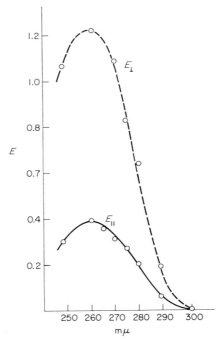

Fig. 6. Ultraviolet dichroism of DNA fibers (Ruch, *6*). Abscissa: wavelength in millimicrons. Ordinate: *E*, extinction; $E_{||}$, $E_{\perp}$ extinction for planes of vibration parallel and normal to the fibers.

molecular orientation introduces serious errors in such measurement with nonpolarized light. For oriented DNA, theoretical and experimental investigations (*9*) gave the following results for absorption measurements: For specimens with fairly high dichroic ratios (up to 3), the error is about 6% for a transmission of 50%. For lower transmission values, the error is much larger. No serious error is concerned with cellular DNA absorption except for material such as elongated sperm heads. In this case the measurements must be carried out in polarized light.

Similar conditions are found for other cellular substances, such as proteins. High degrees of anisotropic absorption are very rare.

References

1. Caspersson, T., Nukleinsäureketten und Genvermehrung. *Chromosoma* **1**, 605–619 (1940).
2. Frey, H. P., Über die Einlagerung des Lignins in der Zellwand. *Holz Roh-Werkstoff* **17**, 313–318 (1959).
3. Frey-Wyssling, A., Ultraviolet and Fluorescence Optics of Lignified Cell Walls.

In "Formation of Wood in Forest Trees," 2nd Symp. M. M. Cabot Found., 1963 (M. H. Zimmermann, ed.), pp. 153–167. Academic Press, New York, 1964.

4. Hengartner, H., Die Fluoreszenzpolarisation der verholzten Zellwand. *Holz Roh-u. Werkstoff* **19**, 303–309 (1961).

5. Ruch, F., Eine Apparatur zur Messung des Ultraviolett-Dichroismus von Zellstrukturen. *Exptl. Cell Res.* **2**, 680–683 (1951).

6. Ruch, F., Birefringence and Dichroism of Cells and Tissue. *In* "Physical Techniques in Biological Research" (G. Oster and A. W. Pollister, eds.), Vol. 3, pp. 149–176. Academic Press, New York, 1956.

7. Ruch, F., Dichroismus und Difluoreszenz der Chloroplasten. *Exptl. Cell Res.* Suppl. **4**, 58–62 (1957).

8. Seeds, W. E., Polarized ultraviolet microspectrography and molecular structure. *Progr. Biophys. Biophysics Chem.* **3**, 27–31 (1953).

9. Thorell, B., and F. Ruch, Molecular orientation and light absorption. *Nature* **167**, 815–817 (1951).

GLOSSARY OF TERMS FOR QUANTITATIVE CYTOCHEMISTRY

compiled by
*George L. Wied**
UNIVERSITY OF CHICAGO
CHICAGO, ILLINOIS

* Supported by a grant from the Illinois Division of the American Cancer Society.

GLOSSARY

The glossary was designed to explain terms of interest for the quantitative cyto-chemist. The original version was compiled to serve as reference material for the International Tutorial on Quantitative Cytochemistry at the University of Chicago, 1965. This version was revised according to suggestions made by Daniel G. Oldfield, Oscar W. Richards, and Günther Beneke. Mrs. Patricia Berg provided valuable edi-torial assistance on both versions. The limitation of space required exercise of judg-ment in the selection and limitation of the material to be discussed. No glossary compiler can claim infallibility and it is conceivable that certain errors of com-mission or of omission evaded scrutiny. The editor and publishers would gratefully accept recommendations for required rectification in subsequent printings.

A

Abbe condenser A simple, two-lens condenser having much spherical aberration and poor field uniformity except for large light sources. The *numerical aperture,* however, can be large.

Abbe sine condition The relationship expressed by the equation (ns) sin $\theta = (n's')$ sin θ', where n and n' are refractive indices; s and s' are the distances from the optical axis; and θ and θ' are the angles *light* rays make with the optical axis. The existence of *coma* in an optical system is shown by the failure of the optical system to satisfy the sine condition.

Aberration In optics, a systematic departure from a theoretically ideal mode of image formation.

Absorption When *light* passes through a transparent substance, part is absorbed, part transmitted, and part reflected. The light absorbed generally increases the temperature of the substance.

Absorption coefficient As applied to electromagnetic radiation and to atomic and subatomic particles, the absorption coefficient is a measure of the rate of decrease in the *intensity* of the incident beam of particles or *photons* as it passes through a substance. Part of this lowering of intensity is due to *scattering* (reflection in all directions) and part to *absorption,* whereby it is converted into other forms of energy. After absorption it may, however, be re-emitted as secondary radiation. Thus, one should differentiate between the true absorption coefficient and the scattering coefficient, but for convenience they are sometimes added together and called the *total absorption coefficient.* Another coefficient sometimes used is the mass absorption coefficient, determined by dividing the absorption co-efficient by the density of the absorbing medium.

Achromatic A lens system that has been corrected for *chromatic aberration,* usually at two wavelengths.

Achromatic objective An *objective* that is corrected chromatically for *light* of two *wavelengths* and spherically for light of one color (usually yellow-green).

Achromatin That nuclear material which does not stain with basic dyes, generally comprising the nuclear sap, linin, and nuclear membrane.

Acrocentric chromosome A chromosome in which the *centromere* or *kinetochore* is situated much closer to one end of the chromosome than to the other.

Adenine A *purine* base found in *nucleic acids*. Specifically, 6-aminopurine.

Albuminate Any compound formed by an acid or a base with an *albumin*.

Albuminoid Syn. *scleroprotein*.

Albumins A group of simple proteins soluble in pure water; the solution is co-agulated by heat. The albumin in egg white is sometimes called egg albumin.

Allelomorphic In Mendelian inheritance, referring to one of a pair of *genes* at the same *locus* on *homologous chromosomes* which govern the occurrence of contrasting characteristics, e.g., tall and short.

Allosome A sex *chromosome,* as differentiated from a somatic chromosome or *autosome*.

Allowed transition A transition between two energy levels in a quantum-mechanical system for which the probability of transition per unit time is relatively large (see *fluorescence*).

Amitosis See *cell division*.

Ampholyte Syn. *amphoteric electrolyte*.

Amphoteric Having both basic and acidic properties; able to act either as a weak base or a weak acid.

Amplification An increase in output *signal* magnitude relative to input signal magnitude.

Amplifier A device for producing *amplification*.

Analog computer See *computer*.

Analyzer The *Nicol prism* in a *polarimeter* through which light passes after traversing the liquid. Any optical device that functions similarly to selectively transmit or absorb *polarized light* according to the orientation of the device.

Anaphase The third stage of *mitosis* (see *cell division*).

Aneuploid cell A cell having *chromosome* numbers which are not integral multiples of the *haploid* value; one of the causes of this condition is *nondisjunction*. Aneuploid cells are found in approximately 12% of all cells (Hauschka, 1961).

Angle of refraction The acute angle between a *refracted* ray and the *normal* to the refracting *surface*.

Angstrom The unit of length equal to 0.00000001 cm or 10^{-10} meter which is customarily used to express the *wavelength* of light. It was named for the spectroscopist Ångström and is sometimes called the "tenth-meter." A micron (0.001 mm) is 10,000 Å.

Angular aperture Referring to a microscope, the angle of the largest cone of light entering the objective from an object point on the axis.

Angular distribution In physics, the distribution of the intensity of photons or particles measured at an angle relative to a reference direction. Usually the angular distribution is that of *scattered* particles or particles resulting from nuclear processes; the specified direction is then the direction of an incident beam. On the other hand, the reference direction may be that of *polarization,* the *emission* direction of associated radiation, or an applied field.

Anion A negatively charged ion.

Anisotropic Describing a material whose properties are different in different directions.

Anode (1) That electrode of a system to which the positive terminal of a voltage source is connected. (2) The electrode toward which an *anion* moves. (3) The negative electrode of a galvanic cell functioning as a source of electromotive force.

Anomalous dispersion Although the *refractive index* n of a medium normally decreases with increasing *wavelength* λ, often in the immediate vicinity of a certain wavelength λ_1, there is a break in the *dispersion curve;* there n increases with increasing λ. These discontinuities correspond to bands or lines in the medium's *absorption spectrum.* This is expressed by the equation $n^2 = 1 + A\lambda^2/(\lambda^2 - \lambda_1^2) + B\lambda^2/(\lambda^2 - \lambda_2^2) + \cdots$, where n is the refractive index; A, B, $\dots$, are *constants,* and λ_1, λ_2, $\dots$ are the absorption wavelengths. If anomalous dispersion is pronounced, the medium appears colored, e.g., transparent *dyes.*

Aperture An opening, usually circular, through which *light* or other radiation can pass.

Aplanatic points The two conjugate points of an optical system for which the system is aplanatic (corrected for *spherical aberration* and *coma*).

Aplanatic surface An optical *surface* of such shape that all rays from one point are brought together in another point by *reflection* or *refraction* processes.

Apochromatic objective A microscope objective corrected at three wavelengths for *spherical* and *chromatic aberration.*

Archoplasm See *ergastoplasm.*

Arginine A basic amino acid with a molecular weight of 174 and an *isoelectric point* of 10.76.

Aster The system of *astral rays* considered collectively.

Astral ray A fibrous process diverging from the *centrosome.*

Astrosphere See *aster*

Attenuation Reduction in concentration, density, or effectiveness. In an electrical communications channel, it is the diminution of power, current, or voltage measured in *decibels* or *nepers,* while in radiation theory it expresses the reduction in *flux* density, or power per unit area, with distance from the source.

Autoradiograph (radioautograph) A photographic emulsion placed in contact with or within a material containing radioactive substances for the purpose of determining the strength and distribution of the sources of radioactivity.

Autosome A somatic *chromosome;* any chromosome other than a sex chromosome.

Auxochrome A chemical group in a dye molecule which can enhance the action of a *chromophore.*

Axis, optical See *optical axis.*

B

Barr bodies (sex chromatin) Marginal *chromatin* bodies found in cell nuclei which lack one X *chromosome.*

Beer law *Light absorption* by solutions is directly proportional to the solution concentration (number of molecules through which the rays pass). The formula is

$\ln(I_0/I) = kcd$, where c is the solution concentration; d, the solution thickness; k, the absorption coefficient; I_0, the intensity of light entering the solution; and I, the intensity of light exiting from the solution.

Bivalent A complex of four *chromatids* formed during *pachytene* stage of *miosis*.

Birefringence The formation by *refraction* within a crystal of two light rays diverging from each other at the point where a single ray is incident on the crystal. The phenomenon is due to the different velocities at which differently polarized components of the incident ray pass through the crystal. Syn. *double refraction*.

Blastomere One of the cells into which a *zygote* divides; a segmentation or *cleavage* cell.

Bouguer law The *absorption* of *radiant energy* by homogeneous materials, e.g., glass or clear liquids, is dependent on the thickness of the material as follows: $-dI/dx = KI$ or $I = I_0 e^{-Kx}$, where I is the *intensity* of the transmitted *light*; K is the linear *absorption coefficient* (equivalent to the kc of the *Beer law*); x is the thickness of the absorbing layer; and I_0 is the intensity of the light entering the material.

Boundary condition A value assigned to the *dependent variable* of a *differential equation* or to the *derivatives* of that variable for certain values of the *independent variables*. The chosen values make the solution specifically applicable to a particular set of states of the system which the differential equation governs.

Brightness That characteristic of *luminous energy* which determines whether the visual sensation produced by two sources of luminous energy having the same color and the same saturation will be judged identical or nonidentical.

C

Calculus When unqualified, the term calculus usually is considered to mean "differential calculus" or "integral calculus," although there are other kinds. "Differential calculus" is concerned with the calculation and properties of the *derivative* of one quantity with respect to another, of which it is a *function;* it deals with continuously varying quantities. "Integral calculus" is the inverse of differential calculus; its concern is finding the value of a function when its derivative is known. This process is called integration and is used, for example, to obtain the trajectory of a *curve*, the length of a curve, or the volume bounded by a given *surface*. Integral calculus is also related to the calculus of variations, which studies the maximal and minimal properties of integrals.

Candela The unit of *luminous intensity*. See *standard candela*.

Candle See *candela*.

Candlepower See *candela*.

Carnoy's solution A fixing fluid composed of 6 parts absolute ethyl alcohol, 3 parts chloroform, and 1 part glacial acetic acid, all by volume.

Cathode (1) That electrode of a system to which the negative terminal of a voltage source is connected. (2) The electrode toward which a *cation* moves. (3) The positive electrode of a galvanic cell functioning as a source of electromotive force.

Cauchy formula An approximate form of the *Sellmeier equation* valid for wavelengths far from absorption bands.

Cell division Cell division is a basic expression of the power of reproduction inherent in all living matter. Although all living cells are the products of such divisions, not all are capable of further division to produce new cells. *Mitosis* is the major visible process of cell division. *Amitosis* consists of simple elongation, constriction, and division of the cell, including its nucleus; it occurs relatively infrequently, chiefly in cells found in certain accessory reproductive structures and other cells of temporary value. Mitosis, a much more complex process of cell division, suggests by its orderly sequence of stages the precise partition of essential cell constituents between the two daughter cells. Mitosis is divided into four stages: *prophase, metaphase, anaphase, telophase.*

In prophase, the *centrioles* separate or, if only one is present, it splits and the halves separate. The *astral rays,* which are a series of radiating lines, form around each. As these asters draw apart, fibers in the form of a *spindle* appear between them; this whole configuration is the mitotic figure. The spindle guides the *chromatids* to opposite ends of the cell in an unknown way; it is a polarized gel. While this is occurring, each *chromosome* contracts from a thin thread into two parallel threads or chromatids, which attain their maximal width and minimal length at the end of prophase. By this time the nucleoli and nuclear membrane have disappeared.

The chromosomes now migrate toward the equator of the spindle, arranging themselves in the equatorial plane; they are attached to the fibers by their *kinetochores.* This is metaphase.

Next, in anaphase, the chromatids (now called chromosomes) move to the spindle poles. Each chromosome's kinetochore begins moving first, thus giving a **V** or **J** shape to each chromosome, depending on the location of the kinetochore.

The migration is finished in the telophase, and the *cytoplasm* divides or is separated by the formation of a partition between the two chromosome groups. The two resulting daughter cells are in the resting stage.

The cell division described is called *somatic* if it involves the *diploid* chromosome number, and equational if it involves the *haploid* chromosome number.

Centriole A cell organelle important for *cell division,* located at or near each end of the *spindle.*

Centromere See *kinetochore.*

Centrosome A specialized area of differentiated *cytoplasm* appearing during *mitosis* and *meiosis* containing the *centrioles* and from which the *astral rays* diverge. Centrosomes are common in the cells of animals, but appear to be confined to the *Thallophyta* among plants.

Centrosphere See *aster.*

Chang cells Cell lines from normal human material, first established by R. S. Chang in 1954 [*Proc. Soc. Exp. Biol. Med.* **87,** 440–443 (1954)]. Although the Chang cells are generally histologically and metabolically similar to tumor cells (see *HeLa cells* and *HE p-1 cells*), it is difficult to establish whether or not these lines are capable of producing an *in vivo* cancer in man. Chang cells inoculated into human volunteers have produced equivocal results.

Chiasma A point at which two homologous chromosomes are in contact during the *diplotene* stage of *meiosis.*

Chromatic aberration That lens defect caused by *light* of shorter wavelength being brought to a focus on the lens axis before and with less magnification than light of longer wavelength. When chromatic aberration is present, the image of an object illuminated by white light exhibits coloration.

Chromatid Either of the two sister bodies formed by the longitudinal splitting of a *chromosome* in preparation for *mitosis* or *meiosis;* this separation occurs in pre-*prophase*. During meiosis there are four chromatids, which form a *bivalent*.

Chromatin The part of the *nucleoplasm* that is deeply staining.

Chrome alum Potassium chromium sulfate; it is used in the *gallocyanin* chrome alum staining reaction for RNA and DNA.

Chromidia *Chromatin* fragments lying free in the *cytoplasm*, not massed to form a nucleus.

Chromophore Chemical group in a dye molecule, such as azo, nitroso, etc., primarily responsible for the characteristic color exhibited by the dye.

Chromoprotein A protein that is colored and conjugated, having respiratory functions and related to the green chlorophyll of higher plants. Some examples are the blue hemocyanin found in many lower animals, the red *hemoglobins* in higher animals, and the red and blue pigments in seaweeds.

Chromosome A deeply staining body, usually V, J, or rod shaped at *mitosis,* located in the nucleus; chromosomes appear during *mitosis (cell division)* and split to form *chromatids*. They carry *genes,* the hereditary factors, and are of constant number in each species. Until 1956 the *diploid* chromosome number in man was believed to be 48, but at that time Tijo and Levan showed the correct number to be 46. Of these 46 chromosomes, 44 (22 pairs) are *autosomes* and 2 (one pair) are sex chromosomes, either XY for males or XX for females. In sperm and ovum the number is *haploid,* i.e., 23.

Cleavage *Cell division* of the *zygote* into *blastomeres*.

Coated optics Optical *reflecting* or *refracting surfaces* that have been coated with metallic or glassy material (e.g., magnesium fluoride, silicon oxide, titanium oxide). The purpose of coating is to reduce reflection. In addition, they provide protection of the surfaces against abrasion, fumes, etc.

Collimating lens See *collimation* and *collimator*.

Collimation The aligning of the various parts of an optical system. (Collimation is derived from the Latin "collineare, -atum" meaning to bring together in a straight line.)

Collimator (1) A tube or lens that transmits only in one prescribed direction some of the light that enters it, e.g., the tube of a *spectroscope* which produces parallel rays which are directed at a *prism*. (2) A small telescope having cross hairs at its focus, which is attached to another telescope or surveying instrument, etc., in order to adjust the sighting.

Color translating microscope A *television microscope* that uses color television to transform the image produced by an ultraviolet microscope into an image visible to the eye. Two or three *frequencies* of ultraviolet *light* are selected for which the cell materials under consideration are different in their *absorption spectrum*. For example, if two bacteria differ in their absorption of two frequencies, a beam of ultraviolet light containing these frequencies is sent through the microscope; the beam transmitted indicates the distribution and number of the two kinds of bacteria present. Then these two beams are used to produce electric currents, which in turn reproduce the microscopic field, colored and greatly enlarged, on a television screen; each organism appears in a different color combination. This principle, called "color translation" or "electronic staining" permits examination of living cells which have been given chemicals, hormones, vitamins, etc. The original instrument did not use television techniques.

Coma A form of lens aberration due to differences in magnification produced by different lens zones; it occurs for points not on the lens axis and produces for a distant point object a comet-shaped image with the tail either away from or toward the lens axis. A condition for the absence of coma is the *abbe sine condition*. If a lens system is corrected for both coma and spherical aberration for a single object position, it is *aplanatic*.

Complex variable A quantity of the form $z = (x + iy)$, where x and y are real *variables* and $i = \sqrt{-1}$ and is called the imaginary unit. A complex number is of the form $(a + ib)$ where a and b are *real numbers*. Thus, it consists of a real part, a, and a pure imaginary part, ib. Complex numbers are subject to the following laws:

(1) Equality: $(a + ib) = (c + id)$ if, and only if, $a = c, b = d$.

(2) Addition: $(a + ib) + (c + id) = (a + c) + i(b + d)$.

(3) Multiplication: $(a + ib)(c + id) = (ac - bd) + i(ad + bc)$.

Computer A machine or device that transforms mechanical, electrical, optical, etc., input signals into output signals of the same or of different type in accordance with a set of mathematical or logical rules. Computers are either *analog* or *digital*. An analog computer uses continuous physical quantities such as length, voltage, etc., to represent input and output. A digital computer uses discrete physical states such as switch open–switch closed to represent the digits 0 and 1, and with the latter, numbers which in turn represent input, output, etc. Output from analog computers can be converted to input for digital computers by an analog-to-digital converter.

Condenser A system of mirrors or lenses that collects, controls, and focuses *light*.

Condenser, dark field See *dark field condenser*.

Condenser, variable-focus See *variable focus condenser*.

Constant An absolute constant is a number always having the same value. An arbitrary constant, or *parameter*, may have different values in different cases. For example, a circle is represented by the equation $x^2 + y^2 = r^2$. If r is an absolute constant there will be exactly one circle represented by this equation, but if r is a parameter, every circle having its center at the origin of a Cartesian *coordinate system* is represented. A given circle of this family of circles is determined by the choice of r since this fixes the circle's radius.

Continuous spectrum The spectrum resulting when a *light* source or other radiation source emitting a continuum of *wavelengths* is analyzed, e.g., any incandescent solid, liquid, or gas under high pressure.

Coordinate system A system of lines, curves and (or) *surfaces* having a fixed, specified relation to each other and with respect to which points can be located. The rectangular Cartesian system is simplest and most frequently used. The coordinate axes are three mutually perpendicular straight lines which intersect in one point O, called the origin. If the axes are labeled OX, OY, and OZ, imagine OX and OY to be drawn on a piece of paper, which is then the XY plane with OX horizontal; let OX increase in going to the right from the origin; OY points toward the top of the page and becomes more positive going up from the origin. The positive direction of OZ is then outward from the page for a right-hand coordinate system. A unit of arbitrary length is chosen and marked off repeatedly on each axis, in both the positive and negative directions. If three numbers are given, each in multiples (or fractions) of this unit distance, they locate the position of a point in space and are called the coordinates of that point. Conventionally, the notation used is (x, y, z), where x is the coordinate of the point on the X axis; y, on the Y axis; and z, on the Z axis. The arrangement described constitutes a right-handed coordinate system, which is the most common one. If a pair of axes is exchanged, the system is then left-handed.

For a point to be located in two dimensions, the X axis, then called the abscissa, and the Y axis, called the ordinate, are used; the point is expressed in the form (x, y).

These conceptions can be generalized a great deal. If the surfaces are mutually perpendicular, the system is orthogonal; if the surfaces are not mutually perpendicular, the system is nonorthogonal or affine. The system is rectilinear when the coordinate surfaces are planes; otherwise it is curvilinear. A Cartesian coordinate system is rectilinear and, most usually, also orthogonal; when not orthogonal, it is called oblique.

Partial differential equations often require a suitable coordinate system so that *separation of variables* can be used for their solution. For further details see P. M. Morse and H. Feshbach, "Methods of Theoretical Physics," Vol. 1, Chap. 5, McGraw-Hill, New York, 1953.

Critical illumination A method of microscopical illumination in which an image of the source is focused by the substage condenser in the plane of the specimen.

Curve (higher plane) A curve which is neither a straight line nor a conic section; the algebraic equation describing the curve is of *order* greater than two. The *transcendental functions* could also be called higher plane curves.

Curve (plane curve) A *function* of two or more *variables* defines a curve, and the graph of the function describes the shape of the curve. Geometrically, a curve may be considered as the path of a point moving according to some equation; it is the *locus* of the equation. A curve in two dimensions is called a plane curve, in three dimensions a space curve. Plane curves may be classed in different ways; the simplest, although not the most important mathematically, is by the *order*. A curve of the first order is a straight line, and one of the second order is a conic section or one of its degenerate cases, such as the circle. Curves of order greater than two and *transcendental* curves are discussed under *curve (higher plane)*.

Cytochemistry The study of the chemical composition, organization, and activity of a cell.

Cytochrome (1) A porphyrin *chromoprotein* similar to *hemoglobin*. (2) Hemochromogens (cytochromes a, b, c) found in animal tissues and yeast; they are important in oxidation and reduction since they accept and transfer hydrogen.

Cytodiagnosis The determination of the nature of a disease by studying the cells in an exudate or transudate.

Cytogenetics The study of inheritance and other genetic phenomena using cytological concepts, methods, and materials.

Cytokinesis Changes occurring in the *cytoplasm* during *cell division*.

Cytokinetics The study of the rates at which processes occur in a cell.

Cytopathology The study of alterations within cells during disease.

Cytophysics The study of the physical (mechanical, electrical, optical, etc.) properties of cells.

Cytopathy Cellular disease.

Cytoplasm Protoplasm of a cell, as opposed to *nucleoplasm*.

Cytopoiesis Cell generation and development.

Cytoscopy The examination of cells for the purpose of diagnosing a disease.

Cytosine A *pyrimidine* base found in *nucleic acids;* 2-hydroxy-6-aminopyrimidine ($C_4H_5N_3O$).

Cytosome The body of a cell exclusive of its nucleus.

Cytothesis Repair of injured cells.

D

Damping Progressive reduction in the amplitude of *oscillation* of a system, due to energy dissipation by, for example, friction in a mechanical system or resistance in an electrical system.

Dark field condenser A condenser producing a hollow cone of *light* focused in the plane of the specimen. Used with an *objective* having a smaller numerical aperture than the minimal numerical aperture of the hollow cone, only light which is scattered by the specimen can enter the objective. Object points thus appear as bright images on a dark background.

Dark field illumination Any method of lighting that illuminates the specimen but does not admit *light* directly to the objective. There are two types of such illumination: that used for large specimens, images being formed by reflected light; that used for small particles or very fine lines, images being formed by scattered light, so that the particles appear as bright stars against a dark background.

De Broglie's equation The equation $\lambda = h/mv$, where λ is the *wavelength* of a particle, m its mass, v its velocity, and h is Planck's constant ($h = 6.6252 \pm 0.0002 \times 10^{-27}$ erg-second). Thus, one can see that heavier particles have shorter wavelength than lighter particles. This consideration has led to the development of the *ion microscope*.

Decibel The unit in which electrical power ratios are sometimes expressed in audio engineering. The decibel value of a given amount of electrical power W_2 relative to an arbitrarily chosen reference amount of power W_1 is expressed by $10 \log_{10}(W_2/W_1)$.

Degree In mathematics, the highest power to which any of the terms of a *function, polynomial,* etc., is raised. If a term has more than one *variable*, the degree is the sum of the degrees of each of the variables, e.g., the degree of $x^3 yz^2$ is 6.

Denaturation The loss of normal properties and functions of an organic substance, especially secondary and tertiary structure by a protein, produced by physical or chemical action.

Density, optical See *optical density.*

Density, specular See *specular density.*

Denumerable A *set* whose elements can be put in one-to-one correspondence with the set of all positive *integers.*

Dependent variable A *variable* whose value is determined when that of one or more other variables is given. For example, if $y = f(x)$, y is determined by the value of x and so is a dependent variable.

Depolymerization The breaking up of a *polymer* molecule into lower molecular weight species.

Derivative In mathematics, the instantaneous rate of change of a *function* with respect to its *independent variable*. *Differentiation* is the process used to find the derivative of a function. The derivative of y with respect to x is usually denoted by dy/dx, but other designations, such as y' and $f'(x)$, are also used. If the function $y = f(x)$ is plotted in the Cartesian *coordinate system,* the *slope* of the *curve* at the point of $x = x_o$ is its derivative, dy/dx, at that point.

Desoxyribonucleic acid (DNA) A nucleic acid of high molecular weight containing *desoxyribose* as the sugar component, in addition to phosphoric acid and four types of bases: two *pyrimidines* (*thymine* and *cytosine*) and two *purines* (*adenine* and *guanine*). The configuration of DNA is that of a double helix, as shown by X-ray analysis.

Desoxyribose An aldopentose found in cells, particularly in *nucleic acid.*

Diakinesis The last stage of *meiotic prophase.*

Dichroism The property, exhibited by some crystals and solutions, of absorbing different wavelengths of *polarized light* to different degrees depending on the relation of the plane of polarization to the optic axis. As a result, different colors may be produced with different directions of transmission of light through the material.

Differential If y is a *function* of x, so that $y = f(x)$, then the differentials of y and x are dy and dx, respectively. For $dx \neq 0$, the ratio of the differentials is the *derivative* of y with respect to x, $dy/dx = f'(x)$.

Differential equation An equation which involves *differentials* or *derivatives* of an unknown *function*. A differential equation is called *ordinary* unless partial derivatives occur; then it is called a *partial differential equation*. The *order* of the equation is the order of the highest derivative present; the highest power of the function or its derivatives is called the *degree*. *Linear differential equations* are equations of the first degree, and other equations are nonlinear.

Differentiation (1) In cytology and histology, an increase in the complexity and organization of cells or tissues during development. (2) In mathematics, the process of determining the *derivative* of a *function* with respect to the *independent variable*. The derivatives of certain elementary functions are obtained directly using the methods of *calculus;* for more complicated functions, various general theorems of calculus can be used to obtain derivatives.

Diffraction Bending of *light* around an obstacle. When rays of light pass through a small opening, as the slit of a *spectroscope,* the light undergoes diffraction, causing the beam to fan out on each side of the slit. A narrow slit causes the paths of the light rays to differ in length; at some points light is concentrated, while at other, alternate points, interference occurs. Thus, in *monochromatic* light, alternating dark and light bands are produced.

Diffuse density The density of a photographic image when measured using diffuse, instead of parallel, *light*. See *specular density.*

Diffuse reflection The reflection of rays from a surface such that the reflected rays have various directions due to surface irregularities.

Diffuse reflectance The ratio of *radiant flux* diffusely reflected to *incident radiant flux.*

Diffuse reflection factor The ratio of the *luminous flux* reflected diffusely from a *surface* to the total luminous flux striking the surface.

Digit   Any one of the symbols 0, 1, 2, ..., 9.

Digital computer   See *computer*.

Diploid   Having two sets of *chromosomes,* or double the *haploid* number.

Diplokaryotic   Exhibiting twice the *diploid chromosome* number.

Diplophase   The phase in the life cycle of an organism in which the nuclei are *diploid*.

Diplosome   A double *centrosome* in the *cytoplasm;* an *allosome* that is paired.

Diplotene   The fourth stage of *meiotic prophase,* which comes between *pachytene* and *diakinesis.* In this stage the chiasmata become visible.

Dispersion   In physics, the process of separating a radiation into its components in accordance with some property such as energy, *wavelength,* or *frequency.* For example, dispersion of light is due to *refraction* by a *prism, diffraction* by a *grating,* or other means. Refractive dispersion occurs because the velocity of light in a given medium, and thus the *refractive index,* varies with the frequency. Dispersion is defined quantitatively as the *derivative* of the deviation Δ with respect to the property (frequency, wavelength, etc.). For example, with respect to wavelength λ, the dispersion D is $D = d\Delta/d\lambda$. For refractive dispersion, considering one refraction at the angle of incidence θ and refractive index n, $D = d\Delta/d\lambda = (\sin \theta / n\sqrt{n^2 - \sin^2 \theta})\,) \, dn/d\lambda$. Several expressions have been derived from this equation which express n as a *function* of λ, e.g.,

$$n^2 = A + \frac{B}{\lambda^2} + \frac{C}{\lambda^4} + \cdots \quad \text{and;} \quad n^2 = 1 + \frac{A\lambda^2}{\lambda^2 - \lambda_1^2} + \frac{B\lambda^2}{\lambda^2 - \lambda_2^2} + \cdots$$

Dissociation   The disjunction of a molecule into simpler molecules or ions.

Distributional error   The error introduced into a photometric calculation which assumes the existence of a uniform, random distribution of *chromophores* in the measuring field when actually the field contains a nonuniform distribution.

DNA   See *desoxyribonucleic acid.*

Double focus method   In *interference* microscopy, the system in which one beam of *light* from the specimen is focused at one point on the *optic axis* and the other beam is focused above it, thus appearing as a halo around the first image. Local changes in the optical thickness of each part of the specimen alter the phase of the beam passing through the specimen, while the average optical thickness of the specimen or the region around it determines the changes in the reference beam.

Double refraction   See *birefringence.*

Dye (dyestuff)   A staining or coloring material, generally used in solution. One class of dyes are azo dyes, which derive from azobenzene and are synthetic and organic, containing the *chromophore* —N=N—. Monazo dyes contain one —N=N— group, and diazo dyes contain two such groups. For staining living cells, vital dyes are used.

Dynode   An electrode in a *photomultiplier* which when bombarded by electrons produces additional electrons by secondary emissions. The emitted electrons are made to strike the dynode of the next stage and the process is repeated.

E

Electrolyte   A solution which is capable of conducting an electric current by its *ions.*

Electron microscope   A type of microscope in which a beam of electrons transmitted through a specimen is focused by magnets to produce an image of the specimen. The image is viewed or photographed using a fluorescent screen. The resolving power of an electron microscope is 50 to 200 times that of the *light* microscope.

Electron tube An evacuated or gas-filled tube in which electrons move under the influence of electric fields existing between two or more electrodes.

Electrostatic dye binding A type of staining in which the dye is held to the substrate by ionic bonds.

Emission Generally, the process of electron ejection from a conducting *surface* caused by *light,* heat, or ion or electron bombardment. Specifically, the total electronic current emitted by a heated *cathode,* also called emission current.

Emission spectrum Any *spectrum* produced by radiation from a source; it may be a line, a band, or a *continuous spectrum,* depending on the source.

Endomitosis *Chromosome* division in a nucleus without subsequent *mitosis,* resulting in duplication of the chromosome complement.

Enzyme A catalytic substance, often a protein, formed by living cells; it accelerates or makes changes in its substrate, for which it is specific. Some examples are proteolytic enzymes (proteases), bacterial enzymes (produced by bacteria), autolytic enzymes (producing autolysis or digestion of the cell), etc.

Epignetic cell changes Cell changes, other than genetic, which explain the transition from normal to tumor cells; the term was introduced by H. J. Muller. Such changes show adaptation, but are not actually adaptive changes since they persist even if the environmental factors causing them are no longer operating. Epigenetic changes are expressed primarily in microsomes, where protein formation occurs (shown by T. Hiltin).

Ergastoplasm A fine reticulum found in the cytoplasm. Syn. *archoplasm, kinoplasm, ergoplasm.*

Ergoplasm See *ergastoplasm.*

Euploid cell A cell containing an integral multiple of the *haploid* number of *chromosomes* (euploidy).

Excitation The addition of energy to a system, which transfers it from the normal or ground state to a higher energy level, called the excited state.

Exponential function In mathematics, a *function* of the form $f(x) = a^x$, where a is a positive *real number* called the base of the exponential function. The *laws of exponents* embody the elementary properties of exponential functions.

Extinction In absorption spectrophotometry, *light absorption* by a dissolved substance (see *extinction coefficient*).

Extinction coefficient A measure of *light absorption* by a solution, given by the formula $E = (1/cd) \cdot \log(I_0/I)$, where E is the extinction coefficient, I the *intensity* of the transmitted light, I_0 the intensity of the incident light, c the concentration of the solution, and d the thickness of the solution. When c is in moles per liter and d is in centimeters, E is called the *molar extinction coefficient.*

Extinction factor Ratio of the *intensity of light* transmitted when the *analyzer* and *polarizer* are parallel, to the intensity transmitted when the analyzer and polarizer are crossed.

Extraordinary ray That ray which is deviated (angle of refraction $\neq 0$) when the incident ray enters the face of a birefringent crystal perpendicularly; thus the extraordinary ray does not obey the ordinary laws of *refraction.* The *refractive* *index* varies with the direction of the ray, but it is customary to state the index of refraction for the extraordinary ray in the direction at right angles to the optic axis, where the velocity is a maximum or a minimum.

F

Fast Resistant to the action of a chemical, drug, or, especially, a dye, e.g., bacteria.

Fast Green FCF An acid dye used as a counterstain; it is of the diamino triphenyl methane series.

Fechner law The perceived magnitude of a sensation is proportional to the logarithm of the magnitude of the physical stimulus that elicits that sensation. See *Weber–Fechner law*.

Fermat principle When *light* passes from a point A to a different point B by some path, the time required for its passage is a minimum or maximum compared to other, adjacent paths. The time is minimized if the light is *reflected* from A to B by a plane *surface* or is *refracted* on its way from A to B by a plane surface. For a curved reflecting or refracting surface, the time is a minimum if the surface is less curved than the corresponding *aplanatic surface* at the point at which the ray is refracted. In such instances the law is called the "principle of least time." On the other hand, if the reflecting or refracting surface has greater curvature than the aplanatic surface at the same point, the actual path time is a maximum, i.e., the light could pass through any other point of the curved surface in less time. The time is equal for all points on a given aplanatic surface, and the light passes through each of them if unobstructed.

Feulgen reaction The Feulgen reaction consists in the reaction between leukofuchsin and the aldehyde in desoxyribose which results in a purple-blue color. Therefore, specimens are first hydrolyzed by HCl to free the aldehyde group of the pentose sugar of DNA and then are treated with leukofuchsin (basic fuchsin in sulfurous acid). DNA is Feulgen positive (assumes the characteristic purple-blue color), and RNA is Feulgen negative.

Field emission microscope A microscope using electrons to determine the structure of substances, as does the *electron microscope*. However, the field emission microscope uses the material being studied as the electron source, rather than directing an external beam of electrons on the substance. Isolated molecules can be made visible by means of field emission microscopy [E. W. Mueller, *Z. Physik* **120**, 270 (1942); E. W. Mueller, *J. Appl. Phys.* **27**, 474 (1956)].

Filar micrometer An eyepiece having a fiducial line mounted in its focal plane, the line being movable by a calibrated micrometer screw for linear measurements on images formed in the focal plane.

Filter A device for absorbing or transmitting specified wavelength ranges of electromagnetic radiation.

Flare Any stray light in an optical system due to *reflection, refraction, scattering,* etc.

Flavoprotein A protein united to a prosthetic group containing a flavin.

Fluorescence The *emission* of electromagnetic radiation by a substance after absorbing energy from particulate or electromagnetic radiation; the emission lasts only as long as the stimulus producing it is maintained, i.e., it ceases within about 10^{-8} second after the end of *excitation* (the time for a normal *allowed transition*).

Fluorescent screen A plate coated with a readily fluorescent material. It is used to observe properties of invisible radiations, as X-rays, from the *fluorescence* emitted by the screen, and to form the visible image in cathode-ray tubes, as in *oscilloscopes* and television tubes. The emission lasts only as long as *excitation* continues, with a very short glow period afterward, whereas the glow period of *phosphorescent* screens is longer.

Fluorite objective An *objective* using lenses of glass containing the mineral fluorite to allow partial correction of both spherical and chromatic *aberration*. The correction usually made produces an objective between *achromatic* and *apochromatic*.

Fluorochrome A dye which, when irradiated by ultraviolet light, fluoresces.

Fluorometer An instrument for measuring *fluorescence*. Also, a device for photometric measurements in the ultraviolet, the measurements being made using the fluorescence produced in a substance by the *ultraviolet radiation*.

Flux With respect to *photons* or particles, flux is the number passing through a *surface* per unit time. Concerning electromagnetic radiation, flux is the energy or power passing through a surface per unit time.

Flying-spot microscope In the flying-spot microscope [J. Z. Young and R. F. Roberts, *Nature* **167**, 231 (1951)] the scanning process is shifted from the image plane (as in the *television microscope*) into the object plane. Frequently, the source of illumination is a *cathode-ray oscilloscope* which, however, cannot provide significant spectral selectivity. Mechanical scanning thus has a definite advantage [J. J. Freed and J. L. Engle, *Ann. N.Y. Acad. Sci.* **97**, 412 (1962)].

Focal length For a spherical surface, the distance from a mirror or *lens surface* to the image of an infinitely distant *light* source.

Form birefringence *Birefringence* due to the presence of asymmetrical, submicroscopic particles which form a regular array, although not necessarily being individually crystalline. Form birefringence disappears when the object is immersed in a medium having the same *refractive index* as that of the particles; in this way, form and *intrinsic birefringence* may be distinguished, and the relative contribution of each to the total birefringence may be estimated.

Freeze drying Method of specimen fixation by freezing rapidly to −160° to −180°C, dehydrating *in vacuo* while frozen, and finally, thawing and embedding in paraffin while still *in vacuo*.

Freeze substitution Method of specimen fixation by freezing rapidly to low temperature followed by treatment with a dehydrating agent which remains liquid at low temperatures, such as alcohol.

Frequency Cycles or vibrations per unit time. In electricity, frequency is the number of complete cycles per second of an alternating current (usually 60 cycles per second in the USA and 50 cycles per second in Europe). For *light,* rather than frequencies (e.g., 5×10^{14} cycles per second for yellow light) either the wave number (the reciprocal of *wavelength*) or wavelength used.

Fresnel–Arago law Two plane polarized *light* rays in a given beam which are out of phase with each other can undergo *interference* only when their planes of *polarization* are parallel.

Function A correspondence between two *sets* of *variables,* called the "domain" and the "range," such that each element of the domain is associated with one and only one element of the range. The domain is composed of *independent variables* and the range of *dependent variables*. If x is the independent variable and y the dependent variable, y is determined explicitly by the equation $y = f(x)$ or implicitly by $f(x, y) = 0$. If there are several independent variables, $x_1, x_2, \ldots, x_n$, the dependent variable y is determined by $y = f(x_1, x_2, \ldots, x_n)$ or $f(x_1, x_2, \ldots, x_n, y) = 0$.

The principal categories of functions are: (1) algebraic, when the variables involve only algebraic operations; (2) *transcendental,* when it is not algebraic, e.g., *logarithmic,* trigonometric, etc.; (3) *real* or complex, depending on whether the variable is real or complex; (4) single-valued, as $y = 2x$, or multi-valued as $x^2 + y^2 = 4$; (5) continuous or discontinuous.

A function is called "even" if $f(x) = f(-x)$ and "odd" if $f(x) = -f(-x)$. For example, x^2 and $\cos x$ are even, while x^3 and $\sin x$ are odd. Other names given to functions having special properties are linear, periodic, harmonic, homogeneous, integral, inverse, and orthogonal.

G

Gallocyanin A basic oxazine dye used as a stain for *Nissl bodies* when in aqueous solution with *chrome alum;* also used as nuclear stain.

Galvanometer An instrument that measures electric currents.

Gametes Male or female reproductive cells which may unite with one another to form a *zygote;* this union is called conjugation or fertilization. The gametes of higher animals are the egg (female) and the sperm (male).

Gametic number The number of *chromosomes* in the nucleus of a *gamete.*

Gametocyte A cell that produces *gametes* by division; an oocyte or spermatocyte.

Gene A zone or locus in a *chromosome* which determines the hereditary transmission and the development of particular characters of that cell and its progeny, including ultimately the organism to which they may give rise. The gene is considered the hypothetical hereditary unit; its existence has been indicated by indirect evidence from the study of hereditary processes. In recent years, the study of giant chromosomes of the salivary gland of fruit flies (*Drosophila melanogaster*) has revealed fine structural details which may be the genes. These chromosomes are longitudinally differentiated into numerous zones whose nature and arrangement seem to be constant, barring recognized types of change; many of these transverse bands have been identified as the points occupied by the hypothetical genes in other studies. Gene action is not definitely known, but genes have been interpreted as self-perpetuating bodies producing *enzymes* which are able to influence the action of other organelles of the cell.

Genome The set of chromosomes donated by either the male or female gamete to the chromosome complement of the *zygote* and all succeeding normal somatic cells derived from it.

Glare The condition existing when a visual field contains an area much brighter than the area under observation or to which the eye is adapted.

Globulin A class of proteins insoluble in water, but soluble in water-soluble proteins (pseudo-globulins) or in acid, alkaline, or salt solutions (euglobulins).

Glutelin A simple protein which is very soluble in quite dilute acids and alkalis, insoluble in all neutral solvents, and heat coagulable. Glutelin is found in cereal seeds.

Glycoprotein Any compound of protein and carbohydrate. The chondroproteins, the mucoids, and the mucins are glycoproteins.

Goniometer An instrument used to measure the angles between the reflecting surfaces of a *prism* or a crystal. Two methods may be used to determine this angle. In the first, the prism or crystal remains stationary, and parallel rays from a *collimator* strike the surfaces of the prism near the apex and are reflected in different directions. The angle between the beams reflected from the two faces is measured by a telescope which can move around a graduated circle; the angle between the two prism faces is half of this angle. In the other method, the telescope remains stationary, while the prism or crystal is rotated so that first one, then the other face has light striking it. The angle between the faces is the supplement of the angle through which the prism or crystal mounting is turned.

Goniometer analyzer A sheet of *polaroid,* graduated in degrees, which rotates in a plane perpendicular to the optic axis. In the Smith–Baker interference microscope, the difference between the reference and the extinction readings is half the phase difference (expressed in degrees) produced by the specimen.

Grating An array of parallel, equally spaced lines, rods, bars, or other long, narrow objects having relatively little space between them. A *diffraction grating* is a light-transmitting or light-reflecting material with rulings on the *surface;* it is used to produce spectra.

Group In mathematics, a *set* of elements which is finite or infinite in number and satisfies certain conditions:

(1) There is an operation defined which associates with each ordered pair of elements a, b of the group G another element, c, of the group; the relationship is expressed $ab = c$. This operation may be any single-valued binary operation, for example, addition or multiplication.

(2) If a, b are in the group G, then ab must necessarily be in G also; this is called "closure."

(3) The operation is associative: $(ab)c = a(bc) = abc$ for any three elements of G.

(4) There exists an element e of G called the identity such that $ea = a$ for every element a of G.

(5) Each element a of G has an element called in the inverse a^{-1} such that $a^{-1}a = aa^{-1} = e$.

Infinite groups are called discrete if the elements are *denumerable,* and continuous if they consist of a nondenumerable number of elements. A finite group having n elements is of *order n*. If there are m of these n elements, $m < n$, that satisfy all of the above requirements, these m elements form a subgroup of the original group. Every group contains at least two subgroups, the group itself and the identity element. If the elements of a group are symbols, with no meaning attached, the group is called abstract, but if the elements represent numbers, matrices, etc., the group is called special.

Guanine A purine base found in *nucleic acids*. Specifically, 2-amino-6-hydroxypurine.

H

Haploid Having a single set of *chromosomes,* as in mature germ cells, as distinguished from the normal *diploid* number in *somatic cells.* (The haploid number is 23 in man.)

Haze Visual effect due to *light scattering* by particles too small to be seen with the unaided eye (of the order of 1–10 microns).

HeLa cells Classical cell lines from human tumor material started by George O. Gey in 1951 from cervical carcinoma [*Cancer Research* **12**, 264–265 (1952)]. The term "He La" was derived from the first two letters of both the first name and the last name of the patient whose cells were brought into culture. See also *HE p–1 cells* and *Chang cells*.

Hemoglobin A conjugated protein consisting of the protein globin and the prosthetic group, heme. Hemoglobin is easily crystallized and both combines with and releases oxygen; it is the respiratory pigment of the erythrocytes.

Hemosiderin An iron-containing pigment found intracellularly and produced upon the decomposition of *hemoglobin* or of myoglobin; removal of iron from the hemosiderin granule leaves an acidic polysaccharide.

HE p 1, HE p 2, HS 1 cells Human cancer tissue culture cell lines (human epidermoid 1, human epidermoid 2, human sarcoma 1) derived from animal transplants and biopsies by Audrey Fjelde in 1952 while at the Sloan Kettering Institute in New York City [*Cancer* **9**, 845–851 (1955)]. HS 1 cells exhibit a *chromosome* number of 49 to 51 [*Cancer* **9**, 648–663 (1956)], which is three to five more than the number exhibited by the normal karyotype. HE p 1 cells show a *stemline* of 72 [*Hereditas* **45**, 449–460 (1959)], while HE p 2 cells have a stemline of around 77 to 80, which is hypertriploid [*Cancer Research* **23**, 197–200 (1963)].

Heterochromatic Staining differently from the surrounding material, usually staining darker. For example, the sex *chromosome* Y stains darker than other chromosomes when stained by ordinary methods.

Heterochromatin Although originally this term meant the substance of *heterochromosomes,* it has since been broadened to include any *chromatin* that has a very large amount of *desoxyribose*-type *nucleoprotein.*

Heterochromosome Syn. *Allosome.*

Heteroploidy Having a *chromosome* number that is not an integral multiple of the *haploid* number.

Histogram A graph that depicts the *frequency* distribution of some quantity.

Histone Any strongly basic protein that is water soluble, but insoluble in, or precipitated by, ammonium hydroxide. Also, they are coagulated by heat. Some examples of histone are the globin of *hemoglobin* and the histone from thymus cell nuclei.

Homologous chromosome Each member *chromosome* of the pair which associates at *synapsis;* they are the corresponding members of the two sets contributed by the *gametes.*

Huygens' principle Each point of a wave front may be considered the source of spherical, secondary waves, spreading out in all directions and having the same velocity as the propagation velocity of the waves.

Hydrogen bond A weak ionic bond formed between a hydrogen atom carried by an electronegative atom and some other electronegative atom such as oxygen, fluorine, nitrogen, etc.

Hydrolysate The fluid resulting from *hydrolysis.*

Hydrolysis Chemical decomposition caused by the addition of water; the reaction is $AB + HOH \rightarrow AOH + HB$.

Hydrolysis curve The curve showing extent of hydrolysis as a function of time during which the hydrolytic agent acts. In absorption spectrophotometry of Feulgen-stained material, a curve of measured *absorption* versus duration of hydrolysis. The hydrolysis time for which the absorption is a maximum is taken to be the optimal time for hydrolysis.

Hyperdiploid Having a chromosome number greater than *diploid*.

Hypodiploid Having a chromosome number less than *diploid*.

I

Idiochromatin The *chromatin* that takes part in the processes of *cell division*.

Idiochromidia *Chromidia* that take part in the process of *cell division;* generative chromidia.

Idiogram A graphical presentation of the chromosome complement of a *metaphase* cell in which the chromosomes are ordered and grouped in accordance with length, shape, position of *kinetochore,* etc.

Illumination The ratio of the *luminous flux* incident on an element of *surface* to the area of that element. The unit of illumination is the *lux*.

Illumination critical See *critical illumination.*

Imaginary number A number of the form ia, where $i = \sqrt{-1}$, and a is a real number.

Incandescence *Light emission* by a body due to the kinetic energy possessed by its molecules (e.g., a glowing electric lamp filament).

Incandescent lamp A lamp that produces *light* by *incandescence* when some substance in it is heated to a white or red heat, e.g., a filament lamp.

Independent variable In mathematics, a *variable* that does not depend on other variables for its value, e.g., x is independent of the value of y in $y = f(x)$.

Integer A *natural number,* the negative of a natural number, or 0 (defined to be that number which, when added to another number, gives that number as its sum, i.e., $a + 0 = a$).

Intensity The quantity of energy or the number of particles passing through unit area per unit of time; e.g., the intensity of radiation is the number of photons or particles passing through a unit area per unit time.

Interference The charge in the resultant amplitude of a wave due to the superposition of two or more waves. To produce optical interference with *light* waves, a light beam is separated into two parts, and each beam made to follow a different optical path so that the two beams are out of phase with each other. When these beams are brought together, they will interfere destructively at some points (dark), constructively at others (light).

Interference filter An optical device that permits only a certain, usually narrow, band of *wavelengths* to be transmitted, the rest being suppressed by the destructive *interference* of waves transmitted through the filter and those reflected $2n$ times, for n an *integer*. (See also *monochromator*.)

Interference fringes The alternate dark and light bands observed when two beams of *light* initially in phase undergo *interference* with each other. One way to ensure that the beams were originally in phase is to use a single light source.

Interference microscopy The simplest interference microscope is a Fabry-Perot *interferometer;* it allows examinations of the surface irregularities (S. Tolansky, "Surface Microtopography," Wiley, New York, 1962), as well as of the *refractive index* variations [A. M. Frederikse, *Z. Wiss. Mikroskopie* **52**, 48 (1935); R. C. Mellors and co-workers, *Cancer* **6**, 372 (1953)]. Apart from this, microscopic interferometers follow different principles, depending on whether they are used for incident or transmitted *light.* However, for cellular research, transmitted light instruments are of greater importance. In the Dyson-type interferometer [J. Dyson, *Proc. Phys. Soc. London* **B62**, 505 (1949); J. Dyson, *Nature* **171**, 743 (1953)], the incident light is split into two rays which, after passing through the specimen, are recombined by semireflecting layers deposited on two glass plates. The specimen is placed between the two plates and can be viewed through a hemispherical glass block by means of a conventional, high-power microscope. In another type of microscopic interferometer, separation and recombination are achieved through *birefringent* elements [A. A. Lebedeff, *Rev. Optique* **9**, 385 (1930); M. Francon, *Bull. Microscop. Appl.* **7**, 14 (1957)]. Depending on how the separated rays pass through the object field, one can characterize the optical systems as shearing or double-focus. In the former, the two beams pass side by side through the sample field; in the latter, they are displaced along the optic axis. A particular wide separation of the two bundles is possible in the Mach–Zehnder interferometer. In its microscopic version, both microscope objectives, one for the substrate, the other for the reference beam, point in the same direction [J. Grehn, *Leitz Mitt. Wiss. Techn.* **1**, 35 (1959)]. In some respects, *phase-contrast* and interference microscopes are alike. In both, a light bundle is divided into two parts and then recombined. The essential difference is that in an interference microscope the light is divided by a beam splitter, while in a phase microscope it is the specimen, in particular its fine details, which divides the light. Since small particles diffract light more strongly, they will give a better spatial separation in a phase microscope than larger particles. Images of small particles are thus less subject to artifacts. The interference microscopes permit easier quantitative measurements. Certain interference microscopes are adapted for scanning [T. Caspersson *et al., Exp. Cell Res.* **7**, 601 (1954); G. Svensson, *Exp. Cell Res.* **4**, 165, Supp. (1957)] and integration [H. G. Davies and E. M. Deeley, *Exp. Cell Res.* **11**, 169 (1956)]. The principal application of the interference microscope in cellular research is the determination of the dry or anhydrous mass [A. J. Hale, "The Interference Microscope in Biological Research," Williams and Wilkins, Baltimore, 1958; R. C. Mellors and J. Hlinka, *Exp. Cell Res.* **9**, 128 (1955)].

Interferometer An instrument in which phase differences resulting in *interference* can be measured.

International candle See *candela.*

Intrinsic Part of the nature of a thing; inherent.

Intrinsic birefringence *Birefringence* caused by a regular molecular structure; it is independent of the medium in which the object is immersed (see also *form birefringence*).

Ion An atom, or a molecularly bound group of atoms, that has lost or gained one or more electrons and thus has a positive or negative electric charge. When ions are characterized by their electric charge state, they are called positive, negative, or *amphoteric* ("Zwitter"); an amphoteric ion carries both positive and negative charges, often at opposite ends of a molecule as in amino acids.

Ion beam scanning A method of analyzing the mass, energy, or velocity *spectrum* of an *ion* beam by moving a probe or by changing the magnetic or electric fields of a mass *spectrometer.*

Ionization The process of forming *ions,* e.g., ions are formed when polar compounds such as acids, bases, or salts are dissolved in water, liquid ammonia, and certain other solvents. The compounds undergo *dissociation,* and positively and negatively charged ions are formed, depending on whether electrons were lost or gained. Gases are ionized by electrical discharge or the passage of radiation through the gas.

Ion microscope Any device in which electric or magnetic fields are used to shape the trajectories of ions or other charged particles so as to produce a magnified image of an initial ion distribution. The latter is usually that which has been transmitted through the specimen to be visualized. As particular types one has the *electron microscope, proton microscope,* etc. [H. Boersch, *Experientia* **4**, 1 (1948); E. W. Mueller, *Am. Scientist* **49**, 88 (1961)]. See also *Field emission microscope.*

I. P. See *isoelectric point.*

Irrational number A number which cannot be expressed as a fraction of the form p/q, where p and q are integers and $q \neq 0$. If expressed in decimal form, an irrational number is infinitely nonrepeating (that is, no fixed sequence of digits is repeated after some finite number of decimal places). Some examples of irrational numbers are $\sqrt{2}$, π, e.

Isochore A graph representing pressure as a *function* of temperature, the volume remaining constant.

Isoelectric point That pH at which a molecule in solution carries no net ionic charge. Here the solution exhibits minimal viscosity, osmotic pressure, and conductivity. Also, the molecules do not move toward either electrode (i.e., do not undergo cataphoresis), they are more easily coagulated, and proteins swell the least.

Isogamy Sexual conjugation in protozoans in which the male and female cells are similar in many respects, rather than dissimilar, as in higher forms.

Isolux A *curve* at each point of which the *illumination* is the same.

Isomerism The phenomenon whereby two or more substances have the same molecular composition and molecular weight, but different molecular configurations. Examples are many organic compounds and complex inorganic salts.

Isometric Referring to a system in which certain lengths are maintained constant.

Isotropic A material having one or more properties that are independent of the choice of direction within the material along which the property is measured.

K

Karyokinesis The process involved in nuclear division, by either *mitosis* or indirect *cell division,* especially nuclear transformation, differentiated from *cytokinesis.* Also called *karyomitosis.*

Karyomere A *chromosome* segment, i.e., one of the *chromatin* granules composing a chromosome.

Karyoplasm Old term for *nucleoplasm.*

Karyosome (1) A false or *chromatin* nucleolus, as opposed to a true nucleolus or *plasmosome*. (2) One of the chromatin masses united as knots in the chromatin network. Also called false nucleolus, net knot.

Karyotype See *idiogram*.

Kinetics The study of the rates at which various interrelated processes occur. For example, in chemical reaction kinetics, the rates at which chemical reactions occur are investigated.

Kinetochore A small region or portion of a *chromosome* often visible during *mitosis* as a constriction and at which a chromosome is attached to a *spindle fiber*. Syn. *centromere*.

Kinoplasm Syn. *ergastoplasm*.

Klinefelter syndrome Males with XXY sex *chromosomes*. They are sterile, with bodily characteristics tending to be feminine [*Acta Endocrinol.* **34**, 488–495 (1960)].

Köhler method of illumination A method of microscopical illumination whereby an image of the source is formed by the source condenser on the iris of the substage condenser diaphragm; this iris lies in the lower focal plane of the substage condenser; the latter then focuses an image of the source iris in the plane of the specimen.

L

Lake An adsorption compound formed by the union of a dye with a metal salt by electrovalent bonding. When insoluble lakes are formed in fibers being dyed, the process is called "mordanting"; the "mordants" are usually hydroxides of iron, chromium, and aluminum.

Lambert cosine law An ideally diffuse *surface* which emits (or transmits or reflects) a *luminous intensity* I_n in the direction of the normal to that surface will emit (or transmit or reflect) a luminous intensity $I_\theta = I_n \cos \theta$ in the direction lying at an angle θ with the normal to the surface.

Lambert law See *Bouguer law*.

Law of Brewster Unpolarized light incident on the surface of a dielectric produces maximal *polarization* of reflected and refracted rays when the angle of incidence is such that these rays are perpendicular to each other.

Laser A solid-state or gaseous device which can produce an intense, monochromatic, parallel beam of coherent *light*. It functions in virtue of the ability of an excited atom to absorb a photon of the particular frequency that the excited atom would emit in falling normally to a lower energy state. When an excited atom absorbs such a photon, the atom instantaneously drops to the lower state, emitting a photon as it falls. If such emitted photons are reflected back and forth through atoms in an excited state by the action of an external energy source, all excited atoms absorbing photons of the characteristic frequency will *simultaneously* emit photons of that particular frequency. Thus, the emitted light is coherent owing to simultaneous emission by all atoms, and it is monochromatic because of the resonance absorption and emission of the particular atoms employed. The light is emitted as a parallel beam owing to the act of the plane-parallel surfaces used to reflect the photons back and forth.

Laws of exponents If a and b are positive *real numbers,* then for any real numbers x and y, the laws of exponents are as follows:

   (1) $a^x a^y = a^{x+y}$;
   (2) $a^x/a^y = a^{x-y}$;
   (3) $a^x b^x = (ab)^x$;
   (4) $a^x/b^x = (a/b)^x$;
   (5) $(a^x)^y = a^{xy}$;
   (6) $a^{-x} = (1/a^x)$ for $x > 0$;
   (7) $a^x > 0$ for all x;
   (8) If $a \neq 1$, $a^x = a^y$, if, and only if, $x = y$;
   (9) If $a > 1$, $a^x > a^y$, if, and only if, $x > y$;
   (10) If $a < 1$, $a^x > a^y$, if, and only if, $x < y$.

Lens A transparent optical element containing at least one polished *refracting* surface, usually spherical, but sometimes systematically altered from the spherical shape for particular applications.

Leptotene The first stage of *meiotic prophase,* in which the ends of the *chromatin* threads acquire polarity with respect to one small area of the nuclear membrane.

Light The range of electromagnetic radiation associated with vision, i.e., the *wavelengths* ranging from 4000 Å (violet) to 7700 Å (red).

Light, velocity of The speed at which a "group" of electromagnetic waves comprising a pulse of light is propagated through a medium. More specifically, this velocity is the "group velocity." Since a light pulse may be composed of a set of superposed monochromatic *waves,* each wave having one particular wavelength and one particular velocity of propagation, the group velocity and the "wave velocity" (also called phase velocity) will not in general be equal. If waves of long wavelength have greater wave velocity than waves of short wavelength, the wave velocity of these waves will be greater than the group velocity.

Linear differential equation The general form for a linear equation of *order n* is $p_0(x)y^{(n)} + p_1(x)\ y^{(n-1)} + \cdots + p_n(x)y = r(x)$, where $y^{(i)}$ is the ith derivative of y. See also *ordinary differential equation.*

Linear function A *function* of the first *degree* having the form $y = mx + b$, where m is the *slope* of the equation and b the value of y, when $x = 0$. Such a function is called linear because, when graphed in a Cartesian *coordinate system,* its graph is a straight line.

Line spectrum A *spectrum* in which values of the property being analyzed group around discrete values, in contrast to a *continuous spectrum.* The spectra of atoms is a line spectrum; the spectra of molecules was unresolved in the early days of *spectroscopy,* but since then it has been shown that the bands of most molecules consist of lines, and it is believed all bands consist of lines.

Lipofuscin A pigment having a lipid or lipoprotein as precursor, possibly formed by oxidation of the precursor. In the presence of a reducing substance such as ascorbic acid, it stains black with silver. Also called "wear and tear pigment."

Locus (1) A system of *curves,* lines, or points that satisfy specified conditions. Thus, the locus of an equation is the *set* of all points for which the equation is satisfied. (2) The position along a chromosome at which a given gene occurs.

Logarithm The logarithm of a number a to the base b is the exponent x or the power to which the base must be raised to equal a. That is, if $a = b^x$, then $x = \log_b a$. The base must be positive and unequal to 1, and a must be positive. The base of the Briggs or ordinary logarithms is 10, so that 1 is the log of 10 since 10 is the first power of 10; 2 is the log of 100, etc. Another type of logarithm, the natural logarithm, uses as base the *irrational* number $e = 2.7182 \ldots$ (expressed as $\log_e N$ or $\ln N$).

The "antilogarithm" is the number corresponding to a given logarithm, and the "cologarithm" is the logarithm of the reciprocal of a number.

Logarithmic amplifier An *amplifier* that has an output *signal* that is a *logarithmic function* of the input signal.

Logarithmic function A *function* whose equation is $y = a \ln x$ in the Cartesian *coordinate system;* the exponential function, $x = e^{y/a}$, is its inverse. When graphed using Cartesian coordinates, values on the abscissa increase geometrically as values on the ordinate increase arithmetically. Using semilogarithmic paper, one sees that the graph of $x + \log y =$ constant or $y + \log x =$ constant is a straight line.

Lumen The unit of *luminous flux*. 1 lumen $= 0.00146$ *watt* of *radiant flux* of *wavelength,* 555 *millimicrons,* or its equivalent with respect to *brightness.*

Luminescence *Light emission* of any type. With regard to the means by which energy is supplied to the emitting object, one may distinguish photoluminescence (*fluorescence, phosphorescence*), thermoluminescence (*incandescence*), chemiluminescence (inluding bioluminescence), and electroluminescence.

Luminosity The quality of *brightness* evaluated subjectively by some specified set of observers.

Luminous efficiency The ratio, expressed in *lumens* per *watt,* of the *luminous flux* to the corresponding *radiant flux.* It is a concept associated with the determination of *luminous flux* using the standard *luminosity function.*

Luminosity function (standard) A standard *function* that has been established by the Commission Internationale de l'Eclairage (CIE) (formerly called, in translation, International Commission on Illumination) which allows a given source of *radiant energy* to be evaluated with respect to its *luminosity.* The *luminous flux* in *lumens* is given by $K \int_{\lambda=0}^{\lambda=\infty} y_\lambda J_\lambda \, d\lambda$, where J_λ is the spectral power density of the source in watts per unit *wavelength;* $y\lambda$, the dimensionless standard luminosity function normalized to a value of 1 at 555 millimicrons; and K, a conversion constant with the value 680 lumens per watt.

Luminous energy The energy possessed by those electromagnetic waves that can elicit the sensation of vision in an average human observer.

Luminous flux A measure of *brightness,* the unit of luminous flux being the *lumen.*

Luminous intensity The number of *lumens* of *luminous flux* emitted from a source per steradian of solid angle with origin at the source. The unit of luminous intensity is the *candela.*

Lux The unit of *illumination.* 1 lux $= 1$ lumen per square meter.

Lysosome A cell organelle containing a number of different hydrolytic enzymes such as acid phosphatase, acid DNase, etc.

M

Magnification (linear) The ratio of the distance between two points in the image plane to the distance between the corresponding two points in the object plane.

Malus cosine-squared law The fractional intensity of plane-*polarized light* transmitted by an *analyzer* is proportional to the square of the cosine of the angle between the plane of *polarization* of the light and the transmission plane of the analyzer.

Malus' theorem If a ray of *light* is traced through a system of refractive media from a point A on any initial wavefront W_i to a point B on any final wavefront W_f, and if the total optical path from A to B is p_{AB}, then every ray traced from W_i to W_f will have exactly the same value of total optical path as did the ray from A to B, viz., p_{AB}.

Marfan syndrome A hereditary malformation caused by greater length variations in the Y *chromosome* than normal for the population. The associated malformations include eye defects, heart-aortic abnormalities, and spider fingers [*Cytogenetics* **1**, 5–19 (1962)].

Marker An abnormal chromosome having an easily identifiable morphology.

Mean The mean (or arithmetic mean) of a number of quantities X_i $(i = 1, \ldots, n)$ is their sum divided by the number of quantities, i.e., $\Sigma X_i / n$.

Meiosis See *miosis*.

Mercury vapor lamp An electric discharge lamp in which the discharge occurs through mercury vapor; the *spectrum* that is emitted is not continuous. (Compare with *xenon lamp*.)

Metacentric chromosome Chromosome in which the *kinetochore* is located very nearly midway along the length of the chromosome.

Metachromasia The staining of different substances different shades or colors when using the same dye.

Metaphase Second stage of *mitosis*. (See *cell division*.)

Microdensitometer An instrument to detect and measure optical density of a photographic emulsion. Some microdensitometers measure the secondary image produced in a microscopic system instead of a photographic negative, e.g., Barr and Stroud Integrating Microdensitometer designed by E. M. Deeley [*J. Sci. Instr.* **32**, 263–267 (1955)]. In this case the instrument is functioning as a *photometer*.

Micrograph A photographic reproduction of an image formed by a microscope or an equivalent optical instrument.

Micrometer, filar See *filar micrometer*.

Micron A unit of length equal to 10^{-6} meter $= 10^{-3}$ millimeter.

Microradiograph The *radiograph* of a very small object which requires examination under a microscope or as a projected image. Low-voltage (i.e., soft) X-rays are used for this purpose. The technique is of importance in mass determinations.

Microspectrograph A special form of *microspectroscope* which is designed particularly for photographing spectra.

Microspectroscope An instrument that is a combined microscope and *spectroscope*.

Microspectroscopy, limitation of The limitations to microspectroscopy can be divided into those due to properties and preparation of the material under investigation and those related to optical and electrical factors [H. G. Davies and P. M. B. Walker, *Progr. Biophysics Biophys. Chem.* **2**, 195 (1952); P. J. Fitzgerald and A. Engstrom, *Cancer* **5**, 643 (1952); L. Lison, "Histochemie et Cytochemie Animales," Gauthier-Villars, Paris, 1953]. Fixation may cause the specimen to shrink and

Nanometer Preferred systematic term for *millimicron*.

Natural number One of the numbers $1, 2, \ldots, 50, \ldots, N, \ldots$.

Neper The unit of *attenuation,* named after Napier (the inventor of natural *logarithms*), which may also be expressed in *decibels.* When I_1 is attenuated to I_2 ($I_2 = I_1 e^{-n}$), then the attenuation is expressed in nepers (n).

Newton's rings A series of bands or rings produced by the *interference* of *light* reflected from two or more nearly parallel surfaces that are in contact at one point.

Nicol prism A device for obtaining plane-*polarized light.* It is composed of a crystal of calcite (Iceland spar) which has been cut and then cemented together again with Canada balsam so that the *ordinary ray* is reflected from the balsam, and the *extraordinary ray* is freely transmitted. This ray is plane polarized by the process of double refraction in the crystal.

Nissl bodies (substance) Basophilic bodies containing RNA which form the reticulum of the *cytoplasm* of nerve cells; described by Franz Nissl (1860–1919), a German neurologist.

Noise A set of undesired oscillations present in a system.

Noise filter A *filter* to prevent the transmission of *noise.*

Nonabsorption light loss Syn. *nonspecific specimen light loss.*

Nondisjunction Nonseparation of two daughter *chromosomes* during *anaphase* of *mitosis,* resulting in one daughter nucleus receiving both chromosomes. Thus, one cell will have more chromosomes than normal; the other will have fewer (*aneuploid cell*).

Nonhistone protein Acidic and neutral protein remaining after DNA and *histone* protein have been removed from a chromosome.

Nonspecific specimen light loss *Light* loss due to the particulate nature of cellular matter and variations of *refractive index* within a substance. It is caused mainly by *scattering.* Syn. *nonabsorption light loss.*

Normal A line making an angle of 90 degrees with another line.

Nuclease An *enzyme* able to break down *nucleic acids* into *nucleotides, nucleosides,* or components of the latter. Nucleases are found in germinating seeds and in such animal organs as the liver, pancreas, and thymus.

Nucleated Having a nucleus.

Nucleic acid (nucleinic acid) Any polynucleotide found in the cell; in general it contains the bases *adenine, cytosine, guanine,* and either *thymine* or *uracil.* Usually, the sugar component is ribose or *desoxyribose.* Nucleic acids are found in nuclei and *cytoplasm.*

Nuclein A colorless, amorphous substance, insoluble in dilute acids, but soluble in dilute alkalis; it is a decomposition product of *nucleoprotein.* The name is attributed to Miescher, the founder of nucleic acid chemistry.

Nucleinase An *enzyme* or group of enzymes which dissociates *nucleic acid* into *nucleotides.*

Nucleohistone A *nucleoprotein* composed of *nucleic acid* and *histone.*

Nucleoliform Having the characteristic appearance of a nucleolus.

Nucleolini A term used in older literature, referring to the masses of ribonucleoproteins present in or around nucleolar vacuoles. The other type of ribonucleoprotein inside the nucleolus is the "pars amorpha," which surrounds and on which is embedded the filamentous network called nucleolonema (the filamentous network continuous with the nucleolini).

Nucleoplasm   Nuclear protoplasm, formerly called *karyoplasm.*

Nucleoprotein   A nuclear constituent consisting of a basic protein and *nucleic acid.* When hydrolyzed, nucleoproteins yield amino acids, *purine,* and *pyrimidine* bases, phosphoric acid, and a sugar. They are soluble in fat solvents or water. Example: *nucleohistone.*

Nucleoside   A compound composed of a *purine* or *pyrimidine* base and a sugar (pentose), which results from the removal of phosphate from a *nucleotide.*

Nucleotide   The basic structural unit of *nucleic acid* consisting of a *purine* or *pyrimidine* base, a pentose sugar, and phosphoric acid.

Numerical aperture   The sine of half the *angular aperture* times the *refractive index* of the substance through which the light reaching the lens passes. Mathematically it is expressed by N. A. $= n \sin \theta$, where n is the index of refraction of the medium and θ half the angular aperture.

O

Objective   The integral set of refracting or reflecting elements (in an optical instrument employing two or more such sets) which produces an image of an object.

Objective, achromatic   See *achromatic objective.*

Objective, fluorite   See *fluorite objective.*

Opacity   The ratio of the incident *light intensity* to the transmitted light intensity, i.e., the reciprocal of *transmission.*

Opaque   In optics, a term used to describe a material that does not transmit radiation.

Optical activity   A molecular property possessed by certain substances such as sugar whereby plane-*polarized light* undergoes a rotation of its plane of polarization in passing through the substance. The total rotation is proportional to the thickness of the substance traversed by the light.

Optical axis   The line that joins the center of *curvature* of the *surfaces* of an optical system.

Optical center of a lens   The point on the axis of a lens or lens system through which a ray having parallel incident and emergent directions passes.

Optical density   The *logarithm* of the *opacity.*

Optical path   The product of the geometrical distance d and the *refractive index* of the medium n. If there are several segments of the *light* path, $d_1, d_2, \ldots, d_p$, in substances with refractive indexes $n_1, n_2, \ldots, n_p$, the optical path is expressed by $n_1 d_1 + n_2 d_2 + \cdots + n_p d_p = \sum\limits_{i=1}^{p} n_i d_i$. In a medium in which the refractive index varies continuously, optical path $= \int n \, ds$, where ds is an element of length along the path. By the *Fermat principle* the optical path between two points has an extreme value.

Optics, coated   See *coated optics.*

Optimum magnification   The greatest theoretically obtainable magnification, determined by the *numerical aperture* of a lens. The maximum value of the numerical aperture of a dry lens is 1.0 and for an oil-immersion objective, 1.65. Thus, the theoretical minimal distance between points which are resolved is 2.8×10^{-5} cm for a dry lens and 1.7×10^{-5} cm for an oil-immersion lens, using oblique illumination of *wavelength* 5500 *angstroms*. The maximal useful magnification is roughly 1000 times the numerical aperture; magnifications greater than this yield no further details in the image.

Order   (1) In a *differential equation,* the order of the highest *derivative* occurring. (2) In a *group,* the number of elements in a finite group. (3) In a *polynomial,* the highest *degree* of any term present. This applies only to the entire equation.

Ordinary differential equation   A single equation with ordinary (not partial) *derivatives* having as its general solution an expression containing arbitrary *constants* equal in number to the *order* of the equation. If *boundary conditions* are imposed, the values of the constants are specified and a particular solution obtained. (A useful collection of ordinary differential equations with solutions is found in "Differential-Gleichungen, Lösungsmethoden und Lösungen" by E. Kamke (3rd ed., Chelsea, New York, 1948).

Ordinary ray   That ray which is undeviated (angle of refraction $= 0$) when the incident ray enters the face of a birefringent crystal perpendicularly; thus *Snell's law* of *refraction* is obeyed by the ordinary ray. See *extraordinary ray.*

Orthochromatic   Producing shades of black and white corresponding to natural colors, as in black and white photographic film. Sensitive to all colors except red.

Oscillation   (1) A motion of an oscillating object which carries it once through its full range of positions and velocities. (2) Variation; instability. Regular, periodic variation between minimal and maximal values, as voltage or current.

Oscillatory scanning   A scanning system in which the scanning spot moves continuously back and forth across the image so that successive lines are scanned in opposite directions (e.g., television).

Oscillogram   A record of a wave form.

Oscillograph   An instrument that records *oscillation.*

Oscilloscope   A type of *oscillograph* that displays electrical *signals* as position or intensity changes of an electron beam incident on a *fluorescent screen.*

P

Pachytene   The third stage (bouquet stage) of *meiotic prophase,* coming between *zygotene* and *diplotene,* in which *homologous chromosomes* shorten, thicken, and intertwine.

Parameter   (1) An arbitrary *constant,* as distinguished from an absolute of fixed constant; an arbitrary value can be assigned to a parameter. (2) In statistics, a constant which specifies certain characteristic properties of a probability distribution such as a *mean, variance,* etc.

Partial derivative   The *derivative* of a *function* having two or more *independent variables* with respect to one of the independent variables. It is calculated by differentiating the function with respect to the variable of interest and treating all other variables as constants during the differentiation. For example, if the function is $f(x, y)$, the partial derivative f_y is obtained by differentiating $f(x, y)$ with respect to y, holding x constant.

Partial differential equation A *differential equation* having two or more *independent variables,* so that the derivatives are *partial derivatives.*

Path difference The difference in linear distance traveled by two waves in a given time. Usually the two waves of interest either propagate along the same direction with different velocities, or they propagate with the same velocity along convergent or divergent paths.

Path, optical See *optical path.*

pH A measure of hydrogen ion concentration defined by $pH = -\log[H]$, where [H] is the concentration of hydrogen ions in moles per liter.

Phase-contrast microscope A compound microscope having a phase plate at the focal plane of the first group of lenses in the objective and an annular diaphragm at the front focal plane of the substage condenser. The phase plate, a glass plate on which is deposited an annular layer of transparent material, changes the phase of rays passing through the layer by one-quarter *wavelength.* Rays diffracted by a point in the specimen take a different path through the system. The interference of these two sets of rays occurs when they are brought together to form an image. Thus, objects differing only in optical path, not necessarily in density, become visible.

Phase difference The difference $(\phi_2 - \phi_1)$ in phase angle between two monochromatic waves given by $A \sin \phi_2$ and $B \sin \phi_1$.

Philadelphia chromosome (Ph¹) A *chromosome,* smaller than any normal human chromosome, which appears in leukemic cells of chronic myoloid leukemia. The Philadelphia chromosome is altered and believed to be No. 21, the same one involved in *mongolism.* Mongoloids, compared with normal individuals, show an increased incidence of leukemia.

Phosphoprotein A conjugated protein in which a hydroxy amino acid and phosphoric acid are esterified, e.g., casein in milk and vitelline in egg yolk.

Phosphopyridine nucleotides Compounds containing adenine, a pentose, phosphoric acid, and nicotinic acid amide; important for hydrogen transfer reactions during cell respiration.

Phosphorescence *Luminescence* which persists longer than 10^{-8} second after *excitation* has ceased.

Photometer An instrument that measures *luminous intensity* or *luminous flux.*

Photomultiplier An *electron tube* having one or more *dynodes* between the output electrode and the photocathode; the electrons emitted from the photocathode due to incident radiation produce additional electrons by secondary emission from each dynode stage. Syn. *multiplier phototube.*

Photon A bundle or quantum of electromagnetic energy.

Phototube A *light*-sensitive electron tube consisting of a photoemissive *cathode,* i.e., one which will emit electrons when illuminated, and an *anode* for collecting the electrons emitted by the cathode.

Phytohemagglutinin A *mucoprotein* from the garden bean (*Psaseolus*); it is used with samples of peripheral blood in which it induces the leukocytes in the plasma to actively divide for *chromosome* study [*Exp. Cell Res.* **20**, 613–616 (1960)].

Pile of plates A device consisting of a stack of glass plates in contact with each other, so arranged that *light* is *reflected* from them at the polarizing angle; the reflected light is then fully plane polarized, and the transmitted light is partially polarized.

Planck's constant A physical constant having the value 6.6252×10^{-27} erg-second, and denoted by the symbol h.

pK The negative logarithm of the equilibrium constant K for the chemical reaction $A_a B_b \cdots \rightarrow aA + bB + \cdots$, where $K = [A]^a \cdot [B]^b \cdots / [A_a B_b \cdots]$, and the brackets denote molar concentrations of the chemical species $A_a B_b \cdots$, A, B, ...

Plasmal reaction A reaction of the *Schiff reagent* with aldehyde groups derived from cytoplasmic acetal phospholipids, thus introducing uncertainty in interpretation of the *Feulgen reaction*. The acetal phospholipids can be removed by treatment with alcohol and in other ways.

Plasmosome (1) The true nucleolus, as differentiated from the nuclear *karyosomes*. (2) Generic term for any cytoplasmic granule.

Ploidy The number of multiples of the *haploid* number of chromosomes which a cell contains.

Polar body Any of the three small cells produced by oogonia during oogenesis.

Polarimeter An instrument used to determine the *optical activity* of a liquid. A *polarizer* is inserted in the path of a *light* ray before it traverses the liquid, and an *analyzer* after traversal; from the relative positions of polarizer and analyzer the optical activity may be determined.

Polariscope An instrument consisting of an *analyzer* and a *polarizer,* with space between them for inserting transparent specimens to be examined.

Polarization The production of *polarized light.*

Polarized light *Light* having wave vibrations confined to one plane, obtained by reflecting ordinary light from a plane *surface* at the angle of polarization, or by passing light through a *Nicol prism.*

Polarizer A device, as a *polaroid* plate or a *prism,* for producing plane-*polarized light.*

Polarizing microscope The polarizing microscope is one of the well-established tools of optics in biology [H. St. Bennett, *in* McClung's "Handbook of Microscopical Technique," Hoeber, New York, 1950; H. J. Jerrad, *Rev. Sci. Instr.* **26,** 1007 (1955); G. Oster, *in* "Physical Techniques in Biological Research," Academic Press, New York (1955)]. The polarizing microscope has a *polarizer* in the condenser and an *analyzer* in the ocular. More recent developments in polarization microscopy are related to increased resolving power, partly achieved by eliminating stray *light* and thus improving contrast [S. Inoue and K. Dan, *J. Morphol. Physiol.* **89,** 423 (1951); M. M. Swann and J. M. Mitchison, *J. Exp. Biol.* **27,** 226 (1950)] and partly by the development of highly sensitive polarization rectifiers [S. Inoue and W. L. Hyde, *J. Biophys. Biochem. Cytol.* **3,** 831 (1957)].

Polaroid A thin, transparent, film-like material used in photography and optics for polarizing *light.* Registered tradename of the Polaroid Corporation.

Polocyte Syn. *polar body.*

Polymer The molecule produced by *polymerization.*

Polymerization The chemical combination of a large number of individual organic molecules of the same type to form a compound,

Polynomial An integral *rational function,* also called a *multinomial,* having n variables. It is of the form

$$c_1 x_1^{a_1} x_2^{b_1} \cdots x_n^{r_1} + c_2 x_1^{a_2} x_2^{b_2} \cdots x_n^{r_2} + \cdots + c_k x_1^{a_k} x_2^{b_k} \cdots x_n^{r_k}.$$

In any term of this expression c_i is the coefficient which is *constant* and may be *real* or complex (see *complex variable*); a_i is the *degree* with respect to x_1 and is an integer; b_i is the degree with respect to x_2 and is an integer, etc. The degree of the entire term is $a_i + b_i + \cdots + r_i$, while the degree of the polynomial is the highest degree of any term having a nonvanishing coefficient. If all of the terms have the same degree, the polynomial is "homogeneous"; it is linear if it has degree 1; quadratic, if degree 2; cubic, if degree 3, etc.

Polynucleotide A *polymer* composed of many *mononucleotides* connected in chain fashion.

Polyploid The condition in which the *chromosome* number is more than *diploid.*

Prism A transparent solid bounded in part by two nonparallel plane faces, cut at certain angles for various optical purposes. Prisms can be used for *reflection, polarization,* or *dispersion.* In the latter use, a triangular prism receives light at one face and passes it through another after two *refractions;* this causes a total deviation of a light ray from its initial direction of Δ after passing through the prism. The deviation depends on the angle of the prism and its *refractive index* for the light used, as follows:

$$\Delta = \theta - \alpha + \arcsin\left[n \sin\left(\alpha - \arcsin\frac{\sin \theta}{n} \right) \right],$$

where θ is the angle of incidence of entering light, α the prism angle, and n the refractive index.

p-RNA and **r-RNA** The two types of nuclear RNA fractions which can be isolated by extracting cells with 0.15 M and 2.0 M NaCl solutions; this was discovered by Logan and Davidson [*Biochim. Biophys. Acta* **24**, 196 (1957)] and Osawa *et al.* [*Biochim. Biophys. Acta* **28**, 271–277 (1958)]. These methods are used to first extract the *ribosomes,* then the desoxyribonucleoproteins from cells. The Kirby technique was used by Sibatani *et al.* [*Biochim. Biophys. Acta* **33**, 590–591 (1959); *Nature* **186**, 215–217 (1960)] and by Yamana *et al.* [*Biochim. Biophys. Acta* **41**, 295–303 (1960); *Exp. Cell Res.* **21**, 535–540 (1960)] to separate RNA into two parts as follows: First the homogenate of the tissue was shaken with phenol saturated by phosphate buffer. Then the phenol layer was separated from the aqueous layer and extracted using phosphate buffer. The remaining residue was called r-RNA; the extracted layer was called p-RNA. There is more p-RNA in the total RNA in neoplastic than in nontumor tissues, but the turnover rate of p-RNA is much less than that of r-RNA. Yamana and Sibatani obtained these results in tumors, as well as in normal live cells. (See also m-RNA and s-RNA.)

Progeny Descendants; offspring.

Prolamine Group of proteins which are soluble in 70–90% alcohol, but insoluble in water and in strong alcohol.

Prophase The first stage of *mitosis.* See *cell division.*

Protamine Any of a group of strongly basic proteins of very simple composition which yield very large amounts of diamino acids. They are found in fish spermatozoa.

Pseudoscalar   A *scalar* quantity that changes sign when its reference *coordinate system* is changed from left-handed to right-handed or vice versa. An example of this is the scalar product of a *vector* with a *pseudovector*.

Pseudovector   A *vector* that changes sign when the *coordinate system* is changed from a left-handed to a right-handed one, or vice versa.

Purine   In general, any derivative of the compound formed by fusion of a pyrimidine ring with an imidazole ring. Specifically, $C_5H_4N_4$. *Adenine* and *guanine* are examples of purines. Those purines deriving from *nuclein cleavage* during metabolic processes are called endogenous.

Pyknosis   The shrinkage and wrinkling of a cell nucleus.

Pyrimidine   In general, any derivative of the six-membered heterocyclic compound containing two nitrogen atoms and four carbon atoms in the ring, the nitrogen atoms being separated by one carbon atom; specifically, N : CHN : CHCH : CH. Some examples of pyrimidines are *thymine, uracil,* and *cytosine.*

Q

Quantum   The discrete amount of energy absorbed or emitted during transitions of an atomic system from one energy level to another.

Quantum efficiency   The number of product molecules produced in a photochemical reaction for each quantum of *light* absorbed.

Quantum theory   Energy is absorbed and emitted by atomic systems only in discrete units called quanta. For radiant energy, such as *light,* of *frequency* ν, the quantum equals $h\nu$, where h is Planck's constant and has value $(6.6252 \pm .0002) \times 10^{-27}$ erg-second. There exists only a discrete set of energies with which electrons can be bound into atoms; energies intermediate between these cannot function in this way.

Quench   To overpower; to extinguish; to arrest by applying voltage, e.g., the discharge of an *ion* counter.

R

Radiant energy   That form of energy which is propagated in the form of electromagnetic waves, and emitted or absorbed as *quanta.*

Radiant flux   The amount of *radiant energy* incident on or emitted from a *surface* of any specified area per unit time.

Raman scattering   The appearance of additional lines near each major line in the *spectrum* caused by the *scattering* of light from the molecules of solids, liquids, and transparent gases. This phenomenon was discovered in 1928 by C. V. Raman, an Indian physicist. The spectrum is characteristic of the scattering material, being composed of more diffuse lines than the associated unscattered line. This effect is due to a change in rotational or vibrational energy of the scattering molecules, so is useful in studying molecular behavior or structure. For example, when light from a mercury arc excites carbon tetrachloride, some of the violet lines in the scattered light (especially at 4358 Å) have a fairly clear Raman spectrum associated with them, consisting of several lines of *wavelength* longer or shorter than the prominent line. The shorter, usually faint lines are anti-Stoke's lines.

Radiograph The image produced on film by radiation which has passed through an object. In practice, the radiation is usually X-rays.

Rational number A number that can be written in the form p/q, where p and q are *integers,* and q is not zero. The rational numbers form part of the system of *real numbers.*

Real number A number that is either *rational* or *irrational.*

Reduction division Syn. *meiosis.*

Reflectance The ratio of reflected *radiant flux* to incident radiant flux.

Reflectance, diffuse See *diffuse reflectance.*

Reflection A change in the direction of propagation of *light* after striking a surface. The law of regular reflection states that the angle formed between an incident light ray and the perpendicular to the point of reflection is equal to the angle between this perpendicular and the reflected ray; the incident ray, reflected ray, and the perpendicular all lie in the same plane.

Reflection X-ray microscopy A method of focusing and magnifying X-rays transmitted through a specimen using reflection at glancing angles from concave mirrors or curved single-crystal surfaces.

Refraction The change of direction of a *light* beam at the *surface* between two media of different *refractive indexes;* this change, caused by different light velocities in the media, is expressed by *Snell's law.*

Refractive index (index of refraction) The ratio of the velocity of *light* of a certain *wavelength* in vacuum to the velocity in a medium is the refractive index of that medium for the light. When light is *refracted,* the index may also be expressed as $n = n'\sin\theta'/\sin\theta$, where n is the refractive index of the first medium, n' of the second, and θ is the angle of incidence, θ' the angle of refraction. (See *Snell's law.*)

Resolution The process of separating or discerning individual elements, or the *degree* to which they can be separated or discerned. In optics, this term denotes the smallest distance between two points still allowing two images to be distinguished or the smallest change in *wavelength* discernible in a *spectrometer* as separate images. In the latter case, resolution is defined to be the ratio of the average wavelength of two lines in the *spectrum* which form a doublet to the actual differences in their wavelengths; resolution may also be defined in the same manner in terms of wave numbers or *frequencies.*

Ribonuclease An *enzyme* present in various body tissues that catalyzes the *depolymerization* of *ribonucleic acid* to yield *mononucleotides.*

Ribonucleic acid (RNA) A compound composed of two *purines, uracil,* and *cytosine,* two *pyrimidines, adenine,* and *guanine,* a sugar, and phosphoric acid. Since its sugar is ribose, the compound is called ribonucleic acid.

Ribosomes The active ribonucleoprotein constituents of microsomes; the ribosomes are composed of RNA having high molecular weight and of one or more basic proteins [*Biochem. J.* **76**, 23P-24P (1960)]. Structurally they consist of two or more types of RNA linked together due to divalent *ions,* especially magnesium [*Proc. Natl. Acad. Sci.* **47**, 1548–1554 (1961)]. Several types of evidence suggest a relationship between the biosynthesis of ribosomes and nucleolar function: (1) evidence that there are many small ribonucleoprotein particles in the nucleolus, in addition to the *nucleolini* there, (2) evidence that many of the ribonucleoprotein granules in the nucleolus may be discharged into the *cytoplasm,* (3) suppression of biosynthesis of microsomal RNA and protein in livers of animals treated with thioacetamide [*Arch. Biochem. Biophys.* **46**, 119–127 (1953)]. Perhaps the parts of the ribosome which differ in size and enzymatic constitution are formed in different parts of the nucleus.

Ring chromosome A *chromosome* having a structural aberration causing it to have the shape of a ring.

Ringer's solution A solution containing 0.33 g of calcium chloride, 0.3 g of potassium chloride, 8.6 g of sodium chloride, and distilled water to make 1000 ml. Ringer's solution is also called an isotonic solution of three chlorides.

Residual protein See *non-histone protein.*

S

Sakaguchi method Histochemical staining procedure for the demonstration of guanidyl groups; based on the chemical method described by Sakaguchi for *arginine* [*J. Biol. Chem.* **5**, 25 (1925); *J. Biochem. Japan* **37**, 231 (1950)].

Scalar A quantity having only magnitude, as differentiated from a *vector,* which also has direction. A true scalar has the same magnitude in all *coordinate systems.* See also *pseudoscalar.*

Scattering The dispersion of diffusion of a set of particles or rays about one or more spatial or other coordinates. For example, *light* is scattered in all directions when it enters a body of isotropic matter.

Schiff reaction A reaction of aldehydes with a reagent (Schiff reagent = fuchsin–sulfurous acid) resulting in production of a purple color.

Schwarzschild-Villiger effect The phenomenon in which a higher photometric transmission level is measured for a small, dark area in a larger, lighter zone owing to the *scattering* of *light* from the light zone into the darker one.

Scleroprotein A fibrous, simple protein which is insoluble; it serves as protection or support in the body. See *albuminoid.*

Self-absorption In optical *emission spectroscopy,* the reduction of relative *intensity* in the central part of spectral lines. This reduction is due to selective *absorption* in the cooler outer vapor of the source of radiation emitted by the hot central core.

Self-reversal The maximal possible degree of *self-absorption.*

Sellmeier equation The equation which expresses the dependence of the *refractive index* of a medium on the *wavelength* of *light* passing through it. The variation of refractive index with wavelength is called refractive *dispersion.*

Separation of variables A method used to find a particular solution to *linear partial differential equation.* A solution is assumed which is the product of certain unknown *functions,* each of which depends on only one of the *independent variables;* this solution is substituted into the original equation, thus separating the equation into two or more *ordinary differential equations* which can be solved by various methods. Any *boundary conditions* which must be imposed are satisfied by choosing suitable values of the *parameters* of the solution.

Set In mathematics, an arbitrary collection of elements with no required relation between the elements and no restriction with respect to the number or nature of these elements. Some examples are the set of all *integers,* all *rational numbers,* all *real numbers,* etc.

Sex chromatin Marginal *chromatin* bodies in cell nuclei. The method of determining the presence of sex chromatin gives information only on the number of *X chromosomes,* not about the absence or presence of a Y chromosome. The greatest number of sex chromatin bodies present in a cell is the number of X chromosomes minus one. Thus XO *Turner syndrome* patients and XY males will show no sex chromatin, while XXY *Klinefelter's syndrome* cases and XX females will exhibit one sex chromatin body. This method cannot distinguish between patients having primary amenorrhea, since some may be XY and others XO. Generally, the sex chromatin tests are performed on the vaginal or buccal mucosa. Papanicolaou, *Feulgen,* or orcein staining reactions demonstrate the marginal chromatin bodies quite well.

SH group Sulfhydryl group. The univalent SH radical is generally attached to a carbon chain. SH groups are important for the activity of many *enzymes.*

Signal The value of some variable constituting or depending on the variable(s) of interest in a system. The signal is frequently measured at a different time and different place from that of the system variable.

Signal-to-noise ratio The ratio of the *signal* magnitude to that of the *noise.* This ratio is determined using the root-mean-square values in the case of random noise or the peak values in the case of impulse noise.

Single cell clone Cell cultures derived from one isolated cell. Generally, clones of tumor cells are obtained from animal ascites tumors which were cultured. In 1950, Japanese scientists obtained the first tumor cell clones in animals using Yoshida's rat sarcoma as material.

Slope The limiting ratio of the change in ordinate to the corresponding change in abscissa at a point. In a Cartesian *coordinate system,* if the path has end points (x_1, y_1) and (x_2, y_2), its slope is given by $m = (y_2 - y_1)/(x_2 - x_1)$. If the path is not straight, its slope is expressed by $\lim_{x_2 \to x_1} (m) = (dy/dx)_{x = x_1}$, where $\lim_{x_2 \to x_1}$ means the limit as x_2 approaches x_1, and (dy/dx) is the *derivative* of y with respect to x at the point $x = x_1$.

Snell's law The law expressing the relationship between the angle of *refraction* of a ray of *light* and its angle of incidence, when the ray traverses media of different *refractive indices.* Snell's law is given by $n \sin \theta = n' \sin \theta'$, where n and n' are the refractive indexes of the two media; θ is the angle of incidence, and θ' is the angle of refraction. The angles are measured relative to a line perpendicular to the boundary surface between the two media at the point where the ray crosses from one medium to the other. If the second medium has a greater refractive index than the first, the ray bends toward the perpendicular, and if the second medium has a smaller refractive index, the ray bends away from the perpendicular.

Somatic cell Body cell, excluding *gametes.*

Spectrograph A type of *spectroscope* especially designed to photograph *spectra.* Spectography extends the scope of spectroscopy beyond the visible range of the light, i.e., into either the ultraviolet or infrared range.

Spectrometer An instrument used to measure spectra (plural of *spectrum*) or determine the *wavelengths* of the different radiations. Its construction is similar to that of a *spectroscope,* but it is used for precise measurements of *refractive indices,* so has divided scales from which may be read the angular position of the telescope and the *prism* table.

Spectrophotometer A device for measuring, as a *function* of *wavelength, radiant flux,* or energy passing through or reflected by a medium. It contains the following parts: (1) a source of radiant energy, (2) a *monochromator,* (3) holders for any substances to be investigated, (4) a device to receive and measure the radiant *intensity* or the radiant flux passing through or reflected by the substances under investigation.

Spectrophotometer, ultra-fast Ultra-fast *spectrophotometers* [G. W. Bethke, *J. Opt. Soc. Am.* **50,** 1054 (1960); M. M. Gurevich and K. I. Kolyadin, Opt. *Spectry. SSSR* **9,** 131 (1960)] are capable of scanning a specimen at a rate of more than 20,000 times per second. Some of these high-speed spectrophotometers are attached to electronic data storage units with print-out systems [S. Bourghardt *et al., Experientia* **11,** 163 (1955); H. Hyden and S. Larsson, *J. Neurochem.* **1,** 134 (1956)] and perform, integrate, and print-out about 3000 individual measurements per minute.

Spectroscope An instrument used to form and view spectra (plural of *spectrum*). *Light* from an illuminated slit is made parallel by a *collimating lens;* then it falls on a *diffraction grating* or *prism,* which disperses it. The spectral light can then be viewed using a telescope.

Spectroscopy The experimental and theoretical study and interpretation of *spectra.*

Spectrum The pattern produced by displaying components in order according to the magnitude of some property. In particular, an optical spectrum, in which images of a narrow slit are arranged in order of *wavelength.* The *prism* and *diffraction grating* are the chief devices for obtaining an optical spectrum.

Specular density The optical density of an image when measured with parallel *light* (contrast with *diffuse density*); the total light, including that dispersed, is measured.

Specular reflection The reflection of rays from a *surface* such that all reflected rays have the same direction.

Spherical aberration The condition in which rays from a point on the axis which are refracted or reflected by noncentral portions of an element are brought to a focus at a different point on the axis than rays which pass through the central portion of the element.

Spindle The framework of protein fibers which is formed during *mitosis* or *meiosis* between the *centrioles.*

s-RNA A *ribonucleic acid* to which amino acids are transferred after being converted to amino acid adenylates; it has a molecular weight of about 25,000. These ribonucleic acids have specific configurations determining their specificity for linkage to individual amino acids and determining their location on the surface of the *ribosomes.* This specificity may be partly related to the presence of *pyrimidine* and *purine* bases, recently found in this ribonucleic acid and present in minute amounts in other ribonucleic acids [*J. Biol. Chem.* **235,** 1488–1499 (1960); *Biochem. J.* **72,** 294–301 (1959)]. Experiments have shown the terminal end of the s-RNA, the amino acid receptor, to be cytidine, cytidine, and adenine (CCA) [*N.Y. Acad. Sci.* **81,** 675–678 (1959); *Biochim. Biophys. Acta* **45,** 133–138 (1960)]; this trinucleotide's linkage to the molecule is much more unstable than the other *nucleotide* linkages. One of the possible functions of the nucleolus is the addition of this trinucleotide to the s-RNA, according to Vincent and Baltus ("The Cell

Nucleus, pp. 18–23, Academic Press, New York, 1960). See also m-RNA, p-RNA, and r-RNA.

Standard candela   That *physical* standard which establishes a unit for the physical characteristic called *luminous intensity*. The latter is the physical counterpart of the subjective characteristic called *brightness* or *luminosity*. The candela is first determined mathematically by the relation 1 candela $= 1$ lumen per steradian, and then defined physically by stipulating that 1 square centimeter of any ideal (blackbody) radiator at the temperature of solidification of platinum (2046° K) produces 60 *lumens* per steradian.

Standard deviation   The square root of the expected value of the squares of the differences of a number of observations subtracted from their *mean*. In statistics, the square root of the *variance* is the standard deviation.

Stemline   *Chromosome* number for a given tumor. This term, introduced by Makino in 1952, is applied to those cells which appear to have been primarily responsible for the growth of the tumor. The first detailed chromosome *ideograms* for human malignant tumor cells were worked out in 1957 by Ising and Levan. For example, Hansen-Melander *et al.*, after examining cancer cells in ascites that accompanied ovarian cystocarcinoma, found two stemlines, one of 58 and the other of 63, situated between the *triploid* number of 69 and the *diploid* number of 46.

Only the chromosome number is considered when one determines the stemline or stemlines of a given tumor, but stemline cells may be characterized by all kinds of structural variation. Ford *et al.* (1958), for example, examined 60 reticulum cell tumors, the majority of which had been induced by irradiation, and found that most of them differed from normal tissue and from each other with respect to stemline numbers, the extent of variation around it, and the different forms of abnormal chromosomes. The stomach cancer analyzed by Ising and Levan contained two ring chromosomes in the stemline cells. Thus, each tumor has a distinct individuality; this individuality does not necessarily indicate, however, any histopathological difference. This may explain the fact that the histopathological classification is of limited value as used in clinical diagnosis to indicate the biochemical nature of the tumor, since different physiological qualities accompany the different stemlines. When the environmental conditions are constant, the stemlines remain stable or become more dominant. An environmental change induces a change in the stemline.

Steradian   A unit of measure of solid angle, the latter being defined as the ratio of projected area subtended to the square of the distance of that area from the origin of coordinates. A hemisphere subtends a solid angle of 2π steradians about the center of the hemisphere; a sphere subtends a solid angle of 4π steradians about its center.

Stoichiometry   That branch of chemistry concerned with the proportions in which elements and compounds react with each other, and with quantitative laws governing such chemical reactions.

Submetacentric chromosome   A chromosome that is nearly *metacentric*.

Sulfhydryl group   See *SH group*.

Super-female   Female having three X *chromosomes* (XXX).

Surface   The *set* of all points (x, y, z) satisfying an equation having three variables, e.g., $f(x, y, z) = 0$.

SV effect   See *Schwarzschild-Villiger effect*.

Synapse The connection of two nerve cells either by the intertwining of the terminal arborizations of their processes or by the embracing of one cell body by the processes of another cell.

Synapsis The point-for-point lateral pairing of *homologous chromosomes* with neither univalent chromosome losing its identity. The resulting bivalent chromosome transmits mixed characteristics from both the parents to the offspring owing to crossing-over of chromosome segments during synapsis. Syn. *syndesis*.

Syndesis Syn. *synapsis*.

T

Talbot A unit of *luminous energy* defined by: 1 talbot = 1 *lumen* per second.

Television microscope A microscope that generally uses ultraviolet *light,* thus greatly extending the range of microscopic investigation since many substances which do not absorb visible light do absorb ultraviolet light, e.g., many living cells and microorganisms. Also, because these substances often differ in *absorption* characteristics for different ultraviolet *frequencies,* one can distinguish between them under the television microscope.

Telocentric chromosome A chromosome in which the *kinetochore* is located at the extreme end of the chromosome.

Telophase The fourth stage of *mitosis*.

Tetrade See *bivalent*.

Tetraploid That state of a cell or nucleus in which the *chromosome* number is four times the *haploid number*.

Thallophyta A phylum of the plant kingdom which includes fungi, bacteria, algae, and many smaller groups. The plant body is a thallus, i.e., undifferentiated into leaf, stem, and root, varying a great deal in complexity among different members of the phylum.

Thermionics The study of the *emission* of electrons from hot bodies, usually including the subsequent behavior and control of the electrons, especially *in vacuo*.

Thermionic tube An *electron tube* in which electron emission occurs by electrical heating of the *cathode*.

Thermionic valve The British equivalent of *thermionic tube*.

Thymine A *pyrimidine* base found in *nucleic acids,* first isolated from the thymus; specifically 2,4-dihydroxy-5-methylpyrimidine.

Thyroglobulin The iodine-protein secreted by the thyroid and lodged in the colloid substance.

Transcendental In mathematics, the term applied to *functions,* equations or numbers which are not algebraic. Transcendental operations cannot be defined by elementary methods. Some examples of transcendental functions are *exponential, logarithmic,* and trigonometric functions. Transcendental equations are equations containing one or more transcendental functions. Generally such equations must be solved by approximations.

Transmission The ratio of *light intensity* transmitted through a medium to that entering the medium.

Transmission level The ratio, expressed in *decibels,* of the power at any point in a transmission system to the power at some reference point, thus giving the level of the *signal* power.

Transmission limit The *frequency* or *wavelength* above or below which a certain type of radiation is almost completely absorbed by a given medium; this medium acts as a sharp *filter* for that radiation if the limits are clearly defined.

Transmission loss The power lost in transmission between two points, expressed as the difference between the net power passing the two points.

Triploid Having three times the *haploid* number of *chromosomes.*

Trisomic Having one chromosome more than the normal diploid complement, so that three homologous chromosomes of the same type exist, rather than the normal two.

Tryptophan An essential amino acid found in proteins; it is freed by tryptic digestion. Its composition is α-amino-β-indole proprionic acid.

Tungsten A heavy, hard, gray-white, metallic chemical element used in electric lamp filaments and in hardening steel for high-speed tools. It is found in tungstite, scheelite, and wolframite.

Tungsten lamp An electric lamp with an *incandescent tungsten* filament, used for quantitative cytochemistry in the visible *light* ranges and in routine microscopy.

Turner syndrome Characterized by poor growth and sexual development; found in persons having only one sex *chromosome,* an X. These apparent females have 45 chromosomes and usually do not exhibit marginal *sex chromatin* bodies in the nuclei of epithelial cells.

Tyrode solution A solution composed of 0.05 g of sodium diphosphate, 0.1 g of magnesium chloride, 1 g of glucose, 1 g of sodium bicarbonate, 0.2 g of potassium chloride, 0.2 g of calcium chloride, 8 g of sodium chloride, and distilled water to make 1000 ml. It is used as an isotonic solution for cell suspensions.

Tyrosine *p*-Hydroxyphenylalanine; an amino acid which is closely related to and probably the precursor of melanin, epinephrine, and thyroxin. It is often found in proteins, especially casein.

U

Ultraviolet radiation Electromagnetic radiation having *wavelengths* from 4000 Å to less than 400 Å, i.e., from above visible violet to the region of very "soft" (i.e., nonpenetrating) X-rays.

UMSP-1 Abbreviation of Universal Microspectrophotometer, Model No. 1. This instrument, designed by T. Caspersson and made by Carl Zeiss, is a scanning microspectrophotometer with quartz lenses and xenon light source.

Uracil A *pyrimidine* base which is a constituent of *nucleic acids;* specifically, 2,6-dihydroxypyrimidine.

V

Variable A quantity to which any of the values of a given *set* may be assigned, as distinguished from a *constant.* The variable may be either *real* or *complex.* When a *function* is implicit, as $f(x, y, z) = 0$, and expresses the relation between two or more variables, it may generally be expressed explicitly as $f(x, z) = y$; x and z

are *independent variables* and *y* is a *dependent variable.* The choice of variables may be arbitrary, but some particular choice may be more convenient than others.

Variable-focus condenser Basically an *Abbe condenser* in which the lower *lens* element is movable and the upper is fixed. The lower lens produces an image of the source between the elements so that the exit beam leaves the stationary lens as a large-diameter parallel bundle of rays. Thus, the field of low-power *objectives* may be filled with light without removing the top element. On the other hand, it can also be adjusted to produce a divergent bundle with a *numerical aperture* as high as 1.3.

Variance In statistics, the expected value of the square of the deviation from the *mean,* i.e., the square of the *standard deviation.*

Vector A quantity having both direction and magnitude, as distinguished from a *scalar,* which has only magnitude. Graphically, a vector is often indicated by an arrow, the length of the arrow being proportional to the scalar magnitude of the vector; the direction of the arrow corresponds to the direction of the vector. The *origin* of the arrow is its initial point or tail, and the terminus of the arrow is its final point or head. Some examples of vectors are velocity and acceleration, while mass, temperature, and density are scalars.

Velocity Change of position per unit time.

W

Watt The unit of electric power; it equals 1 joule per second or 10^7 ergs per second; 1 horsepower = 746 watts.

Wave front reconstruction Strictly, the term implies that an image is rebuilt after the process of image formation has been interrupted somewhere, e.g., with an artificial mask. Since one may start with an artificial mask from which to synthesize an image, without a primary object being present, the term "reconstruction" could also be replaced by "optical synthesis." This process was first developed for crystal analysis [M. J. Buerger, *J. Appl. Phys.* **21**, 909 (1950); E. O. Wallon and A. H. Compton, *J. Opt. Soc. Am.* **24**, 229 (1934)]. Its great potential for biological microscopy, however, lies in the fact that it also may be applied to odd-shaped objects [D. Gabor, *Proc. Roy. Soc. London* **A197**, 454 (1949); P. Kirkpatrick and H. M. A. El-Sum, *J. Opt. Soc. Am.* **46**, 825 (1956); P. Kirkpatrick and H. H. Patee, Jr., X-ray-microscopy, in "Encyclopedia of Physics" (S. Flügge, ed.), Springer, Berlin, 1957, Vol. 30, p. 305; E. N. Leith and J. Upatnieks, *J. Opt. Soc. Am.* **53**, 1377 (1963)]. Reconstruction of the *diffraction* patterns will yield the original structure of the object and, therefore, is called the "hologram." An apparently fundamental limit to any microscopic image formation is the effect of diffraction. "As long as the numerical aperture governs the resolving power of the microscope, there is no hope that much further progress will be made. Perhaps, some day something will be found to overcome this limit" [E. Abbé, *Ges. Abhandlungen* **1**, 149 (1878)]. This "something" is the principle of wave front reconstruction.

Wavelength The distance from any point on a uniform wave train to the next having the same phase.

Weber law The minimum difference between two stimuli detectable by a human observer depends on the *fraction* of the *total* magnitude of the stimulus which that difference represents, and not simply on the magnitude of the difference.

Weber–Fechner law The difference in perceived magnitude between two subjective sensations is proportional to the logarithm of the ratio of the magnitudes of the physical stimulus which induces those sensations.

Wratten filter Tradename of a series of color filters having specified and reproducible optical properties.

X

Xenon lamp Lamp containing xenon (symbol Xe), a colorless, odorless, inert gas. The lamp emits *radiant* energy with a *continuous spectrum* similar to that emitted by the sun. Compare with *mercury vapor lamp* and *tungsten lamp*.

X-Ray diffraction Discovered after Max von Laue suggested that a crystal might act on X-rays in a way similar to a *grating* on *light* [W. Friedrich, P. Knipping, M. von Laue, Sitzungsberichte Bayer, Akad. Wiss. Math.-Phys. Klasse, 1912, p. 303; J. R. Meyer-Arendt and J. K. Wood, *Am. J. Phys.* **29**, 341 (1961)]. In most X-ray microscopic cameras, tubing with bores ranging from 100μ down to 25μ is used to obtain sufficiently *collimated* X-rays which then fall on a small crystal, fiber, or other preselected detail of a biological structure [M. E. Bergman and I. Fankuchen, *Rev. Sci. Instr.* **20**, 696 (1949); F. G. Chesley, *Rev. Sci. Instr.* **18**, 422 (1947); W. Parrish, X-ray diffraction and fluorescence analysis, in "Nondestructive Testing Handbook" (R. C. McMaster, ed.), Ronald, New York, 1959].

Z

Zygonema The *zygotene* stage of *meiotic prophase*.

Zygophase That portion of the life history which is *diploid*.

Zygote (1) The fertilized ovum before the first *cleavage* occurs. (2) The result of the union of two *gametes*.

Zygotene The second stage of *meiotic prophase* in which pairing of *homologous chromosomes* occurs; this stage is between *leptotene* and *pachytene*.

Zygotic number The *diploid* number of *chromosomes*.

AUTHOR INDEX

Numbers in parentheses are reference numbers and indicate that an author's work is referred to although his name is not cited in the text. Numbers in italic show the page on which the complete reference is listed.

H

SUBJECT INDEX

A

Abbe condenser, 559
Abbe microspectral ocular, 7–8
Abbe sine condition, 559
Aberration, 559
Absorbance, 255
Absorption coefficient, 559
Absorption cytophotometry, 201–213
Absorption spectra, 5 ff.
Acetylation, blocking with, 460–461
Achromatin, 560
Acid dye, binding, 456–462
Acid mucopolysaccharides, 489–501
   chemistry, 490–492
Acridine Orange, 494
Acriflavine, 494
Acrocentric chromosome, 560
Adrenal medulla, dry weight of cell nuclei, 82–83
Albumins, 560
Alcian Blue, 494
Alkaline Fast Green reaction, 345–346, 462–464
Alkaline phosphatase, activity, 82
Allelomorphic, 560
Allometric growth equation, 85
Allosome, 560
Allowed transition, 560
Amitosis, 563
Amplification, 560
Analyzer, 560
Aneuploid cell, 560
Angle of refraction, 560
Angstrom, 560
Angular aperture, 560
Angular distribution, 560
Anisotropic materials, 523–524, 536
Anode, 561
Anomalous dispersion, 561
AO-Baker interference microscope, 55–56
Aperture, 561
Aplanatic points, 561

Aplanatic surface, 561
Apochromatic objectives, 16, 561
Area densitometer, 400
Arginine, 561
   Sakaguchi reaction, 454–456
Aster, 561
Astra Blue, 494
Astral ray, 561
Astrol Blue, 500
Atabrine, 494
Attenuation, 561
Auramine, 284
Autoradiography, 561
   RNA, 376–377
Autosome, 561
Auxochrome, 561
Azure A, 494
Azure B, 362, 367–368
   staining with, 344–345

B

Barium rhodizonate method, 495
Barr and Stroud integrating microdensitometer, 184–186, 443–447
Barr bodies, 561
Barrier cells, 9
Barrier filters, 419
Basic dyes, for mucopolysaccharides, 494
Beam splitter, in photomicrography, 262–264
Beer-Lambert law, 437
   testing of in tissue, 312–313
Berberine sulfate, 283–284
Berek compensators, 533
Bi-Col method, 495
Biebrich Scarlet, 347
Binding. See Dye binding
Birefringence, 523–525, 525–526, 562
   of dyes, 539–546
   error in dry weight due to, 74
   in lipid-containing structure, 507 ff.